OXFORD STATISTICAL SCIENCE SERIES

OXFORD STATISTICAL SCIENCE SERIES

Non-linear Time Series

Series

A Dynamical System Approach

HOWELL TONG

Mathematical Institute, University of Kent at Canterbury

CLARENDON PRESS OXFORD

1990

Oxford University Press, Walton Street, Oxford OX2 6DP

Oxford New York Toronto
Delhi Bombay Calcutta Madras Karachi
Petaling Jaya Singapore Hong Kong Tokyo
Nairobi Dar es Salaam Cape Town
Melbourne Auckland

and associated companies in
Berlin Ibadan

Oxford is a trade mark of Oxford University Press

Published in the United States
by Oxford University Press, New York

British Library Cataloguing in Publication Data
Tong, Howell
Non-linear time series: a dynamical system approach.
1. Non-linear time series. Analysis
I. Title
519.5'5
ISBN 0-19-852224-X

Library of Congress Cataloging in Publication Data
Tong, Howell.
Non-linear time series: a dynamical system approach / Howell
Tong.
p.   cm. – – (Oxford statistical science series; 6)
1. Time-series analysis.   2. Nonlinear theories.   I. Title.
II. Series.
QA280.T597   1990   519.5'5 – –dc20   89-29697
ISBN 0-19-852224-X

Set by
The Universities Press (Belfast) Ltd
Printed in Great Britain by
Biddles Ltd.
Guildford & King's Lynn

To Mary, Simon, and Anna, my Lyapunov functions.

Preface

Non-linear time series analysis is a rapidly developing subject. Of necessity, it draws on deeper aspects of probability theory and more sophisticated tools of statistical inference. It demands greater degrees of ingenuity and common sense in model building. In return, once freed from the shackles of linearity, the analyst has the opportunity of gaining a fuller appreciation of the beauty of the real world. Thus, I have included real data sets from animal populations, solar activities, economics, finance, medical sciences, hydrology, environmental sciences, and others. A user-friendly package is available which implements a fair proportion of the modelling and forecasting techniques described in this book.

Although a few specialized books have recently appeared, I believe that there is a need for a fairly comprehensive account, covering the fundamentals of probability theory, statistical inference, model building, and prediction of non-linear time series. In tune with modern developments in other scientific disciplines, I have adopted the dynamical system approach, in that whenever possible I emphasize links with dynamical systems. This is based on my unswerving belief that without well-tried physical underpinnings, no sustainable edifice can be erected. As a reflection of the experimental nature of this undertaking, readers will probably observe non-uniform motions in places in the book. These are also partly due to my desire to keep the level of mathematics as modest as possible, although I cannot claim that I have never yielded to the beauty of mathematics. Readers are usually warned of such instances, which are indicated by the symbols (¶ and ¶¶).

I am enormously indebted to all non-linear time series enthusiasts but would like to mention, in particular, Kung-sik Chan, with whom I have made many exciting excursions over the truly fascinating non-linear terrains. Without his selfless assistance, I am sure that I would have made many more mistakes in my navigation. All remaining errors are naturally mine alone. I am also grateful to Doyne Farmer, Russell Gerrard, Ian Jolliffe, Rahim Moeanaddin, Pham Dinh Tuan, Richard Smith, Akiva Yaglom, and Zhu Zhao-xuan. Mrs Mavis Swain deserves my sincere thanks for rendering my sometimes inscrutable writing intelligible under very difficult conditions. Last but not least, I would like to take this opportunity of thanking my father, whose Chinese calligraphy has adorned this volume.

H.T.

Canterbury
April 1989

Acknowledgements

Grateful acknowledgements are made to the following:

The *Journal of Time Series Analysis* and Professor Peter M. Robinson for permission to reproduce Fig. 5.6.
The American Water Resources Association for permission to reproduce §7.4.
Springer Verlag for permission to reproduce material from the monograph entitled *Threshold models in non-linear time series* by H. Tong.
The Royal Society and Dr. D. A. Jones for permission to reproduce Figs. 4.1, 4.2, and 4.11.

Contents

Some suggested set meals for the readers

(A) Fast food (for applied statisticians in a hurry or with a limited mathematical background):

Chapter 1
Sections 2.1 and 2.2
Chapter 3
Sections 5.1, 5.2, 5.3.3, 5.3.5.3, 5.4, and 5.6
Chapter 7

(B) Vegetarian food (for those with minimal statistical background):

Chapter 1
Chapter 2
Chapter 3
A personal selection from the rest

(C) Gourmet food (for those looking for potential research problems):

Chapter 2
Chapter 4
Chapter 5
Chapter 7
Exercises and complements of all seven chapters

(D) Banquet (for those looking for a fairly comprehensive treatment):

Enjoy your seven-course meal!

The STAR PC package

A user-friendly floppy disk STAR may be purchased from Microstar Software (using the order form provided at the end of the book) which will provide a comprehensive statistical package for threshold modelling. It may be used in conjunction with Chapter 7 to gain hands-on experience. The package may be run on an IBM PC/XT or PC/AT or their compatibles with MS-DOS Version 3 or PC-DOS Version 3. It has extensive graphics.

1
Introduction

出乌呈枉幻直

Non-linearity *begets completeness*;
Misjudgment creates linearity.

Ch. XXII Lao Tzu (circa 600 BC)

1.1 Time series model building

In our endeavours to understand the changing world around us, observations of one kind or another are frequently made sequentially over time. The record of sunspots is a classic example, which may be traced as far back as 28 BC (see e.g. Needham 1959, p. 435).

Let us tentatively call such records *time series*. Possibly the most important objective in our study of a time series is to help to uncover the dynamical law governing its generation. Obviously, a complete uncovering of the law demands a complete understanding of the underlying physics, chemistry, biology, etc. When the underlying theory is non-existent or far from being complete, and we are presented with not much more than the data themselves, we may adopt the following paradigm:

(1) recognize important features of the observed data;

(2) construct an empirical time series model, incorporating as much available background theory as possible;

(3) check that the constructed model is capable of capturing the features in (1) and look for further improvement if necessary.

Fundamentally, an empirical time series model represents a *hypothesis* concerning the probability transition over time, that is the dynamics. Some authors have used the word 'model' in a different sense from the one adopted here. For example, it has sometimes been used to mean a forecast algorithm, the form of which is completely specified except for some defining parameters to be determined from data. Stage (1) in the above model-building paradigm dictates the 'shape' of things to come and stage (3) judges the 'goodness of fit' of the delivered product. Stage (2) may be facilitated by specifying a fairly wide class of models, denoted by C, within which some optimal search technique, that is identification, may then be employed. An obvious requirement is that C should be wide

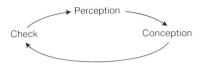

Fig. 1.1. A loop in model building

enough to include models capable of capturing the recognized features in (1). Equally obvious is the fact that the size of C is constrained by the amount of computation at our disposal for the search. A recognition of these two aspects reinforces the belief that model building is as much an art as it is a science.

Philosophically speaking, every specification of a times series model is coloured by some subjective judgement. What we have described in the above paradigm is best viewed as just one loop in a spiral of many and each loop should lead to an empirical model closer to the objective reality, in which the more important features are incorporated and the less important ones discarded (cf. Box 1980) (Fig. 1.1).

The other important function of an empirical model should not be overlooked, and that is it sharpens the perception in the next loop. Whilst an empirical model can never replace the underlying theory, the former can assist the development of the latter. At the same time, each advance in the latter can help bring about a more satisfactory empirical model. It may be argued that statistical modelling in general, and time series modelling in particular, should not be divorced from the underlying scientific discipline that the final product (a statistical model) is supposed to serve.

1.2   Stationarity

Let X_t denote a real-valued random variable representing the observation made at time t. For most of the book we confine our study to observations made at a regular time intervals, and, without loss of generality, we assume that the basic time interval is of duration one unit of time. We may now state the following definition:

Definition 1.1: A *time series*, $\{X_t\}$, is a family of real-valued random variables indexed by $t \in \mathbf{Z}$, where $\mathbf{Z}$ denotes the set of integers.

The more elaborate term 'discrete parameter time series' is not used because we shall study almost exclusively the case with $t \in \mathbf{Z}$. At any rate, the subscript t is reserved exclusively for this case.

In this volume, mainly those important features with time-invariant properties are considered.

Definition 1.2: The time series $\{X_t\}$ is said to be *stationary* if, for any $t_1, t_2, \ldots, t_n \in \mathbf{Z}$, any $k \in \mathbf{Z}$, and $n = 1, 2, \ldots,$

$$F_{X_{t_1}, X_{t_2}, \ldots, X_{t_n}}(x_1, \ldots x_n) = F_{X_{t_1+k}, X_{t_2+k}, \ldots, X_{t_n+k}}(x_1, \ldots, x_n) \qquad (1.1)$$

where F denotes the distribution function of the set of random variables which appear as suffices.

The term 'strictly stationary' is more often used to describe the above situation, while the term 'weakly stationary', 'second-order stationary', 'covariance stationary', or 'wide-sense stationary' is used to describe the theoretically less restricted situation in which

$$E(X_{t_1}) = E(X_{t_1+k}) \qquad \mathrm{cov}(X_{t_1}, X_{t_2}) = \mathrm{cov}(X_{t_1+k}, X_{t_2+k}) \qquad (1.2)$$

for all $t_1, t_2, k \in \mathbf{Z}$, the covariances being assumed to exist. Strict stationarity implies weak stationarity provided var X_t exists. In the Gaussian case, they are equivalent. Unless otherwise stated, we use the terms 'stationary time series' and 'strictly stationary time series' interchangeably. In the main, we consider model building for stationary time series or for time series which may be made stationary after some simple transformation, such as taking differences of consecutive observations, subtracting a polynomial or a trigonometric trend, etc.

Consider a stationary time series $\{X_t\}$ with finite variance. It follows from (1.2) that $\mathrm{cov}(X_{t_1}, X_{t_2})$ is simply a function of $|t_1 - t_2|$. This function is called the *autocovariance function of* $\{x_t\}$ *at* $lag(t_2 - t_1)$. We denote it by $\gamma_{t_2-t_1}$. It has the following properties (see e.g. Priestley 1981, pp. 108–10):

(1) $\gamma_0 = \mathrm{var}\, X_t$

(2) $|\gamma_\tau| \le \gamma_0, \forall \tau \in \mathbf{Z}$

(3) $\gamma_{-\tau} = \gamma_\tau, \forall \tau \in \mathbf{Z}$

(4) $\forall t_1, t_2, \ldots, t_n \in \mathbf{Z}, \forall$ positive $n \in \mathbf{Z}$, and $\forall$ real $z_1, z_2, \ldots, z_n,$

$$\sum_{r=1}^{n} \sum_{s=1}^{n} \gamma_{t_r-t_s} z_r z_s \ge 0.$$

The ratio γ_τ / γ_0, $\tau \in \mathbf{Z}$, is called the *autocorrelation function of* $\{X_t\}$ *of lag* τ. It is denoted by ρ_τ. Properties (2), (3), and (4) still hold if the γ are replaced by the ρ with corresponding subscripts. It is well known that ρ_τ may be interpreted as a measure of *linear* association between X_t and $X_{t\pm\tau}$.

Property (4) is that of positive semi-definiteness and the following theorem describes the positive semi-definite function defined by $\{\rho_\tau : \tau =$

$0, \pm 1, \pm 2, \ldots\}$ as a Fourier transform.

Theorem 1.1: A function defined by $\{\rho_\tau : \tau = 0, \pm 1, \pm 2, \ldots \}$, $\rho_0 < \infty$, is positive semi-definite if and only if it can be expressed in the form

$$\rho_\tau = \int_{-\pi}^{\pi} e^{i\omega\tau} \, dF(\omega) \tag{1.3}$$

where F (defined for $|\omega| \leq \pi$) is monotonic non-decreasing.

For a proof see for example Doob (1953, p. 474).

The Fourier transform F is called the (normalized) *integrated spectrum*. If $\{\rho_\tau\}$ is absolutely summable, then F has the continuous derivative f, given by

$$f(\omega) = \frac{1}{2\pi} \sum_{\tau=-\infty}^{\infty} \rho_\tau e^{-i\omega\tau} \quad \text{almost all } \omega \in [-\pi, \pi]. \tag{1.4}$$

The function f is called the (normalized) *spectral density function*. The analogous equations for γ_τ are

$$\gamma_\tau = \int_{-\pi}^{\pi} e^{i\omega t} \, dH(\omega) \tag{1.3'}$$

and

$$h(\omega) = \frac{dH(\omega)}{d\omega} = \frac{1}{2\pi} \sum_{\tau=-\infty}^{\infty} \gamma_\tau e^{-i\omega\tau} \quad \text{almost all } \omega \in [-\pi, \pi] \tag{1.4'}$$

where H and h are called the (*non-normalized*) *integrated spectrum* and the (*non-normalized*) *spectral density function* respectively. Obviously H and F are related by

$$H(\omega) = \gamma_0 F(\omega), \quad \text{all } \omega. \tag{1.5}$$

(See, for example, Priestley (1981) for a detailed discussion of the branch of time series analysis called *spectral analysis* which is centred around the spectral functions.)

1.3   Linear Gaussian models

It is a remarkable fact that linear Gaussian models have dominated the development of time series model building for the past five decades. It may be said that the era of linear time series modelling began with such linear models as Yule's *autoregressive* (*AR*) *models* (1927), first introduced in the study of sunspot numbers. Specifically, the class of AR models consists of models of the form

$$X_t = a_0 + \sum_{j=1}^{k} a_j X_{t-j} + \varepsilon_t \tag{1.6}$$

where the a_j are real constants $(a_k \neq 0)$, k is a finite positive integer referred to as the *order* of the AR model, and the ε_t are zero-mean uncorrelated random variables, called *white noise*, with a common variance, $\sigma_\varepsilon^2(<\infty)$. Symbolically, we express (1.6) by $X_t \sim \text{AR}(k)$. A more general class of linear models is obtained by replacing ε_t by a weighted average of $\varepsilon_t, \varepsilon_{t-1}, \ldots, \varepsilon_{t-l}$, that is

$$X_t = a_0 + \sum_{j=1}^{k} a_j X_{t-j} + \sum_{j=0}^{l} b_j \varepsilon_{t-j} \tag{1.7}$$

where the b_j are real constants $(b_l \neq 0)$ and b_0 may be set equal to unity without loss of generality. This is the so-called class of *autoregressive/moving average (ARMA) models*. Symbolically, we express (1.7) by $X_t \sim \text{ARMA}(k, l)$. Here, l is a finite non-negative integer referred to as the *order* of the moving-average part of the ARMA model. The special case of $\text{ARMA}(0, l)$ is referred to as the *moving-average (MA)* model of order l, denoted by $\text{MA}(l)$.

We now introduce two conditions on the ARMA models. At the expense of some slight loss of theoretical generality, these two conditions lead to sharper results and some simplification of discussion. In any case, it seems that they are often made in practice, either explicitly or implicitly.

Condition A; The roots of the polynomials

$$A(z) = z^k - \sum_{j=1}^{k} a_j z^{k-j} \tag{1.8}$$

$$B(z) = \sum_{j=0}^{l} b_j z^{l-j} \quad (b_0 = 1) \tag{1.9}$$

all have modulus less than one. A and B will be called the *autoregressive generating function* and *moving-average generating function* respectively.

Condition B: $\{\varepsilon_t\}$ is a sequence of independent identically distributed random variables (an i.i.d. sequence), each with the distribution $\mathcal{N}(0, \sigma_\varepsilon^2)$. $\{\varepsilon_t\}$ is referred to as a *Gaussian white noise*.

Let

$$\mu_X = a_0 \Big/ \left(1 - \sum_{j=1}^{k} a_j\right) \quad \text{and} \quad \sigma_X^2 = \frac{\sigma_\varepsilon^2}{2\pi} \int_{-\pi}^{\pi} \left|\frac{B(e^{-i\omega})}{A(e^{-i\omega})}\right|^2 d\omega.$$

Under these two conditions, and subject to X_0 having a $\mathcal{N}(\mu_X, \sigma_X^2)$ distribution:

1. $\{X_t : t = 1, 2, \ldots\}$ is stationary.
2. $\forall t_1, t_2, \ldots, t_k \in \mathbf{Z}_+$, the set of non-negative integers, and $\forall k$ belonging to the set of positive integers, $(X_{t_1}, X_{t_2}, \ldots, X_{t_k})$ is jointly Gaussian. $\{X_t : t = 1, 2, \ldots\}$ is called a *Gaussian sequence*.

3. X_t admits the *linear (one-sided) model/linear representation*

$$X_t = \mu_X + \sum_{j=0}^{\infty} \beta_j \varepsilon_{t-j} \quad \text{with} \quad \sum_{j=0}^{\infty} \beta_j^2 < \infty, \ \beta_0 = 1, \text{ and } \mu_X = \mathrm{E}X_t. \quad (1.10)$$

3′.   Likewise ε_t admits a linear model in terms of X_s, $s \le t$. This is sometimes called the *invertibility* of $\{X_t\}$ (see e.g. Rosenblatt 1979).

Henceforth, unless otherwise stated, all ARMA models are assumed to satisfy Conditions A and B. We may sometimes emphasize this fact by referring to them as stationary Gaussian ARMA models. On the other hand, if a model for $\{X_t\}$ is of the general form (1.10) which possesses properties (1) and (2) and in which $\{\varepsilon_t\}$ is an i.i.d. sequence (and necessarily Gaussian), it is called a *linear Gaussian model*. Henceforth, by an abuse of terminology, we do not distinguish between a time series model and the time series defined by it. Now, a well-defined linear Gaussian model for $\{X_t\}$ is completely specified by the mean, μ_X, and the autocovariances, γ_t, of $\{X_t\}$, or equivalently by μ_X and the (non-normalized) spectral density function, h. Note that

$$h(\omega) = \frac{\sigma_\varepsilon^2}{2\pi} \left| \sum_{j=0}^{\infty} \beta_j e^{-ij\omega} \right|^2 \quad (1.11)$$

which is a continuous integrable function of ω. On the other hand, an ARMA model has a (non-normalized) spectral density function of the form

$$\frac{\sigma_\varepsilon^2}{2\pi} \left| \frac{B(e^{-i\omega})}{A(e^{-i\omega})} \right|^2 \quad (1.12)$$

which is a rational function of $e^{-i\omega}$. It has been said that ARMA models enjoy the same degree of generality among the class of linear Gaussian models as rational functions among the class of continuous integrable functions (see e.g. Priestley 1980, p. 283). Of course, an ARMA model has the significant property of consisting of only a finite number of parameters. From the point of view of model building, we may conclude that *if and only if the autocovariances are considered an important feature, the class of ARMA models constitutes a useful choice of C.*

1.4   Some advantages and some limitations of ARMA models

The strengths and weaknesses of stationary Gaussian ARMA models are, in fact, already subsumed in the conclusion of the last section. We elaborate them as follows. Proofs of some of the results cited in this section will be given in full in Chapter 4.

1.4.1 SOME ADVANTAGES

In the following discussion, we merely highlight some of the significant achievements of the ARMA models.

1. Mathematically, linear difference equations are the simplest type of difference equations and a complete theory is available. Probabilistically, the theory of Gaussian sequences is readily understood. The theory of statistical inference is the most developed for linear Gaussian models.

The class of stationary Gaussian ARMA models has an elegant and fundamental geometric characterization in terms of the concepts of a *predictor space* and a *Markovian representation* introduced by Akaike (1974a). These concepts are rooted in control systems theory. He has shown that *a stationary Gaussian time series has a stationary Gaussian ARMA representation if and only if its predictor space is finite-dimensional.*

2. The computation time required for obtaining a parsimonious ARMA model for the data is well within the reach of most practitioners. Ready-made packages are available. Over the years, much experience has been accumulated in the application of ARMA models (see e.g. Box and Jenkins 1976).

3. These models have been reasonably successful as a practical tool for analysis, forecasting, and control (see e.g. Box and Jenkins 1976). They have not survived 60-odd years for nothing! We must conclude that they represent the objective world to a good first approximation.

1.4.2 SOME LIMITATIONS

Once again, in the discussion that follows we merely highlight some of the current interests in the subject of time series modelling. The discussion will be interspersed with the introduction of terminology, concepts, and theoretical results mostly relevant to later exposition.

1. On setting the innovation ε_t to a constant for all t (or equivalently on setting var ε_t to zero), eqn (1.7) becomes a *deterministic* linear difference equation in X. Under condition A, X_t will always tend to a unique finite constant, independent of the initial value, as t tends to infinity. The situation is described as a *stable limit point*. If $A(z)$ has one root greater than unity in modulus, $|X_t|$ will tend to infinity with t, and the situation is described as being *unstable*. If $A(z)$ has some roots equal to unity in modulus and the others less than unity in modulus, X_t will eventually osciallate among a set of points whose values depend on the initial value. The situation is described as being *neutrally stable*. We have

here merely restated the well-known result that a linear difference equation does not permit stable periodic solutions independent of initial value. This point will be developed further in Chapter 2.

2. Having symmetric joint distributions, stationary Gaussian ARMA models are not ideally suited for data exhibiting strong asymmetry. Figure 1.2 gives one typical set of hydrological data, a Gaussian model for which would be of limited value.

3. ARMA models are not ideally suited for data exhibiting sudden bursts of very large amplitude at irregular time epochs. This is clear in view of the normality of ARMA models. Essentially, ARMA models are more suitable for data with negligible probability of very high level crossings (and there are plenty of these about). We may recall the elementary result that if the kth order moment of a random variable X exists, then

$$P[|X| > c] = O(|c|^{-k}) \quad \text{as} \quad c \to \infty. \tag{1.13}$$

Thus, the probability of large excursions is connected with the existence of moments. If the set of all possible values of X is bounded from both sides, then the distribution of X has the *moment property*, that is moments of all orders exist (see e.g. Fisz 1963, p. 68). However, boundedness is not necessary since, for example, it is obvious that a Gaussian random variable (and hence a stationary Gaussian sequence) has the moment property.

It is interesting to note that models without the moment property may be constructed by some kind of stochastic 'perturbation' of the ARMA models. Consider a stochastic perturbation of an AR(1) model in the form of

$$X_t = (a + b\varepsilon_t)X_{t-1} + \varepsilon_t \tag{1.14}$$

where $\{\varepsilon_t\}$ is a Gaussian white noise with zero mean and, without loss of generality, unit variance. The coefficient of X_{t-1} is no longer a constant but is a random variable, which is a linear function of ε_t. This model is a special case of the general class of models called *bilinear models*, which will be discussed in more detail later.

Figure 1.3 illustrates the phenomenon of sudden bursts of the above class of models. We may prefer these models to the ARMA models when dealing with a situation of this type.

4. Since the autocovariances, γ_j $(j \in \mathbf{Z})$, are only one aspect of the joint distributions of (X_t, X_{t-j}), $(j \in \mathbf{Z})$, other aspects may contain vital information missed by the γ_j. One such aspect is, for example, *the regression function at lag (j)*, that is $\mathrm{E}(X_t \mid X_{t-j})$, $(j \in \mathbf{Z})$. For the ARMA models, these are all linear because of the joint normality. This

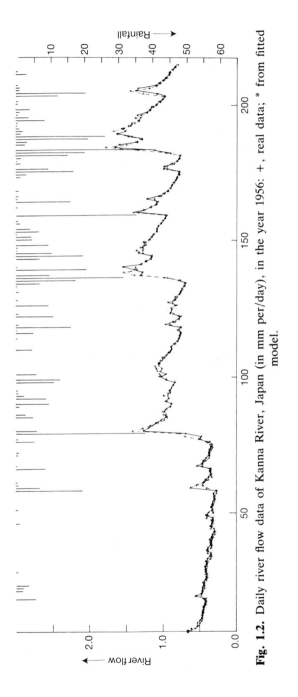

Fig. 1.2. Daily river flow data of Kanna River, Japan (in mm per/day), in the year 1956: +, real data; * from fitted model.

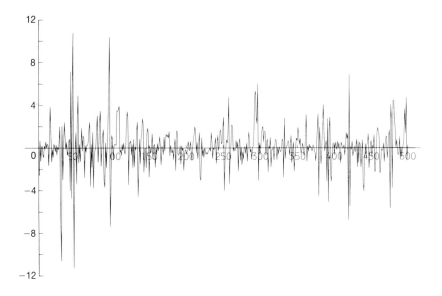

Fig. 1.3. A realization of the model $X_t = (-0.1 + 0.9\varepsilon_t)X_{t-1} + \varepsilon_t$, $\varepsilon_t - \mathcal{N}(0, 1)$.
(The theoretical standard deviation of X_t is 2.357)

characteristic may sometimes weaken the usefulness of ARMA models for data exhibiting strong cyclicity. The following situation seems to have some practical relevance.

The autocorrelation function of strongly cyclical data is also strongly cyclical. At those lags for which the autocorrelation function is quite large in modulus, the corresponding regression functions may be sufficiently well approximated by linear functions. However, at those lags for which the autocorrelation function is quite small in modulus, a linear approximation for the corresponding regression functions is not always unquestionable. Indeed, it is conceivable that the strong cyclicity of the data may be linked with a strong association (not necessarily measurable by the autocorrelation function which measures only linear association) between X_t and X_{t-j}, $j = \pm 1, \pm 2, \ldots, \pm L$, for some finite integer L. In this case, a *non-linear* approximation for the regression functions may well be more appropriate for those lags with small autocorrelations. We may illustrate the above situation with the classic annual Canadian lynx data (1982–1934) (See Figs 1.4–1.6.) We shall return to a more comprehensive analysis of these data later.

In fact, the use of sample regression functions in the time series context goes right back to Yule (1927). The use of sample regression functions

Fig. 1.4. Logarithmically transformed MacKenzie River series of annual Canadian lynx trappings from the years 1821–1934

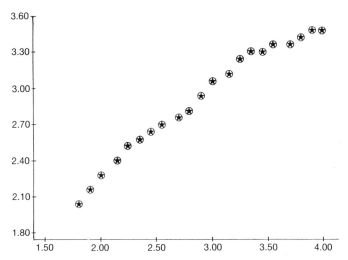

Fig. 1.5. Sample regression function of X_t on X_{t-1} for the data in Fig. 1.4. Sample autocorrelation function of lag 1 is 0.79. Sample estimate of $\gamma_0 \rho_1^2 / \text{var}\{E(X_t \mid X_{t-1})\}$ is roughly 1. The linear fit for the regression of X_t on X_{t-1} implied by a linear Gaussian time series model is quite reasonable

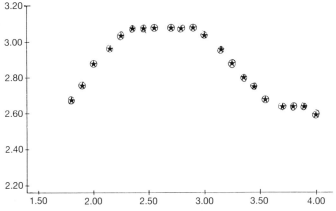

Fig. 1.6. Sample regression function of X_t on X_{t-3} for data in Fig. 1.4. Sample autocorrelation function of lag 3 is -0.13. Sample estimate of $\gamma_0 \rho_3^2 / \text{var}\{E(X_t \mid X_{t-3})\}$ is roughly 0.04. A linear Gaussian time series model for the data would imply an *almost horizontal* linear fit for the regression of X_t on X_{t-3}, which is clearly poor

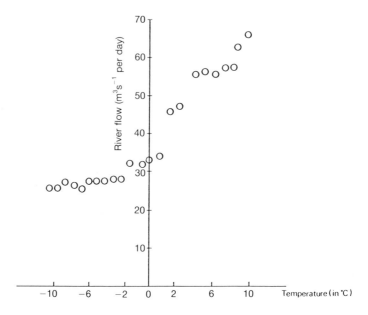

Fig. 1.7. Non-parametric regression, $E\{X \mid Z = z\}$, of river flow (X) on temperature (Z) for the River Jökulsà Eystri, Iceland. The method does not assume an *a priori* functional form but is based on a (kernel) smoothing on the data histograms. Specifically, let $\{\delta_N(z)\}$ denote a sequence of symmetric and non-negative functions of z, of area 1, with the property that $\delta_N(z) \to$ Dirac delta function as $N \to \infty$. Then $E\{X \mid Z = z\} = \sum_{j=1}^{N} x_j \delta_N(z - z_j)/\sum_{j=1}^{N} \delta_N(z - z_j)$, where $(x_1, z_1), \ldots, (x_N, z_N)$ denote the N data points

may be easily extended beyond univariate time series. Figure 1.7 gives an illustration of regressing river flow on temperature. The non-linear effect due to the melting ice of a glacier within the catchment area of the river is clearly evident. More details about the analysis of these data will be given in the final chapter.

5. ARMA models are not ideally suited for data exhibiting *time irreversibility*. Figures 1.2 and 1.4 show examples of such data. A simple yet effective way of visualizing this is by tracing these data on a transparency and then turning it over.

One way of gaining further insights into the effect of time reversibility on the probabilistic structure of the time series $\{X_t\}$ is to introduce higher-order spectra. We will deal with this point in Chapter 4.

1.5 What next?

After six decades of domination by linear Gaussian models, the time is certainly ripe for a serious study of ways of removing the many limitations of these models. Once we decide to incorporate features in addition to the autocovariances, the class of models would have to be greatly enlarged to include those besides the Gaussian ARMA models. We may either retain the general ARMA framework and allow the white noise to be non-Gaussian, or we may completely abandon the linearity assumption.

In the former case, limitations 2, 3, 4, 5 of Gaussian ARMA models can be removed, to some extent, by a *judicious* choice of the distributions of the ε_t. As a typical illustration, let us consider $E(X_t \,|\, X_{t-j})$ for the following non-Gaussian MA(1):

$$X_t = \varepsilon_t - a\varepsilon_{t-1} \tag{1.15}$$

where ε_t has a uniform distribution on $(-\sqrt{3}, \sqrt{3})$. After some non-trivial manipulation $E(X_t \,|\, X_{t-1})$ is shown to be non-linear as illustrated in Figs 1.8 and 1.9.

Shepp *et al.* (1980) have given a detailed study of the regression functions, $E(X_t \,|\, X_{t-1}, \ldots, X_{t-k})$, k being any positive integer, for a non-Gaussian MA(l). Another example, which is probably the simplest although a little extreme, is taken from Whittle (1963a, Section 2.6) and Rosenblatt (1979). Consider the stationary AR(1) model

$$x_t = \tfrac{1}{2}X_{t-1} + \varepsilon_t$$

where

$$\varepsilon_t = \begin{cases} \tfrac{1}{2} \text{ with probability } \tfrac{1}{2} \\ 0 \text{ with probability } \tfrac{1}{2} \end{cases}$$

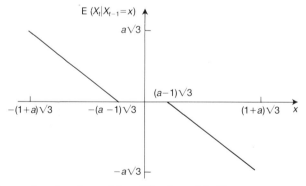

Fig. 1.8. Regression function of lag (1) of model $X_t = \varepsilon_t - a\varepsilon_{t-1}$, ε_t uniformly distributed on $(-\sqrt{3}, \sqrt{3})$; $(a \geq 1)$

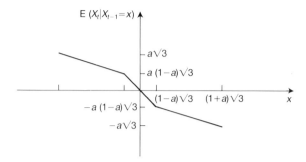

Fig. 1.9. Regression function of lag (1) of model of $X_t = \varepsilon_t - a\varepsilon_{t-1}$, ε_t uniformly distributed on $(-\sqrt{3}, \sqrt{3})$; $(a < 1)$

and ε_t is independent of X_s, $s < t$. X_t is then uniformly distributed on $[0, 1]$ and

$$2X_t = X_{t-1} + 2\varepsilon_t$$

$$= X_{t-1} \text{ (modulo 1)}.$$

Obviously,

$$E(X_t \mid X_{t-1}) = \tfrac{1}{2}X_{t-1} + \tfrac{1}{4}$$

which is linear in X_{t-1}. However,

$$E(X_{t-1} \mid X_t) = 2X_t \quad \text{(modulo 1)}$$

which is non-linear!

There is no doubt that further exploration within the non-Gaussian ARMA framework may be quite fruitful. We may argue that the failure of non-Gaussian ARMA models to remove limitation 1 means that it would be appropriate to look elsewhere for models possessing much richer dynamical properties. The pages which follow will be devoted entirely to the removal of the linearity assumption. To end the chapter the following classification summarizes the situation:

Linear Gaussian models	Linear non-Gaussian models
e.g. ARMA models with Gaussian white noise	e.g. ARMA models with non-Gaussian white noise
Non-linear Gaussian models	Non-linear non-Gaussian Models
e.g. Gaussian output with non-Gaussian white noise input through a non-linear filter	e.g. read on!

Bibliographical notes

The philosophical attitude adopted in this book is similar to that more eloquently discussed by Box (1980). It leans on dialectics. The basic theory of stationary time series is covered in Doob (1953) at a sophisticated level and in Priestley (1981) at a level more readily accessible to the non-specialists of probability theory. Akaike (1974a) is a remarkable paper, which completes the geometric delineation of ARMA models within the class of linear time models. The parallel picture in the class of non-linear time series models has no more than a few strokes on it (see Chapter 4). Serious limitations of linear Gaussian time series models in practical situations were mentioned earlier by Akaike, Cox, Galbraith, and Tunnicliffe-Wilson in the discussions of the papters by Campbell and Walker (1977) and Tong (1977b) on the analysis of the classic Canadian lynx data. More attention seems to be warranted in respect of time irreversibility.

Exercises and complements

(1) Let $\{X_t\}$ denote a stationary Gaussian time series. Prove that
$$E[X_s \mid X_t = x] \equiv E[X_t \mid X_s = x].$$
Generalize the result to higher-order conditional moments.

(2) Consider the strictly stationary AR(1) model
$$X_t = \tfrac{1}{2}X_{t-1} + \varepsilon \qquad t \geq 1$$
where X_0 is uniformly distributed on $[0, 1]$,
$$\varepsilon_t = \begin{cases} \tfrac{1}{2} \text{ with probability } \tfrac{1}{2} \\ 0 \text{ with probability } \tfrac{1}{2} \end{cases}$$

and ε_t is independent of X_s, $s < t$. Show that the joint distribution of (X_0, X_1) is different from that of (X_1, X_0). Let the times series $\{X_t\}$ be instantaneously transformed to the time series $\{Y_t\}$ via

$$Y_t = \Phi^{-1}(X_t), \text{ each } t$$

where Φ denotes the standard Gaussian distribution function. Show that, for each t, Y_t has a standard Gaussian distribution. Is $\{Y_t\}$ time reversible?

(3) Let $\{X_t\}$ be a strictly stationary time series all of whose joint distributions are symmetric about the origin. Prove that $\{X_t\}$ need not be time reversible. Does time reversibility imply symmetry of all joint distributions about the origin?

(4) Suppose that X_0 is uniformly distribution on $(0, 1)$. Let

$$X_t = 2X_{t-1} \text{ (modulo 1)} \qquad t \geq 1$$

that is X_t is the fractional part of $2X_{t-1}$. Prove that the joint distributions of $(X_{t+\tau}, X_t)$ are degenerate and that

$$\text{cov}(X_{t+\tau}, X_t) = \frac{2^{-|\tau|}}{12}.$$

Show that the linear least-squares predictor, $\hat{X}_t$, of X_t given all past values is given by

$$\hat{X}_t = \tfrac{1}{4} + \tfrac{1}{2}X_{t-1}$$

which has mean square error of prediction equal to $\frac{1}{16}$.
[Hint: Consider a binary representation of X_0].

(5) Let $\{X_t\}$ denote a Gaussian time series with zero mean and unit variance. Suppose that it has a (normalized) spectral density function f. Let

$$Y_t = X_t^2 - 1, \quad \text{for each } t.$$

Verify that $\{Y_t\}$ has normalized spectral density, h, given by

$$h(\omega) = \int_{-\pi}^{\pi} f(\omega - \theta)f(\theta)\, d\theta.$$

(6) Let

$$X_t = (a + b\varepsilon_t)X_{t-1}$$

where $\{\varepsilon_t\}$ is a sequence of independent identically distributed random variables with zero mean and unit variance. Suppose that $a^2 + b^2 < 1$. Prove that $X_t \to 0$ in probability as $t \to \infty$.

(7) Show that the sequence $\{X_1, X_2, \ldots\}$ is strictly stationary if and only if there exists a sequence $\{Y_1, Y_2, \ldots\}$ such that, for any n, the joint distribution of $(X_1, X_2, \ldots, X_n)$ is the same as that of $(Y_n, Y_{n-1}, \ldots, Y_1)$.

(Kingman and Taylor 1966, p. 394)

2
An introduction to dynamical systems

It stands alone and does not change,
Goes round and does not weary.

. . .

Receding, it is described as far away,
Being far away, it is described as turn-
ing back.

. . .

Ch. XXV Lao Tzu

2.1 Orientation

As soon as we leave the relatively straightforward world of linearity, we are faced with an infinitude of possible choices of the generic models. Nature is full of surprises and awareness of its infinite variety is an accumulative learning process, which is itself non-linear. It seems therefore that there will always be the necessity of different approaches to non-linear time series model building.

One of the basic objectives of this volume is the quest for a deeper understanding of cyclical phenomena which manifest themselves in the form of cyclical time series. Historically, the development of time series analysis is, in many ways, related to this quest. We need only mention Schuster's periodogram (1898, 1906), Yule's autoregressive models (1927), and the modern industry of spectral analysis (see e.g. Childers 1978 and Priestley 1981). In particular, it is interesting to recall that the papers by Schuster (1906) and Yule (1927) were devoted to the analysis of the cyclical sunspot numbers.

Another basic objective is the exploration of ways of improving forecasting which has been dominated by linear assumptions.

With a view to constructing sufficiently wide classes of models with the above objectives in mind and to developing tools for their analyses, we review some of the fundamental ideas in dynamical systems which have been found useful in other scientific disciplines.

2.2 From linear oscillations to non-linear oscillations:
A bird's-eye view

In 1583, the 19-year-old Galileo timed the oscillations of a swinging chandelier in a church by his pulse, thereby obtaining one of the early records of oscillations in the history of science. It is now well known that, to a first approximation, the period of a simple pendulum is *independent* of the amplitude of oscillation and a theoretical explanation of this observation may be based on the simple harmonic oscillator model in the form of a linear differential equation. The independence mentioned above is, of course, a well-known characteristic of the linear theory of oscillations. However, with the improvement of timing precision, it has been discovered that the period actually increases with increasing amplitude. No linear models can explain this relationship and they have to be replaced by non-linear models, often but not always described by non-linear differential equations. Amplitude–period dependence, which is more commonly referred to as *amplitude–frequency dependence,* is a characteristic of non-linear oscillations.

Nowadays, the study of (non-linear) oscillations has transcended classical mechanics and the tools employed are not confined to non-linear differential equations but include non-linear difference equations, functional equations, etc. This wider science, which studies now a *dynamical system* in its widest possible context, is becoming indispensable in diverse fields such as population dynamics, chemical reactions, biomechanics, economics, etc. It is full of vitality and is, without doubt, one of the most exciting branches of science.

The development of non-linear oscillations has gone through three important historical stages.

The chief architect of the first stage was Henri Poincaré (1854–1912) of France, one of the giants of mathematics. It was the results of his study of the notoriously difficult three-body problem which led him to develop what later became the beginning of the qualitative (i.e. geometric) theory and the quantitative (i.e. analytic) theory of non-linear oscillations. Among his many important contributions to the subject, the revolutionary idea of a *limit cycle,* which is totally absent in the linear theory, and the powerful tool of small-parameter perturbation stand out like two beacons showing the way forward.

The second stage occupied the first 60 years of this century and was closely linked with the technological (mainly mechanical and electrical) development of the period. A typical differential equation studied during this period may be expressed by

$$m\ddot{x} + \phi(\dot{x}) + f(x) = F \cos \omega t \qquad (2.1)$$

where we may interpret $m\ddot{x}$ as the *inertia force*, $\phi(\dot{x})$ as the *damping force*, $f(x)$ as the *restoring force* or *spring force*, and $F \cos \omega t$ (F and ω fixed) as the *external force* or *excitation*. In 1918, G. Duffing introduced the celebrated differential equation for mechanical vibrations, now bearing his name, which includes the non-linear restoring force in a dynamical system under excitation. Around the same time, B. Van der Pol developed the famous equation describing oscillations generated by a triode valve under no excitation by incorporating a damping term which could vary between positive and negative values. (More about the two equations will be given later.) These two equations reveal many phenomena, such as jump phenomena, frequency entrainment, limit cycles, etc., which are beyond the capability of linear models. By far the most significant contributions came from the Soviet school of non-linear osciallations headed by Academician Aleksandr Aleksandrovich Andronov (1901–52), sometimes known as the father of modern oscillations. In 1925, the young Andronov had already recognized the role of Poincaré's geometric or abstract concept of limit cycles in conrete autovibration (in Russian *avtokolebanii*). He was the first to *identify* observable self-sustained oscillations with Poincaré's abstract limit cycles. This was evident in the concluding part of his Moscow University bachelor thesis entitled 'Limit cycles of Poincaré in the theory of oscillations'. As early as 1929, when still a postgraduate student, he pointed out that sustained oscillations/self-excited oscillations could be found in diverse situations—from the vibrating strings of a violin to the triode valve oscillator, from the periodic oscillations of chemical reactions to the predator–prey ecosystem, etc. The remarkable achievement of Andronov was the fruitful fusion of abstract mathematical ideas with concrete applications in natural sciences, engineering, and others. His main weapon was the two-dimensional phase space, or the *phase plane*, with coordinates $(x, \dot{x})$, which he used with the greatest dexterity and in which he was said to have spent his entire life! His voluminous contributions were condensed into the famous treatise entitled *Theory of oscillations* (in collaboration with his students S. E. Khaikin and A. A. Vitt) published in 1937. This masterpiece has been translated into many languages, including English and Chinese. Qualitative results accelerated quantitative studies, to which N. M. Krylov and N. N. Bogoliubov and others in the Soviet Union made numerous contributions. Again, traces of Poincaré's quantatitive method could be found in their works. All in all, Soviet oscillation theorists reigned supreme in the 1930s. Only 10 years later did the West come to feel the full impact of their achievements and enormous efforts had to be mounted in order to bridge the gap.

Going beyond the two-dimensional phase plane in a differential equation system introduces many topological objects much more esoteric than limit cycles. At the same time, very complicated structures have been discovered even in one-dimensional difference equations. The 'quantum leap' was signalled by the discovery of the so-called *strange attractor* in non-linear mathematics and *chaos* in physical systems. For our present purpose, they may be taken to convey the same phenomenon. It was discovered that trajectories almost indistinguishable from realizations of stochastic processes could be generated by deterministic systems. These then set the scene for the third stage, and starting from the 1970s the focus has been on chaos. Here, the interplay between order and disorder, determinism and stochasticity, stability and initial-condition sensitivity, predictability and unpredictability, etc., is undergoing profound changes with very exciting implications on people's view of the world around them. Undoubtedly, unfamiliar concepts from this third stage, such as the KAM theorem, Lyapunov exponents, Smale's horseshoe, Feigenbaum constants, fractal dimensions, and so on, will all find their way into the time series literature sooner or later.

It is hoped that the above bird's-eye view has convinced readers that the subject of *time series analysis* can benefit much from ideas which have proved themselves in the first two stages of the development of non-linear oscillations. One day a rejuvenated *time series analysis* might even have a part to play in the third stage.

2.3 Limit cycles

The bird's-eye view just described shows that it is perhaps not surprising that Yule had to improvise with the linear method in 1927. However, it must be said that he was fully aware of its limitations.

So as to acquaint readers with the bare essentials of non-linear oscillations pertinent to later exposition, we now describe the analysis of the celebrated triode oscillator in some detail. (Of course, there is no substitute for a reading of a standard account such as Minorsky (1962) or Andronov *et al.* (1966).) It has been known to radio engineers since 1913 that a triode valve can be used to generate oscillations of a very pure character. A triode valve (see Fig. 2.1) is a thermionic valve with three electrodes: a cathode, the emitter of electrons; an anode, the collector of electrons; and a grid, a wire with open spaces, placed between the anode and the cathode. The grid has a small negative potential relative to the cathode and controls the electron flow from the cathode to the anode. Consider the following circuits (Fig. 2.2). (For more details see for example Minorsky (1962, p. 173).)

As usual, the grid current, anode reactions, internal capacity of the

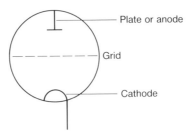

Fig. 2.1. A triode

triode valve, etc., are assumed negligible. By Kirchhoff's law, we have

$$i = -C\frac{dv}{dt'} \qquad Ri = v - L\frac{di}{dt'} - M\frac{di_a}{dt'} \qquad (2.2)$$

or

$$LC\frac{d^2v}{dt'^2} + \left(RC - M\frac{di_a}{dv}\right)\frac{dv}{dt'} + v = 0 \qquad (2.3)$$

where t' denotes the time. The (experimentally determined) functional relation of i_a and v is called the *characteristic* of the valve, which may take the form represented by the solid curve AD in Fig. 2.3. It is said to have the characteristic of a *saturation* above the *threshold* v_0. A function of the form shown by AD will be referred to as a *saturation-type function*.

If the true characteristic is approximated, as suggested by Andronov and Khaikin (1959), by a piecewise linear function (as shown by the lines AB, BC, CD in Fig. 2.3) then under the following linear transformation

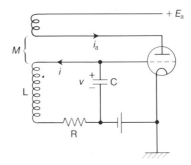

Fig. 2.2. Triode as an oscillator: L = inductance, R = resistance, C = capacitance, i = current in L–R–C circuit, M = mutual inductance, i_a = anode current, v = grid voltage E_a = battery

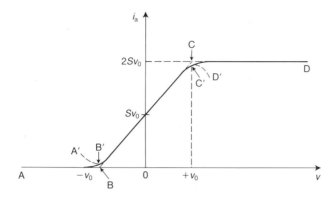

Fig. 2.3. Characteristic of a triode (solid curve AD) (S is a constant and v_0 is the saturation grid potential)

of coordinates and reparametrization:

$$x = v/v_0 \qquad t = \omega_0 t'$$

$$\omega_0 = (LC)^{-1/2} \qquad h_1 = \tfrac{1}{2}\omega_0 RC \qquad h_2 = \tfrac{1}{2}\omega_0(MS - RC)$$

eqn (2.3) may be simplified to

$$\ddot{x} + 2h_1\dot{x} + x = 0 \quad \text{for } |x| > 1 \tag{2.4a}$$

$$\ddot{x} - 2h_2\dot{x} + x = 0 \quad \text{for } |x| < 1. \tag{2.4b}$$

A few remarks are now in order:

1. If $M = 0$, that is the 'anode' coil is absent, then $h_1 = -h_2$ and eqns (2.4) reduce to the ordinary L–C–R equation, which is a second-order linear differential equation and has the well-known solution

$$x(t) = Ae^{\lambda_1 t} + Be^{\lambda_2 t}$$

where A and B are arbitrary constants to be determined by initial conditions, and where λ_1, λ_2 are roots of the characteristic equation

$$\lambda^2 + 2h\lambda + 1 = 0$$

with

$$h = h_1 = -h_2 = \tfrac{1}{2}\omega_0 RC(>0).$$

When $h^2 > 1$, both roots are real (and negative), and $x(t)$ decays exponentially, that is a monotonic damping is obtained. When $h^2 < 1$, the two roots form a complex pair, each with a negative real part, and $x(t)$ is a damped periodic function of t, that is damped oscillations are obtained. To gain a deeper insight, let us consider the loci of $(x, \dot{x})$ with t being the

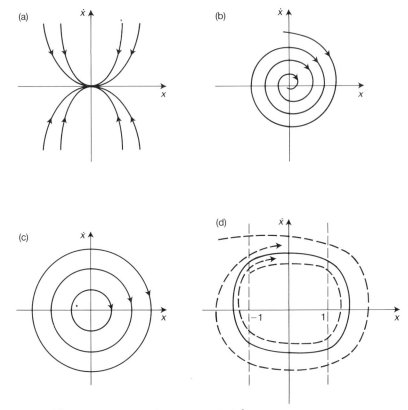

Fig. 2.4. (a) Phase diagram (stable node) $(h^2 > 1)$; (b) phase diagram (stable focus) $(h^2 < 1)$; (c) phase diagram (centre) $(h_1 = h_2 = 0)$; (d) phase diagram (a stable limit cycle) $(0 < h_1 < \infty,\ 0 < h_2 < \infty)$

parameter and with different initial conditions. This is the so-called two-dimensional *phase space* (also called the *phase diagram,* and the *phase plane*), with which Poincaré and Andronov did much of their fundamental qualitative study of second-order differential equations. The most significant point to be noted from Figs 2.4(a) and 2.4(b) is that the origin represents the unique stationary state of oscillation (albeit *static*) *independent of initial conditions.* In Figs 2.4(a) and 2.4(b), the origin is referred to as a *stable node* and a *stable focus* respectively.

2.   If $M = 0$ and $R = 0$, then (2.4) reduce to the simple harmonic motion (SHM)

$$\ddot{x} + x = 0. \tag{2.5}$$

The origin of the associated phase diagram, Fig. 2.4(c), is called the *centre.* It reveals the limitation of a SHM model and models similar to it (called centre-type models) for periodic motion. The initial condition determines uniquely in which circular orbit of the phase diagram the motion will take place. The slightest change of the initial condition will result in a completely different circular orbit. Also, under the slightest perturbation of the parameters, the centre structure disappears. For example, on allowing R to be non-zero but arbitrarily small, Fig. 2.4(c) is replaced by Fig. 2.4(a) or (b). Thus, the SHM is *not physically observable*. Note that the system is conservative (i.e. it does not dissipate energy), which is an unrealistic assumption in practice. Minorsky (1962, Ch. 2, section 9) has given an interesting discussion of another famous centre-type model, namely the so-called simple *Lotka–Volterra predator–prey model:*

$$\frac{dN_1}{dt} = \varepsilon_1 N_1 \qquad \frac{dN_2}{dt} = -\varepsilon_2 N_2$$

where N_1 and N_2 denote the population sizes of the prey and predator respectively, and ε_1 and ε_2 denote the natural multiplication rate of the prey and the natural depletion rate of the predator respectively. Typically, on setting $\varepsilon_1 = a - bN_2$ and $\varepsilon_2 = a' - b'N_1$ (a, b, a', b' are constants >0) the coupled equation describes the interaction between the two populations which, under suitable conditions, can lead to periodic solutions of a similar nature to those of SHM.

3.   It is interesting to note that if attention is confined to the region $|v| < v_0$, then a locally valid cubic approximation of the characteristic (as indicated by the curve A′B′C′D′ in Fig. 2.3) leads to a *locally valid* approximate model in the form of the so-called Van der Pol equation (after some coordinate transformations)

$$\ddot{x} + \beta(x^2 - 1)\dot{x} + x = 0 \qquad\qquad (2.6)$$

where β (>0) is a parameter determined by L, C, R, M, S, and v_0. Analysis is then often carried out *on the assumption that β is sufficiently small*. This represents a 'small-parameter perturbation' of the SHM (2.5), an idea introduced by Poincaré, as mentioned in §2.2. In reference to the triode characteristic, Andronov–Vitt–Khaikin's piecewise linear differential equations (2.4) seem a more realistic approximation of eqn (2.3) than Van der Pol's equation of the form (2.6).

An interesting question for eqn (2.4) must be: does there exist an isolated closed curve on the phase diagram to which all trajectories starting sufficiently near it will approach as t tends to infinity?

To demonstrate that under appropriate conditions the existence is assured, Andronov *et al.* (1966) have used the 'theory of point transformations' developed by the group. We now give an outline of their

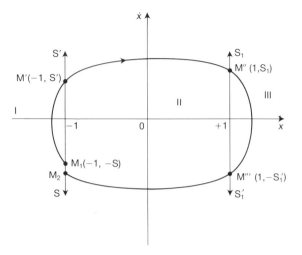

Fig. 2.5. Phase diagram of piecewise linear differential equations (2.4)

arguments. The phase diagram is separated by straight lines $S'S$ and S_1S_1'
into three regions: I, II, and III (Fig. 2.5). In each of these three regions
its own *linear* differential equation is valid. (The piecewise linearity
greatly facilitates the application of the theory of point transformation.)
The equations in I and III have solutions which correspond to either a
stable node or a stable focus. The equation in II has a similar type of
solution if $h_2 < 0$. The case when $h_2 > 0$ is more interesting as we shall
see. It corresponds to a negative damping, that is energy is *absorbed* over
this region! Starting with a general point, say M_1, in I, and solving the
linear differential equations for I, II, III, and II in that order with M_1,
M', M'', and M''' as their respective initial points, and M', M'', M''', and
M_2 as their respective terminal points, we have a *point transformation*, T,
from M_1 to M_2 after the journey I$\rightarrow$II$\rightarrow$III$\rightarrow$II$\rightarrow$I etc. We cannot
form any conclusion after the first journey, but for the subsequent
journeys we can see whether M_2 comes nearer to M_1 or not. If M_2
approaches M_1 and coalesces with it for the repeated journey I$\rightarrow$II$\rightarrow$
III$\rightarrow$II$\rightarrow$I etc., then we obtain a fixed point of the point transformation
T which leads to the following obvious conclusion: the existence of a
fixed point of T is a 'criterion of periodicity' of the piecewise linear
differential equations (2.4). After some tedious algebra involving some
transcendental equations, Andronov and colleagues (1937, 1959) give the
following significant qualitative result: $h_1 > 0$, $h_2 > 0$ is the necessary and
sufficient condition for the existence of *an isolated closed curve on the
phase diagram to which all trajectories starting sufficiently near it will*

approach as t tends to positive infinity. We now define such an isolated closed curve as a *stable limit cycle*. (As a matter of definition, we call the limit cycle *unstable* if the positive infinity is replaced by negative infinity.) Figure 2.4(d) gives an example of a stable limit cycle for (2.4). In fact, when $h_1 > 0$, $h_2 > 0$, it turns out that there is only one such closed curve for (2.4).

As we have seen in §2.2, the concept of a limit cycle introduced by Poincaré in the abstract and identified by Andronov with numerous observable periodic oscillations in the concrete represents a milestone in the development of non-linear oscillations. Physically, *limit cycles represent the (now dynamic) stationary state of sustained oscillations which does not depend on initial conditions but depends exclusively on the parameters of the system, that is they are intrinsic properties.* In addition, *there exist limit cycles which have the properties of being robust, that is insensitive to small perturbations of the parameters of the system* (Andronov actually used the Russian work *grubye*) and are *physically observable.* They arise as a result of a perfect balance between energy dissipation due to the positive damping term $2h_1\dot{x}$ (in regions I and III) and the energy absorption due to the negative damping term $-2h_2\dot{x}$ (in region II) every journey round the limit cycle. (Mathematically, this is equivalent to a vanishing line integral of energy exchange over each round of the limit cycle, that is one period. This is the so-called criterion of Liénard. See e.g. Minorsky 1962, p. 104.) In terms of applications, the most important is in their relation to the so-called *self-sustained oscillations* which characterize, as we have just seen, the oscillatory state of a triode oscillator. Thus, it is immaterial whether the oscillation of a triode oscillator is started by a switch-on or by some arbitrary impulse applied at the instant of a switch-on; the ultimate self-sustained oscillations will be exactly the same, and *the steady* (i.e. non-periodic) *supply of energy* from a (direct current) battery *is converted* by the triode oscillator *into* very pure *physically observable periodic oscillations.*

As far as the search for a suitable class of generic models for the modelling of cyclical data is concerned, the above analysis of the triode valve plays the crucial role of a *feedback controller* of the operating mode of the system. The saturation characteristic of the triode valve allows the existence of two possible operating modes: (i) 'dissipate energy', when the absolute value of the grid voltage v exceeds the *threshold* value v_0, and (ii) 'absorb energy', when otherwise. Generally speaking, the presence, physical or otherwise, of a threshold such as v_0 specifies the operating modes of the system and opens up the possibility of limit-cycle-type oscillations. Thus, *threshold is a generic concept.* It seems that there exists an almost limitless number of examples in which this basic concept plays a crucial role.

2.4 Some examples of threshold models based on piecewise linearity

Tong (1983a) has described numerous examples from diverse fields in which the notion of a threshold is dominant. They have been chosen from the following areas: (i) radio engineering; (ii) marine engineering; (iii) servo-systems; (iv) a steam engine; (v) oceanography; (vi) population biology; (vii) economics; (viii) hydrology; (ix) medical engineering. We do not propose to repeat the examples here with the exception of Example (vi), which is connected with some of the studies of Chapter 7. The above examples drawn from diverse fields all share one common feature, namely the predominance of a threshold, which is merely a reflection of the fact that *saturation is everywhere present* (cf. Kalman 1955, p. 294).

2.4.1 POPULATION BIOLOGY

The idea of a threshold is very natural to the study of population biology because the production of eggs (young) per adult per season is generally a saturation-type function of the available food and food supply is generally limited. Examples abound in this relatively young branch of science (see e.g. May and Oster 1976; Oster and Ipaktchi 1978 and references therein). For example, Readshaw and Cuff (1980) have considered simple threshold models of the form

$$X_t = 0.8X_{t-1} + f(X_{t-15}) \tag{2.7}$$

for the classic Nicholson's blow-fly data. Here X_t denotes the number of adult flies in day t and f is typically characterized by thresholds. For example, in the adult–protein-limited case:

$$f(x) \doteq \begin{cases} 10x & \text{if } x \le 171 \\ 1795 - 0.503x & \text{if } 171 < x \le 3569 \\ 0 & \text{if } x > 3569. \end{cases} \tag{2.8}$$

(See e.g. Gurney *et al.* 1981.) Note that it takes approximately 15 days for an egg to develop into an adult. (All the parameters are determined by what seems to be a trial-and-error method.) Note that eqn (2.7) is an additive version of Pielou's (1974, pp. 79–82) multiplicative equation $X_t = X_{t-1}F(X_{t-d})$.

It seems almost universally accepted in this field that the threshold concept is basic to an understanding of the many observed population cycles. We shall give a detailed time series analysis of some such data in Chapter 7.

2.5 Local linearization of non-linear differential equations

In the examples given in the last two sections, piecewise linearity was quite natural because it was closely linked to the underlying physics of the system (e.g. triode valve characteristics). Whilst it would definitely be unwise to propose that *all* non-linear differential equations could be adequately approximated by piecewise linear differential equations, it would nevertheless be interesting to see how far *piecewise* linearization could lead us. Towards the end of this section we will finish the discussion with the Kalman–Bass theorem.

As an illustration, let us consider the Van der Pol equation (2.6) again, now with β set at unity without loss of generality. We are not concerned with modelling the triode valve oscillator but with Van der Pol 'oscillator' *per se*. Thus, we have

$$\ddot{x} + (x^2 - 1)\dot{x} + x = 0. \tag{2.9}$$

Putting

$$y = \dot{x}$$

we may rewrite (2.9) in the standard *state space* form with $(x, y)^T$ as the state vector:

$$\dot{x} = y \qquad \dot{y} = (1 - x^2)y - x. \tag{2.10}$$

The system defined by (2.10) is said to be *two-dimensional*, the dimensionality being determined by the dimensionality of the state vector. The *state space* here is $\mathbf{R}^2$, which is often called the *two-dimensional phase space*. The trajectory of $(x, y)^T$ is sometimes called a *two-dimensional phase portrait*. Extension of the terminology to higher dimensions is obvious.

Now, solutions of the algebraic equations

$$\dot{x} = 0 \qquad \dot{y} = 0 \tag{2.11}$$

are called the *singular points of* eqn (2.10). For the present case, the origin is the only singular point. The two-term Taylor expansion about this point gives the local linearization as follows:

$$\begin{bmatrix} \dot{x} \\ \dot{y} \end{bmatrix} = \mathbf{L}(0, 0) \begin{bmatrix} x \\ y \end{bmatrix} \tag{2.12}$$

where

$$\mathbf{L}(x, y) = \begin{bmatrix} 0 & 1 \\ -1 - 2xy & 1 - x^2 \end{bmatrix}.$$

Therefore, around the origin the local approximation is

$$\ddot{x} - \dot{x} + x = 0 \tag{2.13}$$

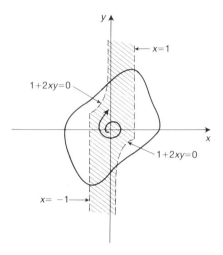

Fig. 2.6. Limit cycle of the Van der Pol equation (closed curve in solid line). The broken lines give a rough estimate of the limit cycle

which may be compared with eqn (2.4b). Now, the characteristic equation associated with (2.13) is given by

$$\det(\lambda\mathbf{I} - \mathbf{L}(0,0)) = \lambda^2 - \lambda + 1 = 0 \tag{2.14}$$

and all its roots are complex with positive real parts. Therefore, the singularity at the origin is an *unstable focus*. (See the outward spiral from the origin in Fig. 2.6.)

To delineate the region on the x–y plane to which the linear approximation (2.13) may apply, we may follow a method due to Chen (1971) by noting that *for each fixed x and y* the equation

$$\begin{pmatrix} \dot{x} \\ \dot{y} \end{pmatrix} = \mathbf{L}(x, y)\begin{pmatrix} x \\ y \end{pmatrix} \tag{2.15}$$

is a valid local linearization at (x, y) and all the roots of the associated characteristic equation

$$\det(\lambda\mathbf{I} - \mathbf{L}) = \lambda^2 - (1 - x^2)\lambda + (1 + 2xy) = 0 \tag{2.16}$$

have positive real parts if and only if

$$1 - x^2 > 0 \quad \text{and} \quad 1 + 2xy > 0. \tag{2.17}$$

(Note that a *naive* characteristic equation associated with (2.9) would read

$$\lambda^2 + (x^2 - 1)\lambda + 1 = 0 \tag{2.18}$$

which leads to the top inequality only.) The region defined by inequality (2.17) is represented by the hatched area in the phase diagram (Fig. 2.6). The broken lines then give a rough estimate of the limit cycle which is known to exist in the Van der Pol oscillator and is represented by the closed curve in a solid line.

So far our discussion has been heuristic but it is based on the fact that frequently we may establish all qualitative features of the trajectories (the 'phase portrait') by examining the field of directions defined by the differential equation at a *finite* (but 'sufficiently large') number of points in the phase space (see e.g. Kaplan 1950). The points chosen are commonly the singular points of the differential equation. In fact, for the two-dimensional system, we have the rigorous results of Kalman and Bass which we state in the form of a theorem without proof. (For details, see Kalman (1957) and references therein.) For higher-dimensional systems, the situation is very complex and is beyond the scope of this book. One complication stems from the fact that chaos will enter the picture once we go beyond the two-dimensional system.

* ¶ Let us consider a two-dimensional system defined by

$$\dot{\mathbf{x}} = \mathbf{h}(\mathbf{x}) \tag{2.19}$$

where $\mathbf{x} = (x, y)^T$ and $\mathbf{h}(\mathbf{x}) = (h_1(x, y), h_2(x, y))^T$.

Theorem 2.1 (Kalman-Bass Theorem): Let the 2-vector function $\mathbf{h}$ of (2.19) satisfy a Lipschitz condition. Suppose that (2.19) is *dissipative*, that is that there is a circular domain $D: x^2 + y^2 \leq r^2$ which all trajectories eventually enter. Suppose that $\mathbf{h}(0) = 0$ but that $\|\mathbf{h}(\mathbf{x})\| \neq 0$ for $\|\mathbf{x}\| \neq 0$, where typically $\|\mathbf{x}\|$ denotes $(x^2 + y^2)^{1/2}$. Then D can be decomposed into the union of certain ('sufficiently small') closed regions D_i $(i = 1, \ldots, N)$ to which corresponds a piecewise linear, continuous vector function $\mathbf{h}^*$ given by

$$\mathbf{h}^*(\mathbf{x}) = \mathbf{A}_i \mathbf{x} \quad \text{in} \quad D_i \ (i = 1, \ldots, N) \tag{2.20}$$

the $\mathbf{A}_i$ being 2×2 matrices, which is such that the two-dimensional phase portraits of (2.19) and

$$\dot{\mathbf{x}} = \mathbf{h}^*(\mathbf{x}) \tag{2.21}$$

are topologically equivalent, that is homeomorphic (with a single possible exception). The exception is that, if (2.19) has one or more limit cycles which are neither stable nor unstable, they may not occur in (2.21). ¶ ¶

---

* Sections which readers may wish to skip at first reading are opened by ¶ and closed by ¶ ¶.

2.6 Amplitude–frequency dependence and jump phenomenon

For definiteness we consider the Duffing equation without damping:

$$\ddot{x} = -\alpha x - \beta x^3 + F \cos \omega t \qquad (2.22)$$

where α, β, F, and ω are real constants. Our discussion will be heuristic and we refer readers to the specialist texts (such as Andronov and Khaikin (1937) or Stoker (1950), etc.) for the missing rigour.

It is clear that $x^{(1)} = A \cos \omega t$ is the solution of (2.22) for the case $\beta = 0$, that is the linear case. Suppose that β is a small parameter. Then, in the spirit of Poincaré's small-parameter perturbation mentioned in §2.2, we may start with $x^{(1)}$ as the first approximation of the solution of (2.22). Substituting this in (2.22) and observing the identity

$$\cos^3 \omega t = \tfrac{3}{4} \cos \omega t + \tfrac{1}{4} \cos 3\omega t$$

we obtain an equation for the next approximation $\bar{x}^{(2)}$:

$$\ddot{\bar{x}}^{(2)} = -(\alpha A + \tfrac{3}{4}\beta A^3 - F) \cos \omega t - \tfrac{1}{4}\beta A^3 \cos 3\omega t. \qquad (2.23)$$

Upon integrating (2.23) twice, the solution is

$$\bar{x}^{(2)} = \frac{1}{\omega^2}(\alpha A + \tfrac{3}{4}\beta A^3 - F) \cos \omega t + \frac{1}{36}\frac{\beta A^3}{\omega^2} \cos 3\omega t. \qquad (2.24)$$

As usual all integration constants are set to zero in the above discussion since we are only interested in periodic solutions. Provided that β, α, A, and F are all sufficiently small it would seem natural to repeat the substitution to obtain successive approximations. However, it turns out that this seemingly natural process *fails to yield all the branches of the response curves* which relate the amplitude of the forced oscillation to ω. Duffing then took a bold step, which led to significant results that apparently even Lord Rayleigh failed to obtain. Duffing argued that if $x^{(1)} = A \cos \omega t$ is truly a reasonable first approximation, then, instead of $\bar{x}^{(2)}$, the next approximation, now denoted by $x^{(2)}$, should be of the form

$$x^{(2)} = A \cos \omega t + B \cos 3\omega t \qquad (2.25)$$

(with $B = 0$ when $\beta = 0$) because it reduces to the exact result for the linear case ($\beta = 0$). Duffing's reasoning leads to

$$A = \frac{1}{\omega^2}(\alpha A + \tfrac{3}{4}\beta A^3 - F) \qquad (2.26)$$

and

$$B = \frac{1}{36}\frac{\beta A^3}{\omega^2}. \qquad (2.27)$$

From (2.26) follows the *basic amplitude (A)–frequency (ω) relation*

$$\omega^2 = \alpha + \tfrac{3}{4}\beta A^2 - \frac{F}{A}. \tag{2.28}$$

The significant point about this basic relation is the multi-value aspect of the relation. To be mathematically meaningful A should be fixed first and the frequency ω considered as a function of A. Duffing's procedure predicts that *for certain values of ω there are three corresponding values of A* as can be seen in the multi-branch response curves (Fig. 2.7).

Duffing's prediction has been checked experimentally in a variety of different cases. In each case experimental results are in good agreement with the theory.

If a positive damping term $c\dot{x}$ $(c > 0)$ is added to the left-hand side of (2.22), then it may be shown (see e.g. p. 92 of Stoker 1950) that the response curves may be obtained from those shown in Fig. 2.7 by 'closing their tops' (see Fig. 2.8).

The above response curves predict several important and interesting physical phenomena, which have been observed experimentally. We mention one of them now.

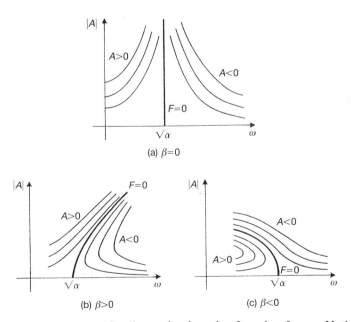

Fig. 2.7. Response curves for linear, hard, and soft spring forces. Notice that figures (b) and (c) may be obtained from (a) by bending the latter to the right and to the left respectively

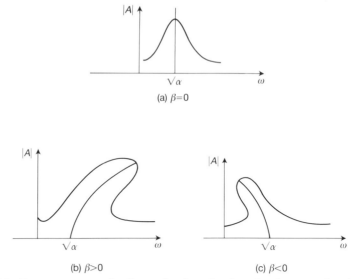

Fig. 2.8. Response curves for linear, hard, and soft spring forces under damping

Let us consider the hard spring case (i.e. $\beta > 0$). Suppose we hold the amplitude F of the excitation constant but allow the frequency ω to decrease gradually from the point 1 (Fig. 2.9). We would observe that the response amplidute $|A|$ increases gradually until point 2 is reached at which position it *jumps* upwards (hence the term *jump phenomenon*) to point 3 and then decreases thereafter. On the other hand, if the frequency ω is allowed to increase, then the response amplitude $|A|$ follows the $1'–2'–3'$ route which is shown by double-headed arrows. Notice that the upward jump and the downward jump occur at different ω values. The jump phenomena for the soft spring case (i.e. $\beta < 0$) may be described in a similar way. Referring to Fig. 2.7, we can see that there can be only a single jump (upwards only for $\beta > 0$ and downwards only

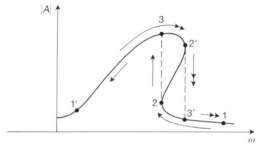

Fig. 2.9. Jump phenomenon

for $\beta < 0$) in the absence of damping (i.e. $c = 0$). It is also obvious that a linear spring (i.e. $\beta = 0$) is jump-free with or without damping.

For other variants of jump phenomena, readers are referred to, for example, Stoker (1950).

In (2.25) the second approximation $x^{(2)}$ involves the *third harmonic* term $\cos 3\omega t$ (ω being the *fundamental* frequency). From this observation, we may infer that a general solution of (2.22) involves all odd harmonics. This is in fact the case (see e.g. Stoker 1950). The important point to note is that *the occurrence of harmonics* besides the fundamental frequency *is another characteristic of a non-linear dynamical system.*

Finally, it should be remarked that, despite its vintage, the Duffing equation is still taxing the best brains in differential equations and its general solution is far from being complete!

2.7 Volterra series and bilinear systems

Before we continue our discussion of dynamical systems in terms of differential equations, it would be appropriate, at this point, to give a fundamentally different description. The description given so far is in terms of *internal* structure in the form of a differential equation which specifies how all its components, that is *states*, are interconnected, how they interact, and how they behave individually. In fact, Kalman (1980) has called this the *internal, state variable,* or *axiomatic* definition of a dynamical system. We could also describe a dynamical system externally by specifying how the system responds to different stimuli, without specifying the internal properties. Kalman called this the *external* or *input/output* or *empirical* definition of a dynamical system. In systems science, constructing the internal description from knowledge of the external description is called the *problem of realization,* which is a vast topic in that science and the interested reader is referred to, for example, Kalman *et al.* (1969).

Now, one basic tool employed in the external description of a non-linear system is the so-called Volterra series, which has a history dating back to early this century. The principal architect of the approach was V. Volterra, who apparently first published his ideas nearly a century ago. (See for example Volterra (1930) and references therein.) Later, others like N. Wiener and his co-workers (Wiener 1958), and Barrett (1963) and Kalman (1980) took up the theme but from different standpoints. However, the subject seems to have lost its momentum shortly afterwards. More recently, there seems to have been a revival of interests (see e.g. Brockett 1976, 1977; Rugh 1981).

To describe the Volterra series properly, we would have to employ the language of functional analysis because the series is really a power series expansion for a functional. This is beyond the scope of this book. However, in order to give our readers a flavour of the topic, we now give an informal account by sometimes relying on heuristics and analogies.

Let $f(t; x(t'), t' \leq t)$ denote the response (i.e. output) at time t to the stimuli (or signal or input) $\{x(t'), t' \leq t\}$. Strictly speaking, f is an example of a *functional* by virtue of its being a function whose argument $x(.)$, is a function and whose value is a real number. The value taken by this functional at t is denoted by $f(t; x(t'), t' \leq t)^*$. Many of the common input/output relations are, in fact, examples of functionals, a few of which we list below.

1. Identity:

$$f(t; x(t'), t' \leq t) = x(t). \tag{2.29}$$

Here, the response always equal the latest stimulus

2. Differentiation:

$$f(t; x(t'), t' \leq t) = \dot{x}(t). \tag{2.30}$$

The functionals here and above for time t depend only on the values of $x(s)$ with s in the immediate neighbourhood of t. They are said to be *instantaneous*.

3. One-sided smoothing:

$$f(t; x(t'), t' \leq t) = \int_{t_0}^{t} g(t, t')x(t') \, dt' \tag{2.31}$$

where g is called a *kernel*.

4. Modulation:

$$f(t; x(t'), t' \leq t) = M(t)x(t). \tag{2.32}$$

Up to now, all the examples are *linear* functionals in that

$$f(t; cx(t'), t' \leq t) = cf(t; x(t'), t' \leq t), \quad \forall c \in \mathbf{R}$$

$$f(t; x(t') + y(t'), t' \leq t) = f(t; x(t'), t' \leq t) + f(t; y(t'), t' \leq t).$$

5. Square-law devices:

$$f(t; x(t'), t' \leq t) = kx^2(t) \tag{2.33}$$

where k is a constant. This is non-linear and instantaneous.

---

* The notation adopted here is unconventional but it seems better suited for this level of discussion. A less clumsy notation would be $f[x](t)$.

6. Regular homogeneous functional of degree n:

$$f(t; x(t'), t' \le t)$$

$$= \int_{t_0}^{t} \ldots \int_{t_0}^{t} g(t; t_1, t_2, \ldots, t_n) x(t_1) x(t_1) x(t_2) \ldots x(t_n) \, dt_1 \, dt_2 \ldots d_{tn}$$

$$(2.34)$$

where g is again called the *kernel*. This functional includes the square-law device as a special case by considering the kernel with $n = 2$ and

$$g(t; t_1, t_2) = k\delta(t - t_1)\delta(t - t_2) \qquad (2.35)$$

where δ denotes the Dirac delta function. This functional is the basic building block of the Volterra series.

There is a natural analogy between functionals and functions of several variables since we can intuitively compare $x(.)$ with a collection of (infinitely) many variables. It is known that if f is a sufficiently well-behaved function near the origin it has a convergent power expansion near the origin:

$$f(x_1, x_2, \ldots, x_n) = k_0 + \sum k_i x_i + \sum \sum k_{ij} x_i x_j + \sum \sum \sum k_{ijk} x_i x_j x_k + \ldots$$

$$(2.36)$$

where the summations are all from 1 to n. By analogy, if f is a sufficiently well-behaved functional near the origin we expect the power expansion near the origin to take the form

$$f(t; x(t'), t' \le t) = k_0(t) + \int k(t; t_1) x(t_1) \, dt_1$$

$$+ \iint k(t; t_1, t_2) x(t_1) x(t_2) \, dt_1 \, dt_2$$

$$+ \iiint k(t; t_1, t_2, t_3) x(t_1) x(t_2) x(t_3) \, dt_1 \, dt_2 \, dt_3 + \ldots \quad (2.37)$$

where the integrals are all from $-\infty$ to t. A compact form of (2.37) is

$$f(t; x(t'), t' \le t)$$

$$= \sum_n \iint \ldots \int k(t; t_1, \ldots, t_n) x(t_1)(t_2) \ldots x(t_n) \, dt_1 \, dt_2 \ldots dt_n. \quad (2.38)$$

It is often more convenient to allow the integrals to range over $(-\infty, \infty)$ but restrict the kernels so that

$$k(t; t_1, \ldots, t_n) = 0 \qquad (2.39)$$

if any of $t_1, t_2, \ldots, t_n$ is greater than t. With this convention, (2.38) defines the *Volterra series* of f. If the range of n is finite, we call the series (2.38) a *finite Volterra series*.

Example 2.1 (Determination of Volterra series for the Duffing equation): Recall the Duffing equation with damping after an obvious change of notation to conform with our present discussion:

$$\ddot{y} + c\dot{y} + \alpha y + \beta y^3 = x(t) \tag{2.40}$$

where $x(t)$ denotes the stimulus (i.e. the forcing term) and is given by, as in the previous section,

$$x(t) = F \cos \omega t. \tag{2.41}$$

The response (i.e. output) is denoted by $\{y(t)\}$. Clearly, $y(.)$ is a functional of $x(.)$ via (2.40). The object is to determine the Volterra series for this functional.

Introduce the operator $D = d/dt$ and write (2.40) as

$$Ly + \beta y^3 = x \tag{2.42}$$

where the variable t is suppressed and

$$L = D^2 + cD + \alpha.$$

Now invert (2.42) in the neighbourhood of the origin treating L as an ordinary number to obtain a power series expansion

$$y = c_1 x + c_2 x^2 + \ldots \tag{2.43}$$

where the coefficients c_i may be obtained by substituting this power series for y in the left-hand side of (2.42) and equating coefficients of powers of x on both sides. Thus,

$$L(c_1 x + c_2 x^2 + \ldots) + \beta(c_1 x + c_2 x^2 + \ldots)^3 = x.$$

$$\therefore \quad Lc_1 = 1$$
$$Lc_2 = 0$$
$$Lc_3 + \beta c_1^3 = 0$$
$$\cdots$$

$$\left.\begin{array}{c} \therefore \quad c_2 = c_4 = c_6 = \ldots = 0 \\ \text{and } c_1 = L^{-1} \\ c_3 = -L^{-1}\beta L^{-3} \\ \cdots\cdots \end{array}\right\} \tag{2.44}$$

The meaning of L^{-1} is provided by the (particular integral) solution of linear differential equation

$$Ly = x \tag{2.45}$$

in the form of

$$y(t) = \int_{-\infty}^{\infty} h(t - t_1)x(t_1)\, dt_1 \qquad (2.46)$$

which is formally written as

$$y(t) = L^{-1}x(t). \qquad (2.47)$$

Here,

$$h(s) = \begin{cases} (\lambda_1 - \lambda_2)^{-1}(e^{\lambda_1 s} - e^{\lambda_2 s}) & \text{for } s > 0 \\ 0 & \text{otherwise} \end{cases} \qquad (2.48)$$

where λ_1 and λ_2 are the roots of the characteristic equation

$$\lambda^2 + c\lambda + \alpha = 0. \qquad (2.49)$$

(We have assumed that $\lambda_1 \neq \lambda_2$ and that they have negative real parts. For the case with equal roots, we need to modify $h(s)$ in a standard way.) The first two non-zero terms of the solution are thus

$$y(t) = \int_{-\infty}^{\infty} h(t - t_1)x(t_1)\, dt_1 - \beta \int_{-\infty}^{\infty} h(t - t_1)\left(\int_{-\infty}^{\infty} h(t - t_2)x(t_2)\, dt_2\right)^3 dt_1$$

corresponding to

$$y = L^{-1}x - \beta L^{-1}(L^{-1}x)^3. \qquad (2.50)$$

After some rearrangement, we may obtain explicitly the first two non-zero terms of the Volterra series for the Duffing equation (2.40) as follows:

$$y(t) = \int_{-\infty}^{\infty} h(t - t_1)x(t_1)\, dt_1$$

$$- \beta \iiint_{-\infty}^{\infty} h(t - t_1, t - t_2, t - t_3)x(t_1)x(t_2)x(t_3)\, dt_1\, dt_2\, dt_3 \qquad (2.51)$$

where

$$h(t - t_1, t - t_2, t - t_3) = \int_{-\infty}^{\infty} h(t - s)h(s - t_1)h(s - t_2)h(s - t_3)\, ds. \qquad (2.52)$$

The analysis is incomplete without considering the question of convergence. However, this is a very delicate problem, on which we shall not dwell beyond quoting a result of Barrett's (1963):

In the case where $\alpha > 0$, $c^2 > 4\alpha$ (linear part overdamped) the functional power series is convergent (i) for all $x(t)$ when $\beta \geq 0$, (ii) for all $x(t)$ satisfying

$$\max_{-\infty < t < \infty} |x(t)| < \frac{\sqrt{2}\,\alpha}{3}\frac{\alpha}{\sqrt{3}\,|\beta|} \qquad (2.53)$$

when $\beta \leq 0$. The convergence is interpreted here in the classical sense for each fixed t. Apparently, unlike our discussion in §2.6, β is not required to be small in Barrett's condition (i). In Barrett's condition (ii), $|\beta|$ may be large provided it is 'compensated' by α. On the other hand, to discern limit cycles, jump phenomena, etc., from the Volterra series description requires deeper structural studies especially of the kernels. (See e.g. Brockett 1977.) □

Example 2.2 (A bilinear system): Consider the so-called *bilinear* input–state –output equation systems in the simplest form

$$\dot{x}(t) = A(t)x(t) + B(t)x(t)u(t) \qquad y(t) = C(t)x(t) \qquad (2.54)$$

where $u(t)$ is the control input, $y(t)$ is the observed output, and $x(t)$ the state at time t. All the variables are scalars in this example. In a more general situation, the state variable may be a vector, and we may also consider multi-inputs and multi-outputs in which case u and y are vectors. The term 'bilinear' derives from the presence of the cross-product $u(t)x(t)$. Generally speaking, $u(t)$ and $y(t)$ are observable and $x(t)$ is not. The role of $x(t)$ usually lies in its abstraction of what may be envisaged as the information about the future trajectory of the system from its past. We may quote Kalman (1980): 'the "state" [his quote] of a dynamical system may be identified with the "memory" [again his quote] that the system retains of a particular input'.

Suppose that the initial value of x is $x(0)$. Then the fundamental solution of the linear differential equation

$$\dot{x}(t) = A(t)x(t) \qquad (2.55)$$

subject to initial value $x(0)$ is

$$x(t) = \Phi_A(t, 0)x(0) \qquad (2.56)$$

where

$$\ln(\Phi_A(t', t)) = \int_t^{t'} A(s)\,\mathrm{d}s. \qquad (2.57)$$

Control engineers have sometimes called $\Phi_A(t', t)$ the *transition matrix*, a term which we shall not use in this book. On making the change of variables

$$Z(t) = \Phi_A(0, t)x(t) \qquad (2.58)$$

and using (2.57), (2.54) is equivalent to

$$\dot{Z}(t) = B(t)\dot{u}(t)Z(t) \qquad y(t) = \bar{C}(t)Z(T) \qquad (2.59)$$

where

$$\bar{C}(t) = C(t)\Phi_A(t, 0). \qquad (2.60)$$

To solve the differential equation for $Z(t)$, we may repeat the same argument as previously and get

$$Z(t) = \Phi_{Bu}(t, 0)Z(0) \qquad (2.61)$$

where

$$\ln(\Phi_{Bu}(t', t)) = \int_t^{t'} B(s)u(s) \, ds. \qquad (2.62)$$

It is quite easy to verify that

$$\Phi_{Bu}(t, 0) = 1 + \int_0^t B(s)u(s) \, ds + \frac{1}{2!} \int_0^t \int_0^t B(s)u(s)B(s')u(s') \, ds' \, ds$$

$$+ \frac{1}{3!} \int_0^t \int_0^t \int_0^t B(s)u(s)B(s')u(s')B(s'')u(s'') \, ds'' \, ds' \, ds + \ldots$$

$$= 1 + \int_0^t B(s)u(s) \, ds + \int_0^t \int_0^{s'} B(s')u(s')B(s)u(s) \, ds \, ds'$$

$$+ \int_0^t \int_0^{s''} \int_0^{s'} B(s')u(s')B(s'')u(s'')B(s)u(s) \, ds \, ds' \, ds''$$

$$+ \ldots \qquad (2.63)$$

Therefore

$$y(t) = C(t)\Phi_A(t, 0)Z(t)$$

$$= C(t)\Phi_A(t, 0)\Phi_{Bu}(t, 0)Z(0)$$

$$= C(t)\Phi_A(t, 0)\Phi_{Bu}(t, 0)x(0)$$

$$= C(t)\Phi_A(t, 0)x(0) + C(t)\left(\int_0^t \Phi_A(t, 0)B(s)u(s) \, ds \right)x(0)$$

$$+ C(t)\left(\int_0^t \int_0^{s'} \Phi_A(t, s')B(s')u(s')\Phi_A(s', 0)B(s)u(s) \, ds \, ds' \right)x(0)$$

$$+ C(t)\left(\int_0^t \int_0^{s''} \int_0^{s'} \Phi_A(t, s'')B(s'')u(s'')\Phi_A(s'', s')B(s') \right.$$

$$\left. \times \Phi_A(s', 0)B(s)u(s) \, ds \, ds' \, ds'' \right)x(0)$$

$$+ \ldots \qquad (2.64)$$

This implies that the bilinear system (2.54) admits a Volterra series with kernels ($r = 0, 1, 2, \ldots$)

$$k(t; t_1, t_2, \ldots, t_r) = C(t)\Phi_A(t, t_1)B(t_1)\Phi_A(t_1, t_2)B(t_2) \ldots$$
$$\times B(t_r)\Phi_A(t_r, 0)x(0). \quad \square \tag{2.65}$$

A few remarks are in order.

Remark 2.1: The above result (2.65) may be generalized to cover the case with a state vector, $\mathbf{x}(t)$, of dimension $n > 1$. Apart from the obvious changes of dimensions, that is $C(t)$ is $1 \times n$, $\Phi_A(t_i, t_j)$ is $n \times n$, $B(t_i)$ is $n \times n$, and $\mathbf{x}(0)$ is $n \times 1$, eqn (2.65) remains unchanged.

Remark 2.2: Noting that $\Phi_A(s, t)$ is separable, that is

$$\Phi_A(s, t) = \Phi_A(s, 0)\Phi_A(0, t) \tag{2.66}$$

we see that the kernel given by (2.65) is expressible as a separable product, namely

$$k(t; t_1, t_2, \ldots, t_r) = \gamma_0(t) \prod_{j=1}^{r} \gamma_j(t_j) \tag{2.67}$$

where

$$\gamma_0(t) = C(t)\Phi_A(t, 0) \tag{2.68}$$

$$\gamma_j(t_j) = \Phi_A(0, t_j)B(t_j)\Phi_A(t_j, 0), \quad j = 1, \ldots, r. \tag{2.69}$$

(For the case $n = 1$, the right-hand side of (2.69) reduces to $B(t_j)$.) We call kernels of the form given by (2.67) *separable kernels*. Thus, bilinear systems have separable kernels on account of (2.65) and (2.66).

Remark 2.3: It is not difficult to verify that the Volterra series, or more specifically the regular homogeneous functional of degree r,

$$y(t) = \int_0^t \cdots \int_0^{t_2} \gamma_0(t)\gamma_1(t_1)\gamma_2(t_2) \ldots \gamma_r(t_r)u(t_1)u(t_2) \ldots u(t_r) \, dt_1 \ldots dt_r \tag{2.70}$$

is *realized* by the bilinear system with state vector

$$\mathbf{x}(t) = (x_1(t), x_2(t), \ldots, x_r(t), x_{r+1}(t))^T$$

and initial value

$$(x_1(0) = x_2(0) = \ldots = x_r(0) = 0, \, x_{r+1}(0) = 1)$$

and

$$\dot{x}_1(t) = u(t)\gamma_1(t)x_2(t)$$
$$\dot{x}_2(t) = u(t)\gamma_2(t)x_3(t)$$
$$\vdots$$
$$\dot{x}_r(t) = u(t)\gamma_r(t)x_{r+1}(t) \tag{2.71}$$
$$\dot{x}_{r+1}(t) = 0$$
$$y(t) = \gamma_0 x_1(t).$$

Summarizing the above discussion, we have:

Theorem 2.2: A finite Volterra series has a bilinear realization if and only if the kernels are separable.

In fact, the theorem applies to systems more general than the bilinear systems. Specifically, it applies to the so-called *linear analytic systems* under a mild condition,

$$\dot{x}(t) = f(t, x(t)) + u(t)g(t, x(t))$$
$$y(t) = h(t, x(t)) \tag{2.72}$$
$$x(0) = x_0$$

where $x(t) \in \mathbf{R}^n$, $u(t) \in \mathbf{R}$, $y(t) \in \mathbf{R}$, and f, g, and h are analytic functions of x and continuous in t. The mild condition alluded to, which we shall assume in all our subsequent discussions, states that there is a finite $T > 0$ such that the solution of

$$\dot{x}(t) = f(t, x(t)), \qquad x(0) = x_0$$

exists on $[0, T]$. The Volterra series is then only concerned with $t \in [0, T]$, which again we shall tacitly assume henceforth.

Theorem 2.3: A finite Volterra series has a linear analytic realization if and only if it has a bilinear realization.

A result due to Frechet (see e.g. Brockett 1976) tells us that any continuous *map* (i.e. *functional*) of the space of continuous functions over $[0, T]$, $T < \infty$, to **R** may be approximated by a finite Volterra series. Together with Theorems 2.2 and 2.3, this result forms the basis of the claim that *the class of bilinear systems is dense in the class of linear analytic systems if the time interval of interest is finite*. The condition of finiteness of the time interval turns out to be crucial. It clearly marks the extent to which bilinear systems may be usefully applied in practical situations. For 'finite-time' problems, bilinearity has a lot to offer. Loosely speaking, the dense property is a quantitative property. However, important qualitative properties of non-linearity such as limit cycles, jump phenomena, etc., which are observed to occur and which cannot be explained by the linear theory, are pertinent to 'infinite-time' problems—they are observed as a form of asymptotic behaviour over time. Brockett (1977) has demonstrated that *bilinear systems do not exhibit limit cycles or jump phenomenon*.

We now end this section with some examples of the bilinear system.

Example 2.3 (Population dynamics): Let $x(t)$ denote the population size of a certain biological species at time t. The simplest population model is

$$\frac{\mathrm{d}x(t)}{\mathrm{d}t} = u(t)x(t) \tag{2.73}$$

where $u(t)$, birth rate minus death rate, may be considered a control input variable. In many realistic situations $u(t)$ depends on $x(t)$, that is there are population constraints. We may construct a simple 'feedback control' model by setting

$$u(x) = a - bx \qquad (2.74)$$

where the constant a is sometimes called the *intrinsic growth rate* and a/b corresponds to the maximum attainable population. Here and later we suppress t whenever convenient. It is sometimes instructive to rewrite this model, the so-called *Verhulst–Pearl logistic model*, as

$$\frac{dx}{dt} = ax\left(\frac{(a/b) - x}{(a/b)}\right) \qquad (2.75)$$

which expresses the real growth rate as a proportion of the intrinsic growth rate. The proportion decreases with increasing population due to limited resources.

Further inhibition may be incorporated in the model. For example, the presence of a competing species or a parasite, x_2, may affect the population of the species, x_1. In either case we may generalize (2.75) to the so-called *two-species Lotka–Volterra model*

$$\frac{dx_1}{dt} = u_1(x_1, x_2)x_1 \qquad \frac{dx_2}{dt} = u_2(x_1, x_2)x_2 \qquad (2.76)$$

where

$$u_1(x_1, x_2) = a_1 - b_{11}x_1 - b_{12}x_2$$
$$u_2(x_1, x_2) = a_2 - b_{21}x_1 - b_{22}x_2. \qquad (2.77)$$

(Recall that a special case of this model was discussed in §2.3.) The parities of the coefficients a and b reflect the mode of interaction between x_1 and x_2. For example: (i) if x_1 and x_2 compete for the same resources, then all coefficients are positive; (ii) if x_1 is the parasite population and x_2 is the host population, then b_{12} is negative because the parasite population grows at the expense of the host population. The coefficient a_1 is negative because the parasite has no alternative 'food' than the host.

The main point to note is that the population control u is, in the above models, multiplicative instead of additive, typically of the form

$$\frac{dx}{dt} = \alpha u + \beta x.$$

Example 2.4 (The Michaelis–Menton model): This is a commonly used model to describe biochemical reactions in the human body which are controlled by an enzyme catalyst. It takes the form

$$\frac{dx_1}{dt} = a_1 x_2 - bux_1 \qquad \frac{dx_2}{dt} = bux_1 - (a_1 + a_2)x_2 \qquad (2.78)$$

where x_1 is the concentration of a chemical substance (i.e. a substrate) acted upon by an enzyme with concentration u and x_2 is the concentration of a complex. The model assumes that the complex formed by a combination of enzyme and substrate further decomposes into an enzyme and end product of concentrate x_3 so that

$$\frac{dx_3}{dt} = a_2 x_2 \qquad \frac{du}{dt} = (a_1 + a_2)x_2 - bux_1 \qquad (2.79)$$

with $x_1 + x_2 + x_3 = s > 0$ and $u + x_2 = E > 0$. Here, s and E arise from the total substrate and total enzyme available in the cell.

2.8 Time delay

The notion of a time delay, which we have briefly touched upon in §2.4 (e.g. eqn (2.7)), is also basic to the understanding of cyclical phenomena. As we have seen, there is often an in-built feedback mechanism which is responsible for the unforced sustained oscillations. Intuitively, it is clear that few feedback mechanisms would produce instantaneous responses. Of course, if the time delay is negligible relative to the sampling period (in the case of discrete time data), then it seems reasonable to assume that the time delay is zero for practical purposes.

The development of *delayed (differential) equations* is relatively recent. One of the earliest comprehensive accounts seems to be Bellman and Cooke (1963); they have used the name of differential–difference equations for delayed differential equations, and the subject is still undergoing development. It seems that analytical tools are much less well developed here than those for piecewise linear equations, for example. However, it is generally recognized that if the time delays are long compared with the natural growth timescales in the equation, the potentially stabilizing feedback can in fact become destabilizing, and the system oscillates in a stable limit cycle (see e.g. Levin and May 1976; Gumowski 1981). Of course, this important property has been recognized for a long time (see e.g. Wiener 1948). Without going into the analytical complexity (for this, the readers may refer to the references cited so far in this section), we may briefly indicate the richness in structure of delayed differential equations. First, we consider a first-order linear delayed differential equation with delay $\delta(>0)$:

$$\dot{x}(t) = -x(t - \delta), \qquad (t \geq 0) \qquad (2.80)$$

subject to

$$x(t) = \theta(t), \qquad (-\delta \leq t \leq 0).$$

In operator form (2.80) may be written as

$$(D + e^{-\delta D})x(t) = 0 \tag{2.81}$$

where D is the operator d/dt. Now, the characteristic equation

$$\lambda + e^{-\delta \lambda} = 0 \tag{2.82}$$

is transcendental and the structure of its roots is much more complex; some of them may be real and some may be complex. (Recall that it is always real for $\delta = 0$.) It turns out that (2.80) admits no oscillatory solutions for $\delta < 1/e$ (i.e. similar to the case of a first-order equation with $\delta = 0$), but it can admit oscillatory solutions for $\delta > 1/e$ (i.e. similar to the case of a second-order equation with $\delta = 0$ whose characteristic roots are complex). This situation is sometimes described as a 'simple root–multiple root type bifurcation at the threshold value $1/e$' (see e.g. Gumowski 1981.) A general conclusion is that delay terms considerably increase the variety of possible qualitatively distinct time evolutions. Damped and sustained oscillations can sometimes occur in the presence of delay while, for the same system but with the delay suppressed, only a constant steady state is obtained. For example, when $\delta = \pi/2$, (2.81) has a solution $x(t) = a \cos t + b \sin t$, $(a, \ b$ arbitrary constants). See also Robinson (1972, 1974, 1975, 1977a) and Tong (1983b) for a stochastic extension of (2.81).

As far as applications of the concept of time delay are concerned, the logistic delay equation of Hutchinson (1948) is probably one of the earliest in population biology. It takes the form

$$\dot{x}(t) = x(t)(a - bx(t - \delta)) \tag{2.83}$$

where $x(t)$ is the population density at t and δ denotes the time delay which corresponds to the development time taken by the newly born to become an adult. There are now an increasing number of applications from many areas including ecology, physics, physical chemistry, chemical engineering, economics, etc. (see for example references in Bonilla and Verlarde (1982)). We describe an example in astrophysics in connection with sunspot numbers. It provides some necessary background to an analysis of these data in Chapter 7.

As we have said in Chapter 1, dark spots on the surface of the Sun have been observed for nearly 2000 years. Recent records of sunspot numbers reveal an intriguing cyclical phenomenon of an approximate 11 year period which has been challenging our intellect every since Samuel Heinrich Schwabe (1789–1875) of Germany first announced the sunspot cycles in 1843 after spending 17 years in painstaking observations. These data are regarded as a good indicator of the overall evolution of the magnetic oscillation of the Sun. They provide an important source of information concerning the fluid motions of the solar dynamo as well. It has been suggested that the Sun may be considered a rotating plasma with a weak magnetic field and acting like a dynamo. According to one astrophysical theory, the differential solar rotation generates a toroidal field (with lines of force running in the W–E direction) which tends to put stress on the poloidal field (with lines of force running in the N–S direction) of the Sun. Magnetic eruption takes place only when the toroidal field strength exceeds some *threshold* (see e.g. Bray and Loughhead 1964). This theory has been further developed (see e.g. Yoshimura 1979) to incorporate a 'time delay' mechanism in the feedback action of the magnetic field on the dynamo process. The dynamo equation of Yoshimura is quite complicated:

$$\frac{\partial \psi}{\partial t} = \left(\frac{(1-\mu^2)}{r^2} \frac{\partial^2}{\partial \mu^2} + \frac{\partial^2}{\partial r^2} \right) \psi + N_R R \Phi \qquad (2.84a)$$

$$\frac{\partial \Phi}{\partial t} = \left(\frac{(1-\mu^2)}{r^2} \frac{\partial^2}{\partial \mu^2} + \frac{\partial^2}{\partial r^2} \right) \Phi + N_G G \psi \qquad (2.84b)$$

$$N_R \propto \exp(-a_N |\Phi(t - t_d)|_{\max}^{N_f}) \qquad (2.84c)$$

$$N_G \propto \exp(-a_N |\Phi(t - t_d)|_{\max}^{N_f}) \qquad (2.84d)$$

where ψ and Φ represent the poloidal and toroidal fields respectively. The standard spherical coordinate system is used, in which symmetry about one of the polar coordinate angles is assumed and $\mu = \sin \theta$, θ being the other polar coordinate angle; R and G are partial differential operators describing the so-called magnetohydrodynamic induction (remember the electromagnetic induction of the triode valve?), $|\Phi|_{\max}$ denotes the spatial maximum of Φ, and (a_N, N_f, t_d) are parameters. A typical value of N_f is 5, which implies that N_R and N_G are like band-pass filters of Φ as a realization of the threshold idea. The time delay is expressed by t_d. The physical idea behind this model is not unlike that of the triode valve oscillator except that the latter has no time delay. Numerical integration of (2.84) leads to periodic solutions (Yoshimura 1979).

2.9 From differential equations to difference equations

So far our discussion has been mainly concentrated on dynamical systems in continuous time expressed in non-linear differential equations. It is included so that we may acquire a *physical point of view*. Thus, we have been exposed to the fundamental ideas that (i) in an unforced dissipative non-linear system (e.g. the Van der Pol equations) we may have periodic solutions in the form of limit cycles, provided there is an energy balance, and (ii) in a periodically forced dissipative non-linear system (e.g. the Duffing equation with damping) the amplitude of the 'output' signal and the frequency of the periodic driving force are interrelated. These ideas are unknown to linear dynamicists.

However, to give a mathematically rigorous expression of these physical ideas is by no means trivial. (Hence, we may begin to appreciate some of the many formidable problems facing pioneers like Andronov.) The task of extending the same level of mathematical rigour to discrete-time dynamical systems is even more formidable. Fairly recent research (e.g. May 1976) shows that the variety of dynamical behaviour is in some respects much richer for discrete-time systems expressed, for example, in non-linear difference equations, with chaos, for instance, being possible even in the one-dimensional case. (Recall that for a differential equation system we would have to go beyond the two-dimensional phase plane for the emergence of chaos, that is for autonomous systems of the form $\dot{\mathbf{x}} = \mathbf{f}(\mathbf{x})$, $\mathbf{f}: \mathbf{R}^2 \to \mathbf{R}^2$.)

The origin of the greater complexity may be explained by reference to the following first-order autonomous differential equations:

$$\dot{x} = g(x;c) \qquad x = x(t),\ t > 0,\ x(0) = x_0 \qquad (2.85)$$

where x_0, c are parameters and g is a single-valued continuous differentiable function of its arguments. Let

$$x(t) = H(x_0, t; c) \qquad (2.86)$$

be the general solution of (2.85). An analogous first-order autonomous recurrence is of the form

$$x_{t+1} = f(x_t; c), \qquad t = 0,\ \pm 1,\ \pm 2, \ldots \qquad (2.87)$$

where c is a parameter and $f(x;c)$ is a single-valued smooth function of both x and c. Similar to (2.86), let

$$x_t = F(x_0, t; c), \qquad (2.88)$$

be the general solution of (2.87). Now, the function H in (2.86) can be determined in principle for $t > 0$ and $t < 0$ with *equal* ease. An analogous situation rarely exists in the case of (2.87) because the function F turns out to be in general extremely complicated (in all non-contrived cases it cannot be expressed explicitly in terms of known elementary and transcendental functions). Another way which leads to the same conclusion is to note that whilst it is easy to iterate forward with (2.87) from x_0, obtaining the so-called *discrete half-trajectory of consequents* of x_0, namely $\{x_1, x_2, \ldots\}$, it is generally difficult to 'invert' (2.87) so as to find the so-called *discrete half-trajectory of antecedents* of x_0, that is $\{x_{-1}, x_{-2}, \ldots\}$. (Just write down a few simple f and try for yourself.) Note that antecedents are similar to, but not identical with, the backcasts introduced by Box and Jenkins (1976, §9.2.4).

With the trajectories consisting of sets of discrete points, we lose immediately all the advantages associated with continuity, differentiability, etc. For example, the method of point transformation for limit cycle investigation described in §2.3 will no longer apply. Moreover, the naive approach of studying difference equations by discretizing differential equations can lead to considerable difficulties. For example, in a recent study Yamaguti and Ushiki (1981) have shown that the discretization of the equation

$$\dot{x} = x(1-x) \tag{2.89}$$

by central difference schemes with fixed 'meshed' size produces some 'ghost solutions', that is pathological behaviour. Above all, the continuous-time/discrete-time relationship is more delicate than is sometimes appreciated. (See for example, Chan and Tong (1987), which gives an unexpected result for a first-order linear model in time series.)

It would seem that, at least for the present, we really have to take the bulls of non-linear difference equations by their horns. Recently, there seems to be an increasing awareness of the need to develop systematically dynamical systems in discrete time *per se*. The proliferation of articles devoted to this area, for example in the journal *Physica D*, is a testimony.

2.10 Limit points and limit cycles of non-linear difference equations

The theory of discrete-time non-linear dynamical systems, in general and non-linear difference equations in particular, is incomplete. It is currently undergoing tremendous development. At the present stage of development, the pragmatic approach of resorting to digital computer experimentation plays a very important part in the learning process. However, so as to aid our discussion, we now introduce some *working* definitions, which are analogous to their continuous-time counterparts. No pretence at complete rigour is intended.

For each integer $t \geq 1$, let $\mathbf{x}_t$ denote a k-dimensional (state) vector $\in \mathbf{R}^k$, satisfying the equation

$$\mathbf{x}_t = \mathbf{f}(\mathbf{x}_{t-1}), \qquad \mathbf{x}_0 \in \mathbf{R}^k \tag{2.90}$$

where $\mathbf{f}$ is a vector-valued function. Let $\mathbf{f}^{(j)}$ denote the jth iterate of $\mathbf{f}$, that is

$$\mathbf{f}^{(j)}(\mathbf{x}) = \mathbf{f}(\mathbf{f}(\ldots \mathbf{f}(\mathbf{x}))\ldots)$$

$$j \text{ of them}$$

Definition 2.1: Let T be a finite positive integer. A k-dimensional vector $\mathbf{x}^*$ is called a *periodic point with period* T of (2.90) if $\mathbf{x}^* = \mathbf{f}^{(T)}(\mathbf{x}^*)$ and $\mathbf{x}^* \neq \mathbf{f}^{(j)}(\mathbf{x}^*)$ for $1 \leq j < T$. (We also sometimes call $\mathbf{x}^*$ a *fixed point* of $\mathbf{f}^{(T)}$.) We say $\mathbf{x}^*$ is *periodic* or is a *periodic point* if $\mathbf{x}^*$ is periodic with period T for some $T \geq 1$. The ordered set $(\mathbf{x}^*, \mathbf{f}^{(1)}(\mathbf{x}^*), \ldots, \mathbf{f}^{(T-1)}(\mathbf{x}^*))$ is called a T-cycle. We say that $\mathbf{x}_0$ is *eventually periodic* if for some positive integer n, $\mathbf{x}^* = \mathbf{f}^{(n)}(\mathbf{x}_0)$ is periodic. We say that $\mathbf{x}_0$ is *asymptotically periodic* if there is a periodic point $\mathbf{x}^*$ for which the Euclidean norm

$$\|\mathbf{f}^{(n)}(\mathbf{x}_0) - \mathbf{f}^{(n)}(\mathbf{x}^*)\| \to 0 \quad \text{as} \quad n \to \infty.$$

Definition 2.2: By an *attractor* for $\mathbf{f}$ we mean a compact set A such that the set

$$B = \left\{ \mathbf{x} : \lim_{n \to \infty} \inf_{\mathbf{y} \in A} \|\mathbf{f}^{(n)}(\mathbf{x}) - \mathbf{y}\| = 0 \right\}$$

has positive Lebesgue measure and A is minimal with respect to (w.r.t.) this property. Here $\|.\|$ denotes the Euclidean norm. The set B is called the *basin of attraction* (or *domain of influence*) for A. It is sometimes, denoted by $B(A)$.

If the attractor is a set of T points $\{\mathbf{x}_1, \ldots, \mathbf{x}_T\}$ such that

$$\mathbf{f}(\mathbf{x}_n) = \mathbf{x}_{n+1}, \qquad n = 1, \ldots, T-1$$

and

$$\mathbf{f}(\mathbf{x}_T) = \mathbf{x}_1$$

we call the attractor A a *limit cycle*. If $T = 1$, we call it a *limit point*. For the map

$$f(x) = 4x(1-x)$$

on the interval $[0, 1]$, it may be checked that $[0, 1]$ is an attractor for f. Attractors of such 'non-degenerate' type are called *strange attractors*. Strange attractors are related to, but not identical with, the objects which we shall call chaotic time series in the next section.

We are primarily interested in the situation where $\mathbf{f}$ is realized through the recurrence

$$x_t = f(x_{t-1}, \ldots, x_{t-k}) \quad (t \geq 0, \ k < \infty). \tag{2.91}$$

Just as is the case with non-linear differential equations, it is conceivable that there may exist regions of $\mathbf{R}^k$ with respect to which the recurrence f diverges. However, in practice we are mainly interested in those regions of $\mathbf{R}^k$ with respect to which the recurrence $\mathbf{f}$ converges to either a limit point or a limit cycle or a bounded set. Various *censoring* devices may be introduced to restrict our attention to the latter. The following is one of many similar devices.

Let d be a prefixed integer chosen from $\{1, 2, \ldots, k\}$, $k < \infty$. We agree to set $x_i = 0$, $\forall i < 0$.

Definition 2.3: Let f be a point transformation from $\mathbf{R}^k$ to $\mathbf{R}$ given by (2.91). Let S be a finite interval of $\mathbf{R}$. f_S is said to be a *censored version** of f induced by S if it is a point transformation from $\mathbf{R}^k$ to $\mathbf{R}$ and has the following properties: (i) $x_{t-d} \in S \Rightarrow f_S(x_{t-1}, \ldots, x_{t-k}) = f(x_{t-1}, \ldots, x_{t-k})$ and (ii) $x_{t-d} \notin S \Rightarrow f_S(x_{t-1}, \ldots, x_{t-k}) = c$, $c \notin S$ and $|c| < \infty$.

Theorem 2.4: f_S defines a stable recursion in the sense of uniform boundedness asymptotically.

Proof. Denote the row vector $(x_t, \ldots, x_{t-k+1})$ by $\mathbf{x}_t$. We agree to call x_i an outlier if $x_i \notin S$. Suppose that $\mathbf{x}_{t_0}$ is the first vector with its first component x_{t_0} being an outlier. Under the recursion f_S,

$$\mathbf{x}_{t_0+d} = (c, x_{t_0+d-1}, \ldots, x_{t_0+d-k+1}).$$

Obviously, $\forall t \geq t_0 + d$, $\mathbf{x}_t$ has at least one component equal to c. It now remains to be shown that the number of components of $\mathbf{x}_t$ equal to c is monotonically non-decreasing as t increases to infinity. There are two possibilities subsequent to $\mathbf{x}_{t_0+d}$. One possibility is that no more outliers will occupy the first component except for the recurring c, in which case f_S defines a stable recursion. The other possibility is that a new outlier will occupy the first component in addition to the recurring c. Because each outlier will subsequently produce one further component equal to c, we have proved by induction that the number of components equal to c is monotonically non-decreasing. Hence, there exists an $M < \infty$, such that for all $t \geq M$,

$$|f_S(x_{t-1}, \ldots, x_{t-k})| < \infty, \qquad \forall(x_{t-1}, \ldots, x_{t-k}) \in \mathbf{R}^k.$$

Therefore, by the finiteness of M,

$$|f_S(x_{t-1}, \ldots, x_{t-k})| < \infty, \qquad \forall(x_{t-1}, \ldots, x_{t-k}) \in \mathbf{R}^k \text{ and all } t. \quad \square$$

Note that globally f_S and f may behave differently.

In one-dimensional cases it is possible to use the standard 'cob-web'-type argument to investigate the existence of limit points and limit cycles. We illustrate the method with Figs 2.10, 2.11, and 2.12, which are self-explanatory.

---

* In Tong (1983*a*), the name stabilizer was used. The present choice seems more descriptive.

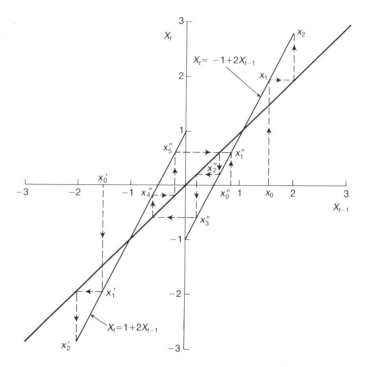

Fig. 2.10. Initial values less than 1 in modulus lead to the limit cycle (0.6, 0.2, −0.6, −0.2). 1 and −1 are fixed points. Initial values greater than 1 in modulus lead to divergence

In higher-dimensional cases, i.e. $k \geq 2$, the situation is much more complex and we need to introduce geometric concepts similar to those described in §2.3. We confine our discussion mainly to the case $k = 2$. For convenience, we denote the state vector by $\xi_t = (x_t, y_t)^T$ and consider the two-dimensional dynamics (mapping) $\phi(\xi_t) = \xi_{t+1}$. Specifically,

$$\phi : \begin{pmatrix} x_t \\ y_t \end{pmatrix} \rightarrow \begin{pmatrix} f(x_t, y_t) \\ g(x_t, y_t) \end{pmatrix}, \qquad f : \mathbf{R}^2 \rightarrow \mathbf{R}, \qquad g : \mathbf{R}^2 \rightarrow \mathbf{R}. \qquad (2.92)$$

The sequence of points on $\mathbf{R}^2$, $\{\xi_i\}_{i=0}^\infty$, is called an *orbit* (or a *trajectory*) of the mapping ϕ. The point $\mathbf{P}(\bar{x}, \bar{y})$ is called a *fixed point* of the mapping if it holds that $\phi : \mathbf{P} \rightarrow \mathbf{P}$, that is

$$\begin{pmatrix} \bar{x} \\ \bar{y} \end{pmatrix} = \begin{pmatrix} f(\bar{x}, \bar{y}) \\ g(\bar{x}, \bar{y}) \end{pmatrix}. \qquad (2.93)$$

It is plausible that the local behaviour of ϕ at $\mathbf{P}$ is governed by its local linearization (cf. §2.5) at $\mathbf{P}$. (We shall state two theorems later which

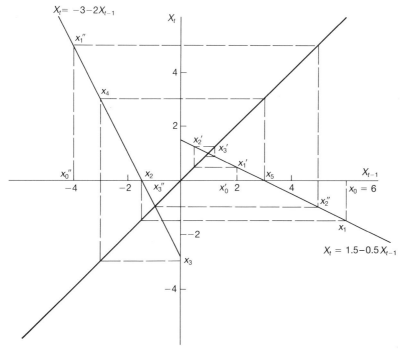

Fig. 2.11. Initial values of the form $3n$ ($n = 0, 2, \dots$), lead to the limit cycle $(-3, 3, 0)$. Other initial values lead to the limit points ± 1. (Note that for a discontinuous map, a cycle of period 3 does not necessarily imply a chaos (cf. Li and Yorke 1975)

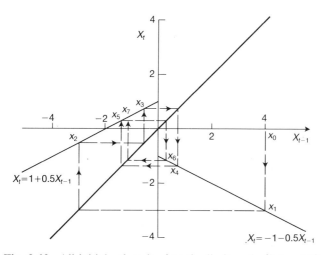

Fig. 2.12. All initial values lead to the limit cycle $(0.4, -1.2)$

justify this statement.) For this we assume that f and g are analytic at $\mathbf{P}$. Let $\mathbf{J}$ denote the Jacobian matrix of first partial derivatives evaluated at $\mathbf{P}$, or in short the *derivative* $(D\phi)$ of ϕ evaluated at $\mathbf{P}$, that is

$$D\phi(\mathbf{P}) = \mathbf{J} = \begin{pmatrix} f_x^{(\mathbf{P})} & f_y^{(\mathbf{P})} \\ g_x^{(\mathbf{P})} & g_y^{(\mathbf{P})} \end{pmatrix} \tag{2.94}$$

where the entries are evaluated at $\mathbf{P}$. Then the locally linear model around $\mathbf{P}$ is

$$\begin{pmatrix} x_{t+1} \\ y_{t+1} \end{pmatrix} = \mathbf{J} \begin{pmatrix} x_t \\ y_t \end{pmatrix} + \text{a constant vector} \tag{2.95}$$

(Without loss of generality, the constant vector may be chosen to be the zero vector by a suitable change of origin.)

Let us recall some basic results concerning the linear model $\xi_{t+1} = \mathbf{B}\xi_t$, namely

$$\begin{pmatrix} x_{t+1} \\ y_{t+1} \end{pmatrix} = \mathbf{B} \begin{pmatrix} x_t \\ y_t \end{pmatrix} \tag{2.96}$$

where $\mathbf{B}$ is a general 2×2 matrix of real constants. Clearly the origin is a fixed point. Let λ_1 and λ_2 ($\lambda_1 \neq \lambda_2$) denote the eigenvalues of $\mathbf{B}$ with $\mathbf{e}_1$ and $\mathbf{e}_2$ denoting the corresponding eigenvectors. Since any initial point generates a unique orbit provided that $\mathbf{B}$ has no zero eigenvalues, we assume that $\mathbf{B}$ has this property. Suppose that $|\lambda_1| \neq 1$ and $|\lambda_2| \neq 1$. In this case, the origin is called a *hyperbolic* fixed point. (This definition may be extended to cover the mapping defined by (2.92) and then $(\bar{x}, \bar{y})^T$ is called a *hyperbolic* fixed point if $\mathbf{J}$ has no eigenvalues of unit modulus.) The eigenvalues λ_1, λ_2 characterize the *trajectories* (i.e. *orbits*) of (2.96) because under the coordinate transformation

$$\boldsymbol{\eta}_t = (\mathbf{e}_1 \mid \mathbf{e}_2)\xi_t, \tag{2.97}$$

the model (2.96) is equivalent to

$$\boldsymbol{\eta}_t = \Delta\boldsymbol{\eta}_{t-1} = \ldots = \Delta^t\boldsymbol{\eta}_0, \tag{2.98}$$

where

$$\Delta = \begin{bmatrix} \lambda_1 & 0 \\ 0 & \lambda_2 \end{bmatrix}.$$

The space spanned by eigenvectors of $\mathbf{B}$ whose eigenvalues have modulus less (greater) than unity is called the *stable* (*unstable*) *manifold*. It is denoted by $E^s(E^u)$. The orbits in $E^s(E^u)$ are characterized by contraction (expansion). The space spanned by the eigenvectors of $\mathbf{B}$ whose eigenvalues have unit modulus is called the *centre manifold*. Depending on the values of λ_1, λ_2, we may have a classification of the orbits similar to that portrayed in Figs 2.4(a), (b), (c). (See Figs 2.13(a), (b), (c), and (d). Note that the *saddle* type is also available in differential equations although not protrayed in Fig. 2.4.)

Note that in Figs 2.13(a) and (b), the arrows will be reversed if $|\lambda_1|$ and

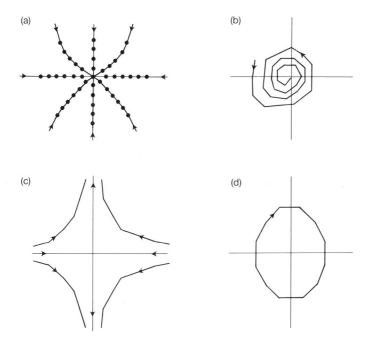

Fig. 2.13. Stable node (λ_1 and λ_2 are real and $0 < |\lambda_1| < 1$, $0 < |\lambda_2| < 1$). Note that only the points, not the lines joining them, are important. Points will not be shown in (b)–(d). (b) Stable focus (λ_1 and λ_2 complex with modulus less than 1). (c) Saddle (λ_1 and λ_2 are real and $0 < |\lambda_1| < 1$, $|\lambda_2| > 1$). (d) Centre (λ_1 and λ_2 complex with unit modulus). If $(\arg \lambda_1)/\pi$ is rational all orbits are periodic. If $(\arg \lambda_1)/\pi$ is irrational then almost all orbits on the same ellipse cover it densely

$|\lambda_2|$ are greater than unity. In general, if $|\lambda_j| < 1$ for all j, then all orbits are attracted to the origin, which is sometimes called a *sink*. If $|\lambda_j| > 1$ for all j, then all orbits are repelled by the origin, which is sometimes called a *source*. We should emphasize once more that *orbits in discrete time* (*solutions of discrete-time dynamical systems*) *differ fundamentally from trajectories in continuous time* (*solutions of continuous-time dynamical systems*) because the former are sequences of points while the latter are curves in $\mathbf{R}^k$. A more descriptive name for a continuous-time trajectory is a *flow*.

We now return to our non-linear set up (2.92). The general idea is then to study the local behaviour around the fixed point, **P**, via the linearized system (2.95), with the classicfication of which we can then hope to have a similar classification of the non-linear system (2.92) around **P**. The hope is the preservation of local behaviours around **P** in going from the linear case (which is easier to handle) to the general non-linear case. We have in mind perhaps something typified by Fig. 2.14.

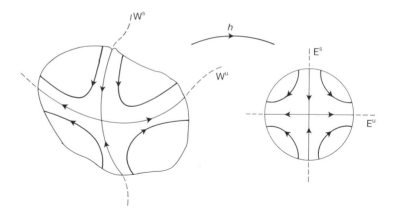

Fig. 2.14. Local linearization around a fixed point

For the linearization to be useful, we would also hope that the stable
and unstable manifolds (E^s and E^u respectively) of the linearized model
will stay close to their non-linear counterparts (W^s and W^u respectively,
say, which are yet to be defined). The hope may be pictured in Fig. 2.15.

Two remarkable theorems show that our hopes are not in vain! ¶ First
we define *local stable manifold*, $W^s_{loc}(\mathbf{P})$, and *local unstable manifold*,
$W^u_{loc}(\mathbf{P})$, of $\mathbf{P}$ of ϕ which is assumed to be a 1–1 and onto mapping and
to have the property that both ϕ and ϕ^{-1} are differentiable (i.e. a
diffeomorphism). Let U denote a neighbourhood of $\mathbf{P}$.

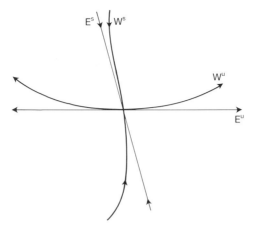

Fig. 2.15. Manifolds

$$W^s_{\text{loc}}(\mathbf{P}) = \{\xi \in U : \phi^t(\xi) \to \mathbf{P} \text{ as } t \to \infty, \text{ and } \phi^t(\xi) \in U, \forall t \ge 0\}$$

$$W^u_{\text{loc}}(\mathbf{P}) = \{\xi \in U : \phi^{-t}(\xi) \to \mathbf{P} \text{ as } t \to \infty, \text{ and } \phi^{-t}(\xi) \in U, \forall t \ge 0\}.$$

Let $W^s(\mathbf{P})$ denote $\bigcup \phi^{-t}(W^s_{\text{loc}}(\mathbf{P}))$ over all $t \ge 0$, and be called the *global stable manifold*. Let $W^u(\mathbf{P})$ denote $\bigcup \phi^t(W^u_{\text{loc}}(\mathbf{P}))$ over all $t \ge 0$, and be called the *global unstable manifold*. We may now state without proof the celebrated Hartman–Grobman theorem and stable manifold theorem of a fixed point for general dimension k (see e.g. Guckenheimer and Holmes 1983, p. 18).

Theorem 2.5 (Hartman–Grobman theorem): Let $\phi : \mathbf{R}^k \to \mathbf{R}^k$ be a diffeomorphism with a hyperbolic fixed point $\bar{\mathbf{x}}$, Then there exists a homeomorphism $\mathbf{h}$ defined on some neighbourhood U of $\bar{\mathbf{x}}$ such that $\mathbf{h}(\phi(\xi)) = D\phi(\bar{\mathbf{x}})\mathbf{h}(\xi)$ for all $\xi \in U$. Here $D\phi(\bar{\mathbf{x}})$ denotes the derivative of ϕ evaluated at $\bar{\mathbf{x}}$.

Theorem 2.6 (Stable manifold theorem for a fixed point): Let $\phi : \mathbf{R}^k \to \mathbf{R}^k$ be a diffeomorphism with a hyperbolic fixed point $\bar{\mathbf{x}}$. Then there are local stable and unstable manifolds $W^s_{\text{loc}}(\bar{\mathbf{x}})$, $W^u_{\text{loc}}(\bar{\mathbf{x}})$, tangent to the eigenspaces E^s, E^u of $D\phi(\bar{\mathbf{x}})$ at $\bar{\mathbf{x}}$ and of corresponding dimensions. $W^s_{\text{loc}}(\bar{\mathbf{x}})$, $W^u_{\text{loc}}(\bar{\mathbf{x}})$ are as smooth as the mapping ϕ. ¶¶

In practice, for cases with dimension not less than 2 we often resort to digital devices in order to explore limit points and limit cycles, etc.

Figure 2.16 shows that the following model (2.99), which arises from an investigation of Wolf's sunspot numbers, appears to admit a limit cycle. However, it is difficult to describe completely its basin of attraction:

$$x_t = \begin{cases} 2.053\,99 + 0.956\,83x_{t-1} - 0.153\,91x_{t-2} - 0.110\,71x_{t-3} \\ \quad + 0.141\,91x_{t-4} - 0.298\,24x_{t-5} + 0.089\,69x_{t-6} \\ \quad + 0.121\,05x_{t-7} - 0.288\,93x_{t-8} + 0.297\,73x_{t-9} \\ \qquad\qquad\qquad\qquad\qquad\qquad \text{if } x_{t-8} \le 12.15 \\ 4{,}716\,29 + 1.388\,96x_{t-1} - 0.791\,86x_{t-2} \quad \text{if } x_{t-8} > 12.15. \end{cases} \qquad (2.99)$$

2.11 Chaos of non-linear difference equations

The iteration defined by (2.90), namely

$$\mathbf{x}_t = \mathbf{f}(\mathbf{x}_{t-1}), \qquad \mathbf{x}_0 \in D \subseteq \mathbf{R}^k$$

has very rich structure even when $k = 1$. Besides limit points and limit cycles, it can exhibit trajectories almost indistinguishable from realizations of a stochastic process! Thus, *randomness can be generated by a strictly deterministic equation*. This phenomenon is loosely described as

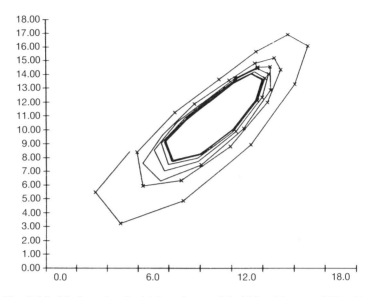

Fig. 2.16. Limit cycle of a high-order model. (After Tong and Wu 1982)

chaos. (The Greek word for chaos is $\chi\acute{\alpha}o\zeta$, which appeared in the passage 'First verily was created chaos, and then broad-bosomed Earth, . . . ' of *Hesiod,* circa 800 BC). The situation should not (although it sometimes does) surprise statisticians for, after all, they throw a coin to randomize their experiments. Fundamentally, *randomness (i.e. chaos) is generated because of the sensitive dependence on initial conditions.* In other words, a small perturbation of the initial condition can lead to vastly different realizations. Thus, although the dynamics governing the trajectory of a tossed coin can be accurately described by a deterministic differential equation, not surprisingly it turns out to be very sensitive to the initial velocity and initial angular momentum. (See for example Fig. 2 on p. 325 of *Statistical Science,* **1,** No. 3, 1986.)

Chaos can occur in both differential equations and difference equations. For simplicity, we shall concentrate on the latter.

One way to characterize sensitive dependence on initial values for difference equations such as (2.90) is by introducing the so-called *Lyapunov exponents* (also called the *characteristic exponents*), a concept due to Oseledec (1968). We sketch the basic idea here, referring the interested readers to Eckmann and Ruelle (1985) and others for a rigorous discussion. For simplicity of discussion, we assume that f is everywhere differentiable, a condition which may be weakened. Let us consider (2.90) with $k = 1$. Let x_0 and x_0' denote two different initial points. Then, after n iterates,

$$(x_n - x_n') = f^{(n)}(x_0) - f^{(n)}(x_0')$$

$$\approx \frac{\mathrm{d}}{\mathrm{d}x} f^{(n)}(x_0)(x_0 - x_0').$$

By the chain rule,

$$\frac{\mathrm{d}}{\mathrm{d}x} f^{(n)}(x_0) = f'(x_0) f'(x_1) \ldots f'(x_{n-1}).$$

If the factors are of comparable size, then $\mathrm{d}f^{(n)}(x_0)/\mathrm{d}x$ increases (or decreases) exponentially with n. That is to say the separation $(x_n - x_n')$ behaves likewise. It therefore makes sense to consider the average rate of change

$$\lambda(x_0) = \lim_{n \to \infty} \frac{1}{n} \ln \left| \frac{\mathrm{d}}{\mathrm{d}x} f^{(n)}(x_0) \right| = \lim_{n \to \infty} \ln \left| \frac{\mathrm{d}}{\mathrm{d}x} f^{(n)}(x_0) \right|^{1/n}.$$

Under some technical conditions pertaining to ergodic theory, $\lambda(x_0)$ turns out to be independent of x_0 almost surely (w.r.t. an underlying invariant measure, say ρ, induced by f). In this case, $\lambda(x_0) = \lambda$, for almost all $x_0 \in \mathbf{R}$ and

$$\delta x_n \approx e^{\lambda n} \delta x_0$$

where $\delta x_j = |x_j - x_j'|$. We call λ the *Lyapunov exponent* of f(w.r.t. ρ) where $\lambda = \int \ln |f'(x)| \rho(\mathrm{d}x)$. Let A be an attractor of f with B as its basin of attraction. If $\mathbf{x}_0 \in B$ almost surely (ρ) and $\lambda > 0$, then we call $\{\mathbf{x}_t : t \geq 0\}$ a *chaotic* time series. Note that global boundedness and local instability are the two basic ingredients of chaotic series . In this case, a line segment of nearby points is stretched on average by a factor of $e^{\lambda n}$ after n iterations. The idea may be generalized to the case $k > 1$. We simply replace $f'(x)$ by the Jacobian matrix $D_{\mathbf{x}}\mathbf{f}$ evaluated at $\mathbf{x}$, that is $D_{\mathbf{x}}\mathbf{f} = (\partial f_i / \partial x_j)$ where f_i denotes the ith component of $\mathbf{f}$, x_j denotes the jth component of $\mathbf{x}$, and the derivative is evaluated at $\mathbf{x}$. We would then replace λ by an array of Lyapunov exponents, sometimes called the *Lyapunov spectrum*. Specifically, let $a_i(n, \mathbf{x})$ denote the modulus of the ith eigenvalue of $D_{\mathbf{x}}\mathbf{f}^{(n)}$ evaluated at $\mathbf{x}$, ordered so that $a_1(n, \mathbf{x}) \geq \ldots \geq a_k(n, \mathbf{x})$. We define the ith *Lyapunov exponent* $\lambda_i(\mathbf{x})$ as

$$\lambda_i(\mathbf{x}) = \lim_{n \to \infty} \frac{1}{n} \ln |a_i(n, \mathbf{x})|, \quad i = 1, \ldots, k.$$

Again, under suitable conditions, the limit exists and is independent of $\mathbf{x}$. The above definition of a chaotic time series may be extended to this case by replacing $\lambda(x_0)$ by $\lambda_1(\mathbf{x}_0)$.

Example 2.5: We now consider the logistic equation which has been made immortal by an exciting review article by the theoretical biologist R. M. May (1976), namely

$$x_{t+1} = ax_t(1 - x_t), \qquad t = 0, 1, 2, \ldots \qquad (2.100)$$

where $x_0 \in [0, 1]$. Clearly for $0 \le a \le 4$, (2.100) defines a map from the unit interval into itself. We concentrate on the 'most chaotic' case in which $a = 4$. In this case (2.100) defines a map from the unit interval on to itself and has a general solution expressible by an *elementary* function

$$x_t = \sin^2(2^t k \pi), \qquad t = 1, 2, \ldots \qquad (2.101)$$

where k lies in $[0, 1)$ and is determined by x_0. It should be stressed that it is the exception rather than the rule that a solution in the form of an elementary function should exist for a non-linear difference equation. It is instructive to write k in diadic form as

$$k = 0 \cdot k_1 k_2 k_3 k_4 \ldots \qquad (2.102)$$

where $k_i \in \{0, 1\}$, each i. Now at each iteration the foremost binary digit is lost. If k is rational, then for sufficiently large $m(\ge 1)$, $\{k_m, k_{m+1}, k_{m+2}, \ldots\}$ is a periodic sequence (say with period p, $1 \le p < \infty$) of 0's and 1's, which implies that the recursion starting with x_0 tends to a limit cycle of period p. For example, corresponding to $k = 1/7$, we have the 3-cycle $(0.188, 0.611, 0.950)$ by first checking that $1/7$ has the diadic expression defined by $k_i = 0$ if $i \equiv 1$ or $2 \pmod 3$, and $k_i = 1$ if $i \equiv 0 \pmod 3$. For this example, $m = 1$. Of course, if x_0 is an arbitrary starting point, k is almost surely an irrational number with an infinite string of 0's and 1's which is in a state of chaos. This implies that $(x_0, x_1, x_2, \ldots)$ is almost surely in a state of chaos for x_0 arbitrarily chosen from $[0, 1]$.

Actually, using the fact that with $a = 4$ (2.100) induces an underlying invariant measure ρ with density (Exercise 6)

$$g(x) = [\pi^2 x(1 - x)]^{-1/2}, \qquad x \in [0, 1],$$

the Lyapunov exponent of (2.100) is given by

$$\lambda = \frac{1}{\pi} \int_0^1 \frac{\ln |4(1 - 2x)|}{[x(1 - x)]^{1/2}} \, dx$$

$$= \ln 2$$

$$> 0$$

which explains the sensitivity of the iteration to initial values. $\square$

It turns out that the Lyapunov spectrum has a close connection with the geometric concept of dimension. to motivate the discussion, let us consider eqn (2.90) with $k = 2$ and suppose that there exists an attractor for which $\lambda_1 > 0 > \lambda_2$. Cover the attractor with squares of side ε. Let $N(\varepsilon)$ denote the number of such squares required. Now, iterate the map q times. For q fixed and ε small enough, the result of the iteration stretches each square into a long thin parallelogram of sides $e^{\lambda_1 q}\varepsilon$ and $e^{\lambda_2 q}\varepsilon$. Suppose we cover the stretched figure with squares of side $e^{\lambda_2 q}\varepsilon$ and let $N(e^{\lambda_2 q}\varepsilon)$ denote the necessary number. Roughly speaking, it holds that

$$\frac{N(e^{\lambda_2 q}\varepsilon)}{N(\varepsilon)} \doteq e^{q(\lambda_1 - \lambda_2)}. \tag{2.103}$$

Suppose that

$$\lim_{\varepsilon \to 0} \frac{\ln(N(\varepsilon))}{\ln(1/\varepsilon)} = d_c. \tag{2.104}$$

Then, (2.103) implies that

$$d_c \doteq 1 - \frac{\lambda_1}{\lambda_2}. \tag{2.105}$$

Now, the limit d_c as defined by (2.104) can be extended to a general set by replacing squares by high-dimensional cubes. The limit is the so-called *Kolmogorov capacity* of a set, which carries the geometric interpretation of dimension. For example, d_c is 0 for a point, 1 for a line, and 2 for an area. Interestingly, $d_c = \ln 2/\ln 3 = 0.630\ldots$ for the *Cantor set* obtained by the process of ever deleting the middle thirds starting with the unit interval $[0, 1]$. Sets with non-integral dimensions are now popularly known as *fractals*, a term due to B. Mandelbrot. The above discussion motivates the definition of the so-called *Lyapunov dimension*, d_L. Let $\lambda_1 \geq \lambda_2 \geq \ldots \geq \lambda_k$ denote the Lyapunov spectrum of the map (2.90), where we have assumed λ_i to be independent of $\mathbf{x}$ for each i. We define

$$d_L = m - \frac{\lambda_1 + \lambda_2 + \ldots + \lambda_m}{\lambda_{m+1}} \tag{2.106}$$

where m is the largest integer for which $\lambda_1 + \lambda_2 + \ldots + \lambda_m \geq 0$. If $\lambda_1 < 0$, define $d_L = 0$; if $\lambda_1 + \lambda_2 + \ldots + \lambda_k \geq 0$, define $d_L = k$. There are many other definitions of dimension, which we shall not pursue (see e.g. Farmer *et al.* 1983).

The notion of a dimension is quite important in the current understanding of chaos. Indeed a chaotic time seies is associated with a *finite-dimensional* attractor.

We now illustrate the calculation of d_L with a fairly typical case.

Example 2.6 (Generalized baker's transformation): The map is piecewise linear ($t = 0, 1, 2, \ldots$):

$$x_{t+1} = \begin{cases} \lambda_a x_t & \text{if } y_t < \alpha \\ \frac{1}{2} + \lambda_b x_t & \text{if } y_t > \alpha \end{cases} \tag{2.107a}$$

$$y_{t+1} = \begin{cases} \alpha^{-1} y_t & \text{if } y_t < \alpha \\ (y_t - \alpha)/(1 - \alpha) & \text{if } y_t > \alpha \end{cases} \tag{2.107b}$$

where $0 \le x_0 \le 1$ and $0 \le y_0 \le 1$. Let λ_a, λ_b, and $\alpha \in (0, \frac{1}{2}]$ and $\lambda_b \ge \lambda_a$ so that $0 \le x_t \le 1$ and $0 \le y_t \le 1$ for all $t \ge 0$. Note that the map (2.107) effectively *stretches* the unit square and then *folds* it as shown in Fig. 2.17, rather like the noodle making at a Peking restaurant. The stretching and folding provide the necessary local instability and global boundedness respectively.

Repeated applications of the stretching–folding action produce the many *similar* 'noodle sticks'. Thus in Fig. 2.18, which shows the result of applying (2.106) twice, we can see that if the x interval $[0, \lambda_a]$ is magnified by a factor $1/\lambda_a$, it becomes an exact replica of Fig. 2.17(d). Similarly, if the x interval $[\frac{1}{2}, \frac{1}{2} + \lambda_b]$ is magnified by $1/\lambda_b$, an exact replica of Fig. 2.17(d) is again obtained. In fact, *self-similarity* is often another manifestation of chaos.

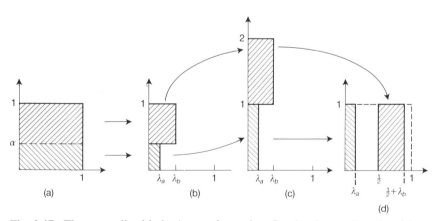

Fig. 2.17. The generalized baker's transformation. It takes in one iteration (a) to (d). Steps (b) and (c) are conceptual intermediate stages, which exhibit stretching. Stage (d) shows the folding. (After J. D. Farmer, E. Ott & J. A. Yorke in *Physica 7D* (1983), p. 165)

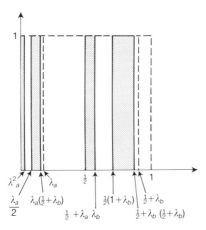

Fig. 2.18. Two applications of the generalized baker's transformation (After Farmer, Ott, and Yorke (1983). See Fig. 2.17)

Now, the Jacobian matrix, $D(x, y)$, at the point (x, y) is given by

$$D(x, y) = \begin{cases} \begin{bmatrix} \lambda_a & 0 \\ 0 & 1/\alpha \end{bmatrix} & \text{if } y < \alpha \\ \begin{bmatrix} \lambda_b & 0 \\ 0 & 1/(1-\alpha) \end{bmatrix} & \text{if } y > \alpha \end{cases} \qquad (2.108)$$

It can be shown that (2.107) induces a uniform distribution over $[0, 1]$. Therefore the two Lyapunov exponents are $\lambda_2 = \alpha \ln \lambda_a + (1 - \alpha) \ln \lambda_b$ and $\lambda_1 = \alpha \ln(1/\alpha) + (1 - \alpha) \ln(1/(1 - \alpha))$. Note that λ_1 is just the *entropy* as defined in information theory of a Bernoulli experiment in which the probability of 'success' is α. It is obvious that $\lambda_1 > 0 > \lambda_2$. Thus

$$d_L = 1 - \frac{\lambda_1}{\lambda_2}. \qquad (2.109)$$

It may be shown that (Farmer *et al.* 1983) in general $d_L \neq d_c$. $\square$

In practice, we often have to resort to digital exploration for chaos, especially when we come to deal with higher-dimensional cases. This is simply due to the infancy of the subject. On this note, we complete our discussion with Fig. 2.19, which illustrates what is possibly a chaos associated with the following high-dimensional difference equation as

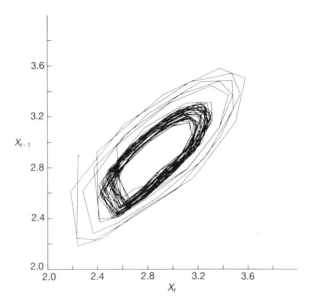

Fig. 2.19. A possible chaotic state

suggested by digital experimentation:

$$x_t = \begin{cases} 0.5890 + 1.1114x_{t-1} - 0.1232x_{t-2} - 0.1430x_{t-3} & \text{if } x_{t-1} \leq 2.5563 \\ 0.9333 + 1.1918x_{t-1} - 0.7569x_{t-2} + 0.2723x_{t-3} - 0.3867x_{t-4} \\ \qquad + 0.1679x_{t-5} - 0.0812x_{t-6} + 0.0728x_{t-7} - 0.0399x_{t-8} \\ \qquad + 0.2149x_{t-9} + 0.0162x_{t-10} & \text{if } x_{t-1} > 2.5563. \end{cases}$$

(This equation was suggested during an analysis of the Canadian lynx data. The data will be discussed in Chapter 7.)

2.12 Stability theory of difference equations

This section may be skipped at first reading. We shall present only the basic elements of the theory here.

As we have seen in §§2.10 and 2.11, we are frequently interested in what happens to $\mathbf{f}^{(j)}$, the jth iterate of $\mathbf{f}$, for large values of j. This concern with the asymptotic behaviour of $\mathbf{f}^{(j)}(\mathbf{x})$ is the subject matter of stability theory. In particular, it is concerned with the behaviour of $\mathbf{f}^{(j)}(\mathbf{x})$ when $\mathbf{x}$ is slightly perturbed.

As usual, let $\mathbf{Z}$ denote the set of all integers and $\mathbf{Z}_+$ the set of all non-negative integers. $\mathbf{R}^m$ is the real m-dimensional Euclidean space with the usual norm

$$\|\mathbf{x}\| = (x_1^2 + x_2^2 + \ldots + x_m^2)^{1/2}$$

defined on vectors $\mathbf{x} = (x_1, x_2, \ldots, x_m)^T \in \mathbf{R}^m$. For a sequence of vectors $\{\mathbf{x}^1, \mathbf{x}^2, \mathbf{x}^3, \ldots\}$, by $\mathbf{x}^k \to \mathbf{y}$ as $k \to \infty$ we mean $\|\mathbf{x}^k - \mathbf{y}\| \to 0$ as $k \to \infty$. Let $\mathbf{f} \colon \mathbf{R}^m \to \mathbf{R}^m$. We are concerned with the difference equation

$$\mathbf{x}_{t+1} = \mathbf{f}(\mathbf{x}_t), \qquad t \in \mathbf{Z}_+, \qquad \mathbf{x}_0 = \mathbf{x}^0 \in \mathbf{R}^m. \tag{2.110}$$

If $\mathbf{f}$ is linear, that is

$$\mathbf{x}_{t+1} = \mathbf{A}\mathbf{x} \tag{2.111}$$

where $\mathbf{A}$ is an $m \times m$ matrix, then a proper question is: 'When does $\mathbf{A}^j \to \mathbf{0}$, the zero matrix, (by $\mathbf{A}^j \to \mathbf{0}$ we mean that each of the $m \times m$ components of $\mathbf{A}^j \to 0$), as $j \to \infty$?'. This is equivalent to the question: 'When does $\mathbf{x}_t \to \mathbf{0}$ as $t \to \infty$ starting from $\mathbf{x}^0$?'. Of course, as we have seen in §2.10, the linear case is solved via the eigenvalues of the matrix $\mathbf{A}$.

If $\mathbf{x} \in \mathbf{R}^m$ and S is a closed set of $\mathbf{R}^m$ (e.g. a closed m-dimensional rectangle), we define the *distance of* $\mathbf{x}$ *from* S *by* $\min\{\|\mathbf{x} - \mathbf{y}\|; \mathbf{y} \in S\}$ and denote it by $\rho(\mathbf{x}, S)$. By $\mathbf{f}^{(k)}(\mathbf{x}^0) \to S$ we mean that $\rho(f^{(k)}(\mathbf{x}^0), S) \to 0$ as $k \to \infty$.

Thus, the existence and location of a closed set to which $\mathbf{f}^{(n)}(\mathbf{x}^{(0)})$ approaches as $n \to \infty$ provides information on the asymptotic behaviour of the difference equation (2.110).

Definition 2.4 (Birkhoff): A point $\mathbf{y}$ is a *positive limit point* of $\mathbf{f}^{(k)}(\mathbf{x})$ if there is a sequence of integers k_i such that $k_i \to \infty$ and $\mathbf{f}^{(k_i)}(\mathbf{x}) \to \mathbf{y}$ as $i \to \infty$. The *positive limit set* $\Omega(\mathbf{x})$ of $\mathbf{f}^{(k)}(\mathbf{x})$ is the set of all its positive limit points.

For ordinary differential equations whose solutions are *continuous* curves, it is known that positive limit sets of bounded solutions are connected. In the case of difference equations, we cannot expect connectedness because of the discrete nature of the parameter space, i.e. $\mathbf{Z}_+$. However, the notion may be modified.

Suppose that $H \subset \mathbf{R}^m$ is such that $\forall \mathbf{x} \in H$, $\mathbf{f}(\mathbf{x}) \in H$. We call such an H a *positively invariant set*. Suppose that $H \subset \mathbf{R}^m$ is such that $\forall \mathbf{x} \in H$, $\exists \mathbf{y} \in H$ such that $\mathbf{f}(\mathbf{y}) = \mathbf{x}$. We call such an H a *negatively invariant set*. H is said to be an *invariant set* if it is both a positively and a negatively invariant set. A closed invariant set H is said to be *invariantly connected* if it is not the union of two non-empty disjoint invariant closed sets.

There are many different modes of stability. The most interesting case is when $\mathbf{f}^{(k)}(\mathbf{x})$ is bounded for all $k \geq 0$, in which case $\mathbf{f}$ is said to be *positively stable in the sense of Lagrange with initial condition* $\mathbf{x}$. If $\mathbf{f}$ is positively stable in the sense of Lagrange with every initial condition $\mathbf{x}$ in $\mathbf{R}^m$, then we say that $\mathbf{f}$ is *positively stable in the sense of Lagrange*, or simply *Lagrange stable*. The following theorem lists some important consequences of positive stability in the sense of Lagrange.

Theorem 2.7 (La Salle 1977): Suppose that $\mathbf{f}$ is continuous. Then every positive limit set is closed and positively invariant. If $\mathbf{f}^{(k)}(\mathbf{x})$ is bounded for all $k \in \mathbf{Z}_+$, then $\Omega(\mathbf{x})$ is non-empty, compact, invariant, invariantly connected, and the smallest closed set that $\mathbf{f}^{(k)}(\mathbf{x})$ approaches as $k \to \infty$.

Proof. Let $\mathbf{x}_i \in \Omega(\mathbf{x})$, the positive limit set, and $\lim \mathbf{x}_i = \mathbf{x}_\infty$. Suppose $\mathbf{x}_\infty \notin \Omega(\mathbf{x})$. This implies the existence of an open ball $\mathbf{B}$ about $\mathbf{x}_\infty$ such that $\mathbf{f}^{(k)}(\mathbf{x}) \in \mathbf{B}$ for only finitely many k. This contradicts the fact that $\mathbf{B}$ contains some positive limit points $\in \Omega(\mathbf{x})$ and hence there are infinitely many k such that $\mathbf{f}^{(k)}(\mathbf{x})$ lies within $\mathbf{B}$. Hence, $\Omega(\mathbf{x})$ is closed. Let $\mathbf{x}_\infty \in \Omega(\mathbf{x})$. Then there exists a monotone subsequence $\{k_i\}$ such that $\mathbf{f}^{(k_i)}(\mathbf{x}) \to \mathbf{x}_\infty$. By the continuity of $\mathbf{f}$, $\mathbf{f}^{(k_i+1)}(\mathbf{x}) \to \mathbf{f}(\mathbf{x}_\infty)$ and hence $\mathbf{f}(\mathbf{x}_\infty) \in \Omega(\mathbf{x})$. This demonstrates the positive invariance of $\Omega(\mathbf{x})$.

Since $\{\mathbf{f}^{(k)}(\mathbf{x}), k = 1, 2, \dots \}$ is bounded, it follows from the Bolzano–Weierstrass theorem that it admits a limit point. Therefore, $\Omega(\mathbf{x})$ is non-empty. As $\Omega(\mathbf{x})$ is readily seen to be bounded and closed, it is compact.

To show that $\Omega(\mathbf{x})$ is invariant, it suffices to show that it is negatively invariant. Let $\mathbf{x}' \in \Omega(\mathbf{x})$. Then there exists a monotone subsequence k_i such that $\mathbf{f}^{(k_i)}(\mathbf{x}) \to \mathbf{x}'$. Then $\mathbf{f}(\mathbf{f}^{(k_i-1)}(\mathbf{x})) \to \mathbf{x}'$. Now $\{\mathbf{f}^{(k_i-1)}(\mathbf{x}), i \in \mathbf{Z}_+\}$ is bounded and therefore it admits a limit point, say, $\mathbf{x}''$. Without loss of generality, let $\mathbf{f}^{(k_i-1)}(\mathbf{x}) \to \mathbf{x}''$. Then it is immediately seen that $\mathbf{f}(\mathbf{x}'') = \mathbf{x}'$. so $\Omega(\mathbf{x})$ is negatively invariant.

We now demonstrate that $\Omega(\mathbf{x})$ is invariantly connected. Suppose not; $\exists \Omega_1, \Omega_2$ closed non-empty invariant sets such that $\Omega(\mathbf{x}) = \Omega_1 \cup \Omega_2$. It follows from the continuity of $\mathbf{f}$ and the compactness of Ω that there exists open sets A_1, A_2 such that $A_1 \cap A_2 = \phi$; $\Omega_i \subseteq A_i$, $i = 1, 2$; $\mathbf{f}(A_1) \cap A_2 = \phi$; and $\mathbf{f}(A_2) \cap A_1 = \phi$. Let $I_i = \{k : \mathbf{f}^{(k)}(\mathbf{x}) \in A_i\}$. Clearly, $(I_1 \cup I_2)^c$ is finite and hence $\exists k_0$ such that $\{i \in \mathbf{Z}_+, i \geq k_0\} \subseteq I_1 \cup I_2$. Also, I_i is infinite, $i = 1, 2$. Without loss of generality, let $k_0 \in I_1$. Suppose $i \in I_1$ and $i \geq k_0$. Then $\mathbf{f}^{(i)}(\mathbf{x}) \in A_1$ and hence $\mathbf{f}^{(i+1)}(\mathbf{x}) \notin A_2$. Therefore $i + 1 \in I_1$. By mathematical induction, we must have $\{i \in \mathbf{Z}_+, i \geq k_0\} \subseteq I_1$. However, this implies that I_2 is finite and hence a contradiction. Thus, $\Omega(\mathbf{x})$ must be invariantly connected.

For the proof of the final assertion, let C be a closed set such that $\mathbf{f}^{(k)}(\mathbf{x}) \to C$ as $k \to \infty$. Then any limit point of $\mathbf{f}^{(k)} \in C$ and so $\Omega(\mathbf{x}) \subseteq C$. This proves that $\Omega(\mathbf{x})$ is the smallest invariant closed set attracting $\mathbf{f}^{(k)}(\mathbf{x})$. $\square$

The above theorem shows that under continuity of $\mathbf{f}$ and Lagrange stability, Birkhoff's positive limit set, $\Omega(\mathbf{x})$, of $\mathbf{f}^{(k)}(\mathbf{x})$ is the smallest closed set that $\mathbf{f}^{(k)}(\mathbf{x})$ approaches as $k \to \infty$. In this sense, locating $\Omega(\mathbf{x})$ is the 'best' information we can hope for. However, the task of locating $\Omega(\mathbf{x})$ can be quite daunting once we leave linearity because it is not always trivial even to establish Lagrange stability. (How are the $\Omega(\mathbf{x})$ located if $\mathbf{f}$ is linear?) We illustrate the point with the following examples.

Example 2.7: Consider the following difference equation $(t = 1, 2, \ldots)$:

$$x_t = \begin{cases} \phi_1 x_{t-1} & \text{if } x_{t-1} > 0 \\ \phi_1' x_{t-1} & \text{if } x_{t-1} \leq 0. \end{cases} \tag{2.112}$$

Here $\mathbf{f}$ is continuous.

It is clear that $|\phi_1| \leq 1$ and $|\phi_1'| \leq 1$ will ensure Lagrange stability (why?). It may come as a surprise to readers to find that the condition may be relaxed to $\phi_1 \leq 1$, $\phi_1' \leq 1$, and $\phi_1 \phi_1' \leq 1$!

We consider four possible cases: (i) $\phi_1 > 0$, $\phi_1' > 0$; (ii) $\phi_1 > 0$, $\phi_1' < 0$; (iii) $\phi_1 < 0$, $\phi_1' > 0$; (iv) $\phi_1 < 0$, $\phi_1' < 0$.

Case (i): If $x_0 > 0$, then $x_k = \phi_1^k x_0$, $k = 1, 2, \ldots$. Therefore we need $\phi_1 \leq 1$ for Lagrange stability with initial condition $x_0 > 0$. Similarly we need $\phi_1' \leq 1$ for Lagrange stability with initial condition $x_0 < 0$.

Case (ii): If $x_0 > 0$, then $x_k = \phi_1^k x_0$, $k = 1, 2, \ldots$. Therefore we need $\phi_1 \leq 1$ for Lagrange stability with initial condition $x_0 > 0$. If $x_0 < 0$, then $x_1 = \phi_1' x_0 > 0$ and $x_k = \phi_1^{k-1} x_1$ for $k = 1, 2, \ldots$. Therefore $\phi_1 \leq 1$ also ensures Lagrange stability with initial condition $x_0 < 0$.

Case (iii): By symmetry with Case (ii), $\phi_1' \leq 1$ will ensure Lagrange stability.

Case (iv): Two iterates of (2.112) give $x_k = \phi_1 \phi_1' x_{k-2}$, $k = 2, 3, \ldots$, from which it is clear that we need $\phi_1 \phi_1' \leq 1$ to ensure Lagrange stability.

In all cases $x_0 = 0$ leads to the trivial case in which $x_t = 0$, all $t > 0$.

Combining the four cases together, we have proved that $\phi_1 \leq 1$, $\phi_1' \leq 1$, and $\phi_1 \phi_1' \leq 1$ ensure Lagrange stability of (2.112). $\square$

Example 2.8: Let $\xi \in \mathbf{R}^2$ and

$$\xi_t = \begin{bmatrix} x_t \\ x_{t-1} \end{bmatrix}.$$

Let

$$\mathbf{A} = \begin{bmatrix} \phi_1 & \phi_2 \\ 1 & 0 \end{bmatrix} \qquad \mathbf{B} = \begin{bmatrix} \phi_1' & 0 \\ 1 & 0 \end{bmatrix}$$

where ϕ_1, ϕ_1', $\phi_2 \in \mathbf{R}$. Suppose that

$$\xi_t = \begin{cases} \mathbf{A} \xi_{t-1} & \text{if } x_{t-2} > 0 \\ \mathbf{B} \xi_{t-1} & \text{if } x_{t-2} \leq 0. \end{cases} \tag{2.113}$$

Here $\mathbf{f}$ is not continuous. Let us consider first the case $\phi_1 \geq 0$, $\phi_2 < 0$, $\phi_1' < 0$, and $\phi_1^2 + 4\phi_2 < 0$. Because of the last condition, the matrix $\mathbf{A}$ has complex eigenvalues and is therefore similar to a rotation followed by a contraction (or expansion).

First, we introduce the following notation:

$$U = \{(x, y) : y > 0\} \qquad L = \{(x, y) : y \leq 0\}$$
$$Q_1 = \{(x, y) \in U : x > 0\}$$
$$Q_2 = \{(x, y) \in U : x \leq 0\}$$
$$Q_3 = \{(x, y) \in L : x < 0\}$$
$$Q_4 = \{(x, y) \in L : x = 0\}$$
$$Q_5 = \{(x, y) \in L : x > 0\}.$$

For every $\xi_t \in U$, ξ_{t+1} is obtained by the action of $\mathbf{A}$ on ξ_t. We say that $\mathbf{A}$ controls U. similarly $\mathbf{B}$ controls L.

As

$$\mathbf{A}\begin{pmatrix} 1 \\ 0 \end{pmatrix} = \begin{pmatrix} \phi_1 \\ 1 \end{pmatrix} \quad \text{and} \quad \mathbf{A}\begin{pmatrix} 0 \\ 1 \end{pmatrix} = \begin{pmatrix} \phi_2 \\ 0 \end{pmatrix}$$

we have the pictorial representation of Figs 2.20(a) and (b), which displays the action of $\mathbf{A}$ on U.

Now $\mathbf{A}$ is a rotation followed by a contraction or expansion after a change of basis. Hence, there exists a positive integer k, such that (s.t.) for every vector $\xi_0 \in U$, there exists a positive integer $k(\xi_0) < k$ s.t.

$$\mathbf{A}^{k(\xi_0)} \xi_0 \in L \quad \text{and} \quad \mathbf{A}^j \xi_0 \notin L, \qquad 0 \leq j < k(\xi_0).$$

In particular, $\forall \xi_0 \in Q_2$, $k(\xi_0) = 1$.

The action of $\mathbf{B}$ on L is displayed in Figs 2.21(a) and (b).

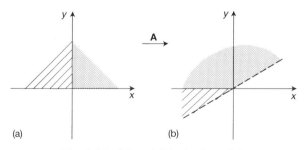

Fig. 2.20. (a) and (b): Action of $\mathbf{A}$

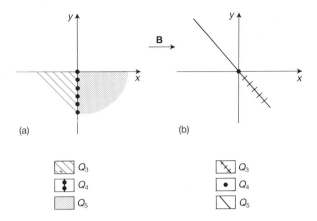

Fig. 2.21. (a) and (b): Action of **B**

Let

$$\mathbf{x} = \begin{pmatrix} x_1 \\ x_2 \end{pmatrix} \in \mathbf{R}^2 \quad \text{and} \quad T : \mathbf{R}^2 \to \mathbf{R}^2 \text{ by } T\mathbf{x} = \begin{cases} \mathbf{Ax} & \text{if } x_2 > 0, \\ \mathbf{Bx} & \text{otherwise.} \end{cases}$$

Then (2.113) is equivalent to

$$\xi_t = T(\xi_{t-1}). \tag{2.114}$$

Given ξ_0, $\{\xi_i ; i = 0, 1, 2, \ldots\}$ is the trajectory under T with initial state ξ_0. We now abstract these trajectories in terms of the symbols **A**, **B**, and the zero matrix, **0** (i.e. we study the symbolic dynamics—see for example Guckenheimer and Holmes (1983)). Let $\xi_0 \in U$; then let $k = k(\xi_0)$. We say that the trajectory is of the type $(S_1, S_2, S_3, \ldots, S_k; S_0', S_1', \ldots, S_{l-1}')$ iff, for $j \geq 1$,

$$T^j \xi_0 = \begin{cases} S_j T^{j-1} \xi_0 & \text{if } 1 \leq j \leq k, \\ S_{j-k-1}' (\text{mod } l) T^{j-1} \xi_0 & \text{if } j \geq k \end{cases}$$

where S_i and S_i' are **A** or **B** or **0**, $T^0 \xi_0 = \xi_0$.

Table 2.1 summarizes all possible types of trajectories under study.

Types are not uniquely represented because $(\mathbf{B}, \mathbf{A}, \mathbf{B}) = (\mathbf{B}, \mathbf{A}; \mathbf{B}, \mathbf{B}, \mathbf{A})$.

Thus, it is readily seen that the 'tail' of the trajectory starting from any initial (point), excepting those in Q_4, can be understood by examining the trajectory starting from

$$\mathbf{A} \begin{pmatrix} \phi_1' \\ 1 \end{pmatrix}.$$

Table 2.1. The semi-colon is omitted inside the parentheses when $k = 0$

Region	Type
Q_1 & Q_2	$(\mathbf{A}, \mathbf{A}, \ldots, \mathbf{A}; \mathbf{B}, \mathbf{B}, \mathbf{A})$
	$k(\xi_0)$ of them
Q_3	$(\mathbf{B}, \mathbf{B}, \mathbf{A})$
Q_4	$(\mathbf{B}; 0)$
Q_5	$(\mathbf{B}, \mathbf{A}, \mathbf{B})$

Now

$$\mathbf{AB}^2 = \begin{pmatrix} \phi_1 & \phi_2 \\ 1 & 0 \end{pmatrix} \begin{pmatrix} \phi_1' & 0 \\ 1 & 0 \end{pmatrix} \begin{pmatrix} \phi_1' & 0 \\ 1 & 0 \end{pmatrix} = \begin{pmatrix} \phi_1 \phi_1'^2 + \phi_2 \phi_1' & 0 \\ \phi_1'^2 & 0 \end{pmatrix}$$

and

$$\mathbf{A} \begin{pmatrix} \phi_1' \\ 1 \end{pmatrix} = \begin{pmatrix} \phi_1 \phi_1' + \phi_2 \\ \phi_1' \end{pmatrix}$$

giving

$$\mathbf{AB}^2 \begin{pmatrix} \phi_1 \phi_1' + \phi_2 \\ \phi_1' \end{pmatrix} = \phi_1'(\phi_1 \phi_1' + \phi_2) \begin{pmatrix} \phi_1 \phi_1' + \phi_2 \\ \phi_1' \end{pmatrix}. \qquad (2.115)$$

Therefore, we may claim that for $\{\xi_t\}$ satisfying (2.113) and for $\phi_1 \geq 0$, $\phi_2 < 0$, $\phi_1' < 0$, and $\phi_1^2 + 4\phi_2 < 0$, the system is Lagrange stable iff $\phi_1'(\phi_1 \phi_1' + \phi_2) \leq 1$. For, we only need note that the tail behaviour of points except those in Q_4 is the same as that of

$$\begin{pmatrix} \phi_1 \phi_1' + \phi_2 \\ \phi_1' \end{pmatrix}$$

and the latter is bounded if $\phi_1'(\phi_1 \phi_1' + \phi_2) \leq 1$. (Recall that by assumption $\phi_1'(\phi_1 \phi_1' + \phi_2) \geq 0$.) Points in Q_4 remain at the origin after the action of **B**. $\quad \square$

Example 2.9 (One country, two systems):

$$x_t = \begin{cases} 1.8 x_{t-1} - 0.9 x_{t-2} & \text{if } x_{t-2} > 0 \\ -0.9 x_{t-1} & \text{otherwise} \end{cases}. \qquad (2.116)$$

Note that (2.116) may be written in the form (2.113) with

$$\mathbf{A} = \begin{bmatrix} 1.8 & -0.9 \\ 1 & 0 \end{bmatrix} \qquad \mathbf{B} = \begin{bmatrix} -0.9 & 0 \\ 1 & 0 \end{bmatrix}.$$

This system is not Lagrange stable because $\phi_1'(\phi_1 \phi_1' + \phi_2) = 2.268 > 1$. Rather interestingly, each of the subsystems

$$x_t = 1.8 x_{t-1} - 0.9 x_{t-2} \quad \text{and} \quad x_t = -0.9 x_{t-1}$$

is Lagrange stable! Thus subsystem stability does not imply system stability because the interaction between the two subsystems may induce instability. □

On the other hand, interactions between subsystems, not all stable, may induce stability. The next example illustrates this.

Example 2.10:

$$x_t = \begin{cases} 0.6x_{t-1} - 0.1x_{t-2} & \text{if } x_{t-2} > 0 \\ -1.1x_{t-1} & \text{otherwise} \end{cases}. \tag{2.117}$$

This system is Lagrange stable because $\phi_1'(\phi_1\phi_1' + \phi_2) = 0.836 < 1$. Note that the subsystem

$$x_t = -1.1x_{t-1}$$

is not Lagrange stable! □

The above results may be generalized in the form of the following theorem:

Theorem 2.8: Let $\{\xi_n\}$ satisfy (2.113). Suppose $\phi_1^2 + 4\phi_2 < 0$. Then $\{\xi_n\}$ is Lagrange stable iff one of the following conditions holds:

(1) $\phi_1' < 0$, $\phi_1 \geq 0$, and $\phi_1'(\phi_1\phi_1' + \phi_2) \leq 1$;
(2) $\phi_1' < 0$, $\phi_1 < 0$, $\phi_1\phi_1' + \phi_2 < 0$, and $\phi_1'(\phi_1\phi_1' + \phi_2) \leq 1$;
(3) $\phi_1' < 0$, $\phi_1 < 0$, and $\phi_1\phi_1' + \phi_2 = 0$;
(4) $\phi_1' < 0$, $\phi_1 < 0$, $\phi_1\phi_1' + \phi_1 > 0$, and $\phi_1\phi_1' + \phi_2 \leq 1$;
(5) $\phi_1' = 0$;
(6) $1 \geq \phi_1' > 0$, $\phi_1 \geq 0$;
(7) $1 \geq \phi_1' > 0$, $\phi_1 < 0$, $(\phi_1^2 + \phi_2)\phi_1' + \phi_1\phi_2 \leq 0$;
(8) $1 \geq \phi_1' > 0$, $\phi_1 < 0$, $(\phi_1^2 + \phi_2)\phi_1' + \phi_1\phi_2 > 0$,
     $\qquad\qquad\qquad\qquad$ and $\phi_1'(\phi_1^2 + \phi_2) + \phi_1\phi_2 \leq 1$.

Proof. We omit the proof but refer the reader to Tong (1989). The result is due to Chan and Tong (1984). □

The danger of stretching the physical intuition too far is exposed by the following example.

Example 2.11:

$$x_t = (-0.9 - e^{-x_{t-1}^2})x_{t-2}. \tag{2.118}$$

This is a difference equation of the type to be discussed in §2.13. The 'eigenvalues for high amplitude' are $\pm\sqrt{(0.9)}i$, which have moduli less than unity implying an attraction of x_t towards the origin for given large $|x_{t-1}|$. The 'eigenvalues for low amplitude' are $\pm\sqrt{(1.9)}i$, which have moduli greater than unity implying a repulsion of x_t away from the origin for given small $|x_{t-1}|$. It is physically plausible that the 'energy dissipation' and 'energy absorption' may balance each other here and that limit cycles ensue. However, it is easy to see that the model is not even Lagrange stable on setting, for example, $x_0 = 0$ and $x_1 = 100$. From then on, for $k = 0, 1, 2, 3, \ldots, x_{2k} = 0$ and $x_{2k+1} = 100(-1.9)^k$. The fact that the model is not Lagrange stable has a serious implication in studying the ergodicity of the stochastic model which is obtained by adding a white noise term to the right-hand side of eqn (2.118). We shall return to this in Chapter 4. □

Once Lagrange stability has been established for eqn (2.110), we can set about locating the positive limit sets for continuous f. One obvious approach is via the explicit orbits. Although this approach may be useful sometimes (e.g. in Example (2.7), it is not always so. The following example illustrates the point.

Example 2.12 (La Salle 1976): Consider the two-dimensional system $(t \geq 0)$

$$\begin{bmatrix} x_{t+1} \\ y_{t+1} \end{bmatrix} = \begin{bmatrix} \dfrac{ay_t}{1 + x_t^2} \\ \dfrac{bx_t}{1 + y_t^2} \end{bmatrix} \qquad (2.119)$$

where $a, b \in \mathbf{R}$ and $a^2 \leq 1$, $b^2 \leq 1$. Because $x_t^2 + y_t^2 \leq x_0^2 + y_0^2$, $\forall t \geq 0$, the system is therefore Lagrange stable. Although clearly it is possible to obtain explicit orbits by iterating forward in t for *each* initial condition $(x_0, y_0)^T \in \mathbf{R}^2$, the approach is tedious if not impractical. □

An alternative is the *direct approach* (i.e. without having to solve the difference equation) due to the great Russian mathematician, A. M. Lyapunov, who laid the foundation of stability theory late last century.

Let $V : \mathbf{R}^m \to \mathbf{R}$. Relative to eqn (2.110), define

$$\dot{V}(\mathbf{x}_t) = V(\mathbf{x}_{t+1}) - V(\mathbf{x}_t) \qquad (2.120)$$

which we sometimes write as

$$\dot{V}(\mathbf{x}) = V(f(\mathbf{x})) - V(\mathbf{x}) \qquad (2.121)$$

where $\mathbf{x} \in \mathbf{R}^m$.

Definition 2.5: Let G be any set in $\mathbf{R}^n$. We say that V is a *Lyapunov function* of $\mathbf{f}$ of (2.110) on G if (i) V is continuous on $\mathbf{R}^m$ and (ii) $\dot{\mathbf{V}}(\mathbf{x}) \leq 0$, $\forall \mathbf{x} \in G$.

Suppose that V is a Lyapunov function of (2.110) on G. We define

$$E = \{\mathbf{x} : \dot{V}(\mathbf{x}) = 0, \mathbf{x} \in \bar{G}\}.$$

Here, $\bar{G}$ denotes the *closure* of G, that is the smallest closed set containing G. Let M denote the largest invariant set in E. For $c \in \mathbf{R}$, the set $\{\mathbf{x} : V(\mathbf{x}) = c, \mathbf{x} \in \mathbf{R}^m\}$ is called a *level surface* (or *level set*) of height c and is denoted by $V^{-1}(c)$.

There is a deep relationship between Lyapunov functions and the location of positive limit sets as shown by the following theorem due to La Salle (1976) and called the *invariance principle*.

Theorem 2.9 (Invariance principle): Suppose the $\mathbf{f}$ of (2.110) is continuous. If (i) V is a Lyapunov function of (2.110) on G and (ii) $\mathbf{x}_t$ is a solution of (2.110) bounded and in G, $\forall t \geq 0$, then $\exists c \in \mathbf{R}$ such that

$$\mathbf{x}_t \rightarrow M \cap V^{-1}(c) \quad \text{as} \quad t \rightarrow \infty.$$

Proof. Let $\mathbf{x}_t = \mathbf{f}^{(t)}(\mathbf{x}_0)$. Since $\{\mathbf{x}_t\}$ is bounded, $\{V(\mathbf{x}_t)\}$ is a decreasing sequence of numbers bounded below. Hence, $\exists c$ such that $V(\mathbf{x}_t) \rightarrow c$ and thus $\dot{V}(\mathbf{x}_t) \rightarrow 0$. It follows from the boundedness of $\{\mathbf{x}_t\}$ and Theorem 2.7 that $\Omega(\mathbf{x}_0)$ is a non-empty, invariant, and compact subset of $\bar{G}$. Also, $\forall \mathbf{x}' \in \Omega(\mathbf{x}_0)$, $\dot{V}(\mathbf{x}') = 0$, and $V(\mathbf{x}') = c$. Thus, $\Omega(\mathbf{x}_0) \subseteq E \cap V^{-1}(c)$ and therefore $\Omega(\mathbf{x}_0) \subseteq M \cap V^{-1}(c)$ by the largest property of M. Hence, $\mathbf{x}_t \rightarrow M \cap V^{-1}(c)$ as $t \rightarrow \infty$.   □

We return to Example 2.12 to illustrate how the invariance principle helps in locating positive limit sets.

Example 2.12 (Again): Take

$$V(x, y) = x^2 + y^2. \tag{2.122}$$

Then

$$\dot{V}(x, y) = \left(\frac{b^2}{(1 + y^2)^2} - 1\right)x^2 + \left(\frac{a^2}{(1 + x^2)^2} - 1\right)y^2. \tag{2.123}$$

Case 1: $a^2 < 1$, $b^2 < 1$. Here, $\dot{V} \leq (b^2 - 1)x^2 + (a^2 - 1)y^2$, and V is a Lyapunov function of (2.120) on $\mathbf{R}^2$. Since $M = E = \{(0, 0)\}$, therefore, by the invariance principle, *every* orbit approaches the origin as $t \rightarrow \infty$ regardless of (x_0, y_0).

Case 2: $a^2 \leq 1$, $b^2 \leq 1$, and $a^2 + b^2 < 2$. We may without loss of generality assume that $a^2 < 1$ and $b^2 = 1$. Then V is still a Lyapunov function of (2.120) on $\mathbf{R}^2$. $E = \{(x, 0); x \in \mathbf{R}\}$. However, $(x, 0)$ is mapped to $(0, bx)$. Therefore, $M = \{(0, 0)\}$ as in Case 1 and we obtain the same conclusion as there.

Case 3: $a^2 = b^2 = 1$. V is still a Lyapunov function of (2.120) on $\mathbf{R}^2$. Here $E = M = \{(x, 0); x \in \mathbf{R}\} \cup \{(0, y); y \in \mathbf{R}\}$. Therefore, by the invariance principle, $\mathbf{x}_t \to M \cap V^{-1}(c^2)$, where $V^{-1}(c^2) = \{(x, y): x^2 + y^2 = c^2\}$ is a circle of radius c. That is, each orbit approaches $\{(c, 0), (-c, 0), (0, c), (0, -c)\}$, the intersections of the x and y axes with the circle $x^2 + y^2 = c^2$. There are two sub-cases: (i) $ab = 1$. Then $(c, 0) \to (0, bc) \to (abc, 0) = (c, 0)$ under two iterations of (2.120). Since positive limit sets are invariantly connected, every orbit approaches one of these cycles of period 2 or the origin. (ii) $ab = -1$. Then $(c, 0) \to (0, bc) \to (abc, 0) = (-c, 0) \to (0, -bc) \to (0, -abc) = (0, c)$ under four iterations of (2.120). As in (i), every orbit approaches one of these cycles of period 4 or the origin.

Case 4: $a^2 > 1$, $b^2 > 1$. We may still use the Lyapunov function approach to study this case. Let $N_\varepsilon = \{(x, y): x^2 + y^2 < \varepsilon^2\}$. For $(x, y) \in N_\varepsilon$ and ε sufficiently small,

$$-V \leq -\left(\frac{b^2}{1 + \varepsilon^2} - 1\right)x^2 - \left(\frac{a^2}{1 + \varepsilon^2} - 1\right)y^2 \leq 0, \qquad (2.124)$$

and $-V$ is a Lyapunov function of (2.120) on N_ε for ε sufficiently small. $E = M = \{(0, 0)\}$. No orbit starting at a point in N_ε other than the origin can approach the origin from within N_ε, its distance from the origin being non-decreasing by (2.124). Besides, the inverse image of $(0, 0)$ under (2.120) is $(0, 0)$. Therefore, by the invariance principle, each orbit must leave N_ε. Since no orbit can jump to the origin in finite time except the 'trivial' orbit starting from the origin, there is no orbit starting anywhere except $(0, 0)$ that can approach the origin as $t \to \infty$. $\square$

Note that there is no unique choice of Lyapunov functions. It is well known that 'two Lyapunov functions are better than one'. In Lyapunov's original work, the function is often motivated by energy considerations and is positive definite (compare 2.122))—hence a Lyapunov function is sometimes known as a generalized energy. As we have seen in Case 4 above, this need not be the case.

We now introduce stability in the spirit of Lyapunov (1892), which deals with the continuity with respect to initial conditions. Let $\mathbf{f}$ be continuous and $\mathbf{f}(W) = \{\mathbf{f}(\mathbf{x}): \mathbf{x} \in W\}$, $W \subseteq \mathbf{R}^m$. We now introduce some definitions which are specialized versions for continuous $\mathbf{f}$ of earlier ones in §2.10.

Definition 2.6: A set H is said to be *stable in the sense of Lyapunov* (or simply *stable*) w.r.t. $\mathbf{f}$ if given a neighbourhood U of H (i.e. an open set containing $\bar{H}$, the closure of H), there is a neighbourhood W of H such that $\mathbf{f}^{(t)}(W) \subset U \; \forall t \in \mathbf{Z}_+$.

Definition 2.7: A set H is an *attractor* w.r.t. $\mathbf{f}$ if there is a neighbourhood U of $\bar{H}$ such that $\forall \mathbf{x}_0 \in U$, $\mathbf{f}^{(t)}(\mathbf{x}_0) \to \bar{H}$ as $t \to \infty$. It is a *global attractor* w.r.t. $\mathbf{f}$ if $\mathbf{f}^{(t)}(\mathbf{x}_0) \to \bar{H}$ as $t \to \infty$, $\forall \mathbf{x}_0 \in \mathbf{R}^m$. If H is both stable and an attractor, then H is said to be *asymptotically stable*. If H is stable and is a global attractor, H is said to be *globally asymptotically stable*. *Unstable* means not stable. If H is neither stable nor an attractor, we say that H is *strongly unstable*.

If H is stable, it must be positively invariant. Furthermore, if H is invariantly connected and a finite set, it is a limit cycle. In particular, if H is a singleton set, it is a limit point. If $\exists K > 0$, $\alpha > 0$ such that $\rho(\mathbf{f}^{(t)}(\mathbf{x}), H) \le k e^{-\alpha t} \rho(\mathbf{x}, H)$, $\forall \mathbf{x} \in U$, then H is said to be *exponentially asymptotically stable*.

Recall Definition 2.5 for the next theorem.

Theorem 2.10 (La Salle 1976): Let G be a bounded open positively invariant set. If V is a Lyapunov function of $\mathbf{f}$ on G, and $M \subset G$, then M is an attractor and $G \subset B(M)$. If, further, V is constant on M, then M is asymptotically stable.

Proof. We first show that $\bar{M}$ is an invariant set $\subseteq E$. Let $\mathbf{x} \in \bar{M}$. Then $\exists \mathbf{x}_n \in M$ such that $\mathbf{x}_n \to \mathbf{x}$. By continuity, $\dot{V}(\mathbf{x}) = 0$. Hence $\bar{M} \subseteq E$. By the invariance of M, $\mathbf{f}(\mathbf{x}_n) \in M$ and $\mathbf{f}(\mathbf{x}_n) \to \mathbf{f}(\mathbf{x})$. So $\mathbf{f}(\mathbf{x}) \in \bar{M}$. Therefore $\bar{M}$ is invariant. Since M is the largest invariant set $\subseteq E$, so $M = \bar{M}$ and hence M is closed.

As $M \subseteq G$ and G is bounded, M is compact. To show that M is an attractor, it suffices to show that $G \subseteq B(M)$. The latter readily follows from the invariance principle stated in Theorem 2.9.

We now show that M is stable if V is constant on M, say, with value $= c$. It is clear that $c = \min\{V(\mathbf{x}): \mathbf{x} \in G\}$ because, otherwise, $\exists \delta > 0$ and $\mathbf{x} \in G$ such that $V(\mathbf{x}) < c - \delta$ but then $V(\mathbf{f}^{(t)}(\mathbf{x})) < c - \delta$, $\forall t$, and $\mathbf{f}^{(t)}(\mathbf{x})$ would not tend to M, leading to a contradiction. Let U be a neigbourhood of M. Let $d = \inf\{V(\mathbf{x}): \mathbf{x} \in G \backslash U\}$. Then $d > c$. It is because, otherwise, $\exists \mathbf{x}_n \in G \backslash U$ and $V(\mathbf{x}_n) \to c$ and therefore $\dot{V}(\mathbf{x}_n) \to 0$. Let $\mathbf{x}^*$ be a limit point of $\mathbf{x}_n$. Then $V(\mathbf{x}^*) = c$ and $\dot{V}(\mathbf{x}^*) = 0$. Since V is a Lyapunov function, we see that $V(\mathbf{f}^{(t)}(\mathbf{x}_n)) \to c$ and $\dot{V}(\mathbf{f}^{(t)}(\mathbf{x}_n)) \to 0$ for all $t \in \mathbf{Z}_+$. Thus $V(\mathbf{f}^{(t)}(\mathbf{x}^*)) = c$ and $\dot{V}(\mathbf{f}^{(t)}(\mathbf{x}^*)) = 0$. So $\{\mathbf{f}^{(t)}(\mathbf{x}^*), t = 0, 1, 2, \ldots\}$ is an invariant subset of E. Hence $\mathbf{x}^* \in M$ and therefore $\mathbf{x}_n \to M$, leading again to a contradiction.

Let $W = \{\mathbf{x} \in G : V(\mathbf{x}) < (d + c)/2\}$. Then W is a neighbourhood of M and $W \subseteq U$. Now, $\forall \mathbf{x} \in W$, $V(\mathbf{f}^{(t)}(\mathbf{x})) < (d + c)/2$ and hence W is a positively invariant set. So $\mathbf{f}^{(t)}(W) \subseteq W \subseteq U$ and this establishes the stability of M and hence the asymptotic stability of it. $\square$

Of course, there are points of contact between the discussions in this section and those in connection with local linearization in §2.10. The latter concern local results and give no information about the basin of attraction. Indeed, the region of asymptotic stability of the origin, say, may be so small that as far as a given practical application is concerned the origin may be considered unstable. By contrast, the Lyapunov function approach takes account of the non-linearity and gives information about the extent of stability or instability.

Finally, we may note that there are 'coverse' theorems in the Lyapunov theory (see Appendix 1).

2.13   A physical approach

We now describe a *physical* approach to dynamical systems essentially due to Ozaki (1985*a*).

First consider a linear equation

$$x_t = a_1 x_{t-1} + a_2 x_{t-2}. \tag{2.125}$$

Suppose that $a_2 < 0$ and that $a_1^2 < -4a_2$, so that the roots of the associated characteristic equation (i.e. the eigenvalues)

$$\Lambda^2 - a_1 \Lambda - a_2 = 0 \tag{2.126}$$

are complex, say λ and $\bar{\lambda}$ (Fig. 2.22). Suppose that $|a_2| < 1$, so that $|\lambda| = \sqrt{-a_2} < 1$. In polar coordinates,

$$\lambda = \sqrt{-a_2} \exp(i\theta) \tag{2.127}$$

where

$$\tan \theta = (a_1^2 + 4a_2)^{1/2}/a_1.$$

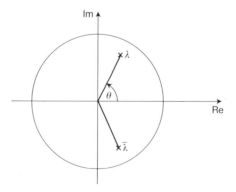

Fig. 2.22. Roots of characteristic equation (2.126)

So far, our discussion has been quite standard, which lies within the linear framework. Now, on following Ozaki (1985a), it may be proposed, perhaps on physical grounds, that we retain the *formal* expressions in (2.127) and (2.128) even when a_1 and a_2 become functions of x_{t-1} and x_{t-2}, and *pretend* that λ retains the status of an eigenvalue (i.e. characteristic root), which becomes *amplitude dependent* (on x_{t-1}, x_{t-2}). (Note that the 'physical' approach suggested here is not the same as the mathematical approach described (in continuous time) in §2.5. In the latter the eigenvalues are well defined as a result of the local linearization. In the former, λ and $\bar{\lambda}$ cease to be genuine eigenvalues.) Continuing in the same vein, we may study the behaviour of $|\lambda|$ as x_{t-1} and x_{t-2} vary. Let us illustrate the approach with an example.

Example 2.13 (A difference equation with exponentially weighted coefficients): Suppose that the constant a_2 in (2.125) is replaced by $\alpha + \beta x_{t-1}^2$ ($\alpha < 0$, $\beta < 0$), in which case $|\lambda|$ as given by $(-\alpha - \beta x_{t-1}^2)^{1/2}$ increases with increasing x_{t-1}^2 (the 'square amplitude') even though β may be very small but negative. It seems that this has sometimes been taken as a *physical* explanation for the expanding orbit, that is $|x_t| \to \infty$ as $t \to \infty$. Implementing a suggestion originally attributed to H. Akaike (see Ozaki and Oda 1978), Ozaki has proposed a heavy damping on the growing amplitude so that $|x_t| < \infty$, $\forall t$, under suitable conditions on α and β. Specifically, he has proposed the class of difference equations with exponentially weighted coefficients, of which the following is a typical member:

$$x_t = (\phi_1 + \pi_1 e^{-x_{t-1}^2})x_{t-1} + (\phi_2 + \pi_2 e^{-x_{t-1}^2})x_{t-2}. \tag{2.129}$$

He has argued that much of the dynamical behaviour of (2.129) may be introduced from two 'extreme' characteristic equations, (CL) and (CH) say, corresponding respectively to the case of extremely low amplitude and the case of extremely high amplitude. The two equations are

$$\text{(CL):} \quad \Lambda^2 - (\phi_1 + \pi_1)\Lambda - (\phi_2 + \pi_2) = 0 \tag{2.130}$$

$$\text{(CH):} \quad \Lambda^2 - \phi_1\Lambda - \phi_2 = 0. \tag{2.131}$$

Let λ_0 and $\bar{\lambda}_0$ (assumed complex) denote the roots of (2.130) and λ_∞ and $\bar{\lambda}_\infty$ (again assumed complex) those of (2.131). It seems physically plausible that if $|\lambda_0| > 1$, then x_t starts to oscillate and diverges away from the origin. Put another way, the origin acts as a repeller. When repelled sufficiently far from the origin, that is when x_t^2 is sufficiently large, (CH) takes over. If $|\lambda_\infty| < 1$, then x_{t+1} tends to be attracted towards the origin. If the coefficients ϕ_i and π_i are so chosen that the repelling energy balances the attracting energy, then limit cycles may ensue. This physical argument is reminiscent of that pertinent to the limit cycles generated by a triode valve, which was described in §2.3. *We should point out that there is a danger if we stretch the physical arguments too far.* As we have seen in Example 2.11, physical arguments cannot replace the mathematical analysis. □

We summarize the discussion of this section by saying that a physical approach is sometimes useful in suggesting interesting models, although it would be prudent not to give the arguments too forcibly unless we could back them up with mathematical rigour.

2.14 Non-linear phenomena under external excitations in discrete time

We have discussed previously the multi-valued amplitude–frequency function in the case of a differential equation, namely the Duffing equation, which has a forcing term. It is therefore of interest to experiment with a similar set-up in discrete time. Specifically, we introduce an external forcing term to the 'right-hand side' of a non-linear difference equation and observe the response. Non-linear phenomena such as *jump phenomena, amplitude–frequency relation, subharmonics, higher harmonics, and synchronization* are reported to have been observed in digital experimentations and we shall reproduce some of these. Before doing so, we should make two remarks:

1. These non-linear phenomena appear to be quite commonly found among many different parameterizations of non-linear systems, in particular, many different non-linear difference equations. For the sake of convenience, only those computer graphics and figures readily accessible to us will be reproduced. This explains the choice of piecewise linear equations in our demonstrations although many other choices will do equally well.

2. Mathematical explanations of these phenomena in discrete time are not always easy to construct. The case of jump phenomena seems to be particularly difficult and we are not aware of any rigorous mathematical explanations in the literature.

We now produce some of the experimental results as follows.

2.14.1 JUMP PHENOMENON

As we have seen previously the output amplitude of a non-linear system, unlike the linear case, may have a 'jump' at different frequencies depending on whether the input frequency (of constant amplitude) is monotonically increasing or monotonically decreasing (see Figs 2.23(a)–(c)).

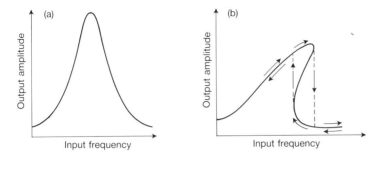

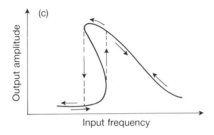

Fig. 2.23. (a) Linear spring; (b) hard spring; (c) soft spring

The time plots of Figs 2.24(a) and (b) clearly show that non-linear difference equations can capture this engineering notion. Recall that the engineering terminology of a *hard spring* and a *soft spring* is an indication of the mode of the *restoring force* of the system. Figures 2.24(a) and (b) correspond to eqns (2.132) and (2.133) respectively.

$$x_t = \begin{cases} 0.4655 + 1.1448x_{t-1} - 0.4801x_{t-2} + 0.1273x_{t-3} \\ \quad - 0.3580x_{t-4} + 0.2565x_{t-5} - 0.0781x_{t-6} - 0.0493x_{t-7} \\ \quad + 0.2186x_{t-8} + 0.0526x_{t-9} + \text{input} \quad \text{if } x_{t-5} \le 3.05 \\ 1.1940 + 1.1181x_{t-1} - 0.5017x_{t-2} - 0.0504x_{t-3} + \text{input} \\ \qquad\qquad\qquad\qquad\qquad\qquad \text{if } x_{t-5} > 3.05. \end{cases} \quad (2.132)$$

(Both eqn (2.132) here and (2.133) later arose out of an analysis of the Canadian lynx data.)

$$x_t = \begin{cases} 1.3003 + 1.3243x_{t-1} - 0.7023x_{t-2} - 0.0750x_{t-3} \\ \quad + \text{input} \quad \text{if } x_{t-6} \le 3.31 \\ 0.2004 + 1.2112x_{t-1} - 0.6971x_{t-2} + 0.6191x_{t-3} \\ \quad - 1.0178x_{t-4} + 0.9967x_{t-5} - 0.7688x_{t-6} + 0.6119x_{t-7} \\ \quad - 0.0551x_{t-8} + \text{input} \quad \text{if } x_{t-6} > 3.31. \end{cases} \quad (2.133)$$

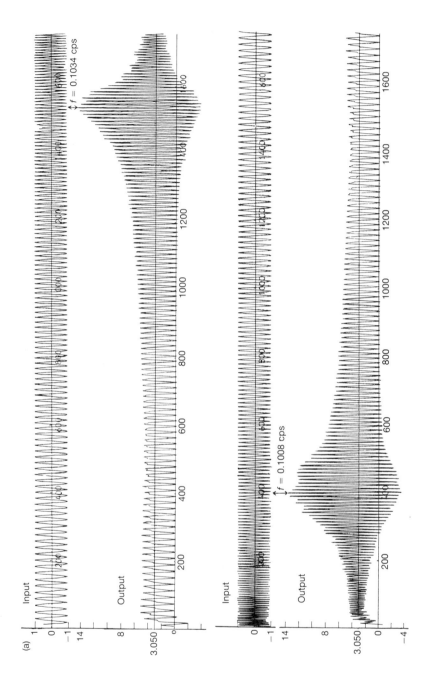

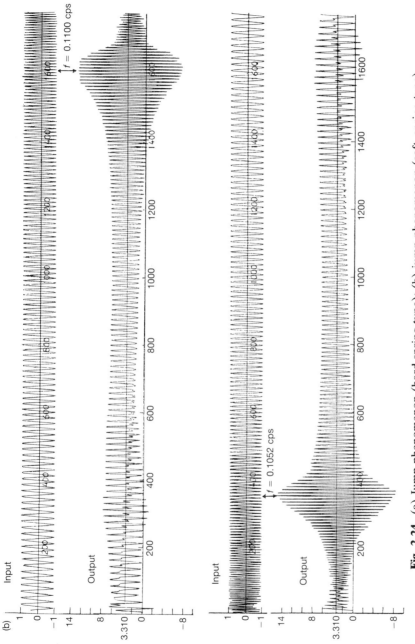

Fig. 2.24. (a) Jump phenomenon (hard spring type); (b) jump phenomenon (soft spring type)

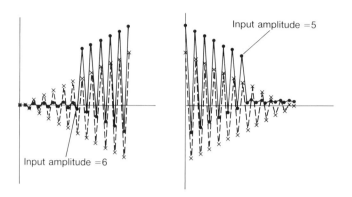

Fig. 2.25. Jump phenomenon with different input amplitudes: $- - -$, input; ———, output

The output amplitude of a non-linear system may also have a jump at different amplitudes depending on whether the input amplitude (of constant frequency) is monotonically increasing or monotonically decreasing. Figure 2.25 corresponds to the time plots of the following model:

$$x_t = \begin{cases} x_{t-1} + 2(y_t - y_{t-1}) & \text{if } |y_{t-1} - y_{t-2}| \geq 10 \\ x_{t-1} + 0.1(y_t - y_{t-1}) & \text{if } |y_{t-1} - y_{t-2}| < 10 \end{cases}.$$

2.14.2 AMPLITUDE–FREQUENCY RELATION

It is well known that, unlike a linear system, the output signal may show different frequencies of oscillations for different amplitudes. The time plots of Figs 2.26(a) and (b) correspond respectively to eqns (2.134) and (2.135). Unlike the previous experiments, the inputs here are Gaussian white noise. We note that this example lies outside the domain of deterministic equations.

$$X_t = \begin{cases} 1.6734 - 0.8295X_{t-1} + 0.1309X_{t-2} - 0.0276X_{t-3} + \varepsilon_t^{(1)} \\ \qquad\qquad\qquad \text{if } X_{t-1} > 0.5 \\ 1.2270 + 1.0516X_{t-1} - 0.5901X_{t-2} - 0.2149X_{t-3} + \varepsilon_t^{(2)} \\ \qquad \text{if } X_{t-1} \leq 0.5, \quad \text{var } \varepsilon_t^{(i)} = 0.003^2, \quad i = 1, 2 \end{cases} \quad (2.134)$$

$$X_t = \begin{cases} 0.15 + 0.85X_{t-1} + 0.22X_{t-2} - 0.70X_{t-3} + \varepsilon_t^{(1)} \\ \qquad\qquad\qquad \text{if } X_{t-1} \leq 3.05 \\ 0.30 - 0.80X_{t-1} + 0.20X_{t-2} - 0.70X_{t-3} + \varepsilon_t^{(2)} \\ \qquad \text{if } X_{t-1} > 0.5, \quad \text{var } \varepsilon_t^{(i)} = 0.003^2, \quad i = 1, 2. \end{cases} \quad (2.135)$$

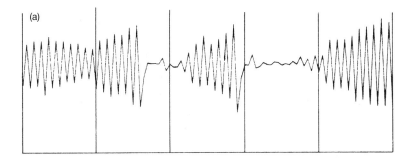

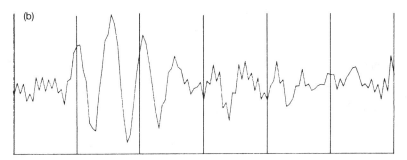

Fig. 2.26. (a) and (b): Amplitude–frequency relation

Note that Fig. 2.26(a) shows the tendency of high frequency of oscillations when the amplitudes are high. Figure 2.26(b) shows the reverse tendency. The size of the noise variance does not seem very critical.

2.14.3 SUBHARMONICS

By a subharmonic is usually meant an output oscillation at a fraction of the input oscillation frequency. The time plots of Fig. 2.27 correspond to the following equation with periodic input $\{y_t\}$:

$$x_t = \begin{cases} 2x_{t-1} + y_t & \text{if } |x_{t-1}| \le 2 \\ y_t & \text{if } |x_{t-1}| > 2 \end{cases} \qquad (2.136)$$

where

$$y_t = \begin{cases} -1 & \text{if } t \text{ is odd} \\ 1 & \text{if } t \text{ is even} \end{cases}.$$

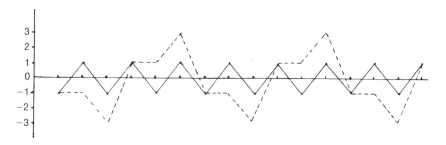

Fig. 2.27. Subharmonics: ——, input; – – –, output

2.14.4 HIGHER HARMONICS

By a higher harmonic is usually meant an output oscillation at a multiple of the input oscillation frequency. The time plots of Fig. 2.28 correspond to the following equation with a periodic input $\{y_t\}$:

$$x_t = \begin{cases} -(2+\sqrt{2})y_t - (1+\sqrt{2}) & \text{if } -1 < y_t \le -1/\sqrt{2} \\ \sqrt{2}\,y_{t-1} & \text{if } -1/\sqrt{2} < y_t \le 0 \\ \sqrt{2}\,y_{t-1} & \text{if } 0 < y_t \le 1/\sqrt{2} \\ (2+\sqrt{2})y_t - (1+\sqrt{2}) & \text{if } 1/\sqrt{2} < y_t \le 1 \end{cases} \qquad (2.137)$$

2.14.5 SYNCHRONIZATION

The phenomenon of *synchronization*, also known as *frequency entrainment* and *phase locking*, was the first non-linear phenomenon to be studied among many others and was apparently observed for the first time by C. Huygens (1629–95) during his experiments with clocks. (He was reputed to be the inventor of the pendulum clock.) He observed that

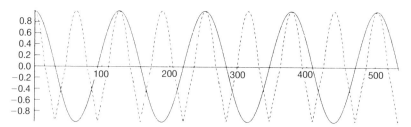

Fig. 2.28. High harmonics: ——, input; – – –, output

two clocks which were slightly out of step when hung on a wall became in step when placed on a piece of soft wood. It has since been observed in electrical, mechanical, acoustical, electroacoustical, electronics, and control systems. Names like Lord Rayleigh, J. H. Vincent, H. G. Moller, E. V. Appleton, Van der Pol, A. Andronov, and J. J. Stoker have been closely connected with it. In control systems, this phenomenon is usually associated with relays, that is *piecewise linear responses*. There also seems to be a considerable interest in this phenomenon in physiological systems (see e.g. Hyndman *et al.*, 1971; Baconnier *et al.* 1983).

Consider a non-linear system, say an electron tube, oscillating with a self-excited (i.e. a limit cycle) frequency ω_0, called the *autofrequency*. Suppose that it is then excited by an extraneous periodic oscillation of frequency ω, called the *heterofrequency*. 'Beats' of the two frequencies may be observed. The frequency of the beats decreases as ω approaches ω_0, but this happens only up to a certain value of the difference $|\omega - \omega_0|$ after which the beats disappear suddenly and the output oscillates with frequency ω. There is thus a non-trivial zone, $\{\omega : \omega_0 - \Delta' < \omega < \omega_0 + \Delta\}$, in which the autofrequency is *entrained* by or *locked* into the heterofrequency (Fig. 2.29).

Now over the dynamic range of 3 ± 1.5 the following system has an autofrequency of period 9:

$$
x_t = \begin{cases}
0.5239 + 1.0359x_{t-1} - 0.1756x_{t-2} + 0.1754x_{t-3} \\
\quad -0.4339x_{t-4} + 0.3456x_{t-5} - 0.3032x_{t-6} \\
\quad +0.2165x_{t-7} + 0.0043x_{t-8} \quad \text{if } x_{t-2} \leq 3.1163 \\
2.6559 + 1.4246x_{t-1} - 1.1618x_{t-2} - 0.1093x_{t-3} \\
\hspace{4cm} \text{if } x_{t-2} > 3.1163.
\end{cases}
\tag{2.138}
$$

(This model will be discussed again in Chapter 7 in connection with the

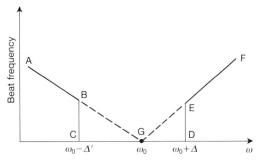

Fig. 2.29. Zone of entrainment (ABCDEF for non-linesr case; ABGEF for linear case)

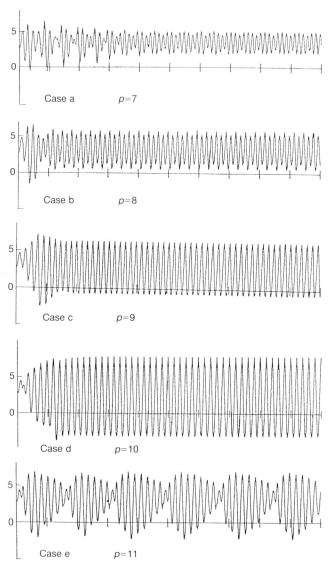

Fig. 2.30. For input periodic signals with period 9 (Case c) and period 10 (Case d), output signals show no beats once the system has 'warmed up'. For input periodic signals with period 7 (Case a), period 8 (Case b), and period 11 (Case e), output signals show beats

modelling of the Canadian lynx data.) Driving this periodic system with periodic signals of period 7, 8, 9, 10, and 11 in succession reveals that no beats occur when the input periods are 9 and 10, at which the output periods are locked in at the corresponding input periods (see Fig. 2.30).

2.15 Delayed difference equations

We have previously discussed linear differential equations with delay and observed how periodic solutions may emerge.

A similar situation exists in delayed difference equations. Levin and May (1976) have considered the simple case

$$x_{t+1} = x_t F(x_{t-T}) \tag{2.139}$$

T being the delay parameter. Non-zero equilibrium points x^* of eqn (2.139) satisfy the equation

$$F(x^*) = 1. \tag{2.140}$$

On following the standard stability analysis by writing $x_t = x^* + \varepsilon_t$, linearizing, and expressing $\varepsilon_t = \lambda^t \varepsilon_0$. (see e.g. Hsu 1970), it holds under suitable regularity conditions on F that

$$\lambda = 1 - b\lambda^{-T} \tag{2.141}$$

where

$$b = -(x \, dF/dx)_{x^*} \quad (F \text{ is assumed differentiable}).$$

(Equation (2.141) may be compared with eqn (2.82).) Here, λ is complex in general. It turns out that analogous bifurcations are obtained. Specifically, Levin and May (1976) have obtained the following bifurcations: (i) $b < T^T/(1 + T)^{1+T} \Rightarrow$ monotonic damping to a constant steady state; (ii) $2 \cos(\pi T/(2T + 1)) > b > T^T/(1 + T)^{1+T} \Rightarrow$ damped oscillation to a constant steady state; (iii) $b > 2 \cos(\pi T/(2T + 1)) \Rightarrow$ no constant state and there could be asymptotically undamped oscillations. Note that as $T \to 0$, $T^T/(1 + T)^{1+T} \to 1$ and $2 \cos(\pi T/(2T + 1)) \to 2$. Note also that as T increases, the likelihood of falling into Case (iii) increases provided $b > 0$. Again, delay leads to the tendency of periodic oscillations.

Bibliographical notes

The historical note on non-linear oscillations has been facilitated by Minorsky (1962) and Zhu (1985). The notion of limit cycles is basic in non-linear oscillations and is covered by every respectable text on the subject. The introduction of this notion via piecewise linear differential equations seems novel and is based on Andronov *et al.* (1966). The novelty lies in the theory of point transformation, which may be exploited to the full in the case of piecewise linearity. Piecewise linearization has also been advocated by control engineers, notably Kalman (1957). Another important contribution by the control engineers is the bilinear system, which has an intimate connection with the Volterra series. We have relied on Barrett (1963) and Brockett (1976, 1977) for orientation. Time delay is another important concept long recognized by the vibrationists and control engineers. The attitude adopted in this book is one which considers the discrete-time dynamical system more basic than the continuous-time dynamical system, although we do not hesitate to incorporate ideas found useful in the latter since the former is a relatively new entry. We have found Gumowski and Mira (1980), Guckenheimer and Holmes (1983), and Holden (1986) valuable besides original papers which have yet to be filtered into book form. The infancy of the subject is reflected by the fact that digital exploration plays probably too significant a role. Physical approaches have not been ignored. For example, Chen (1971) and Ozaki (1985*a*), etc. have been consulted, although their views are not always adopted uncritically. Last but not least, we have benefited substantially from La Salle (1977) and the unpublished thesis of Chan (1986) in our discussion of the very important topic of stability, the significance of which in time series analysis does not seem to be fully appreciated yet.

We have included a number of original results perhaps not readily accessible in the West.

Exercises and complements

(1) Consider the map ($t = 0, 1, 2, \ldots$)

$$x_{t+1} = \begin{cases} 2x_t & \text{if } 0 \le x_t < \frac{1}{2} \\ 2x_t - 1 & \text{if } \frac{1}{2} \le x_t \le 1 \end{cases}.$$

What values will $x_{3002}, x_{3003}, x_{3004}, x_{3005}, \ldots$ take if $x_0 = 13/28$? Repeat the exercise for $x_0 = (13/28)(1 - 8^{-1000})$ and observe the sensitivity of iterations to initial values.

(2) Consider the following system:

$$\frac{dP}{dt} = \begin{cases} -2(P - \alpha) & \text{if } H < 15 \\ 0.5(P - \beta) & \text{if } H \ge 15 \end{cases}$$

$$\frac{dH}{dt} = \begin{cases} H - \gamma & \text{if } P < 10 \\ -2(H - \delta) & \text{if } P \ge 10 \end{cases}.$$

Using the point transformation method, prove that for (i) $\alpha = 5$, $\beta = 5$, $\gamma = 8$, $\delta = 8.4$, (ii) $\alpha = 5$, $\beta = 4.6$, $\gamma = 8.4$, $\delta = 8$, and (iii) $\alpha = 4.6$, $\beta = 5$, $\gamma = 8$, $\delta = 8.4$, we have respectively (i) a stable focus at $(15, 10)$, (ii) a stable limit cycle, and (iii) an unstable limit cycle.

(Private communication from Z. X. Zhu (1987))

(3) Experiment with the iteration

$$x_{k+1} = \frac{x_{k-1}^2 + C}{x_k}, \qquad k \geq 3$$

with $x_0 = 1$, $x_1 = 2$, and $C = -7, -5, -3, -1, +1, \ldots$ and then even integers. What can you say about the sequence when $C = 1$ in particular?

(Powell 1976)

(4) Consider the following mapping from $[0, 1]$ to $[0, 1]$:

$$x_{t+1} = f(x_t) = \begin{cases} (2 - \lambda) + \lambda x_t & \text{if } 0 \leq x_t \leq 1 - 1/\lambda \\ \lambda(1 - x_t) & \text{if } 1 - 1/\lambda \leq x_t \leq 1 \end{cases}$$

where λ is a constant satisfying $1 < \lambda < 2$. Let $x_0 = 0$. Let $x_{(0)} < x_{(1)} < x_{(2)} \ldots$ denote the ordered sequence of $x_0, x_1, x_2, \ldots$. We say then the system is in state E_i at time t if $x_t \in (x_{(i)}, x_{(i+1)}]$. The system is said to move from E_i to E_j at time t if $x_t \in (x_{(i)}, x_{(i+1)}]$ and $f(x_t) \in (x_{(j)}, x_{(j+1)}]$. Find the invariance distribution associated with the Markov chain so constructed with state $E_1, E_2, E_3, \ldots$.

(Yu 1986)

(5) Using the technique described in §2.5, obtain a piecewise lineariza-tion of the following pendulum equation:

$$\begin{pmatrix} \dot{x} \\ \dot{y} \end{pmatrix} = \begin{pmatrix} \sin y \\ \sin x \end{pmatrix}$$

(Chen 1971)

(6) Verify that the logistic model

$$x_{t+1} = 4x_t(1 - x_t), \qquad x_0 \in [0, 1]$$

is related to the piecewise linear model

$$\xi_{t+1} = \begin{cases} 2\xi_t & \text{if } 0 \leq \xi_t \leq \frac{1}{2} \\ 2 - 2\xi_t & \text{if } \frac{1}{2} \leq \xi_t \leq t \end{cases}$$

$\xi_0 \in [0, 1]$ via the transformation $x = \sin^2(\pi\xi/2)$. Prove that the stationary density, f, of the chaos defined by the piecewise linear model satisfies

$$2f(\xi) = f(\xi/2) + f(1 - \xi/2), \qquad \xi \in [0, 1].$$

Solve the above functional equation for f and then deduce that the invariant density, g, of the chaos defined by the logistic model is given by

$$g(x) = \{\pi^2 x(1 - x)\}^{-1/2}, \qquad x \in [0, 1].$$

(7) Let $x_{t+1} = f(x_t)$, $t \geq 0$, define a model giving rise to chaos. Does the time series $\{x_t\}$ admit a spectral analysis?
[Hint: Consider first the logistic model $x_{t+1} = 4x_t(1 - x_t)$, $t \geq 0$, $x_0 \in [0, 1]$.]

(8) Let $x_{t+1} = x_t/(1 + x_t)$, $t = 0, 1, \ldots$, $x_0 \neq 0$. Put $y_t = 1/x_t$. Verify that the non-linear equation in x is reduced to a linear equation in y.

(9) By substituting y_{n+1}/y_n for x_n, reduce the equation

$$x_{n+1}^2 - 3x_{n+1}x_n + 2x_n^2 = 0$$

to

$$\left(\frac{y_{n+2}y_n}{y_{n+1}} - 1\right)\left(\frac{y_{n+2}y_n}{y_{n+1}} - 2\right) = 0.$$

Show that the two solutions of the x-equation are $x_n \equiv x_0$ all n, and $x_n = x_0 2^n$.

(10) Two concave mirrors A_1 and A_2 of focal lengths k_1 and k_2 respectively are placed facing each other (as these parentheses do) at a distance of α units. An object is placed on the line segment passing through the two foci at a distance y_1 from A_1 forming an image at a distance x_1 in front of A_1. This image is now the object for A_2 and forms an image in front of A_2 at a distance y_2 from A_1, etc., giving a series of images with distances x_n and y_n. Check that

$$\frac{1}{y_n} + \frac{1}{x_n} = \frac{1}{k_1}$$

$$\frac{1}{\alpha - y_{n+1}} + \frac{1}{\alpha - x_n} = \frac{1}{k_2}.$$

Eliminate x_n between the two equations to get

$$y_{n+1} = \frac{ay_n + b}{cy_n + \alpha}.$$

Substitute v_n/u_n for y_n to reduce the y-equation to a pair of linear equations.

(Boole 1880)

(11) Determine the Lyapunov exponent for the logistic model

$$x_{t+1} = 4x_t(1 - x_t), \quad x_0 \in [0, 1].$$

(12) Consider the Hénon map

$$x_{t+1} = y_t$$

$$y_{t+1} = -x_t + 2y_t^2.$$

Prove that it is area preserving. Show that the origin is a centre and the point $A = (1, 1)$ is a saddle. Investigate the 'symbolic dynamics' based on the symbols

$$\mathbf{M} = \begin{bmatrix} 0 & -1 \\ 1 & 0 \end{bmatrix} \quad \text{and} \quad \mathbf{N} = \begin{bmatrix} 4 & -1 \\ 1 & 0 \end{bmatrix}$$

as described in §2.12. Suppose we replace $2y_t^2$ by $f(y_t)$ where

$$f(y) = \begin{cases} 0 & \text{if } y < \frac{1}{2} \\ 3y - 1 & \text{if } y > \frac{1}{3} \end{cases}.$$

Study the stable manifold and the unstable manifold at A of the piecewise linearized Hénon map, using the method of Example 2.6.

Starting with $\binom{3/8}{3/8}$, trace out on the x–y plane a periodic solution with period 21 consisting of 5 sub-cycles. (This is sometimes referred to as a periodic solution with period 21/5.) Are there other periodic solutions?

(Zhu 1984)

(13) Let $\mathbf{x} \in \mathbf{R}^k$. Show that the solution of the linear differential equation

$$\dot{\mathbf{x}} = \mathbf{A}\mathbf{x}, \quad \mathbf{x}(0) = \mathbf{x}^0$$

where $\mathbf{A}$ is a $k \times k$ matrix of constants, is given by

$$\mathbf{x}(t) = \exp(\mathbf{A}t)\mathbf{x}^0,$$

where

$$\exp(\mathbf{A}t) = \mathbf{I} + \mathbf{A}t + \frac{\mathbf{A}^2 t^2}{2!} + \ldots$$

and $\mathbf{B}_s = (b_{ij}s)$ for any matrix $\mathbf{B} = (b_{ij})$ and any scalar s.

Show that $\mathbf{x}(t) \to \mathbf{0}$ as $t \to \infty$ if and only if all the eigenvalues of $\mathbf{A}$ have negative real parts.

Suppose that we want to construct a Lyapunov function in the form of a quadratic form $\mathbf{x}^T \mathbf{P} \mathbf{x}$, say, where $\mathbf{P}$ is a positive definite symmetric matrix. Show that $\mathbf{P}$ must satisfy the Lyapunov matrix equation

$$PA + A^T P = -Q$$

for some some positive definite symmetric matrix Q.

(14) Consider the discrete dynamical system defined by

$$\begin{pmatrix} x \\ y \end{pmatrix} \rightarrow \begin{cases} A \begin{pmatrix} x \\ y \end{pmatrix} & \text{if } y \geq 0 \\ \\ B \begin{pmatrix} x \\ y \end{pmatrix} & \text{otherwise} \end{cases}$$

where A and B are 2×2 matrices. Suppose that the rank of B is 1. Using the following notation:

$$i_B = \{Bu : u \in R^2\} \qquad i_B^+ = \left\{ \begin{pmatrix} x \\ y \end{pmatrix} \in i_B : y > 0 \right\}$$

$$i_B^- = \left\{ \begin{pmatrix} x \\ y \end{pmatrix} \in i_B : y < 0 \right\}$$

$$U^+ = \left\{ \begin{pmatrix} x \\ y \end{pmatrix} : y > 0 \right\} \qquad U^- = \left\{ \begin{pmatrix} x \\ y \end{pmatrix} : y < 0 \right\}$$

$$B^+ = \{u \in U^- : Bu \in i_B^+\} \qquad B^- = \{u \in U^- : Bu \in i_B^-\}$$

$$A^+ = \{u \in U^+ : A^n u \notin i_B^-, \forall n\}$$

$$A^- = \{u \in U^+ : A^n u \in i_B^- \text{ for some } n\}$$

study the 'symbolic dynamics' in terms of A and B as in §2.12 for each of the following cases:

Case 1(a): $i_B^+ \subset A^+$, $i_B^- \subset B^-$;

Case 1(b): $i_B^+ \subset A^+$, $i_B^- \subset B^+$;

Case 2(a): $i_B^+ \subset A^-$ with $A^k i_B^+ \subset U^+$ for $k = 1, 2, 3, \ldots, n-1$ and $A^n i_B^+ \subset B^-$, and $i_B^- \subset B^-$;

Case 2(b): i_B^+ as in Case 2(a) but $i_B^- \subset B^+$;

Case 3(a): $i_B^+ \subset A^-$ with $A^k i_B^i \subset U^+$ for $k = 1, 2, 3, \ldots, n-1$ and $A^n i_B^+ \subset B^+$, and $i_B^- \subset B^-$;

Case 3(b): i_B^+ as in Case 3(a) but $i_B^- \subset B^+$.

Obtain conditions for Lagrange stability in each case. Prove that the system does not admit chaos.

(In part based on private communication from Pham Dinh Tuan (1987))

(15) Prove that the following dynamical system converges to the origin regardless of initial values:

$$x_{t+1} = \begin{cases} 0.5x_t - 0.6x_{t-1} & \text{if } x_t \geq 0 \\ 0.7x_t - 0.4x_{t-1} & \text{if } x_t < 0 \end{cases}.$$

Investigate the Lagrange stability of the following system:

$$x_{t+1} = \begin{cases} 1.5x_t - 0.9x_{t-1} & \text{if } x_t \leq 0 \\ -1.5x_t - 0.9x_{t-1} & \text{if } x_t < 0 \end{cases}.$$

(Huang and Li 1987)

(16) Let $\{x_t\}$ be generated by the dynamical system

$$x_t = \begin{cases} \phi_1 x_{t-1} & \text{if } x_{t-1} > 0 \\ \phi_2 x_{t-1} & \text{if } x_{t-1} < 0 \end{cases}$$

where $\phi_1 < 1$, $\phi_2 < 1$, $\phi_1 \phi_2 < 1$. Let a and b be real positive numbers such that $1 > \phi_1 > -a/b$ and $1 > \phi_2 > -b/a$. Verify that

$$V(x) = \begin{cases} ax & \text{if } x > 0 \\ -bx & \text{if } x < 0 \end{cases}$$

defines a Lyapunov function of the above dynamical system for $\{x_t\}$ or $\mathbf{R}$. Using the invariance principle, show that

$$x_t \to 0 \quad \text{as} \quad t \to \infty.$$

(17) Let

$$\dot{x} = \phi(x) \tag{A.1}$$

denote a differential equation in one dimension. Suppose that ϕ is continuous and has a finite derivative everywhere. Let $\xi_1 < \xi_2 < \ldots < \xi_p$ denote all critical points of the differential equation, that is points at which ϕ is zero. Suppose also that

$$d\phi(\xi_i)/dx \neq 0, \qquad i = 1, 2, \ldots, p.$$

Prove that the phase portrait of (A.1) is homeomorphic with that of the following piecewise linear differential equation obtained by a straight-line approximation of ϕ:

$$\dot{x}^* = \phi^*(x^*) \tag{A.2}$$

where

$$\phi^*(x^*) = (x^* - \xi_i)(d\phi(\xi_i)/dx)$$

for all

$$xk_i \leq x^* \leq \bar{x}_i, \qquad i = 1, 2, \ldots, p$$

where

$$xk_i = \frac{\xi_i \, d\phi(\xi_i)/dx - \xi_{i-1} \, d\phi(\xi_{i-1})/dx}{x\phi(\xi_i)/dx - d\phi(\xi_{i-1})/dx}$$

$$\bar{x}_i = x_{i+1}$$

(Kalman 1956)

(18)   Consider the first-order differential equation

$$\dot{x}(t) = f(x(t)), \quad f \text{ continuous everywhere.}$$

Consider the quantization which converts the above model to a first-order difference equation for $\{x(t), \ x(t \pm \Delta t), x(t \pm 2 \Delta t), \ldots\}$:

$$x(t + \Delta t) - x(t) = \bar{f}(x(t)) \, \Delta t$$

where

$$\bar{f}(x(t)) = \begin{cases} (\Delta t J(t))^{-1}\{\exp[\Delta t J(t)] - 1\} f(x(t) & \text{if } J(t) \neq 0 \\ f(x(t)) & \text{if } J(t) = 0 \end{cases}.$$

$J(t) = \mathrm{d}f/\mathrm{d}x$ evaluated at $x(t)$.

Verify that

$$\bar{f}(x(t)) \rightarrow f(x(t)) \quad \text{as} \quad \Delta t \rightarrow 0.$$

Suppose h is a $1:1$ differentiable mapping from **R** to **R** and let

$$y(t) = h(x(t)), \quad \text{each } t \in \mathbf{R}.$$

Show that this quantization does not commute with h, that is applying h before this quantization and applying h after this quantization lead to two different difference equations. Repeat the above discussion with the quantization which replaces $\bar{f}$ by

$$\hat{f}(x(t)) = (\Delta t)^{-1}[\exp(\Delta t \mathrm{D}) - 1]x(t)$$

where D denotes the time derivative.

(19)   Suppose that by *embedding* a discrete-time second-order stationary time series in a continuous-time second-order stationary time series we mean that the autocovariance function of the latter coincides with that of the former over the integers. Verify that

$$X_{t+1} - \alpha X_t = \varepsilon_{t+1}, \qquad t = 0, \pm 1, \pm 2, \ldots$$

where $0 < \alpha < 1$, and $\{\varepsilon_t\}$ is a white noise, may be embedded in

$$\mathrm{d}X(t) - \ln \alpha \, X(t) \, \mathrm{d}t = \mathrm{d}W(t)$$

where $\{W(t)\}$ is a Wiener process with zero mean. Show that, for the case $-1 < \alpha < 0$, embedding is not unique and an embedding model may be written in the form

$$X(t) = \dot{Y}(t) + [(\ln |\alpha|)^2 + \pi^2 m^2]^{\frac{1}{2}} Y(t)$$

$$\mathrm{d}\dot{Y}(t) - 2 \ln |\alpha| \, \dot{Y}(t) \, \mathrm{d}t + [\pi^2 m^2 + (\ln |\alpha|)^2] Y(t) \, \mathrm{d}t = \mathrm{d}W(t).$$

Here, $\dot{Y}(t)$ denotes the derivative of $Y(t)$ in the mean square sense,

m is any odd integer, $\{W(t)\}$ is Wiener process with $E(W(t)) = 0$, $E(\{dW(t)\}^2) = \sigma_w^2 \, dt$, $\sigma_w^2 = -2(\ln |\alpha|)/(1 - \alpha^2)$.

(Chan and Tong 1987)

(20) Show that an alternative definition of the Birkhoff positive limit set $\Omega(\mathbf{x})$ is

$$\Omega(\mathbf{x}) = \bigcap_{j=0}^{\infty} \bigcup_{n=j}^{\infty} \mathbf{f}^{(n)}(\mathbf{x}).$$

(21) Let A and B be attractors of $\mathbf{f}$. Verify that if $A \cap B \neq \phi$, then $A = \mathbf{b}$, that is the attractors are unique.

3
Some non-linear time series models

To be constantly aware of the models is known as black virtue.

Ch. LXV Lao Tzu

3.1 Introduction

In recent years, quite a few non-linear time series models have been proposed. We list some of these in this chapter and, whenever appropriate, include a brief description of the background. Detailed analyses of a selection of these models will be given in later chapters. In many cases, results are still incomplete and much research is going on at present.

3.2 Non-linear autoregression

Possibly the single most important class of non-linear time series models which are directly motivated by dynamical systems is the class of *non-linear autoregression*. Specifically, $\{X_t\}$ is said to follow a *non-linear autoregressive model of order k with general noise* if there exists a function $\tilde{f}: \mathbf{R}^{k+1} \to \mathbf{R}$ such that

$$X_t = \tilde{f}(X_{t-1}, X_{t-2}, \ldots, X_{t-k}, \varepsilon_t), \qquad t \in \mathbf{Z} \qquad (3.1)$$

where $\{\varepsilon_t\}$ is a sequence of independent, identically distributed random variables. Typically, ε_t is independent of X_s, $s < t$. For the moment, we do not assume the existence of moments of ε_t. Clearly, in the absence of ε_t (e.g. by setting $\varepsilon_t = 0$, all t), eqn (3.1) is just a non-linear difference equation of order k, the properties of which were summarized in Chapter 2. We refer to the noise-free case as a *skeleton*. It is often useful to think of (3.1) as a stochastic clothing of a (deterministic) skeleton ($\varepsilon_t \equiv 0$) because many stochastic models are obtained by random perturbation, in one way or another, of deterministic models. We shall return to this viewpoint with greater emphasis in Chapter 4.

It is sometimes more convenient to rewrite eqn (3.1) in a vector form by first introducing a k-dimensional state vector $\boldsymbol{\xi}_t$ by

$$\boldsymbol{\xi}_t = (X_t, X_{t-1}, \ldots, X_{t-k+1})^T \qquad (3.2)$$

and a k-dimensional noise vector $\boldsymbol{\eta}_t$ by

$$\boldsymbol{\eta}_t = (\varepsilon_t, 0, 0, \ldots, 0)^T. \tag{3.3}$$

Then (3.1) may be rewritten as

$$\boldsymbol{\xi}_t = \phi(\boldsymbol{\xi}_{t-1}, \boldsymbol{\eta}_t) \tag{3.4}$$

where $\phi : \mathbf{R}^{2k} \to \mathbf{R}^k$ is defined by

$$\begin{aligned}
\xi_t^{(1)} &= \tilde{f}(\xi_{t-1}^{(1)} \ldots \xi_{t-1}^{(k)}, \eta_t^{(1)}) \\
\xi_t^{(2)} &= \xi_{t-1}^{(1)} \\
&\;\;\vdots \\
\xi_t^{(k)} &= \xi_{t-1}^{(k-1)}
\end{aligned} \tag{3.5}$$

where typically $\xi_t^{(j)}$ denotes the jth component/coordinate of $\boldsymbol{\xi}_t$.

It may be noted that every 'reasonable' discrete parameter Markov chain $\{\mathbf{X}_t\}$ on $\mathbf{R}^k$ admits a representation of the form

$$\mathbf{X}_t = f(\mathbf{X}_{t-1}, \mathbf{e}_t)$$

where $f : \mathbf{R}^{2k} \to \mathbf{R}^k$, $\{\mathbf{e}_t\}$ is a sequence of independent and identically distributed k-dimensional random vectors and $\mathbf{e}_t$ is independent of $\mathbf{X}_s$, $s < t$ (Kifer 1986, p. 8; Rosenblatt 1971, p. 169).

Specifically, we quote Lemma 2 of Rosenblatt (1971) for the case $k = 1$ as follows. First, given two distribution functions F, G we shall say that they are *equivalent* if the jumps of F and G can be mapped on to each other in a 1–1 manner so that jump sizes are preserved.

Lemma 3.1: Let $\{X_t\}$ be a stationary real-valued Markov chain with conditional distribution function $F(x \mid x') = P\{X_t \leq x \mid X_{t-1} = x'\}$ a Borel function of two variables x, x' (i.e. a measurable function from $(\mathbf{R}^2, \mathbb{B})$ into itself, $\mathbb{B}$ being the usual σ-algebra of Borel sets). There is a random variable e_t measurable w.r.t. $\mathbb{B}^{(t)}$, the sigma algebra generated by $\{X_s, s \leq t\}$, such that e_t is independent of $\mathbb{B}^{(t-1)}$ and $\mathbb{B}^{(t)}$ is generated by $\mathbb{B}^{(t-1)}$ and the sigma algebra generated by e_t, if and only if the distribution functions $F(x \mid x')$ (as functions of x) are equivalent for almost all x' with respect to the invariance measure of the chain $\{X_t\}$.

We may give a heuristic discussion as follows[*].

Suppose that $\{X_t, t = 0, 1, \ldots\}$ is a discrete-time Markov process with state space E which may be discrete or continuous. For the moment suppose $E \subseteq \mathbf{R}$ and denote the distribution function of X_{t+1} given $X_t = x$ by F_x:

$$F_x(y) = p(X_{t+1} \leq y \mid X_t = x).$$

---

[*] I owe the discussion to Professor P. J. Donnelly.

Let F_x^{-1} be the usual inverse of F_x and recall that if U has a uniform distribution on $[0, 1]$, then $F_x^{-1}(U)$ has a distribution function F_x. The idea behind this construction is that if $X_t = x$ and U is uniformly distributed on $[0, 1]$ independently on everything else, then taking $X_{t+1} = F_x^{-1}(U)$ gives a random variable with the correct distribution.

Suppose $U_1, U_2, \ldots$ are i.i.d. uniform $[0, 1]$. Define $f : \mathbf{R} \times [0, 1] \to \mathbf{R}$ by $f(x, u) = F_x^{-1}(u)$. The construction $X_{t+1} = f(X_t, U_{t+1})$, with X_0 chosen according to the appropriate initial distribution, gives a realization of the Markov chain $\{X_t, t = 0, 1, \ldots\}$. $\quad\square$

Returning to the general case, if ϕ satisfies

$$\phi(\xi_{t-1}, \eta_t) = \phi(\xi_{t-1}, \mathbf{0}) + \eta_t \tag{3.6}$$

eqn (3.6) is said to define an *additive noise model*. Equation (3.6) is equivalent to

$$X_t = \bar{f}(X_{t-1}, \ldots, X_{t-k}, 0) + \varepsilon_t \tag{3.7}$$

which we write simply as

$$X_t = f(X_{t-1}, \ldots, X_{t-k}) + \varepsilon_t \tag{3.8}$$

where $f : \mathbf{R}^k \to \mathbf{R}$. Frequently in the literature, the acronym NLAR (k) refers to the restricted class defined by (3.8). We shall follow this convention.

Consider the case $k = 1$. Writing $Y_t = f(X_t)$, we may rewrite (3.8) as

$$Y_t = f(Y_{t-1} + \varepsilon_t). \tag{3.9}$$

We may similarly extend the reformulation to $k \geq 2$.

As yet the functional forms of $\bar{f}$ and f have not been specified. In a practical situation, we may leave them unspecified and let the data 'speak' for them directly; this leads to the so-called *non-parametric autoregressive function approach*. Alternatively we may parametrize $\bar{f}$ and f and this leads to the so-called *finite parameteric autoregressive approach*.

Note that it is sometimes instructive to think of an NLAR model in the form

$$\mathbf{X}_t = E[\mathbf{X}_t \mid \mathbf{X}_{t-1}] + \{\mathrm{Var}[\mathbf{X}_t \mid \mathbf{X}_{t-1}]\}^{1/2} \mathbf{e}_t,$$

which may be compared with a diffusion process in continuous time.

3.3 Threshold principle and threshold models

The concept of a *threshold* was discussed in Chapter 2. The basic idea is the local approximation over the states, i.e. the introduction of regimes via thresholds. For convenience, we refer to this idea as the *threshold principle*, which allows the analysis of a complex stochastic system by decomposing it into simpler subsystems. Under the threshold principle, we may group a number of finite parametric non-linear time series models.

3.3.1 PIECEWISE LINEAR MODELS

Let $\{\mathbf{X}_t\}$ be a k-dimensional time series and, for each t, let J_t be an indicator random variable, taking integer values $\{1, 2, \ldots, l\}$. A *canonical form of a threshold model in time series analysis* may be given by

$$\mathbf{X}_t = \mathbf{B}^{(J_t)}\mathbf{X}_t + \mathbf{A}^{(J_t)}\mathbf{X}_{t-1} + \mathbf{H}^{(J_t)}\varepsilon_t + \mathbf{C}^{(J_t)} \tag{3.10}$$

where, for $J_t = j$, $\mathbf{A}^{(j)}$, and $\mathbf{H}^{(j)}$ are $k \times k$ (non-random) matrix coefficients, $\mathbf{C}^{(j)}$ is a $k \times 1$ vector of constants, and $\{\varepsilon_j\}$ is a sequence of i.i.d. k-dimensional random vectors with zero mean and a covariance matrix.

In the above canonical form, J_t indicates the mode of the dynamic mechanism. The choice of J_t is purposely allowed to be quite flexible so that a fairly large number of different situations may be catered for. Of course, that choice of J_t which is a function of $\mathbf{X}_t$ itself will be of immediate interest, since this choice is closely related to the concepts of threshold and time delay introduced in the last chapter.

We now single out a few interesting special cases of model (3.10) for further development.

First, let $\{r_0, r_1, \ldots, r_l\}$ denote a linearly ordered subset of the real numbers, such that $r_0 < r_1 < \ldots < r_l$, where r_0 and r_l are taken to be $-\infty$ and $+\infty$ respectively. They define a partition of the real line $\mathbf{R}$, that is $\mathbf{R} = R_1 \cup R_2 \ldots \cup R_l$, say, where $R_i = (r_{i-1}, r_i]$.

3.3.1.1 The class of self-exciting threshold autoregressive/moving average models Writing $\mathbf{X}_t = (X_t, X_{t-1}, \ldots, X_{t-k+1})^T$,

$$\mathbf{A}^{(j)} = \left[\begin{array}{c|c} a_1^{(j)}(a_2^{(j)} \ldots a_{k-1}^{(j)} & a_k^{(j)} \\ \hline \mathbf{I}_{k-1} & \mathbf{0} \end{array}\right] \quad \text{(a companion matrix)}$$

$$\mathbf{B}^{(j)} = \mathbf{0}$$

$$\mathbf{H}^{(j)} = \left[\begin{array}{c|c} h_1^{(j)} & \mathbf{0} \\ \hline \mathbf{0} & \mathbf{0} \end{array}\right]$$

$$\varepsilon_t = (\varepsilon_t, \varepsilon_{t-1}, \ldots, \varepsilon_{t-k+1})^T$$

$$\mathbf{C}^{(j)} = (a_0^{(j)}, 0, \ldots, 0)^T$$

and $R_{j,d}^{(k)} = \mathbf{R} \times \mathbf{R} \times \ldots \times \mathbf{R} \times R_j \times \mathbf{R} \times \ldots \times \mathbf{R}$, the cylinder set in the Cartesian product of k real lines, on the interval R_j with a dth coordinate space (d some fixed integer belonging to $\{1, 2, \ldots, k\}$), and setting $J_t = j$ if $\mathbf{X}_{t-1} \in R_{j,d}^{(k)}$, we have

$$X_t = a_0^{(j)} + \sum_{i=1}^{k} a_i^{(j)} x_{t-i} + h_1^{(j)} \varepsilon_t \tag{3.11}$$

conditional on $X_{t-d} \in R_j$; $j = 1, 2, \ldots, l$. Since $\{J_t\}$ is now a function of $\{X_t\}$ *itself*, we call the univariate time series $\{X_t\}$ given by (3.11) a *self-exciting threshold autoregressive model of order* $(l; k, \ldots, k)$ or SETAR $(l; k, \ldots, k)$, where k is repeated l times. Figure 3.1 illustrates a realization.

If, for $j = 1, 2, \ldots, l$,

$$a_i^{(j)} = 0 \quad \text{for } i = k_j + 1, k_j + 2, \ldots, k \tag{3.12}$$

then we call $\{X_t\}$ a SETAR $(l; k_1, k_2, \ldots, k_l)$. We call $r_1, \ldots, r_{l-1}$ the *threshold parameters* and d the *delay parameter*. Note that a SETAR

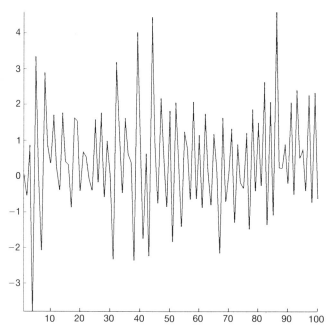

Fig. 3.1. A realization of

$$X_t = \begin{cases} 1.0 + 0.6X_{t-1} + \varepsilon_t & \text{if } X_{t-1} \leq 0 \\ -1.0 + 0.4X_{t-1} + \varepsilon_t & \text{if } X_{t-1} < 0 \end{cases}$$

where $\varepsilon_t \sim \mathcal{N}(0, 1)$

$(1; k)$ is just a *linear* AR model of order k. We sometimes simplify the notation $h_1^{(j)} \varepsilon_t$ to $\varepsilon_t^{(j)}$ and refer to $\{\varepsilon_t^{(j)}\}$ as a (heterogeneous) *white noise sequence*. If the first row of $\mathbf{H}^{(j)}$ is of the form $(h_1^{(j)}, h_2^{(j)}, \ldots, h_k^{(j)})$, $h_k^{(j)} \neq 0$, $(j = 1, 2, \ldots, l)$, then we have the obvious generalization of SETAR to a *self-exciting threshold autoregressive/moving-average model of order* $(l; k, \ldots k, k-1, \ldots, k-1)$ or SETARMA $(l; k, \ldots, k; k-1, \ldots k-1)$. In full, it takes the form

$$X_t = a_0^{(j)} + \sum_{i=1}^{k} a_i^{(j)} X_{t-i} + \sum_{i=0}^{k-1} h_i^{(j)} \varepsilon_{t-i} \qquad (3.13)$$

conditional on $X_{t-d} \in R_j$, $j = 1, 2, \ldots, l$. Again, under conditions similar to (3.12), we may consider SETARMA $(l; k_1, k_2, \ldots, k_l; k_1', k_2', \ldots, k_l')$, where k_j and k_j' refer to the AR order and MA order respectively, conditional on $X_{t-d} \in R_j$.

3.3.1.2   The class of open-loop threshold autoregressive systems
(X_t, Y_t) is called an *open-loop threshold autoregressive system* with $\{X_t\}$ as the observable output and $\{Y_t\}$ as the observable input, if

$$X_t = a_0^{(j)} + \sum_{i=1}^{m_j} a_i^{(j)} X_{t-i} + \sum_{i=0}^{m_j'} b_i^{(j)} Y_{t-i} + \varepsilon_t^{(j)} \qquad (3.14)$$

conditional on $Y_{t-d} \in R_j$ $(j = 1, \ldots, l)$, where $\{\varepsilon_t^{(j)}\}$, $(j = 1, \ldots, l)$ are heterogeneous white noise sequences with zero mean and finite variances and each being independent of $\{Y_t\}$. These l sequences are assumed to be independent of one another. We denote this system by TARSO $(l; (m_1, m_1'), \ldots, (m_l, m_l'))$. Incorporation of 'moving-average' terms is fairly obvious. Here, the indicator variable J_t is a function of the 'exogenous' variable Y_{t-d}. In the above formulation, the value of the exogenous variable indicates which subsystem (assumed linear for simplicity) is activated. Naturally, there are situations where other choices of J_t are more appropriate.

3.3.1.3   The class of closed-loop threshold autoregressive systems
$\{X_t, Y_t\}$ is called a *closed-loop threshold autoregressive system*, or TARSC, if (X_t, Y_t) and (Y_t, X_t) are both TARSO. Again, all heterogeneous white noise sequences involved are assumed to be independent of one another. Finally, incorporation of 'moving-average' terms is fairly obvious.

3.3.1.4   The class of exponential autoregressive (EAR) models   The
class of EAR models and its extensions introduced by Lawrance, Lewis, and others in a series of papers (see e.g. Lawrance and Lewis 1980) may

be formally regarded as a sub-class of the threshold models with $\{J_t\}$ independent of $\{X_t\}$. We may illustrate this point with the following threshold representation of an EAR(2):

$$X_t = a^{(J_t)}X_{t-1} + b^{(J_t)}X_{t-2} + \varepsilon_t \tag{3.15}$$

where $\{J_t\}$ is a sequence of i.i.d. random variables with the following distribution:

$$J_t = \begin{cases} 1 & \text{with probability } 1 - \alpha_2 \\ 2 & \text{with probability } \alpha_2 \end{cases}.$$

Here, $\{J_t\}$ is independent of $\{X_t\}$ and $\{\varepsilon_t\}$, and

$$a^{(1)} = \alpha_1 \qquad a^{(2)} = 0 \qquad b^{(1)} = 0 \qquad b^{(2)} = \alpha_2$$

where α_1 and α_2 are constants $(0 < \alpha_1, \alpha_2 < 1)$.

3.3.1.5 The Class of ARMA models with periodic coefficients This class of models was studied by Gladyshev (1961), within a general context, and by Jones and Brelsford (1967) within the meteorological context. The essential idea is to allow the a_j and b_j coefficients of an ARMA model to be periodically varying over time. A simple example is

$$X_t = a_0(t) + a_1(t)X_{t-1} + \varepsilon_t \tag{3.16}$$

where for $i = 0$, 1, and all integers n, $a_i(2n) = a_i^{(1)}$, say, and $a_i(2n + 1) = a_i^{(2)}$, say. This type of model can be easily put into the threshold framework as follows:

$$X_t = a_0^{(J_t)} + a_1^{(J_t)}X_{t-1} + \varepsilon_t \tag{3.17}$$

where, with probability 1 and for all integer t, $J_{2t} = 1$ and $J_{2t+1} = 2$.

3.3.1.6 The class of threshold models without additive noise A typical example takes the form

$$X_t = a_1^{(J_t)}X_{t-1} + a_0^{(J_t)} \tag{3.18}$$

where $\{J_t\}$ is a sequence of i.i.d. random variables and J_t is independent of X_s, $s < t$. Figure 3.2 illustrates realizations of models of this class, which may be identified as *fractals* (see §2.11).

3.3.1.7 The class of Markov-chain-driven models Typically the models take the form of eqn (3.10) with $\{J_t\}$ being a Markov chain on a finite number of states, say $(1, 2, \ldots, k)$ and

$$P[J_t = j \mid J_{t-1} = i, \mathbb{B}_{t-1}] = P[J_t = j \mid J_{t-1} = i]$$

where $\mathbb{B}_s$ denotes the σ-algebra generated by $\mathbf{X}_s, \mathbf{X}_{s-1}, \ldots$. Figure 3.3 gives a realization of a model of this class.

3.3.1.8 The class of asymmetric moving-average models Typically the model is of the form

$$X_t = \varepsilon_t + h^{(J_t)}\varepsilon_{t-1} \tag{3.19}$$

where

$$J_t = \begin{cases} 1 & \text{if } \varepsilon_{t-1} \text{ is positive} \\ 2 & \text{if } \varepsilon_{t-1} \text{ is negative} \end{cases} \tag{3.20}$$

and $\{\varepsilon_t\}$ is a sequence of i.i.d. random variables. Equation (3.19) may be extended in an obvious way to incorporate ε_{t-2}, ε_{t-3}, etc. This class may be considered a threshold moving average with ε_{t-1} replacing X_{t-1} in the definition of J_t.

3.3.2 PIECEWISE POLYNOMIAL MODELS

A natural way of constructing a class of non-linear time series models is to start with a *polynomial skeleton*, for example $x_t = f(x_{t-1})$, where f is a polynomial of finite degree. However, an analysis of stability will readily demonstrate the inefficacy of the approach without modification. For example, let

$$x_t = ax_{t-1}(1 - x_{t-1}), \qquad a \neq 1. \tag{3.21}$$

Equation (3.21) has two equilibrium points, namely 0 and $(a - 1)/a$. A cobweb diagram (Fig. 3.4) shows that at least one of them is unstable. Thus, a polynomial skeleton of degree not less than 2 requires some modification before it can be 'clothed' into a usable non-linear times series model.

We now describe two possible modifications based on the censoring idea (cf. §2.10).

3.3.2.1 Hard censoring This replaces $f(x)$ by $[f(x)]_{-A}^{+A}$, where

$$[y]_{-A}^{+A} = \begin{cases} A & y > A \\ y & -A \leq y \leq A \\ -A & y < -A \end{cases} \tag{3.22}$$

where A is a positive real constant.

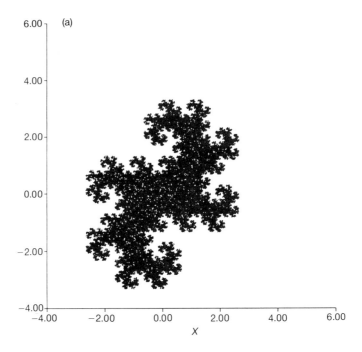

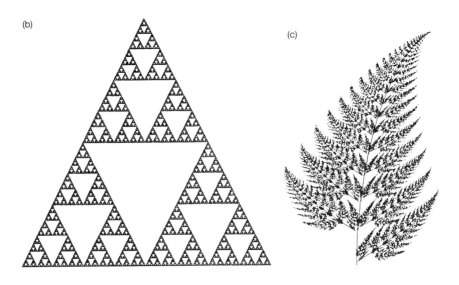

Fig. 3.2.(a) A realization of

$$\begin{bmatrix} x_t \\ y_t \end{bmatrix} = \mathbf{A}\begin{bmatrix} x_{t-1} \\ y_{t-1} \end{bmatrix} + \begin{bmatrix} 1 \\ 1 \end{bmatrix}$$

with probability $\frac{1}{2}$,

$$\mathbf{A}\begin{bmatrix} x_{t-1} \\ y_{t-1} \end{bmatrix} + \begin{bmatrix} -1 \\ -1 \end{bmatrix}$$

with probability $\frac{1}{2}$.

$$\begin{bmatrix} x_0 \\ y_0 \end{bmatrix} = \begin{bmatrix} 1 \\ 1 \end{bmatrix} \qquad \mathbf{A} = \begin{bmatrix} 0.5 & -0.5 \\ 0.5 & 0.5 \end{bmatrix}.$$

The random mechanism is a sequence of independent Bernoulli trials

Fig. 3.2(b) A realization of

$$\begin{bmatrix} x_t \\ y_t \end{bmatrix} + \mathbf{A}\begin{bmatrix} x_{t-1} \\ y_{t-1} \end{bmatrix} = \begin{bmatrix} 0 \\ 0 \end{bmatrix}$$

with probability 0.33, $\begin{bmatrix} 0.5 \\ 0 \end{bmatrix}$ with probability 0.33, $\begin{bmatrix} 0.25 \\ 0.50 \end{bmatrix}$ with probability 0.34

$$\mathbf{A} = \begin{bmatrix} -0.5 & 0 \\ 0 & -0.5 \end{bmatrix} \qquad \begin{bmatrix} x_0 \\ y_0 \end{bmatrix} = \begin{bmatrix} 1 \\ 1 \end{bmatrix}.$$

The random mechanism is a sequence of independent trials with three states

Fig. 3.2(c) A realization of

$$\begin{bmatrix} x_t \\ y_t \end{bmatrix} = \begin{bmatrix} 0 & 0 \\ 0 & 0.25 \end{bmatrix}\begin{bmatrix} x_{t-1} \\ y_{t-1} \end{bmatrix} + \begin{bmatrix} 0 \\ 0 \end{bmatrix}$$

with probability 0.01,

$$\begin{bmatrix} 0.85 & 0.04 \\ -0.04 & 0.85 \end{bmatrix}\begin{bmatrix} x_{t-1} \\ y_{t-1} \end{bmatrix} + \begin{bmatrix} 0 \\ 1.6 \end{bmatrix}$$

with probability 0.85,

$$\begin{bmatrix} 0.20 & -0.26 \\ 0.26 & 0.22 \end{bmatrix}\begin{bmatrix} x_{t-1} \\ y_{t-1} \end{bmatrix} + \begin{bmatrix} 0 \\ 0.8 \end{bmatrix}$$

with probability 0.07,

$$\begin{bmatrix} -0.15 & 0.28 \\ 0.26 & 0.24 \end{bmatrix}\begin{bmatrix} x_{t-1} \\ y_{t-1} \end{bmatrix} + \begin{bmatrix} 0 \\ 1 \end{bmatrix}$$

with probability 0.07.

$$\begin{bmatrix} x_0 \\ y_0 \end{bmatrix} = \begin{bmatrix} 1 \\ 1 \end{bmatrix}.$$

The random mechanism is a sequence of independent trials with four states

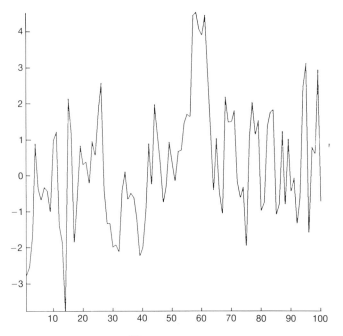

Fig. 3.3. A realization of $X_t = a^{(J_t)} x_{t-1} + \varepsilon_t$, where $\varepsilon_t - \mathcal{N}(0, 1)$, $\{J_t\}$ is a Markov chain on $(1, 2)$ with transition matrix

$$
\begin{array}{c}
J_{t+1} \\
\begin{array}{cc}
\quad 1 & \quad 2
\end{array} \\
J_t \begin{array}{c} 1 \\ 2 \end{array}
\begin{bmatrix} 0.1 & 0.9 \\ 0.3 & 0.7 \end{bmatrix}
\end{array}
$$

and $a^{(1)} = -0.9$, $a^{(2)} = 0.9$

3.3.2.2 Soft censoring This replaces $f(x)$ by $\bar{f}(x)$, where

$$
\bar{f}(x) = \begin{cases} f(x) & \text{for } |x| \le A \\ l(x) & \text{for } |x| > A \end{cases} \tag{3.23}
$$

where A is a positive real constant and $l(x)$ is linear in x.

It is clear that the censoring idea may be extended to skeletons

$$
x_t = f(x_{t-1}, x_{t-2}, \ldots, x_{t-x}) \tag{3.24}
$$

where f is a polynomial in $x_{t-1}, x_{t-2}, \ldots, x_{t-k}$. The modulus operation may be replaced by any suitable norm of a vector, say $(x_{t-1}^2 + \ldots + x_{t-k}^2)^{1/2}$.

The class of censored polynomial autoregressive models obtained by clothing a censored polynomial skeleton with additive noise is, of course,

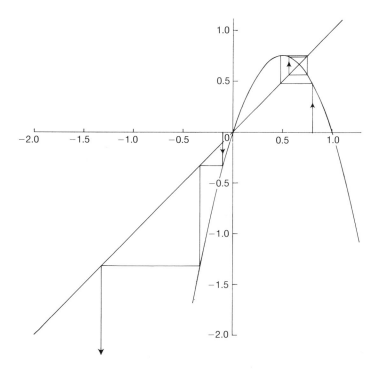

Fig. 3.4. Cobweb diagram of $x_t = 3x_{t-1}(1 - x_{t-1})$. $(0, 1)$ is the basin of attraction of the limit point at $\frac{2}{3}$

an application of the threshold principle. The constants A and $-A$ are the thresholds.

3.3.3 SMOOTH THRESHOLD AUTOREGRESSIVE (STAR) MODELS

Let us consider a SETAR $(2; k, k)$ model, which may be written in the equivalent form

$$X_t = a_0 + \sum_{j=1}^{k} a_j(X_{t-j} + \left(b_0 + \sum_{j=1}^{k} b_j X_{t-j}\right) I_r(X_{t-d}) + \varepsilon_t \qquad (3.25)$$

where I_r is an indicator function such that

$$I_r(x) = \begin{cases} 0 & \text{if } x \leq r \\ 1 & \text{if } x > r \end{cases}. \qquad (3.26)$$

Replacing I_r by a 'smooth' function F yields a class of *smooth threshold autoregressive (STAR) models*. The choice of F is purposely left very flexible, the minimal requirement being that it is continuous and non-decreasing. For example, we may replace $I_r(x)$ by $\Phi((x - r)/\delta)$, Φ being the standard Gaussian distribution, or by $\{1 + \exp[(r - x)/\delta]\}^{-1}$, the logistic distribution, etc. The general motivation is that we may wish to model the data without prior assumption of abrupt changes over the states; we let the data tell us if the changes are abrupt or not by watching, for example, the size of the 'scale' parameter δ.

3.4   Amplitude-dependent exponential autoregressive (EXPAR) models

The discussion of Example 2.13 motivates the class of non-linear autoregressive models under the name of *amplitude-dependent exponential autoressive models*. These models were independently introduced by Jones (1976) and Ozaki and Oda (1978). The basic form of an EXPAR model of order k is

$$X_t = \sum_{j=1}^{k} [\alpha_j + \beta_j \exp(-\delta X_{t-1}^2)]X_{t-j} + \varepsilon_t, \qquad \delta > 0 \qquad (3.27)$$

where $\{\varepsilon_t\}$ is a sequence of i.i.d. random variables, usually with zero mean and finite variance. (Jones only considered the case of $k = 1$.) The above model may be extended by replacing β_j by $f_j(X_{t-1})$, where

$$f_j(x) = \sum_{i=0}^{k_j} \gamma_i^{(j)} x^i. \qquad (3.28)$$

We shall see later that there is sometimes a need to modify the above formulation by replacing $\beta_j \exp(-\delta X_{t-1}^2)$ by $\beta_j \exp(-\delta X_{-j}^2)$ and likewise $f_j(X_{t-1})$ by $f_j(X_{t-j})$ (cf. Example 2.11). Note that the above models contain no 'constant terms', because Ozaki (1981, p. 447) seems to take the view that *if the vibration process starts from the zero initial state it stays at* 0. This, however, may be unduly restrictive in many applications other than pure vibrations. We illustrate this point in §7.2.10.

3.5   Fractional autoregressive (FAR) models

It is well known in approximation theory that we may approximate $\Phi(x)$, $\exp(-\frac{1}{2}x^2)$, etc. by rational functions. For example, for $0 \le x < \infty$,

$$\Phi(x) = 1 - \frac{1}{2}(1 + c_1 x + c_2 x^2 + c_3 x^3 + c_4 x^4)^{-4} + \varepsilon(x) \qquad (3.29)$$

where $|\varepsilon(x)| < 2.5 \times 10^{-4}$, $c_1 = 0.196\,854$, $c_2 = 0.115\,194$, $c_3 = 0.000\,344$, $c_4 = 0.019\,527$, and

$$\frac{1}{(2\pi)^{1/2}} e^{-1/2x^2} = (a_0 + a_2 x^2 + a_4 x^4 + a_6 x^6)^{-1} + \varepsilon(x) \tag{3.30}$$

where $|\varepsilon(x)| < 2.7 \times 10^{-3}$, $a_0 = 2.490\,895$, $a_2 = 1.466\,003$, $a_4 = -0.024\,393$, $a_6 = 0.178\,257$ (see e.g. Abramowitz and Stegun 1972, p. 932).

We may alternatively consider continued fraction approximations. For this, we introduce the notation

$$\frac{a_1}{x+} \frac{a_2}{x+} \frac{a_2}{x+} \frac{a_4}{x+} \frac{a_5}{x+} \cdots$$

to mean

$$\cfrac{a_1}{x + \cfrac{a_2}{x + \cfrac{a_3}{x + \cfrac{a_4}{x + \cfrac{a_5}{x + \ldots}}}}}$$

For example, it is known that for $x > 0$

$$1 - \Phi(x) = \frac{1}{(2\pi)^{1/2}} e^{-1/2x^2} \left\{ \frac{1}{x+} \frac{1}{x+} \frac{2}{x+} \frac{3}{x+} \frac{4}{x+} \cdots \right\}. \tag{3.31}$$

Equation (3.31) reveals the intimate relation between the skeletons of STAR models and EXPAR models. For the order 1 case, both classes may be subsumed in *the class of fractional autoregressive (FAR) models of order* 1:

$$X_t = \frac{a_0 + \sum\limits_{j=1}^{p} a_j X_{t-1}^j}{b_0 + \sum\limits_{j=1}^{q} b_j X_{t-1}^j} + \varepsilon_t \tag{3.32}$$

where $\{\varepsilon_t\}$ is a sequence of i.i.d. random variables, $0 \le p \le q + 1 < \infty$, $a_p \ne 0$, $b_q \ne 0$. Clearly model (3.32) may be extended to include higher-order lags, that is X_{t-s}, $s > 1$.

3.6 Product autoregressive (PAR) models

So far all the non-linear autoregressive models we have listed involve *additive* noise. This, of course, is not essential. As an example of a non-linear autoregressive model with non-additive noise, let

$$X_t = \varepsilon_t X_{t-1}^{\alpha} \tag{3.33}$$

where $\{\varepsilon_t\}$ is a sequence of i.i.d. positive random variables.

3.7 Random coefficient autoregressive (RCA) models

The idea of multiplicative noise implicit in the last class of models may be exploited further to the extent that a fully fledged class of RCA models may be entertained. One motivation for incorporating multiplicative noise is based on the observation that a panel of time series (e.g. growth curves) may correspond to different subjects (e.g. mice) observed under similar conditions (e.g. of similar age and under similar environmental conditions), and we are interested in some universal features (e.g. general growth mechanism). Another motivation is to study the result of random perturbations of an assumed dynamical system. Specifically, a time series $\{X_t\}$ is said to follow a *random coefficient autoregressive model of order* k, $RCA(k)$, if X_t satisfies an equation of the form

$$X_t = \sum_{i=1}^{k} [\beta_i + B_i(t)]X_{t-i} + \varepsilon_t, \tag{3.34}$$

where

(1) $\{\varepsilon_t\}$ is a sequence of i.i.d. random variables with zero mean and variance σ^2;

(2) the β_i, $i = 1, \ldots, k$, are constants;

(3) on letting $\mathbf{B}(t) = [B_k(t), \ldots, B_1(t)]$, $\{\mathbf{B}(t)\}$ is a sequence of independent $1 \times k$ vectors with zero mean and $E[\mathbf{B}^T(t)\mathbf{B}(t)] = \mathbf{C}$;

(4) $\{\mathbf{B}(t)\}$ is independent of $\{\varepsilon_t\}$.

It is fairly straightforward to extend eqn (3.34) to a p-dimensional vector time series $\{\mathbf{X}_t\}$ by replacing the β_i, $B_i(t)$ by $p \times p$ matrices and $\{\varepsilon_t\}$ by a p-dimensional time series. Conditions (1)–(4) are easily generalized:

(1′) $\{\varepsilon_j\}$ is a sequence of i.i.d. random vectors with zero mean and covaraince matrix G;

(2′)   as (2);

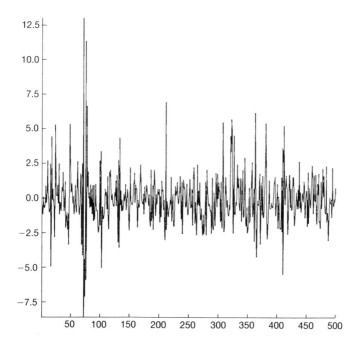

Fig. 3.5. A realization of $X_t = [-0.1 + B_1(t)]X_{t-1} + \varepsilon_t$, where $B_1(t) \sim \mathcal{N}(0, 0.9^2)$, $\varepsilon_t \sim \mathcal{N}(0, 1)$, $\{B_1(t)\}$ and $\{\varepsilon_t\}$ are independent

(3′) $\{\mathbf{B}(t)\}$ is a sequence of independent $p \times kp$ matrices with zero mean and $E[\mathbf{B}(t) \otimes \mathbf{B}(t)] = \mathbf{C}$, $\otimes$ denoting the Kronecker product operation;

(4′) as (4).

Figure 3.5 illustrates a realization of an RCA model. Note the similarity of Figs 1.3 and 3.5 here.

3.8 Newer exponential autoregressive (NEAR) models

These models form formally a sub-class of RCA models, with the marginal distribution specified as exponential. The motivation seems to be the desire to focus more specifically on non-negative time series which assume low values with high probability.

Let $\{J(t); t \in \mathbf{Z}\}$ and $\{\varepsilon_t; t \in \mathbf{Z}\}$ be two independent sequences of i.i.d. random variables. For each t, $J(t)$ is a discrete random variable with the following distribution:

$$J(t) = \begin{cases} 0 & \text{with probability } \alpha_0 \\ 1 & \text{with probability } \alpha_1 \\ \vdots \\ p & \text{with probability } \alpha_p. \end{cases} \tag{3.35}$$

Here, $\alpha_0, \alpha_1, \ldots, \alpha_p$ are non-negative and sum to unity. Let $\beta^{(0)} = 0$, $\beta^{(1)}, \ldots, \beta^{(p)}$ be $p + 1$ constants, satisfying $0 \le \beta^{(j)} \le 1$, $1 \le j \le p$. The following gives one possible formulation of a NEAR model of order p, NEAR(p):

$$X_t = \beta^{(J(t))} X_{t-J(t)} + \varepsilon_t \tag{3.36}$$

where $J(t)$ is independent of $X_{t-1}, X_{t-2}, \ldots$.

Formally, NEAR models are also special cases of Markov-chain-driven threshold models.

3.9   Autoregressive models with discrete state space

Hitherto, X_t takes real values. However, in many areas of applications, X_t are counts taken over time, for example annual sunspot numbers. It is therefore quite natural to consider purpose-built models with discrete state space. Clearly, a kth order non-linear autoregressive model over $\mathbf{R}$ may be considered a Markov chain over $\mathbf{R}^k$. Similarly, a kth order non-linear autoregressive model over $\mathbf{Z}$ may be considered a Markov chain over $\mathbf{Z}^k$. The latter represents a model for dependent discrete data. Therefore we seek a suitable function f and a sequence of i.i.d. random vectors, ε_t, with a suitable distribution such that through

$$X_t = f(X_{t-1}, X_{t-2}, \ldots, X_{t-k}, \varepsilon_t) \tag{3.37}$$

$\{X_t\}$ has a desired marginal (discrete) distribution and a desired autocorrelation function. We give a gew examples in the form of Table 3.1. First, we introduce a notation. Let X be a discrete random variable and α be a real number such that $0 \le \alpha \le 1$. Let $\{B_i(\alpha)\}$ be a sequence of i.i.d. binary random variables such that

$$P[B_i(\alpha) = 1] = \alpha. \tag{3.38}$$

We define the *-operation, called the binomial thinning operation, by

$$\alpha * X = \sum_{i=1}^{X} B_i(\alpha). \tag{3.39}$$

Table 3.1. AR models with discrete state space

Marginal distribution of X_t	Autocorrelation corr(X_0, X_k)	Model form	Distribution of ε_t
(1) Poisson with mean θ ($0 < \theta < \infty$)	α^k	$X_t = \alpha * X_{t-1} + \varepsilon_{1t}, \ t \geq 1, \ 0 < \alpha < 1$; X_0 is Poisson with mean θ	ε_{1t} is Poisson with mean $\theta(1-\alpha)$
(2) Negative binomial, NB(β, θ), namely $P[X_t = x] = \binom{\beta + x - 1}{x}(1-\theta)^\beta \theta^x$, $x = 0, 1, 2, \ldots$, $(0 < \theta < 1)$	α^k	$X_t = \varepsilon_{1t} * X_{t-1} + \varepsilon_{2t}, \ t \geq 1$; X_0 is NB(β, θ)	ε_{1t} is a β random variable with parameters $\alpha\beta$ and $(1 - \alpha)\beta$; ε_{2t} is NB$((1 - \alpha)\beta, \theta)$; $0 < \alpha < 1$
(3) Binomial, $B_i(N, \theta)$, namely $P[X_t = x] = \binom{N}{x}\theta^x(1 - \theta)^{N-x}$, $x = 0, 1, \ldots, N$, $(0 < \theta < 1)$	$\left(\dfrac{\alpha - \theta}{1 - \theta}\right)^k$	$X_t = \alpha * X_{t-1} + \beta * (N - X_{t-1}), \ t \geq 1$, $0 < \alpha < 1, \ 0 < \beta < 1, \ X_0$ is $B_i(N, \theta)$	Not applicable
(4) Bernoulli, namely $P[X_t = 1] = \theta = 1 - P[X_t = 0]$	p^k	$X_t = \varepsilon_{1t}X_{t-1} + (1 - \varepsilon_{1t})\varepsilon_{2t}, \ t \geq 1$, X_0 is Bernoulli with parameter θ	ε_{1t} is Bernoulli with parameter p and ε_{2t} is Bernoulli with parameter θ; $\{\varepsilon_{1t}\}$ and $\{\varepsilon_{2t}\}$ are independent of each other

We note that the above framework may be extended to higher-order autoregressive/moving-average cases. We refer interested readers to McKenzie (1985) and references therein.

3.10 Bilinear (BL) models

Somewhere between the 'fixed coefficient' autoregressive models and the random coefficient autoregressive models lies the class of *bilinear models*. A dynamical system background of a bilinear system was described at some length in §2.7.

The time series $\{X_t\}$ is said to follow a *bilinear model* if it satisfies the equation

$$X_t + \sum_{i=1}^{p} a_i X_{t-i} = \alpha + \sum_{j=1}^{r} \sum_{k=1}^{s} b_{jk} X_{t-j}\varepsilon_{t-k} + \varepsilon_t \tag{3.40}$$

where $\{\varepsilon_t\}$ is a sequence of i.i.d. random variables, usually but not always with zero mean, and the a, b, and α are real constants. By introducing $a_i = 0$, $i \geq p + 1$, and $b_{jk} = 0$, $j \geq r + 1$, we may rewrite (3.40) as

$$X_t + \sum_{j=1}^{(p,r)} [a_j + A_j(t)]X_{t-j} = \alpha + \varepsilon_t \tag{3.41}$$

where

$$(p, r) = \max(p, r) \qquad A_j(t) = -\sum_{k=1}^{s} b_{jk}\varepsilon_{t-k}. \tag{3.42}$$

The difference between the BL models and the RCA models is that in (3.41), the random coefficients $a_j + A_j(t)$ are not necessarily independent of the X_t. In fact, the coefficients are linear functions of the ε_t. The adjective 'bilinear' derives from the fact that (i) X_t is linear in X_s, $s < t$ for fixed ε_s, $s \leq T$, and (ii) X_t is linear in ε_s, $s \leq t$ for fixed X_s, $s < t$. Figure 1.3 gives a realization of a bilinear model.

It should be noted that there is a difference between the (deterministic) bilinear system discussed in §2.7 and the (stochastic) bilinear models here. In the latter the 'control input', ε_t, is *random and unobservable*. This implies that the properties of bilinear systems described in §2.7 require careful reformulation in probabilistic terms before they can be used in the present context. For example, what is the meaning of the claim that *the class of bilinear systems is dense in the class of linear analytic systems if the time interval of interest is finite*?

In the formulation (3.40), there is no difficulty in incorporating 'moving-average' terms. Thus, we may consider an *extended class of BL models* of the form

$$X_t + \sum_{i=1}^{p} a_i X_{t-i} = \alpha + \sum_{i=0}^{q} c_i \varepsilon_{t-i} + \sum_{j=1}^{r} \sum_{k=1}^{s} b_{jk} X_{t-j} \varepsilon_{t-k} \qquad (3.43)$$

where $c_0 = 1$. Henceforth, by the class of BL models we mean the extended class. Occasionally we allow k to run from 0 to S in (3.4).

3.11 Non-linear moving-average models

It is intuitively clear that as a 'dual' to a non-linear autoregressive model we may have a *non-linear moving average* (NLMA) model of the form (loosely speaking)

$$X_t = g(\varepsilon_t, \varepsilon_{t-1}, \ldots, \varepsilon_{t-1}; \boldsymbol{\theta}) \qquad (3.44)$$

$\boldsymbol{\theta}$ *being a vector of parameters*, which is the non-linear analogue of a linear moving-average model

$$X_t = \sum_{j=0}^{q} a_j \varepsilon_{t-j} \qquad (3.45)$$

where $\{\varepsilon_t\}$ is a sequence of i.i.d. random variables. Motivated by the 'external specification' of a dynamical system discussed in §2.7, we may consider a parametrization of (3.44) in the form (cf eqn (2.36))

$$X_t = k_0 + \sum k_i \varepsilon_{t-i} + \sum\sum k_{ij} \varepsilon_{t-i} \varepsilon_{t-j} + \ldots + \sum \ldots \sum k_{ij\ldots r} \varepsilon_{t-i} \varepsilon_{t-j} \ldots \varepsilon_{t-r}$$
$$(3.46)$$

where the summations are all from 0 to q.

Allowing q and r to tend to infinity, we have (formally) a non-linear analogue of the *linear Wold representation*

$$X_t = \sum_{j=0}^{\infty} a_j \varepsilon_{t-j}. \qquad (3.47)$$

We return to this point in Chapter 4.

Other parameterizations of NLMA models are, of course, possible. For example,

$$X_t = \min(\varepsilon_t, \theta \varepsilon_{t-1}). \qquad (3.48)$$

3.12 Autoregressive models with conditional heteroscedasticity (ARCH)

Let $\mathbb{B}_s$ denote the σ-algebra generated by $X_s, X_{s-1}, \ldots$. We note that for NLAR models of the form

$$X_t = f(X_{t-1}, X_{t-2}, \ldots, X_{t-k}) + \varepsilon_t \qquad (3.49)$$

where $\{\varepsilon_t\}$ is a sequence of i.i.d. random variables with finite variance

σ^2, the variance of X_t conditional on $\mathbb{B}_{t-1}$ is a *constant*, namely σ^2. This may be a serious restriction in some applications, for example in economics. This restriction is to some extent removed in the SETAR models, where ε_t is replaced by $h^{(J_t)}\varepsilon_t$, J_t being measurable w.r.t. $\mathbb{B}_{t-1}$ and taking integer values, 1, 2, ..., k say, and the $h^{(j)}$ are real constants not necessarily all equal.

An alternative approach is to consider a 'whole-hearted' multiplicative noise model for X_t. For example, let

$$X_t = \varepsilon_t \sqrt{V_t} \qquad (3.50)$$

where $\{\varepsilon_t\}$ are i.i.d. random variables with standard normal distribution, and

$$V_t = \gamma + \phi_1 X_{t-1}^2 + \ldots + \phi_q X_{t-q}^2 \qquad (3.51)$$

where $\gamma > 0$, $\phi_i \geq 0$ for all i. $\{X_t\}$ is then said to follow an *ARCH model*. It is obvious that $\{X_t^2\}$ follows a BL model if $\{X_t\}$ follows an ARCH model.

More generally, we may drop the normality requirement of ε_t as well as replace (3.51) by

$$V_t = \gamma + \sum_{i=1}^{q} \phi_i X_{t-i}^2 + \sum_{i=1}^{p} \psi_i V_{t-i}, \qquad \psi_i \geq 0 \text{ all } i. \qquad (3.52)$$

In this case, $\{X_t\}$ is said to follow a *generalized ARCH model*, in short, a *GARCH model*.

3.13 Second-generation models

It is possible, in principle at least, to combine the above-mentioned *first-generation* models to produce *second-generation* models, *third-generation* models, and so on. The variety and complexity is clearly unlimited.

For example, we may have a *SETAR–ARCH model*

$$X_t = f(X_{t-1}, \ldots, X_{t-k}) + \varepsilon_t \sqrt{V_t} \qquad (3.53)$$

where f is piecewise linear in its arguments and V_t is given by (3.51). This model combines the advantages of a SETAR model, which targets more on the conditional mean of X_t (given $\mathbb{B}_{t-1}$), and an ARCH model which concentrates on the conditional variance of X_t (given $\mathbb{B}_{t-1}$).

Another example is a BL–ARCH model in which the $\{\varepsilon_t\}$ sequence of a BL model follows an ARCH model.

3.14 Doubly stochastic models

Since the single most important linear time series model is the ARMA model

$$X_t + a_0 + \sum_{j=1}^{p} a_j X_{t-j} = \varepsilon_t + \sum_{j=1}^{q} b_j \varepsilon_{t-j} \tag{3.54}$$

it would seem natural to consider developing non-linear models by 'bending' the a, b coefficients. To a large extent, that is what the above models have done in various specific ways. If we are mainly interested in the general rather than the specific, then a possible approach to achieve greater generality (at least formally) is to allow the coefficients almost complete flexibility. Our view is that there is a need for both the general approach and the specific approach. A possible danger is over-generalization. Paraphrasing K. Popper (1972, p. 36), we suggest that *a model family which is not inappropriate/refutable by any conceivable event is non-scientific. Irrefutability is not a virtue of a model family (as people often think) but a vice.*

We now give a formal definition of a *doubly stochastic model* for the scalar case and refer the interested readers to Tjøstheim (1968a) for the vector case. Now, a scalar doubly stochastic model is given by

$$X_t + a_0(t-1, X) + \sum_{j=1}^{p} a_j(t-1, X)\theta_j(t)X_{t-j} = \varepsilon_t + \sum_{j=1}^{q} b_j(t-1, X)\varepsilon_{t-j} \tag{3.55}$$

where $\{a_i(t-1, X)\}$ and $\{B_j(t-1, X)\}$, $i = 0, 1, \ldots, p$ and $j = 1, \ldots, q$, are stochastic processes and for each t, $a_i(t, X)$ and $b_j(t, X)$ are measurable w.r.t. $\mathbb{B}_t$, the σ-algebra generated by X_s, $s \le t$. The $\{\varepsilon_t\}$ is a sequence of i.i.d. random variables with zero mean and $\{\theta_i(t)\}$, $i = 1, \ldots, p$, are stochastic processes indexed by $t \in \mathbf{Z}$. We may assume that $\{X_t\}$, $\{\varepsilon_t\}$, and $\{\theta_i(t)\}$ are defined on the same probability space. In this quite general form, the doubly stochastic model encompasses many first generation models.

1. *ARMA models*: The a, b, and θ are constants.

2. *Time-dependent ARMA models*: The a and b do not depend on X but only on t, and $\{\theta_i(t)\}$ are constants.

3. *Self-exciting threshold autoregressive moving average models*: The a and b are given by

$$a_j(t-1, X) = a_j^{(J_t)}, \qquad j = 0, \ldots, p \tag{3.56}$$

$$b_j(t-1, X) = b_j^{(J_t)}, \qquad j = 1, \ldots, q \tag{3.57}$$

where J_t is measurable w.r.t. $\mathbb{B}_{t-1}$ and takes values in $\{1, 2, \ldots, l\}$, and $\{\theta_i(t)\}$ are constants.

4. *Random coefficient AR models*: The a and b are constants and $\{\theta_i(t)\}$ are independent of $\{\varepsilon_t\}$.

5. *Dynamic linear state space models*: The models were developed by Harrison and Stevens (1976) and in the simplest scalar case take the form

$$X_t = H_{t-1}\theta_t + \varepsilon_t \tag{3.58}$$

and

$$\theta_t = F\theta_{t-1} + \eta_t \tag{3.59}$$

where F is a known constant and H_{t-1} is known at time $t-1$. $\{\varepsilon_t\}$ and $\{\eta_t\}$ are independent sequences of i.i.d. Gaussian random variables. These models are capable of great generalization, especially in higher dimensions. We refer the interested readers to the above paper and West *et al.* (1985) for details. The latter also gives an algorithmic approach (based on non-linear Kalman filtering) to non-linear time series analysis. As the approach seems to focus on prediction, and makes no assumption of stationarity, we pursue the approach no further; but see Exercise 4 of Chapter 6*.

6. *Bilinear models*: The a are constants, the b are constants over t but linear in $X_{t-1}, X_{t-2}, \ldots$, and the θ are constants.

7. *EXPAR models*: a_0 and the b and $\{\theta_i(t)\}$ are constants, and

$$a_j(t-1, X) = \phi_j + \psi_j \exp(-\gamma X_{t-1}^2). \tag{3.60}$$

3.15 'State'-dependent models

The concept of a *state* and the technique of *Kalman filter* are fundamental in systems science/control engineering, which are assuming an ever increasing importance in time series analysis. This development, together with the desire in generalizing ARMA in the manner described in the last section, has led to another general class of non-linear models. Again the motivation lies in generality. For a *suitable k* and a *suitable l*, we write

$$\xi_t = (1, \varepsilon_{t-l+1}, \ldots, \varepsilon_t, X_{t-k+1}, \ldots X_t)^T \tag{3.61}$$

where as previously $\{\varepsilon_t\}$ is a sequence of i.i.d. random variables. We call ξ_t a *carrier vector*. Using the carrier vector and choosing *suitable* matrices, F, G, and H, we may achieve the *generalization* (perhaps more

---

* I understand that a book is being written by Professors P. J. Harrison and M. West on the subject of dynamic state space models.

appropriately *non-linearization*) of ARMA models by introducing the following model

$$\xi_t = F(\xi_{t-1})\xi_{t-1} + G(\xi_{t-1})\varepsilon_t$$
$$X_t = H\xi_t. \tag{3.62}$$

Alternatively, we may achieve the same goal by introducing the following model

$$X_t + \sum_{j=1}^{k} a_j(\xi_{t-1})X_{t-j} = c(\xi_{t-1}) + \varepsilon_t + \sum_{j=1}^{l} b_j(\xi_{t-1})\varepsilon_{t-j}. \tag{3.63}$$

Structural theory of linear ARMA models (to be covered later in Chapter 4) suggests that models (3.62) and (3.63) may be *formally* equivalent under suitable choices of F, G, and H. This may be shown to be the case (Priestley 1980). It is therefore tempting to regard the carrier vector ξ_t as a *state vector*, and christen the above model a '*state*'*-dependent model* (SDM). Now, it will be clear from our discussion in §4,3 that as a prerequisite *a state vector must carry with it the property of uniqueness, in the sense that its dimension is uniquely defined.* This is universally accepted in systems science. Typically a state (vector) possesses *minimal* dimension, which represents the highest condensation of information. To date we do not know of any theory which shows that ξ_t as defined by eqn (3.61) always possesses the property of uniqueness.

Again, the SDM class encompasses, at least formally, a number of first-generation models such as SETAR, EXPAR, BL, etc.

Bibliographical notes

The foundation of *non-linear autoregressive models* was laid by D. A. Jones (1976).

The *threshold principle* was formally announced in Tong (1987) and the threshold models were first mentioned in Tong (1977*a*). Various special cases of *threshold models* were described in Tong (1983*a*) and are repeated here. New cases included here are:

(1) *threshold models without additive noise*, which have a point of contact with fractals;

(2) *asymmetric moving-average models* (Wecker 1981);

(3) *piecewise polynomial models* (Tong and Lim 1980; Pemberton 1985; Ozaki 1985*a*; Cobb and Zacks 1988);

(4) *smooth threshold autoregressive models* Tong 1983*a*; Chan and Tong 1986*a*; Luukkonen *et al.* 1988*a*).

Pole and Smith (1985) have discussed threshold models in economet-rics from the Bayesian viewpoint.

The idea of *amplitude-dependent exponential autoregressive models* was first proposed by D. A. Jones (1976) and reappeared apparently independently and in a more general form in Ozaki and Oda (1978). The *fractional autoregressive (FAR) model* was originally proposed by R. H. Jones (1965) in an experiment in non-linear prediction in meteorology. Our emphasis is different and appears to be new. Multiplicative noise models are also listed, including *product autoregressive models* introduced by McKenzie (1982), *random coefficient autoregressive models* apparently introduced by Andel (1976), briefly studied by Robinson (1978), and systematically studied by Nicholls and Quinn (1982), *NEAR models of* Lawrance and Lewis (1985), and the *(G)ARCH models* of Engle (1982) and Bollerslev (1986). We follow Chan (1988*a*) in our formulation of NEAR(p) models. *Autoregressive models with discrete state space* require radically different handling (McKenzie 1985).

The *bilinear models* were introduced by Granger and Andersen (1978) and mor systematically studied in Subba Rao and Gabr (1984).

Non-linear moving-average models do not seem to have received as much attention as non-linear autoregressive models in so far as modelling is concerned. Robinson (1977*b*) is a useful reference.

The idea of producing *second-generation models* etc. from first-generation models was mentioned as early as 1980 (Tong 1980*b*; Tong and Lim 1980). Weiss (1986) has considered BL–ARCH models.

The *doubly stochastic models* introduced by Tjøstheim (1986*a*) and the *state-dependent models* of Priestley (1980) aim for generality.

Exercises and Complements

(1) For eqn (3.11), write

$$\eta_t = h_1^{(J_t)} \varepsilon_t.$$

Verify that $\{\eta_t\}$ defines a Martingale difference, that is

$$E[\eta_t \mid \mathbb{B}_{t-1}] = 0$$

where $\mathbb{B}_{t-1}$ is the σ-algebra generated by η_s, $s \leq t-1$.

(2) Experiment with models generating Figs 3.2(a)–(c) using different sets of parameters.

(3) For $k \geq 2$, compare realizations from models (3.27) and the modified models obtained by replacing $\beta_j \exp(-\delta X_{t-1}^2)$ by $\beta_j \exp(-\delta X_{t-j}^2)$. In each case, choose your α_j such that the roots of

$z^k - \sum_{j=1}^{k} \alpha_j z^{k-j}$ lie inside the unit circle. Is the claim that this root condition ensures stationarity valid?

(Chan and Tong 1985)

(4) Study the Lagrange stability of the model

$$x_{n+1} = \frac{ax_n}{1+x_n}.$$

(Private communication from K. S. Chan (1987))

(5) Consider a non-linear autoregressive model

$$X_t = g(X_{t-1})X_{t-1} + \varepsilon_t \qquad (*)$$

where g is 1–1 and continuously differentiable. Show that this is a special case of SDM with carrier vector $\xi_t = (X_t)$. Now, transform x to y by

$$y = g(x)x.$$

Verify that corresponding to eqn (*) we have

$$Y_t = g(Y_{t-1} + \varepsilon_t)Y_{t-1} + g(Y_{t-1} + \varepsilon_t)\varepsilon_t. \qquad (\dagger)$$

Is this an SDM with the carrier vector $h(\xi_t)$ for some suitable h? Compare the carrier vector for eqn (*) and that for eqn (†) in respect of their 'dimensions' (however defined).

4
Probability structure

恒芳恍芳之中有象　　*Indistinct and shadowy,*
Yet within it is a skeleton.

Ch. XXI Lao Tzu

4.1 Deterministic stability, stochastic stability, and ergodicity

Let us start with a simple example which illustrates the intimate relation between stability and stationarity. This important topic is often neglected in standard time series texts. Readers might wish to refresh their memories of §2.12.

First, let us consider the simple autoregressive model

$$X_{t+1} = \alpha X_t + \varepsilon_{t+1} \tag{4.1}$$

where $\{\varepsilon_t\}$ is a sequence of i.i.d. random variables. Henceforth we adopt the abbreviation $\varepsilon_t \sim$ IDD. If ε_t has mean μ and variance σ^2, we may use $\varepsilon_t \sim$ IID(μ, σ^2). Without loss of generality, we assume that ε_t has zero mean here. When $|X_t|$ is large, and if $|\alpha| < 1$, the pull towards the origin (the strength being related to $|\alpha|$) outweighs the noise term. On the other hand, when $|X_t|$ is small, the noise term 'destabilizes' the system and X_{t+1} has a tendency of being pushed further away from the origin. It will pay dividends for us to realize that *the condition* $|\alpha| < 1$ *ensures the strict stationarity of model* (4.1) *because the same condition ensures that the origin is globally asymptotically stable w.r.t. the skeleton of model* (4.1), namely

$$x_{t+1} = \alpha x_t. \tag{4.2}$$

Conversely, because $|\alpha| > 1$ implies that the origin is strongly *unstable* (recall Definition 2.7) w.r.t. the skeleton (4.2), the same condition implies that model (4.1) is *not strictly stationary*.

4.1.1 THE DRIFT CRITERION

The idea of *stochastic stability* has been around in an *implicit* form in the theory of Markov chains for quite some time, although it was really systematically developed in control theory. For example, let $p_{ij}(n) =$ $\mathbf{P}(X_n = j \mid X_0 = i)$ denote the n-step transition probability of a homogeneous Markov chain $\{X_t: t = 0, 1, 2, \ldots\}$ with a finite state space. Then a modified Markov theorem (see e.g. Fisz 1963, p. 256) states that as long as at least one column of the matrix $\mathbf{P}(r) = (p_{ij}(r))$ is wholly positive for some r, it holds that

$$\lim_{n \to \infty} p_{ij}(n) = \pi_j \geq 0, \quad \text{independent of } i \qquad (4.3)$$

where $\sum \pi_j = 1$, the summation being over all the states. Those states corresponding to the wholly positive columns constitute the *centre of attraction*. The chain is strictly stationary w.r.t. the initial distribution defined by $\{\pi_j\}$. The full power of the idea in Markov chains with a countable number of states is vividly demonstrated in Foster (1953). Let $\{X_t\}$ denote an irreducible aperiodic Markov chain with countable state space $\{0, 1, \ldots\}$. He has then shown that the chain is recurrent if $\exists$ a function g s.t. $g(j) \to \infty$ as $j \to \infty$ and

$$\mathrm{E}[g(X_{t+1}) \mid X_t = j] - g(j) \leq 0, \qquad (j = 1, 2, \ldots). \qquad (4.4)$$

(See e.g. Cox and Miller 1965, p. 113 or Parzen 1962, p. 260.] Foster's idea has generated a circle of results. For example, for the case of an irreducible aperiodic Markov chain on $\{0, 1, \ldots\}$, suppose that there exist a continuous function g on the states and a finite set $C \subset \{0, 1, \ldots\}$ s.t. $g(i) \geq 0$, all i, (e.g. $g(i) = i$) and satisfies (i) and (ii):

(i) $\mathrm{E}[g(X_{t+1}) \mid X_t = j] - g(j) \leq K < \infty, \; j \in C$, for some fixed $K > 0$

(ii) $\mathrm{E}[g(X_{t+1}) \mid X_t = j] - g(j) \leq -1, \; j \neq C.$

$$(4.5)$$

Then eqn (4.3) holds. We may interpret g as a *generalized energy* and C as the *centre of attraction*. For continuous state space, say $\mathbf{R}$ (or $\mathbf{R}^m$), we only have to replace *finite* C by a *compact* C with $\phi(C) > 0$ for some measure ϕ and appropriately generalize the notion of irreducibility. The generalized notion is called *ϕ-irreducibility*: the Markov chain $\{X_t\}$ is *ϕ-irreducible* if, for some (σ-finite) measure ϕ on $(\mathbf{R}, \mathbb{B})$, $\mathbb{B}$ being the usual σ-algebra of Borel sets in $\mathbf{R}$,

$$\sum_{t>0} P(X_t \in A \mid X_0 = x) > 0$$

for all $x \in \mathbf{R}$, whenever $\phi(A) > 0$ and $A \in \mathbb{B}$. (The verification of ϕ-irreducibility is a technically delicate matter. See Appendix 1. Briefly, for non-linear autoregressive models of order p, $(0 \leq p < \infty)$, with additive noise, ϕ-irreducibility is obtained if the noise distributions are of infinite support.) Then, subject to some smoothness condition of the transition probability, condition (4.5) ensures the existence and uniqueness of a stationary distribution. Effectively we require $E[h(X_{t+1}) \mid X_t = x]$, as a function of x, to be continuous for each bounded continuous function h on $\mathbf{R}$. The technical term for this property is *weakly continuous*. An alternative is to show that the centre C is small. (Small sets are defined in §4.2.8.) Let us call this criterion (4.5) the *drift criterion* for short. (See Appendix 1 for further details.)

4.1.2 STOCHASTIC STABILITY

We now study stochastic stability in a systematic but informal way, leaving the technical details to Appendix 1. Further, we restrict the discussion mostly to scalar X_t for simplicity, leaving the higher-dimensional cases to Appendix 1, which gives additionally other aspects of stochastic stability.

To be specific, we consider the stochastic difference equation

$$X_{t+1} = f(X_t, \varepsilon_{t+1}), \quad t \in \mathbf{Z}_+ \tag{4.6}$$

where $f: \mathbf{R}^2 \to \mathbf{R}$, $\varepsilon_t \sim$ IID. This defines a Markov chain with state space $\mathbf{R}$. Let the associated skeleton be defined by setting ε_t constant (say zero), that is

$$x_{t+1} = f(x_t, 0) = \phi(x_t), \quad \text{say } t \in \mathbf{Z}_+. \tag{4.7}$$

In §2.10, we have studied the stability of trajectories in the state space $\mathbf{R}$ defined by eqn (4.7) starting with the initial state $x^0 \in \mathbf{R}$, say. It is perfectly natural to generalize and study the *stability* (in an appropriate sense—see Appendix 1) *of trajectories in a space $\mathcal{L}$ of probabilities (measures) on $\mathbf{R}$* defined by (4.6) starting with the initial probability μ_0 of X_0.

Let $\{\mu_t(\mu_0): t = 1, 2, \ldots\}$ denote the trajectory in $\mathcal{L}$ starting with the initial probability $\mu_0 \in \mathcal{L}$. Here $\mu_t(\mu_0)$ denotes the probability of X_t given that X_0 has distribution μ_0. It is interesting to note that from the Markov property of (4.6), we have the *semi-group property*

$$\mu_{t+s}(\mu_0) = \mu_t(\mu_s(\mu_0)), \quad (s, t = 1, 2, \ldots) \tag{4.8}$$

which mimics the equation

$$\phi_{t+s}(x_0) = \phi_t(\phi_s(x_0)) \tag{4.9}$$

deduced from eqn (4.7); here

$$\phi_s(x_0) = \underbrace{\phi(\phi(\ldots (\phi(x_0) \ldots).}_{s \text{ of them}}$$

It is clear that the stability (in an appropriate sense) of $\{\mu_t : t \in \mathbf{Z}_+\}$ resembles the stability of $\{x_t : t \in \mathbf{Z}_+\}$. We refer to the former as *stochastic stability* (in an appropriate sense) and the latter as *deterministic stability*. In both cases the concept of a Lyapunov function is dominant.

Definition 4.1: Let B be any set in $\mathbf{R}$. We say that V is a *stochastic Lyapunov function* of f of (4.6) on B if (i) V is continuous and non-negative and (ii) $E[V(X_{t+1}) - V(X_t) \mid X_t = x] \le 0$, $\forall x \in B$.

Let $\dot{V}(X_t)$ denote $E[V(X_{t+1}) - V(X_t) \mid X_t]$. We may compare V and B with g and C^c of (4.5) respectively.

Let Q_λ denote the set $\{x \in \mathbf{R} : V(x) > \lambda\}$, $\lambda > 0$. In the deterministic case, $V(\phi(x)) - V(x) \le 0$ for $x \in Q_\lambda$ implies that if $x_0 \in Q_\lambda$ then $V(x_t)$ is non-increasing in t and $x_t \in Q_\lambda$, $\forall t \in \mathbf{Z}_+$. In the stochastic case, we can only make probability statements such as

$$\forall x \in Q_\lambda, \quad P\left[\sup_{\infty > t \ge 0} V(X_t) < \lambda \mid X_0 = x \right] \ge 1 - \frac{V(x)}{\lambda} \quad (4.10)$$

(i.e. once started with $x \in Q_\lambda$, $X_1, X_2, \dots$ will all stay in Q_λ with probability greater than or equal to $1 - V(x)/\lambda$).

We can now develop an analogue of the invariance principle of Theorem 2.7.

Suppose that the Markov chain $\{X_t\}$ satisfies (4.6). Suppose that the chain is weakly continuous. Let $\mathscr{L}$ be the space of probability measures on $\mathbf{R}$ and let $U : \mathscr{L} \to \mathscr{L}$ by

$$(U\mu)(A) = \int P(x, A)\mu(\mathrm{d}x) \quad (4.11)$$

for any $\mu \in \mathscr{L}$ and any Borel set A of $\mathbf{R}$. If μ is the probability (measure) of X_0, then we may identify $U\mu$ with $\mu_1(\mu)$, $U(U\mu)$ with $\mu_2(\mu)$, etc.

Theorem 4.1: Suppose that for the above set-up, there exists a continuous non-negative function $V : \mathbf{R} \to \mathbf{R}$ s.t. (i) $E[V(X_1) \mid X_0 = x] - V(x) \le 0$, $\forall x \in \mathbf{R}$ and (ii) $V(x) \to \infty$ as $|x| \to \infty$, $\forall x \in \mathbf{R}$. Then, for each $\mu \in \mathscr{L}$, the positive limit set $\omega(\mu)$ (i.e. the set of limit points of the sequence $\{\mu_t(\mu), \ t = 0, 1, 2, \dots\}$) is non-empty, compact, invariant, invariantly connected, and the smallest closed set that $\mu_t(\mu)$ approaches as $t \to \infty$.

Proof. See Appendix 1. $\square$

Example 4.1: ('The Emperor's clothes'): Consider the bilinear model

$$X_{t+1} = (\tfrac{1}{2} + \varepsilon_{t+1})X_t, \qquad \varepsilon_t \sim \mathrm{IID}(0, \tfrac{1}{2}). \quad (4.12)$$

Consider the function $V(x) = x^2$. Then

$$\dot{V}(X_t) = E[(\tfrac{1}{2} + \varepsilon_{t+1})^2 X_t^2 \mid X_t] - X_t^2$$
$$= -\tfrac{1}{4} X_t^2.$$

Now, V is stochastic Lyapunov function on **R**. Because $\dot{V}(x) = 0$ iff $x = 0$, therefore $X_t \to 0$ in probability as $t \to \infty$. (In fact, $X_t \to 0$, almost surely as $t \to \infty$.) The clothed model is stripping off! $\square$

It is important to note that the same function V, which as we have seen mimics the g function of the drift criterion, serves as a (deterministic) Lyapunov function on **R** of the skeleton

$$x_{t+1} = \tfrac{1}{2} x_t \tag{4.13}$$

which has a globally asymptotically stable equilibrium (i.e. fixed) point at the origin.

4.1.3 ERGODICITY

The emphasis of this section is *generality*. Specialized techniques for special cases are not described in any detail although they may be mentioned and some references included. The aim is to equip readers with some powerful tools, with the aid of which readers can themselves attack problems that they may encounter in future.

The general message of §4.1.2 is this. We may appeal to a *converse theorem* (Theorem A1.7 of Appendix 1) to secure the *existence* of a deterministic Lyapunov function V from the knowledge, however acquired, that 0, say, is a stable equilibrium point of some sort for the skeleton (4.7). It turns out that under quite general conditions *this V may be used to construct the g function for the drift criterion*, which may then be used to demonstrate the general drifting towards a central set for large excursions of the stochastic trajectories and thereby facilitate the establishment of positive recurrence of the Markov chain defined by (4.6). In other words, this function V ultimately leads to the existence and uniqueness of a probability π on **R** (or **R**^{m}) to which $\mu_t(\mu_0)$ tends in a suitable norm $\|.\|$ as $t \to \infty$, irrespective of μ_0. It should be emphasized that the explicit form of V may not be required. This is indeed the case to be stated in Theorem 4.2. This area of results is sometimes collectively known as *ergodic theorems*. If the rate of convergence is geometric (i.e. there exists a $\rho \in (0, 1)$ s.t. $\rho^{-t} \|\mu_t(\mu_0) - \pi\| \to 0$ as $t \to \infty$. $\forall \mu_0 \in \mathcal{L}$), then they are called *geometric ergodic theorems*. If we set $\mu_0 \equiv \pi$, then the Markov chain is strictly stationary. *This practice will be adopted without further mention and π will be referred to as the stationary distribution and the Markov chain is said to be stationary.*

Appendix 1, kindly written by K. S. Chan, is devoted exclusively to this stochastic stability approach to ergodic theorems. We single out two important results here for immediate mention. The first deals with the general case where $\{\mathbf{X}_t\}$ is a Markov chain with state space $\mathbf{R}^m$ defined by the stochastic difference equation

$$\mathbf{X}_t = f(\mathbf{X}_{t-1}, \varepsilon_t), \qquad t \geq 1 \qquad (4.14)$$

where $\varepsilon_t \sim$ IID and is scalar valued. (Note that we have abandoned the use of bold type to denote a vector-valued function.) The function $f : \mathbf{R}^{m+1} \rightarrow \mathbf{R}^m$ is assumed to be decomposable as follows:

$$f(\mathbf{X}_{t-1}, \varepsilon_t) = T(\mathbf{X}_{t-1}) + S(\mathbf{X}_{t-1}, \varepsilon_t) \qquad (4.15)$$

where $T : \mathbf{R}^m \rightarrow \mathbf{R}^m$ and $S : \mathbf{R}^{m+1} \rightarrow \mathbf{R}^m$. The skeleton of eqn (4.14) is given by the 'T-bone'

$$\mathbf{x}_t = T(\mathbf{x}_{t-1}), \qquad t \geq 1 \qquad (4.16)$$

and S supplies the 'skin'. Note that the decomposition (4.15) need not be unique and parallels 'TIME SERIES = TREND + NOISE'. (Tong 1989).

Condition A:

A1. $\mathbf{0} \in \mathbf{R}^m$ is an equlibrium state for eqn (4.16), that is $\mathbf{0} = T(\mathbf{0})$, and is *exponentially asymptotically stable in the large*, that is $\exists K$, $x > 0$ s.t. $\forall t \geq 0$, and starting with $\mathbf{x}_0 \in \mathbf{R}^m$, $\|\mathbf{x}_t\| \leq K e^{-ct} \|\mathbf{x}_0\|$, where $\|.\|$ denotes the Euclidean norm in $\mathbf{R}^m$.

A2. $\forall \mathbf{x} \in \mathbf{R}^m$ and for all neighbourhoods W of $\mathbf{0} \in \mathbf{R}^m$ there is a non-null conditional probability of $S(\mathbf{X}_{t-1}, \varepsilon_t)$ being in W given that $\mathbf{X}_{t-1} = \mathbf{x}$.

A3. The distribution of ε_t has an absolutely continuous component (w.r.t. Lebesgue measure) with positive probability density function over some open interval $(-\delta, \delta)$.

A4. $\{U, JU, \ldots, J^{m-1}U\}$ is a linearly independent set where J is the partial derivative of f w.r.t. $\mathbf{X}$ at $(\mathbf{0}, 0)$ and U is the partial derivative of f w.r.t. ε at $(\mathbf{0}, 0)$.

A5. T is Lipschitz continuous over $\mathbf{R}^m$, that is $\exists M > 0$, s.t. $\forall \mathbf{x}, \mathbf{y} \in \mathbf{R}^m$, $\|T(\mathbf{x}) - T(\mathbf{y})\| \leq M \|\mathbf{x} - \mathbf{y}\|$.

A6. For some $\tau > 0$, $E[\|S(\mathbf{X}_{t-1}, \varepsilon_t)\| \text{ given } \mathbf{X}_{t-1} = \mathbf{x}] \leq \tau$, $\forall \mathbf{x} \in \mathbf{R}^m$.

Condition A1 is crucial because it implies through a 'converse' theorem in the deterministic Lyapunov theory of stability the *existence* of a deterministic Lyapunov function V of **T** of (4.16) on a neighbourhood of **0**. Different modes of stability may be used leading to different analytic properties of V. This same V then serves as an appropriate stochastic

Lyapunov function of f of (4.14) on the complement of some *centre set of attraction*. Generally speaking, a stronger mode of stability of $\mathbf{0}$ is needed if we wish to weaken regularity conditions on f and T, that is A1 and A5 interact. Conditions A2–A4 ensure irreducibility and aperiodicity of the Markov chain in some sense.

Condition A6 specifies the kind of persistent random perturbation which may be allowed on the skeleton. As we shall see, the uniform boundedness is still quite restrictive for applications to models with multiplicative noise. However, it seems possible that both this restriction and the restriction of ε_t being scalar valued could be weakened.

Theorem 4.2: Under Condition A, the Markov chain defined by (4.14) is goemetrically ergodic, provided that f is continuous everywhere and continuously differentiable in a neighbourhood of the origin.

Proof. Detailed proof is given in Appendix 1. □

Next, we state and prove in sketch a closely related theorem, which deals specifically with the additive noise case. We shall need the following condition.

Condition B:

B1.   Same as Condition A1.
B2.   *Either* $\{\varepsilon_t\}$ are IID, the marginal distribution function of which is absolutely continuous and has an everywhere positive probability density function over $\mathbf{R}^m$. Also $\mathrm{E}\,\|\varepsilon_t\| < \infty$. *Or* $\varepsilon_t = (e_t, 0, \ldots, 0)'$ with $\{e_t\}$ being IID, each having an absolutely continuous distribution with an everywhere positive probability density function over $\mathbf{R}$. Also $\mathrm{E}\,|e_t| < \infty$.
B3.   Same as Condition A5.

Theorem 4.3 (Chan and Tong 1985): Under Condition B, the Markov chain defined by

$$\mathbf{X}_t = T(\mathbf{X}_{t-1}) + \varepsilon_t, \qquad t \geq 1, \qquad T: \mathbf{R}^m \rightarrow \mathbf{R}^m \qquad (4.17)$$

is geometrically ergodic.

Proof. *We can actually identify a suitable g function for the drift criterion with a Lyapunov function assured by Condition B1, namely* $g: \mathbf{R}^m \rightarrow \mathbf{R}$,

$$g(\mathbf{z}) = \sup_{t \geq 0} \left(\|\mathbf{x}(t; \mathbf{z})\|\, \mathrm{e}^{qct} \right)$$

where $0 < q < 1$, $\gamma < 1$, and $\mathbf{x}(t; \mathbf{z})$ is the solution of $\mathbf{x}_t = T(\mathbf{x}_{t-1})$, $t \geq 1$, with $\mathbf{z}$ as the starting point, i.e. $\mathbf{x}_0 = \mathbf{z}$.

This g function satisfies (i) $\|\mathbf{z}\| \leq g(\mathbf{z}) \leq K\,\|\mathbf{z}\|$, (ii) $|g(\mathbf{z}) - g(\mathbf{y})| \leq L\,\|\mathbf{z} - \mathbf{y}\|$ for some positive constant L, $\forall \mathbf{z}, \mathbf{y} \in \mathbf{R}^m$, (iii) $g(T(\mathbf{z})) \leq$

$e^{-qc}g(\mathbf{z})$. These properties of g lead to the following:

$$E[g(\mathbf{X}_t) \mid \mathbf{X}_{t-1} = \mathbf{z}] = E[g(T(\mathbf{z}) + \boldsymbol{\varepsilon}_t) \mid \mathbf{X}_{t-1} = \mathbf{z}]$$

$$\leq g(T(\mathbf{z})) + K_1, \ K_1 < \infty,$$

(because (ii) $\Rightarrow g(\mathbf{x} + \mathbf{y}) \leq g(\mathbf{x}) + L\,\|\mathbf{y}\|$ and because $E\,\|\boldsymbol{\varepsilon}_t\| < \infty$ under Condition B2),

$$\leq \theta g(\mathbf{z}) + K_2, \ 0 < \theta < 1, \ K_2 < \infty, \ \text{on using (iii).}$$

Let $1 < \theta' < 1/\theta$. Then on using (i) $\exists\, r > 0$ sufficiently large s.t. if C denotes the compact set $\{\mathbf{x} \in \mathbf{R}^m : \|\mathbf{x}\| \leq r\}$, then

$$E[\theta' g(\mathbf{X}_t) - g(\mathbf{X}_{t-1}) \mid \mathbf{X}_{t-1} = \mathbf{z}] < 0, \qquad \forall \mathbf{z} \notin C$$

and

$$\sup_{\mathbf{z} \in C} E[g(\mathbf{X}_t) \mid \mathbf{X}_{t-1} = \mathbf{z}] < \infty.$$

Conditions B2 and B3 guarantee that $\{\mathbf{X}_t\}$ is ϕ-irreducible and aperiodic; ϕ may be chosen as the Lebesgue measure. Further, they ensure that the non-null compact set C is small. (These very technical points are left to Appendix 1.)

On appealing to the drift criterion, we have proved the theorem. □

Remark 4.1: Conditions A and B give only sufficient conditions for ergodicity. Appendix 1 gives a partial converse, which demonstrates the relationship between the exponential asymptotic instability in the *large* of the origin w.r.t. T (i.e. $\exists K, \ c > 0$ s.t. $\forall t \geq 0$ and starting with $\mathbf{x}_0 \in \mathbf{R}^m$, $\|\mathbf{x}_t\| \geq K e^{ct} \|\mathbf{x}_0\|$) and the transiency of the Markov chain $\{\mathbf{X}_t\}$.

Example 4.2 (FAR models): Suppose we clothe the two-dimensional skeleton of Example 2.12 by adding $(e_{t+1}, 0)'$ to the right-hand side of eqn (2.119).

Here, $\{e_t\}$ are i.i.d. $\mathcal{N}(0, 1)$ random variables. Condition B1 is satisfied if $a^2 < 1$ and $b^2 < 1$. Other parts of Condition B are straightforward. Hence, geometric ergodicity is attained if $a^2 < 1$ and $b^2 < 1$. □

The next example may be tackled with either Theorem 4.2 or Theorem 4.3. we shall use the former and leave readers to try the latter.

Example 4.3 (Modified EXPAR model): Consider the *modified* EXPAR model

$$X_t = \sum_{j=1}^{m} [a_j + b_j \exp(-\gamma X_{t-j}^2)] X_{t-j} + \varepsilon_t \tag{4.18}$$

$\varepsilon_t \sim \text{IID}$. Without much loss of generality, assume $\varepsilon_t \in \mathcal{N}(0, 1)$. This model is of the form (4.15) on defining $\mathbf{X}_{t-1} = (X_{t-1}, \dots, X_{t-m})'$. Then we have the skeleton

$$\mathbf{x}_t = T\mathbf{x}_{t-1} = \begin{pmatrix} \sum_{j=1}^{m} a_j x_{t-j} \\ x_{t-1} \\ \vdots \\ x_{t-m+1} \end{pmatrix} \tag{4.19}$$

which has the origin as the exponentially asymptotically stable equilibrium state in the large if all roots of the characteristic equation

$$z^m - \sum_{j=1}^{m} a_j z^{m-j} = 0 \tag{4.20}$$

lie inside the unit circle

$$S(\mathbf{X}_{t-1}, \varepsilon_t) = \begin{pmatrix} \sum_{j=1}^{m} b_j \exp(-\gamma X_{t-j}^2) X_{t-j} + \varepsilon_t \\ 0 \\ \vdots \\ 0 \end{pmatrix} \tag{4.21}$$

Because $|xe^{-\gamma x^2}| \le c < \infty$ and $E\,|\varepsilon_t| = c' < \infty$ for some c and c', therefore Condition A6 is satisfied. The other parts of Condition A are fairly straightforward. Hence, the root condition of (4.20) establishes geometric ergodicity of the modified EXPAR models. $\square$

Remark 4.2: Recalling Example 2.11 and appealing to a 'converse' theorem of Theorem 4.2 (see Appendix 1), we note that it is an open problem whether the root condition of (4.20) is sufficient for the ergodicity of the unmodified EXPAR models, namely

$$X_t = \sum_{j=1}^{m} [a_j + b_j \exp(-\gamma X_{t-1}^2)] X_{t-j} + \varepsilon_t \tag{4.22}$$

$\varepsilon_t \sim$ IID (cf. Exercise 2 of this chapter).

Example 4.4 (SETAR (2; 1, 1)): Consider the SETAR model

$$X_t = \begin{cases} \phi_1 X_{t-1} + \varepsilon_t & \text{if } X_{t-1} > 0 \\ \phi_2 X_{t-1} + \varepsilon_t & \text{if } X_{t-1} \le 0 \end{cases} \tag{4.23}$$

where $\varepsilon_t \sim$ IID and satisfies Condition B2 of Theorem 4.3.
   Clearly, with

$$T(x) = \begin{cases} \phi_1 x & \text{if } x > 0 \\ \phi_2 x & \text{if } x \le 0 \end{cases} \tag{4.24}$$

T is Lipschitz continuous. The analysis of Example 2.7 shows the 0 is an exponentially asymptotically stable equilibrium point in the large of T, provided $\phi_1 < 1$, $\phi_2 < 1$, and $\phi_1\phi_2 < 1$. Thus, by Theorem 4.3, $\{X_t\}$ is geometric ergodic provided $\phi_1 < 1$, $\phi_2 < 1$, $\phi_1\phi_2 < 1$. □

Remark 4.3: Petruccelli and Woolford (1984) have shown that $\phi_1 < 1$, $\phi_2 < 1$, $\phi_1\phi_2 < 1$ is both a necessary and a sufficient condition for ergodicity of model (4.23). Further, the *boundary* cases such as $\phi_1\phi_2 = 1$ merit further research. Do we have a *null-recurrent* chain in these cases? Moreover, a similar analysis may be extended to the more general cases such as

$$X = \begin{cases} c_1 + \phi_1 X_{t-1} + \varepsilon_t & \text{if } X_{t-1} > r \\ c_2 + \phi_2 X_{t-1} + \varepsilon_t & \text{if } X_{t-1} \le r. \end{cases} \qquad (4.25)$$

(See Exercise 14.)

The next example is a negative example and suggests that there is room for refinement in Theorem 4.2.

Example 4.5 (A first-order random coefficient autoregressive model and a first-order bilinear model): Consider the first order RCA model

$$X_t = (\alpha + A_t)X_{t-1} + \varepsilon_t \qquad (4.26)$$

where $A_t \sim \text{IID}(0, \sigma_A^2)$ and $\varepsilon_t \sim \text{IID}\mathcal{N}(0, \sigma_\varepsilon^2)$ are random variables independent of X_s, $s < t$. $\{A_t\}$ and $\{\varepsilon_t\}$ are independent of each other and α is a real constant. Let $g(x) = x^2$. Let A denote the compact set $\{x : x^2 \le (1 + \sigma_\varepsilon^2)/|1 - (\alpha^2 + \sigma_A^2)|\}$. Then, on using the drift criterion, $\alpha^2 + \sigma_A^2 < 1$ is a sufficient condition for model (4.26) to be ergodic.

We have omitted the verification of ϕ-irreducibility ($\phi \equiv$ Lebesgue measure) and weak continuity. Note also that other choices of the function $g(x)$, for example $1 + |x|$, $\log(1 + |x|)$, etc. will lead to different sufficient conditions for ergodicity (see Exercise 5). Note that the model cannot be written in the form of eqn (4.15) because there are two random noise terms involved, that is ε_t and A_t in

$$X_t = f(X_{t-1}, \varepsilon_r, A_t). \qquad (4.27)$$

Careless application of Theorem 4.2 might lead to the erroneous conclusion that $|\alpha| < 1$ implies ergodicity.

Replacing A_t by $\beta\varepsilon_t$ in (4.26), we have a first-order bilinear model. The same function g may be constructed leading to the same sufficient condition, namely $\alpha^2 + \beta^2\sigma_\varepsilon^2 < 1$, for ergodicity. However, again Theorem 4.2 may not be useful because Condition A6 is violated if we use the obvious choice of T, that is $T(x) = \alpha x$. □

The next example illustrates the kind of difficulties which may occur in applying the drift criterion. It may be skipped at first reading if readers so wish as it is fairly technical.

¶ **Example 4.6** (Markovian bilinear models): Consider the following sub-class of the bilinear models sometimes called the class of *subdiagonal bilinear models**;

$$X_t - \sum_{j=1}^{l} a_j X_{t-j} = \sum_{j=0}^{r} c_j \varepsilon_{t-j} + \sum_{i=1}^{q} \sum_{j=0}^{p} b_{ij} X_{t-i-j} \varepsilon_{t-i} \tag{4.28}$$

where $c_0 = 1$, $\varepsilon_t \sim \text{IID}(0, \sigma^2)$ with a symmetric probability satisfying Condition A3 and has finite fourth-order moment. Let $n = \max(l, r + p, q + p)$, $s = \max(r, q)$, and $m = \max(l - s, p) = n - s$.

We now introduce some notation:

1.
$$\gamma_t(j) = c_j + \sum_{k=0}^{p} b_{jk} X_{t-k}, \qquad j = 1, \ldots, s,$$

where $b_{jk} = 0$ if $j > q$ or $k > p$, and $c_j = 0$ if $j > r$.

2. $\xi_t(j) = X_{t-m+j}, \qquad j = 1, 2, \ldots, m,$

$$\xi_t(m + j) = \sum_{k=j}^{n} a_k X_{t+j-k} + \sum_{k=j}^{s} \gamma_{t+j-k}(k) \varepsilon_{t+j-k}, \qquad j = 1, \ldots, s,$$

where $a_k = 0$ if $k > l$. We call the n-vector $\boldsymbol{\xi}_t$ a *state vector* (—we justify this term later) which is given by

$$\boldsymbol{\xi}_t = (\xi_t(1), \ldots, \xi_t(m), \xi_t(m + 1), \ldots, \xi_t(n))^T.$$

3.
$$\mathbf{A}_{n \times n} = \left[\begin{array}{c|c} \mathbf{U} & \mathbf{0} \\ \scriptstyle m \times (m+1) & \scriptstyle m \times (s-1) \\ \hline \mathbf{J} & \mathbf{V} \\ \scriptstyle s \times (m+1) & \scriptstyle s \times (s-1) \end{array} \right]$$

where $\mathbf{U}$ is an $m \times (m + 1)$ matrix with $u_{i,i+1} = 1$, $i = 1, \ldots, m$, and 0 elsewhere, $\mathbf{V}$ is an $s \times (s - 1)$ matrix with $v_{i,i} = 1$, $i = 1, \ldots, s - 1$ and 0 elsewhere, $\mathbf{0}_{m \times s}$ is an $m \times s$ matrix with all 0 entries, and $\mathbf{J}$ is the matrix

$$\begin{bmatrix} & & & a_1 \\ & \mathbf{0} & & a_2 \\ & \scriptstyle (s-1) \times m & & \vdots \\ a_n & \ldots & a_{s+1} & a_s \end{bmatrix}.$$

4.
$$\mathbf{B}_{n \times n} = \left[\begin{array}{c|c} \mathbf{0} & \mathbf{0} \\ \scriptstyle m \times (m+1) & \scriptstyle m \times (s-1) \\ \hline \tilde{\mathbf{B}} & \mathbf{0} \\ \scriptstyle s \times (m+1) & \scriptstyle s \times (s-1) \end{array} \right]$$

---

* There is some confusion in the literature concerning this choice. For example Pham Dinh Tuan (1985) and Subba Rao and Gabr (1984) have used this term. However, Guegan (1987) has called model (4.28) superdiagonal. A better term may be 'Markovian', which we have used.

where

$$\underset{s\times(m+1)}{\tilde{\mathbf{B}}} = \begin{bmatrix} b_{1m} & \cdots & b_{10} \\ \vdots & & \vdots \\ b_{sm} & \cdots & b_{s0} \end{bmatrix}.$$

5. $\underset{n\times 1}{\mathbf{c}} = (0, \ldots, 0, 1, c_1 + a_1, \ldots, c_s + a_s)^T.$

6. $\underset{n\times 1}{\mathbf{d}} = (\overbrace{0, \ldots, 0}^{m}, b_{10}, \ldots, b_{s0})^T.$

7. $\underset{1\times n}{\mathbf{H}} = (\overbrace{0, \ldots, 0}^{m}, 1, 0, \ldots 0).$

After some tedious algebra (details are given in Pham Dinh Tuan (1985)), we may rewrite model (4.28) in the *Markovian* form

$$\boldsymbol{\xi}_t = \mathbf{A}\boldsymbol{\xi}_{t-1} + \mathbf{B}\boldsymbol{\xi}_{t-1}\varepsilon_t + \mathbf{c}\varepsilon_t + \mathbf{d}(\varepsilon_t^2 - \sigma^2) \qquad (4.29)$$

and

$$X_t = \mathbf{H}\boldsymbol{\xi}_{t-1} + \varepsilon_t. \qquad (4.30)$$

This representation is quite remarkable for at least two reasons: (i) The state vector $\boldsymbol{\xi}_t$ has a unique *finite* dimension, namely n, under general conditions. (See §4.3.2 later.) (ii) $\{\boldsymbol{\xi}_t\}$ is a Markov chain over $\mathbf{R}^n$. However, the presence of σ^2 in (4.29) has the consequence that the Markovian form will reproduce (4.28) only up to an additive constant. If it is desirable to reproduce (4.28) exactly, we only need to add an appropriate constant term to the right-hand side of (4.30). (See also the comments following A2 of §4.3.2.)

At first sight, it would seem quite straightforward to appeal to the drift criterion by choosing an obvious vector norm, say $g(\boldsymbol{\xi}) = \boldsymbol{\xi}^T\boldsymbol{\xi}$, the Euclidean norm, as the g function. This leads to a sufficient condition for ergodicity of model (4.28) in the form of

$$I - \mathbf{A}^T\mathbf{A} - \sigma^2\mathbf{B}^T\mathbf{B} > 0 \qquad (4.31)$$

where by $\mathbf{W} > 0$ we mean that the matrix $\mathbf{W}$ is positive definite. Unfortunately, this condition is often vacuous. For example, take the case $\sigma^2 = 1$, $l = 2$, $r = 0 = p$, $q = 1$. (Details are left to the readers.)

It turns out that a more productive g function is provided by

$$g(\boldsymbol{\xi}) = 1 + \boldsymbol{\xi}'\mathbf{U}\boldsymbol{\xi} \qquad (4.32)$$

where the $n \times n$ matrix $\mathbf{U}$ is defined by

$$\text{vec}(\mathbf{U}) = (\mathbf{I} - \mathbf{A}^T \otimes \mathbf{A}^T - \sigma^2\mathbf{B}^T \otimes \mathbf{B}^T)^{-1} \text{vec}(\mathbf{W}) \qquad (4.33)$$

where the matrix $\mathbf{W} > 0$ and $n \times n$, the symbol $\otimes$ denotes the Kronecker product of the matrices, and vec denotes the 'stacking' operation of putting the first column above the second, the second above the third, and so on. Thus

$$\mathbf{P}_{r \times s} \otimes \mathbf{Q}_{u \times v} = \begin{bmatrix} p_{11}\mathbf{Q} & p_{12}\mathbf{Q} & \cdots & p_{1s}\mathbf{Q} \\ \vdots & \vdots & & \vdots \\ p_{r1}\mathbf{Q} & p_{r2}\mathbf{Q} & \cdots & p_{rs}\mathbf{Q} \end{bmatrix} \quad (4.34)$$

and

$$\mathrm{vec}\left(\mathbf{P}_{r \times s}\right) = (p_{11} \cdots p_{r1} | p_{12} \cdots p_{r2} | \cdots | p_{1s} \cdots p_{rs})^T. \quad (4.35)$$

We shall use the basic identities concerning compatible matrices A, B, C:

$$\mathrm{vec}(ABC) = (C^T \otimes A)\,\mathrm{vec}(B) \quad (4.36)$$

$$(A \otimes B)^T = (A^T \otimes B^T). \quad (4.37)$$

We now *sketch* a proof which shows that the following is a sufficient condition for the ergodicity of model (4.28):

$$\rho(\mathbf{A} \otimes \mathbf{A} + \sigma^2 \mathbf{B} \otimes \mathbf{B}) < 1 \quad (4.38)$$

where $\rho(\mathbf{Q})$ denotes the maximum eigenvalue of $\mathbf{Q}$ in modulus, and is called the *spectral radius* of $\mathbf{Q}$.

1. $g(\xi) > 0$ and continuous. The latter result is obvious. The former is due to the fact that $\mathbf{U} - \mathbf{W}$ is positive semi-definite. This follows from the identity

$$\mathrm{vec}(\mathbf{U}) = \sum_{j=0}^{\infty} (\mathbf{A}^T \otimes \mathbf{A}^T + \sigma^2 \mathbf{B}^T \otimes \mathbf{B}^T)^j \,\mathrm{vec}(\mathbf{W}) \quad (4.39)$$

by virtue of (4.33) and Condition (4.38) (see e.g. Nicholls and Quinn 1982, p. 22).

2.
$$\mathrm{E}[g(\boldsymbol{\xi}_{t+1}) \mid \boldsymbol{\xi}_t = \mathbf{x}] = 1 + \mathbf{x}^T \{\mathbf{A}^T \mathbf{U} \mathbf{A} + \sigma^2 \mathbf{B}^T \mathbf{U} \mathbf{B}\}\mathbf{x} + \mathrm{E}[\mathbf{r}_t^T \mathbf{U} \mathbf{r}_t]$$
$$+ 2\mathrm{E}[(\mathbf{x}^T \mathbf{A}^T + \varepsilon_t \mathbf{x}^T \mathbf{B}^T)\mathbf{U}\mathbf{r}_t] \quad (4.40)$$

where

$$\mathbf{r}_t = \mathbf{c}\varepsilon_t + \mathbf{d}(\varepsilon_t^2 - \sigma^2).$$

3.
$$\mathbf{x}^T \mathbf{A}^T \mathbf{U} \mathbf{A} \mathbf{x} = (\mathbf{x}^T \otimes \mathbf{x}^T)(\mathbf{A}^T \otimes \mathbf{A}^T)\,\mathrm{vec}(\mathbf{U}) \quad (4.41)$$

$$\sigma^2 \mathbf{x}^T \mathbf{B}^T \mathbf{U} \mathbf{B} \mathbf{x} = \sigma^2 (\mathbf{x}^T \otimes \mathbf{x}^T)(\mathbf{B}^T \otimes \mathbf{B}^T)\,\mathrm{vec}(\mathbf{U}) \quad (4.42)$$

$$\mathrm{E}[\mathbf{r}_t^T \mathbf{U} \mathbf{r}] = \mathrm{tr}(\mathbf{U}\mathbf{G}) \quad (4.43)$$

where

$$\mathbf{G} = \sigma^2 \mathbf{c}\mathbf{c}^T + \mathrm{E}(\varepsilon_t^2 - \sigma^2)^2 \mathbf{d}\mathbf{d}^T \quad (4.44)$$

$$\mathrm{E}[\mathbf{x}^T \mathbf{A}^T \mathbf{U}\mathbf{r}_t] = 0 \quad (4.45)$$

$$\mathrm{E}[\varepsilon_t \mathbf{x}^T \mathbf{B}^T \mathbf{U}\mathbf{r}_t] = \sigma^2 \mathbf{x}^T \mathbf{B}^T \mathbf{U}\mathbf{c}. \quad (4.46)$$

4. Equations (4.33), (4.40), and (3) above give

$$E[g(\xi_{t+1}) \mid \xi_t = \mathbf{x}] = g(\mathbf{x}) - \mathbf{x}^T \mathbf{W} \mathbf{x} + \text{tr}(\mathbf{UG}) + L(\mathbf{x}) \qquad (4.47)$$

where

$$L(\mathbf{x}) = 2\sigma^2 \mathbf{x}^T \mathbf{B}^T \mathbf{U} \mathbf{c} \qquad (4.48)$$

a linear form in $\mathbf{x}$. Therefore

$$E[g(\xi_{t+1}) \mid \xi_t = \mathbf{x}] = g(\mathbf{x})\left(1 - \frac{\mathbf{x}^T \mathbf{W} \mathbf{x} - \text{tr}(\mathbf{UG}) - L(\mathbf{x})}{g(\mathbf{x})}\right). \qquad (4.49)$$

Let

$$A^* = \{\mathbf{x} \in \mathbf{R}^n : \mathbf{x}'\mathbf{U}\mathbf{x} \le K\} \qquad (4.50)$$

denote a compact set, where K is to be chosen suitably. For K sufficiently large and for $\mathbf{x} \notin A^*$ being a linear form, $L(\mathbf{x})$ is negligible in comparison with the quadratic form $\mathbf{x}^T \mathbf{W} \mathbf{x}$, which will be the dominant term in the numerator of eqn (4.49). Now, let $\lambda_1(\mathbf{P}) \ge \lambda_2(\mathbf{P}) \ge \ldots \ge \lambda_n(\mathbf{P}) > 0$ denote the eigenvalues of a positive definite matrix $\mathbf{P}$. Ignoring $L(\mathbf{x})$ for the moment, we may deduce for $\mathbf{x} \notin A^*$

$$\frac{\mathbf{x}^T \mathbf{W} \mathbf{x} - \text{tr}(\mathbf{UG})}{g(\mathbf{x})} \ge \frac{\lambda_n(\mathbf{W})}{2\lambda_1(\mathbf{U})} - \frac{\text{tr}(\mathbf{UG})}{K} \ge \delta \qquad (4.51)$$

provided $0 < \delta < \frac{1}{2}\lambda_n(\mathbf{W})/\lambda_1(\mathbf{U})$ and

$$K \ge K(\delta) = \text{tr}(\mathbf{UG})\left(\frac{\frac{1}{2}\lambda_n(\mathbf{W})}{\lambda_1(\mathbf{U})} - \delta\right). \qquad (4.52)$$

The inclusion of $L(\mathbf{x})$ will not affect the conclusion that, for sufficiently large K, the compact set A^* serves as the 'centre' for the drift criterion with g defined as in eqn (4.32). The ϕ-irreducibility and the weak continuity may also be checked. Hence, under the condition $T : \rho(\mathbf{A} \otimes \mathbf{A} + \sigma^2 \mathbf{B} \otimes \mathbf{B}) < 1$ the Markov chain $\{\xi_t\}$ is (geometrically) ergodic and so the Markovian bilinear model (4.28) is stationary under the same condition. $\square$¶¶

Remark 4.4. Almost identical arguments as above show that for the n-vector times series $\{\xi_t\}$ generated by the RCA model

$$\xi_t = (\boldsymbol{\alpha} + \mathbf{A}_t)\xi_{t-1} + \boldsymbol{\varepsilon}_t \qquad (4.53)$$

where α is an $n \times n$ non-random matrix, $\{\mathbf{A}_t\}$ is a sequence of independent random $n \times n$ matrices, $\{\boldsymbol{\varepsilon}_t\}$ is a sequence of independent random n-vectors and is independent of $\{\mathbf{A}_t\}$, and

$$E[\boldsymbol{\varepsilon}_t] = \mathbf{0} \qquad E[\boldsymbol{\varepsilon}_t \boldsymbol{\varepsilon}_t^T] = \underset{n \times n}{\mathbf{G}}$$

$$E[\mathbf{A}_t] = \mathbf{0} \qquad E[\mathbf{A}_t \otimes \mathbf{A}_t] = \underset{n^2 \times n^2}{\mathbf{C}}$$

and the vector version of Condition A3 is satisfied, the condition

$$\rho(\mathbf{a} \otimes \mathbf{a} + \mathbf{C}) < 1 \qquad (4.54)$$

is sufficient for the (geometric) ergodicity of $\{\xi_t\}$. In fact, the term $L(\mathbf{x})$ will be absent in this case. However, for specific types of RCA models, sharper conditions can sometimes be obtained by more direct/detailed analyses. Exercise 10 addresses the special case of NEAR(p) models, in which Chan's (1988a) detailed analysis has yielded a sharper condition than the general spectral radius condition (4.54). Another special case is the ARCH model, which may be expressed in the equivalent form

$$X_t^2 = \eta_t^2 \{ \gamma + \phi_1(X_{t-1}^2 - \gamma) + \ldots + \phi_p(X_{t-p}^2 - \gamma) \}$$

where the η_t are i.i.d. standard normal random variables and η_t is independent of X_s, $s < t$, $\gamma > 0$, $\phi_i \geq 0$ for all i. Note the connection between a BL model and an ARCH model is revealed by the above way of expressing an ARCH model. Clearly, $\{X_t^2\}$ is a BL model if $\{X_t\}$ is an ARCH model. A direct analysis by Milhøj (1985) has obtained the sufficient condition

$$\phi_1 + \ldots + \phi_p < 1.$$

(Is it sharper than that deduced from (4.38) using $(X_t^2 - \gamma, \ldots, X_{t-p+1}^2 - \gamma)$ as the state vector?) Finally, it would seem that the analysis of Chan (1988a) may be adapted for the stationarity problem of the autoregressive models with the discrete state space of McKenzie (1985).

Remark 4.5: Let us consider the general bilinear model BL(l, r, m, q), that is

$$X_t + \sum_{j=1}^{l} a_j X_{t-j} = \sum_{j=0}^{r} c_j \varepsilon_{t-j} + \sum_{i=1}^{m} \sum_{j=1}^{q} b_{ij} X_{t-i} \varepsilon_{t-j}, \qquad t \in \mathbf{Z} \qquad (4.55)$$

where $\varepsilon_t \sim \text{IID}(0, \sigma^2)$ and has a symmetric distribution with moments up to order $2q$, and $c_0 = 1$. This general model can be rewritten in a Markovian representation, but with a much higher dimension of the state vector than that for Example 4.6. We do not pursue this in depth and for details we refer the interested reader to Pham Dinh Tuan (1986), who has obtained the most general result to date for ergodicity, stationarity, and mixing. We now give a heuristic derivation of the 'spectral radius' condition for stationarity.

First, let $p = \max(l, m)$. We need the $p \times p$ matrices,

$$\mathbf{A} = \begin{bmatrix} -a_1 & -a_2 & \cdots & -a_l & 0 & \cdots & 0 \\ 1 & 0 & \cdots & 0 & 0 & \cdots & 0 \\ 0 & 1 & & & & & 0 \\ \vdots & \vdots & \vdots & \vdots & \vdots & \vdots & \vdots \\ 0 & 0 & \cdots & \cdots & 0 & 1 & 0 \end{bmatrix}$$

$$\mathbf{B}_j = \begin{bmatrix} b_{1j} & b_{2j} & \cdots & b_{mj} & 0 & \cdots & 0 \\ 0 & & \cdots & 0 & 0 & \cdots & 0 \\ \vdots & \vdots & & \vdots & \vdots & & \vdots \\ 0 & 0 & \cdots & 0 & 0 & 0 & 0 \end{bmatrix}, \quad j = 1, 2, \ldots, q$$

and the $p \times (r + 1)$ matrix

$$\mathbf{C} = \begin{bmatrix} c_0 & c_1 & \cdots & c_r \\ 0 & 0 & \cdots & 0 \\ \vdots & \vdots & & \vdots \\ 0 & 0 & \cdots & 0 \end{bmatrix}.$$

We may rewrite eqn (4.55) in the form

$$\boldsymbol{\xi}_t = \mathbf{C}\boldsymbol{\zeta}_t + \mathbf{A}\boldsymbol{\xi}_{t-1} + \sum_{j=1}^q \mathbf{B}_j\boldsymbol{\xi}_{t-1}\varepsilon_{t-j} \qquad (4.56)$$

where

$$\boldsymbol{\xi}_t = \begin{bmatrix} X_t \\ \vdots \\ X_{t-p+1} \end{bmatrix} \quad \text{and} \quad \boldsymbol{\zeta}_t = \begin{bmatrix} \varepsilon_t \\ \vdots \\ \varepsilon_{t-r} \end{bmatrix}.$$

Note that this is *not* in general Markov. The basic idea is to obtain a condition on $\mathbf{A}$, the $\mathbf{B}_j$, and $\mathbf{C}$ to ensure the existence of a measurable function $f : \mathbf{R}^\infty \to \mathbf{R}$ s.t.

$$X_t = f(\varepsilon_t, \varepsilon_{t-1}, \ldots) \text{ almost surely for } t \in \mathbf{Z}. \qquad (4.57)$$

This is sometimes called the *non-linear Wold representation*. Now we write eqn (4.56) as

$$\left[\mathbf{I} - \left(\mathbf{A} + \sum_{j=1}^q \mathbf{B}_j\varepsilon_{-j} \right) U \right] \boldsymbol{\xi}_t = \mathbf{C}\boldsymbol{\zeta}_t \qquad (4.58)$$

or

$$(\mathbf{I} - \mathbf{D}_t)\boldsymbol{\xi}_t = \mathbf{C}\boldsymbol{\zeta}_t \qquad (4.59)$$

where U is the backshift operator s.t. $U\boldsymbol{\xi}_t = \boldsymbol{\xi}_{t-1}$, and

$$\mathbf{D}_t = \left(\mathbf{A} + \sum_{j=1}^q \mathbf{B}_j\varepsilon_{-j} \right) U. \qquad (4.60)$$

Suppose that we may write

$$(\mathbf{I} - \mathbf{D}_t)^{-1} = \mathbf{I} + \mathbf{D}_t + \mathbf{D}_t\mathbf{D}_{t-1} + \mathbf{D}_t\mathbf{D}_{t-1}\mathbf{D}_{t-2} + \ldots \qquad (4.61)$$

where by definition

$$\mathbf{D}_t\mathbf{D}_{t-1} = \left(\mathbf{A} + \sum_{j=1}^{q} \mathbf{B}_j\varepsilon_{t-j}\right)\left(\mathbf{A} + \sum_{j=1}^{q} \mathbf{B}_j\varepsilon_{t-1-j}\right)U^2$$

$$\mathbf{D}_t\mathbf{D}_{t-1}\mathbf{D}_{t-2} = \left(\mathbf{A} + \sum_{j=1}^{q} \mathbf{B}_j\varepsilon_{t-j}\right)\left(\mathbf{A} + \sum_{j=1}^{q} \mathbf{B}_j\varepsilon_{t-1-j}\right)\left(\mathbf{A} + \sum_{j=1}^{q} \mathbf{B}_j\varepsilon_{t-2-j}\right)U^3, \quad \text{etc.}$$

In this case we may deduce

$$\xi_t = (\mathbf{I} - \mathbf{D}_t)^{-1}\mathbf{C}\zeta_t$$

$$= \mathbf{C}\zeta_t + \sum_{n=1}^{\infty} \prod_{i=1}^{n} \left(\mathbf{A} + \sum_{j=1}^{q} \mathbf{B}_j\varepsilon_{t-j-i+1}\right)\mathbf{C}\zeta_{t-n} \qquad (4.62)$$

from which we may obtain the non-linear Wold representation of X_t by noting that it is the first component of ξ_t. Now, to make sense of the expansion of (4.61), it is natural to consider the 'spectral radius' of the operator $\mathbf{D}_t$. Consider the case $q = 2$ first. Let us write

$$\Gamma = \begin{bmatrix} \mathbf{A} \otimes \mathbf{A} + \sigma^2\mathbf{B}_1 \otimes \mathbf{B}_1 & \mathbf{A} \otimes \mathbf{B}_2 + \mathbf{B}_2 \otimes \mathbf{A} & \mathbf{B}_2 \otimes \mathbf{B}_2 \\ \sigma^2(\mathbf{A} \otimes \mathbf{B}_1 + \mathbf{B}_1 \otimes \mathbf{A}) & \sigma^2(\mathbf{B}_2 \otimes \mathbf{B}_1 + \mathbf{B}_1 \otimes \mathbf{B}_2) & 0 \\ \sigma^2\mathbf{A} \otimes \mathbf{A} + \gamma^4\mathbf{B}_1 \otimes \mathbf{B}_1 & \sigma^2(\mathbf{A} \otimes \mathbf{B}_2 + \mathbf{B}_2 \otimes \mathbf{A}) & \sigma^2\mathbf{B}_2 \otimes \mathbf{B}_2 \end{bmatrix},$$
$$\gamma^4 = E\varepsilon^4. \qquad (4.63)$$

It turns out that if $\rho(\Gamma) < 1$—we shall call this condition β—then the expansion (4.62) is meaningful with $q = 2$. For $q > 2$, the sufficient condition β, namely $\rho(\Gamma) < 1$, remains unchanged although the matrix Γ becomes much more complicated (see Liu and Brockwell 1988). Hence, if $\rho(\Gamma) < 1$ then $\{X_t\}$ given by eqn (4.55) is stationary, admitting almost surely a unique non-linear Wold representation. (For $q = 1$, the condition reduces to $\rho(\mathbf{A} \otimes \mathbf{A} + \sigma\mathbf{B}_1 \otimes \mathbf{B}_1) < 1$.)

Note that although conditions T of Example 4.6 and β here are similar, they are quite different because of the different ways the $\mathbf{A}$ and the $\mathbf{B}$ are defined. It should perhaps be remarked that it may require substantially more computation to verify the spectral radius condition for Kronecker products.

Conclusion: The construction of a suitable deterministic Lyapunov function such as that given in Exercise 32 requires some ingenuity and experience. This is where the hard work usually lies. On the other hand, a direct analysis of the trajectories without recourse to the deterministic Lyapunov function, such as those in Examples 2.7, 2.8, 2.9, and 2.10, may sometimes be more expedient in verifying Condition A1. We often reap the full benefits of a dynamical system approach because we can call

on two 'stones'— the deterministic Lyapunov function and the deterministic trajectory analysis— to kill one 'bird', that is to establish
ergodicity of the stochastic system! In practical terms, when analysing a
complex non-linear autoregressive model, especially with additive noise
only, digital experimentations with the skeleton will often provide us with
substantial information about the stationarity/non-stationarity of the
stochastic model. This is sometimes the only available channel for
complex models which is justifiable.

Finally, Appendix 1 gives one general approach to the question of
necessity of ergodicity of non-linear (Markov) stochastic difference
equation models. For other types of models, we refer to the references
quoted in the bibliographical notes of this chapter. In the former cases,
the intimate connection between the stochastic difference equation
models and their skeletons is again exploited. Table 4.1 summarizes the
position.

An outstanding problem is the connection between neutral stability of
the skeleton and the null recurrency of the associated Markov chain.

4.2 Stationary distributions

Suppose that $\{\mathbf{X}_t\}$ is an n-dimensional stationary time series. We may
wish to evaluate the stationary distribution, say π. This is a non-trivial
problem if an analytic solution is closed form is desired. However, an
implicit solution is always available if $\{\mathbf{X}_t\}$ is an ergodic *Markov chain
over* $\mathbf{R}^n$, which is given by

$$\pi(A) = \int_{-\infty}^{\infty} P(A \mid \mathbf{x})\pi(\mathrm{d}\mathbf{x}) \tag{4.64}$$

where π denotes the limiting distribution of $\{\mathbf{X}_t\}$, which we shall take to
be the initial distribution (and hence π is the stationary distribution we
seek), A is a Borel set of $\mathbf{R}^n$, and $p(\cdot|\cdot)$ is the usual conditional (i.e.
transition) probability. Needless to say, in this case once π is determined
all the joint distributions follow in principle. It is usually very difficult to
solve the integral equation (4.64) explicitly *in closed form* except in
special cases. The most trivial special case is, of course, that of a linear
AR model driven by Gaussian white noise. Indeed for a linear AR model
driven by i.i.d. random variables with a stable distribution, then π is also
stable, whose characteristic function may be obtained explicitly via eqn
(4.64) which is a convolution in this case. (See Exercise 11.) We are then
'only' left with the problem of inverse transform of a characteristic
function. We now describe a special case which is non-trivial.

Table 4.1 Connection between the behaviour of (Markov) stochastic difference equation models and that of their skeletons

Skeleton	Stochastic difference equation models
$x_{t+1} = f(x_t, 0) = \phi(x_t)$, $t \in \mathbf{Z}_+$	$\mathbf{X}_{t+1} = f(\mathbf{X}_t, \varepsilon_{t+1})$, $t \in \mathbf{Z}_+$, ε_{t+1} are iid random variables
$x_0 = $ *initial value*	$\mu_0 = $ *initial probability*
$\{x_t : t = 0, 1, 2, \ldots\}$ is a *trajectory* in the *state space* $\mathbf{R}^m$	$\{\mu_t(\mu_0) : t = 0, 1, \ldots\}$ is a *trajectory* in the space $\mathscr{L}$ *of probability measures on* $\mathbf{R}^m$
$\phi_{t+s}(x_0) = \phi_t(\phi_s(x_0))$, *where* $\phi_t(x_0) = \underbrace{\phi(\phi(\ldots(\phi(x_0))\ldots))}_{t}$ —*semi-group property*	$\mu_{t+s}(\mu_0) = \mu_t(\mu_s(\mu_0))$, *where* $\mu_t(\mu_0) = $ prob of $\mathbf{X}_t$ given $\mathbf{X}_0$ *has probability* μ_0 —*semi-group property*
B any set in $\mathbf{R}^m$ V is a *Lyapunov function* of ϕ on **B** if (i) V is continuous and ≥ 0 (ii) $\dot{V}(\mathbf{x}) = V(\phi(x_t)) - V(x_t) \leq 0$ $\forall \mathbf{x} \in B$ (energy dissipation)	*B any set in* $\mathbf{R}^m$ v is a *stochastic Lyapunov function* of f on **B** if (i) V is continuous and ≥ 0 (ii) $E[V(\mathbf{X}_{t+1}) - V(\mathbf{X}_t)\mid \mathbf{X}_t = \mathbf{x}] \leq 0$ $\forall \mathbf{x} \in B$
For continuous ϕ, if (i) V is a Lyapunov function on $\mathbf{R}^m$ (ii) x_t is a bounded solution in $\mathbf{R}^m$ $\forall t \geq 0$, then for each $\mathbf{x} \in \mathbf{R}^m$, $\Omega(\mathbf{x})$ is non-empty, compact, invariant, invariantly connected, and the smallest closed set that $\phi_t(\mathbf{x})$ approaches as $t \rightarrow \infty$, and starting with $\mathbf{x}$, x_t tends to the largest invariant set in $\{\mathbf{x} : \dot{V}(\mathbf{x}) = 0\}$	For a weakly continuous chain with U as defined in (4.11), if (i) and (ii) above hold $\forall \mathbf{x} \in \mathbf{R}^m$, and $V(\mathbf{x}) \rightarrow \infty$ as $\|\mathbf{x}\| \rightarrow \infty$ $\forall \mathbf{x} \in \mathbf{R}^m$, then for each $\mu \in \mathscr{L}$, $\omega(\mu)$ is non-empty, compact, invariant, invariantly connected, and the smallest closed set that $\mu_t(\mu)$ approaches as $t \rightarrow \infty$, and starting with μ as the initial probability $\mathbf{X}_t$ tends to the largest invariant (support) set in $\{\mathbf{x} : \dot{V}(\mathbf{x}) = 0\}$ a.e. (μ).
Exponential asymptotic stability in the large of the equilibrium points	Geometric ergodicity of the Markov chains defined by the models
Exponential asymptotic instability in the large of equilibrium points	Transiency of the Markov chains defined in the models

4.2.1 SOME CLOSED-FORM RESULTS

Example 4.7 ('Absolute' autoregression): Consider the very special SETAR model

$$X_t = -\alpha |X_{t-1}| + \varepsilon_t \tag{4.65}$$

where $\{\varepsilon_t\}$ are i.i.d. random variables whose distributions are absolutely continuous with a symmetric density f and with $E|\varepsilon_t| < \infty$. Obviously,

$|\alpha| < 1$ is sufficient for the stationarity of $\{X_t\}$. Let h denote the stationary probability density of X_t. It therefore holds that

$$h(y) = \int_{-\infty}^{\infty} h(x)f(y + \alpha |x|) \, dx$$

$$= \int_{0}^{\infty} h(x)f(y + \alpha x) \, dx + \int_{-\infty}^{0} h(x)f(y - \alpha x) \, dx. \qquad (4.66)$$

By symmetry of f, we also have

$$h(-y) = \int_{0}^{\infty} h(x)f(y - \alpha x) \, dx + \int_{-\infty}^{0} h(x)f(y + \alpha x) \, dx. \qquad (4.67)$$

Let

$$\bar{h}(y) = h(y) + h(-y).$$

Then from eqns (4.66) and (4.67), we have

$$\bar{h}(y) = \int_{-\infty}^{\infty} \bar{h}(x)f(y + \alpha x) \, dx \qquad (4.68)$$

which is the integral equation for the stationary density of $\{\xi_t\}$ satisfying the model

$$\xi_t = -\alpha \xi_{t-1} + \varepsilon_t. \qquad (4.69)$$

Now, from eqn (4.66)

$$h(y) = \int_{0}^{\infty} h(x)f(y + \alpha x) \, dx + \int_{0}^{\infty} h(-x)f(y + \alpha x) \, dx$$

$$= \int_{0}^{\infty} \bar{h}(x)f(y + \alpha x) \, dx. \qquad (4.70)$$

Hence, to find the stationary density of model (4.65), we only need to find that of model (4.69) which is *linear*; that is we may exploit the symmetry of the model literally to straighten out (or linearize) the non-linear model model first!

It may be checked as an exercise that for $0 < \alpha 1$

(1) if $\varepsilon_t \sim \mathcal{N}(0, 1)$

$$h(x) = [2(1 - \alpha^2)/\pi]^{1/2} \exp[-\tfrac{1}{2}(1 - \alpha^2)x^2]\Phi(-\alpha x), \qquad (-\infty < x < \infty)$$

$$(4.71)$$

where Φ is the distribution function of $\mathcal{N}(0, 1)$;

(2)   if $\varepsilon_t \sim$ Cauchy with density

$$\frac{1}{\pi}\frac{1}{1+x^2}, \qquad (-\infty < x < \infty)$$

$$h(x) = k\left[\frac{1}{2A}\frac{(1+A)\pi}{1+A^2+x^2} - \frac{x\ln[A^{-2}(1+x^2)]+(A^2-1+x^2)\tan^{-1}x}{4A^2x^2+(1-A^2x^2)^2}\right],$$

$$(-\infty < x < \infty) \quad (4.72)$$

where $A = \alpha/(1-\alpha)$, $k = 2A/\pi^2$. $\square$

The technique employed in the above example may be extended to more general situations. Since the basic idea is symmetry it is natural to introduce a group. We now follow some fairly abstract discussion in the next subsection.

4.2.2   AN EXTENSION

¶ Let G be a subgroup of the general linear group on $\mathbf{R}^n$ which consists of invertible linear automorphisms on $\mathbf{R}^n$. Sometime, we write $g\mathbf{x}$ for $g(\mathbf{x})$, $g \in G$. The orbit of $\mathbf{x}$ under g is defined as

$$\langle \mathbf{x} \rangle = \{\mathbf{y} \in \mathbf{R}^n; \exists g \in G \text{ s.t. } g\mathbf{x} = \mathbf{y}\}.$$

Let $\varepsilon \subseteq \mathbf{R}^n$, a Borel set, be such that $\varepsilon \cap \langle \mathbf{x} \rangle$ is a singleton set for all $\mathbf{x} \in \mathbf{R}^n$. Let $T: \mathbf{R}^n \to \mathbf{R}^n$ be Borel measurable and $T|_\varepsilon$ the restriction of T on ε. The extension of $T|_\varepsilon$ w.r.t. G is defined as

$$\hat{T}_G(\mathbf{x}) = T|_\varepsilon (\mathbf{y})$$

where $\langle \mathbf{y} \rangle = \langle \mathbf{x} \rangle$ and $\mathbf{y} \in \varepsilon$. We shall write $\hat{T}$ instead of $\hat{T}_G$ whenever G is known from the context. It is assumed that $\hat{T}$ is Borel measurable. Consider the following difference equation:

$$\mathbf{X}_{t+1} = \hat{T}(\mathbf{X}_t) + \mathbf{e}_{t+1} \qquad (4.73)$$

where $\mathbf{e}_{t+1}$ is i.i.d. with Borel measurable probability-density function $f(\mathbf{x})$. Assuming $h(\mathbf{x})$ is a stationary density of $\mathbf{X}_t$ of (4.73), then

$$h(\mathbf{y}) = \int_{\mathbf{R}^n} f(\mathbf{y} - \hat{T}\mathbf{x})h(\mathbf{x})\,d\mathbf{x} \qquad (4.74)$$

holds. Typically, the integral equation (4.74) is rather awesome and it is difficult to write down any explicit solution. However, if f and T are not complicated, then symmetry may help linking up a solution (if it exists) of (4.74) with that of an integral equation of the following form:

$$\bar{h}(\mathbf{y}) = \int_{\mathbf{R}^n} f(\mathbf{y} - T\mathbf{x})\bar{h}(\mathbf{x})\,d\mathbf{x}. \qquad (4.75)$$

Under certain conditions, (4.75) may admit solutions. For example, T may be linear. It is readily seen that every solution of (4.75) is a stationary marginal density of $\mathbf{X}_n$ of (4.73) with $\hat{T}$ replaced by T, that is

$$\mathbf{X}_{t+1} = T(\mathbf{X}_t) + \mathbf{e}_{t+1}. \tag{4.76}$$

The following assumptions will be made:

(1) G is compact;
(2) $T(g\mathbf{x}) = g(T\mathbf{x})$, $\forall g \in G$;
(3) $f(g\mathbf{x}) = f(\mathbf{x})$, $\forall g \in G$;
(4) the Lebesgue measure is invariant w.r.t. G;
(5) there exists μ, an invariant Haar measure on G, and v, a measure on ε, such that, for any non-negative measurable function f on $\mathbf{R}^n$, we have

$$\int_\varepsilon \int_G f(g\mathbf{x})\mu(dg)v(d\mathbf{x}) = \int_G \int_\varepsilon f(g\mathbf{x})v(d\mathbf{x})\mu(dg) = \int_{\mathbf{R}^n} f(\mathbf{x})\, d\mathbf{x}.$$

For a general reference of the theory of Haar measure, see for example Nachbin (1965). As Condition (5) is rather difficult to verify, the following two examples may be instructive.

Example 4.8: Let G be a finite subgroup of the special linear group on $\mathbf{R}^n$. Suppose that ε is a fundamental domain for G, namely $\{g(\varepsilon) : g \in G\}$ is almost surely a *partition* of $\mathbf{R}^n$. Then, for any non-negative measurable function w on $\mathbf{R}^n$,

$$\int_{\mathbf{R}^n} w(\mathbf{x})\, d\mathbf{x} = \sum_{g \in G} \int_{g(\varepsilon)} w(\mathbf{x})\, d\mathbf{x} = \sum_{g \in G} \int_\varepsilon w(g\mathbf{x})\, d\mathbf{x} = \int_\varepsilon \sum_{g \in G} w(g\mathbf{x})\, d\mathbf{x}.$$

Then Condition (5) holds with μ being the counting measure on G and v the Lebesgue measure restricted on ε. $\quad\square$

Example 4.9: Let $S_{n-1} = \{\mathbf{x} \in \mathbf{R}^n : \|\mathbf{x}\| = 1\}$ and ds the geometric measure on S_{n-1}. For the definition of geometric measure and some of its properties, see Tjur (1980). Let G be the orthogonal group on $\mathbf{R}^n$. Then G is compact and let μ, the Haar measure on G, be normalized so that $\mu(G) = \int_{S_{n-1}} ds$. Now G acts on S_{n-1} and the latter is left homogeneous w.r.t. G. Let $e \in S_{n-1}$. It follows from the compactness of G and the G-invariance of ds that for any non-negative measurable function w on S_{n-1},

$$\int_{S_{n-1}} w(s)\, ds = \int_G w(ge)\mu(dg).$$

See also Theorem 1(p. 138) and the Remark (p. 140) of Nachbin (1965).

Thus, if we let $\varepsilon = \{re : r > 0\}$ and $v(dx) = r^{n-1} dr$ on ε, for any non-negative function w on $\mathbf{R}^n$,

$$\int_{\mathbf{R}^n} w(\mathbf{x}) \, d\mathbf{x} = \int_0^\infty \int_{S_{n-1}} w(rs) \, ds r^{n-1} \, dr$$

$$= \int_{S_{n-1}} \int_0^\infty w(rs) r^{n-1} \, dr \, ds = \int_\varepsilon \int_G w(g\mathbf{x}) \mu(dg) v(dx)$$

$$= \int_G \int_\varepsilon w(g\mathbf{x}) v(dx) \mu(dg).$$

Hence, Condition (5) holds. □

By Condition (5), eqn (4.74) becomes

$$h(\mathbf{y}) = \int_{\mathbf{R}^n} f(\mathbf{y} - \hat{T}\mathbf{x}) h(\mathbf{x}) \, d\mathbf{x}$$

$$= \int_\varepsilon \int_G f(\mathbf{y} - \hat{T}g\mathbf{x}) h(g\mathbf{x}) \mu(dg) v(dx)$$

$$= \int_\varepsilon f(\mathbf{y} - T\mathbf{x}) \int_G h(g\mathbf{x}) \mu(dg) v(dx). \tag{4.77}$$

Theorem 4.4: Let $h(x)$ be a non-negative integrable solution of (4.77). Then $\bar{h}(\mathbf{x}) = \int_G h(g\mathbf{x}) \mu(dg)$ is an integrable solution of (4.75). Conversely, if $h(\mathbf{x})$ is a non-negative integrable solution of (4.75), then h can be chosen such that $h(g\mathbf{x}) = h(\mathbf{x})$, $\forall g \in G$ and $\bar{h}(\mathbf{y}) = \int (\mathbf{y} - T\mathbf{x}) h(\mathbf{x}) v(dx)$ is an integrable solution of (4.77).

Proof. ($\Rightarrow$) By the invariance of μ, $\bar{h}(g\mathbf{x}) = \bar{h}(\mathbf{x})$, for any $g \in G$. Therefore,

$$\int_{\mathbf{R}^n} \bar{h}(\mathbf{x}) \, d\mathbf{x} = \int_\varepsilon \int_G \bar{h}(g\mathbf{x}) \mu(dg) v(dx)$$

$$= \mu(G) \int_\varepsilon \bar{h}(\mathbf{x}) v(dx) = \mu(G) \int_{\mathbf{R}^n} h(\mathbf{x}) \, d\mathbf{x} < \infty.$$

Hence $\bar{h}(\mathbf{x})$ is integrable. It remains to verify that $\bar{h}$ satisfies (4.75). Equation (4.77) can be written as

$$h(\mathbf{y}) = \int_\varepsilon f(\mathbf{y} - T\mathbf{x}) \bar{h}(\mathbf{x}) v(dx)$$

and then

$$\bar{h}(\mathbf{y}) = \int_G h(g\mathbf{y})\mu(dg) = \int_G \int_\varepsilon f((g\mathbf{y}) - T\mathbf{x})\bar{h}(\mathbf{x})v(d\mathbf{x})\mu(dg)$$

$$= \int_G \int_\varepsilon f(\mathbf{y} - g^{-1}T\mathbf{x})\bar{h}(\mathbf{x})v(d\mathbf{x})\mu(dg)$$

$$= \int_\varepsilon \int_G f(\mathbf{y} - gT\mathbf{x})\bar{h}(\mathbf{x})\mu(dg)v(d\mathbf{x})$$

$$= \int_\varepsilon \int_G f(\mathbf{y} - Tg\mathbf{x})\bar{h}(g\mathbf{x})\mu(dg)v(d\mathbf{x})$$

$$= \int_{\mathbf{R}^n} f(\mathbf{y} - T\mathbf{x})\bar{h}(\mathbf{x})\, d\mathbf{x}.$$

($\Leftarrow$) Now, with $h(x)$ given as a non-negative integrable solution of (4.75), it may readily be verified that $t(\mathbf{x}) = \int_G h(g\mathbf{x})\mu(dg)$ is a non-negative integrable solution of (4.75) with $t(g\mathbf{x}) = t(\mathbf{x})$, $\forall g \in G$. Then we may rename t as h. By (4.75)

$$h(\mathbf{y}) = \int_{\mathbf{R}^n} f(\mathbf{y} - T\mathbf{x})h(\mathbf{x})\, d\mathbf{x}$$

$$= \int_G \int_\varepsilon f(\mathbf{y} - Tg\mathbf{x})h(g\mathbf{x})v(d\mathbf{x})\mu(dg)$$

$$= \int_G \int_\varepsilon f((g^{-1}\mathbf{y}) - T\mathbf{x})h(\mathbf{x})v(d\mathbf{x})\mu(dg)$$

$$= \int_\varepsilon \int_G f((g\mathbf{y}) - T\mathbf{x})h(\mathbf{x})\mu(dg)v(d\mathbf{x})$$

$$= \int_G \bar{h}(g\mathbf{y})\mu(dg).$$

Now,

$$\bar{h}(\mathbf{y}) = \int_\varepsilon f(\mathbf{y} - T\mathbf{x})h(\mathbf{x})v(d\mathbf{x})$$

$$= \int_\varepsilon f(\mathbf{y} - T\mathbf{x})\int_G \bar{h}(g\mathbf{x})\mu(dg)v(d\mathbf{x}).$$

Thus $\bar{h}$ is a non-negative integrable solution of (4.77). $\quad\square$

Example 4.10: Let $\mathbf{x} = (x_1, x_2, \ldots, x_n)' \in \mathbf{R}^n$ and τ_i be the reflection about the hyperplane perpendicular to the ith axis. That is $\tau_i(\mathbf{x}) = (x_1, x_2, \ldots, -x_i, \ldots, x_n)'$. let G be the finite group generated by $\{\tau_i, 1 \le i \le n\}$ with composition as the group operation. Let α be fixed s.t. $-1 < \alpha < 1$ and T is the map defined by $T(\mathbf{x}) = \alpha \mathbf{x}$. If we let $\varepsilon = \{\mathbf{x}: x_i \ge 0, 1 \le i \le n\}$ then $\hat{T}(\mathbf{x}) = \alpha |\mathbf{x}|$ where $|\mathbf{x}| = (|x_1|, \ldots, |x_n|)'$. Suppose e_n is i.i.d. as $\mathcal{N}(0, I)$ where I is the identity matrix. Then the unique non-negative solution (up to a multiplicative constant) to (4.75) is

$$\bar{h}(\mathbf{x}) = [(1 - \alpha^2)/2\pi]^{n/2} \exp[-\tfrac{1}{2}(1 - \alpha^2)\mathbf{x}'\mathbf{x}]. \tag{4.78}$$

By Theorem 4.4, after suitable normalization, we have the following p.d.f.-type solution to (4.77):

$$c \cdot t(\mathbf{x}) = [2(1 - \alpha^2)/\pi]^{n/2} \exp[-\tfrac{1}{2}(1 - \alpha^2)\mathbf{x}\mathbf{x}'] \prod_{i=1}^{n} \Phi(-\alpha x_i)$$

where $\Phi(.)$ is the cumulative distribution function of the standard normal. When $n = 1$, the solution reduces to (4.71). This is expected since, in this case, the stationary marginal density is unique. This example can be extended in several directions, for example, $T : \mathbf{x} \to (\alpha_1 x_1, \ldots, \alpha_n x_n)'$. The covariance matrix of ε_t may be orthogonal instead of a unit matrix.

However, the explicit solution of (4.77) and the evaluation of $t(\cdot)$ may not be straightforward in the general case.¶¶

4.2.3 NUMERICAL TECHNIQUES FOR SMOOTH CASES

We describe a method which seeks a numerical solution of the integral equation (4.64). The method is concerned with a general first-order non-linear autoregression of the form

$$X_t = \lambda(X_{t-1}) + \varepsilon_t, \quad (t = 0, \pm 1, \pm 2, \ldots) \tag{4.79}$$

where $\varepsilon_t \sim$ IID. *The function λ is assumed to be continuously differentiable.* The specific integral equation to solve is

$$F(x) = \int_{-\infty}^{\infty} F_\varepsilon(x - \lambda(y)) \, dF(y) \tag{4.80}$$

where F and F_ε denote the stationary distribution of X_t and the distribution of ε_t respectively. The basic idea involved is to consider (4.79) as one of a *family of models*, $\{X_t(\beta)\}$, generated by

$$X_{t+1}(\beta) = a + bX_t(\beta) + \beta[\lambda\{X_t(\beta)\} - bX_t(\beta) - a] + \varepsilon_{t+1},$$

$$(t = 0, \pm 1, \pm 2, \ldots) \tag{4.81}$$

where a and b are fixed constants. Thus, $X_{t+1}(\beta)$ is decomposed into a 'linear part' and a 'residual part'. A functional-type expansion about the linear part may then be envisaged. The methods built on (4.81) are essentially of the perturbation type and may be compared with Poincaré's power series solutions for nonlinear differential equations (see for example §2.2 and Minorsky 1962, Ch. 9).

For example, suppose that we represent the random variable $X_t(\beta)$ from the stationary time series $\{X_t(\beta)\}$ by

$$X_t(\beta) = X_t^{(0)} + \beta X_t^{(1)} + \tfrac{1}{2}\beta^2 X_t^{(2)} + \ldots \qquad (4.82)$$

where each of the time series $\{X_t^{(r)}: t = 0, \pm1, \pm2, \ldots\}$ $(r \geq 0)$ is also stationary. When the expansion (4.82) is substituted in (4.81) and power series expansions made as necessary, the following generating equations for the component processes $\{X_t^{(r)}\}$ are found:

$$X_{t+1}^{(0)} = a + bX_t^{(0)} + \varepsilon_{t+1} \qquad (4.83a)$$

$$X_{t+1}^{(1)} = bX_t^{(1)} + \Lambda(X_t^{(0)}) \qquad (4.83b)$$

$$X_{t+2}^{(2)} = bX_t^{(2)} + 2\Lambda^{(1)}(X_t^{(0)})X_t^{(1)}, \text{ etc.} \qquad (4.83c)$$

where $\Lambda(x) = \lambda(x) - bx - a$ and $\Lambda^{(r)}(x)$ denotes the rth derivative of $\Lambda(x)$ (assumed to exist). By identifying $\{X_t^{(0)}\}$ with $\{X_t(0)\}$, a linear AR model, its properties are known. Note that we have assumed that exactly the same input noise sequence, $\{\varepsilon_t\}$, is used in generating each of the individual processes.

Let $F(x; \beta)$ denote the stationary distribution of $X_t(\beta)$, and let $\phi(s; \beta)$ be the corresponding characteristic function. We therefore need to solve the family of integral equations

$$F(x; \beta) = \int F_\varepsilon\{(x - \lambda(y; \beta))\} \, dF(x, \beta). \qquad (4.84)$$

It will be *assumed* that $F(x; \beta)$ is expressible as a powers series in β (cf eqn (4.82)) *convergent at $\beta = 1$. It is not clear exactly when this assumption of convergence at $\beta = 1$ will hold.* Under the assumption, $\phi(s; 1)$ is then the characteristic function of the stationary distribution of X_t, which is sought. It turns out that it is more convenient to start with characteristic functions.

From eqn (4.81), we may deduce that

$$\phi(s; \beta) = \frac{\phi_\varepsilon(s)}{2\pi} \iint \exp[ix(bs - t) + isa + is\beta\Lambda(x)]\phi(t; \beta) \, dt \, dx \qquad (4.85)$$

where ϕ_ε denotes the characteristic function of ε_t. Let

$$\phi(s; \beta) = \sum_{r=0}^{\infty} \theta_r(s)\beta^r. \qquad (4.86)$$

Then

$$\sum_{r=0}^{\infty} \theta_r(s)\beta^r = \frac{e^{isa}\phi_\varepsilon(s)}{2\pi} \int\int \exp[ix(bs-t)] \sum_{j=0}^{\infty} \frac{\{i\beta s\Lambda(x)\}^j}{j!} \sum_{r=0}^{\infty} \theta_r(t)\beta^r \, dt \, dx.$$

Equating powers of β gives, for $r \geq 0$,

$$\theta_r(s) = \frac{e^{isa}\phi_\varepsilon(s)}{2\pi} \int\int \exp[ix(bs-t)] \sum_{j=0}^{r} \frac{\{is\Lambda(x)\}^j}{j!} \theta_{r-j}(t) \, dt \, dx.$$

For $r = 0$, we have

$$\theta_0(s) = e^{isa}\phi_\varepsilon(s)\phi_0(bs) \tag{4.87}$$

and, for $r \geq 1$,

$$\theta_r(s) = e^{isa}\phi_\varepsilon(s)\theta_r(bs)$$

$$+ \frac{e^{isa}\phi_\varepsilon(s)}{2\pi} \int\int \exp[ix(bs-t)] \sum_{j=1}^{r} \frac{\{is\Lambda(x)\}^j}{j!} \theta_{r-j}(t) \, dt \, dx. \tag{4.88}$$

Note that $\theta_0(s)$ is the characteristic function of the stationary distribution of the initial process (4.83a), a linear model. Let $f_0(x)$ be the density corresponding to $\theta_0(s)$. (We assume that the distribution of ε_t is absolutely continuous.) Assuming that each $\theta_r(s)$ is continuous at $s = 0$ with $\theta_r(0) = 0$ $(r \geq 1)$ and $|b| < 1$, we have after some tedious algebra that

$$\theta_r(s) = \sum_{l=0}^{\infty} \frac{\rho_l(s)}{2\pi} \int\int \exp\{ix(b^{l+1}s - t)\} \sum_{j=1}^{r} \frac{\{ib^l s\Lambda(x)\}^j}{j!} \theta_{r-j}(t) \, dt \, dx \tag{4.89}$$

where

$$\rho_l(s) = \frac{\theta_0(s)}{\theta_0(b^{l+1}s)} \tag{4.90}$$

the characteristic function of Y_l following the model

$$Y_t = a + bY_{t-1} + \varepsilon_t, \quad (t = 0, 1, \ldots, l)$$

with $Y_{-1} = 0$. Let $f_r(x)$ denote the inverse Fourier transform of $\theta_r(s)$. The density of $F(x; \beta)$ (assumed to exist) is approximately given by

$$f(x; \beta) = f_0(x) + \beta f_1(x) + \beta^2 f_2(x). \tag{4.91}$$

This approximation has been found sometimes to give negative values. Jones (1976) has recommended setting $b = 0$ and choosing a to be a 'typical' value of $\lambda(X)$ when X has the distribution $F(x)$. It seems that by 'typical' he has meant approximating $y = \lambda(x)$ by $y = a$ which is 'optimal' in some sense. The choice of a may affect the rate of convergence of the numerical procedure. It seems difficult to assess the accuracy of the procedure. Once an approximation $f_X(x; \beta)$ for the stationary marginal density is available, an approximation for the joint density $f_1(x, y; \beta)$ of $(X_t(\beta), X_{t+1}(\beta))$ is (setting $b = 0$)

$$\hat{f}_1(x, y; \beta) = f_\varepsilon \{ y - [a + \beta(\lambda(x) - a] \} \hat{f}_X(x, \beta). \qquad (4.92)$$

Approximations for joint density $f_k(x, y; \beta)$ of $(X_t(\beta), X_{t+k}(\beta))$, $k = 2, 3, \ldots$, are available but rather unwieldy and their reliability perhaps also suspect.

Figures 4.1 and 4.2 are taken from Jones (1976, p. 153), who has also proposed two other methods besides the one just described. One of these two methods is described in §4.2.4 below. In principle, all three methods may be extended to higher-order AR models.

As yet another approach we suggest the following. We consider, instead of (4.81), the perturbed model

$$X_{t+1}^\delta = f(X_t^\delta, \delta\varepsilon_t), \qquad X_0^\delta = x \qquad (4.93)$$

where δ denotes a small parameter. Suppose that we write X_{t+1}^δ as an expansion in δ:

$$X_{t+1}^\delta = X_{t+1}^{(0)} + \delta X_{t+1}^{(1)} + \delta^2 X_{t+1}^{(2)} + \ldots . \qquad (4.94)$$

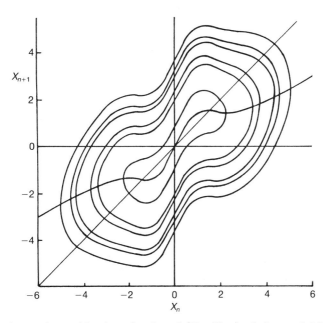

Fig. 4.1. Approximate bivariate density of (X_n, X_{n+1}) of the model in Fig. 4.2 (after Jones 1978)

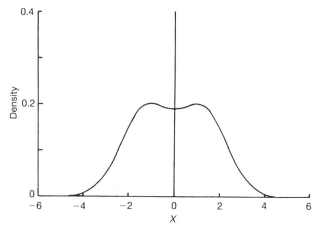

Fig. 4.2. Approximate marginal density of the EXPAR model $X_t = \frac{1}{2}X_{t-1}[1 + 3\exp(-\frac{1}{2}X_{t-1}^2)] + \varepsilon_t$, $\varepsilon_t \sim \mathcal{N}(0, 1)$ (after Jones 1978)

If f is sufficiently smooth, it can also be expanded in powers of δ as

$$f(X_t^\delta, \delta\varepsilon_t) = f(X_t^{(0)}, 0) + \delta\left[\frac{\partial f(x, y)}{\partial x} X_t^{(1)} + \frac{\partial f(x, y)}{\partial y} \varepsilon_t\right]_{(X_t^{(0)}, 0)}$$

$$+ \frac{\delta^2}{2!}\left[\frac{\partial^2 f(x, y)}{\partial x^2} X_t^{(1)2} + \frac{\partial f(x, y)}{\partial x} 2X_t^{(2)}\right.$$

$$\left. + 2\frac{\partial^2 f(x, y)}{\partial x\, \partial y} X_t^{(1)}\varepsilon_t + \frac{\partial^2 f(x, y)}{\partial y^2} \varepsilon_t^2\right]_{(X_t^{(0)}, 0)} + \dots \quad (4.95)$$

where all the partial derivatives are evaluated at $(X_t^{(0)}, 0)$. Equating like powers of δ in (4.94) and (4.95), we have a system of equations:

zero*th* approximation: $X_{t+1}^{(0)} = f(X_t^{(0)}, 0)$

first approximation: $X_{t+1}^{(1)} = B_1(X_t^{(0)}, 0)X_t^{(1)} + B_2(X_t^{(0)}, 0)\varepsilon_t$

second approximation: $X_{t+1}^{(2)} = B_1(X_t^{(0)}, 0)X_t^{(2)} + \Psi_2(X_t^{(0)}, X_t^{(1)}, \varepsilon_t)$

$\vdots$

kth approximation: $X_{t+1}^{(k)} = B_1(X_t^{(0)}, 0)X_t^{(k)}$
$$+ \Psi_k(X_t^{(0)}, X_t^{(1)}, \dots, X_t^{(k-1)}, \varepsilon_t)$$

where

$$B_1(X_t^{(0)}, 0) = \frac{\partial f(x, y)}{\partial x}\bigg|_{(X_t^{(0)}, 0)} \qquad B_2(X_t^{(0)}, 0) = \frac{\partial f(x, y)}{\partial y}\bigg|_{(X_t^{(0)}, 0)}$$

and, on writing $X(\delta) = c_0 + c_1\delta + c_2\delta^2 + \dots + c_k\delta^k + \dots$ and for $k \geq 1$,

$$\Psi_k(c_0, c_1, \dots, c_{k-1}, y) = \Phi_k - B_1(c_0, 0)c_k$$

where

$$\Phi_k = \Phi_k(c_0, c_1, \ldots, c_k, y) = \frac{1}{k!} \frac{d^k f(X(\delta), \delta y)}{d\delta^k}\bigg|_{\delta=0}.$$

To this system of equations we add the initial conditions

$$X_0^{(0)} = x$$

$$X_0^{(1)} = X_0^{(2)} = \cdots = X_0^{(k)} = \ldots = 0.$$

Note that the zeroth approximation is in fact the skeleton! The first approximation is Gaussian if ε_t is Gaussian. The jth approximation is a linear time-dependent AR(1) model if $X_t^{(0)}, \ldots, X_t^{(j-1)}$ are known. The discussion can be fairly easily extended to vector $\mathbf{X}_t^\delta$ and vector $\mathbf{\varepsilon}_t$. The perturbation is usually only valid for $t \in (0, T)$, $T < \infty$.

2.4 NUMERICAL TECHNIQUES CAPABLE OF HANDLING UNSMOOTH CASES

If λ is not continuously differentiable (e.g. as in a SETAR model), then the above method is not strictly applicable. Some difficulty has been reported (Pemberton 1985, p. 198) when λ is piecewise linear and the variance of ε_t is 'small'.

4.2.4.1 Jones's method of conditional distributions However, Jones (1978) has described an alternative technique based on expansions for *conditional* distributions, which may cope with this case. Basically, the processes $\{X_t(\beta): t = 0, \pm 1, \pm 2, \ldots\}$ are treated separately for different β so that it is not necessary to specify the relation of the sequences $\{\varepsilon_t\}$ entering into the generation of the different processes. Also, $b = 0$ and ε_t *is assumed to have a continuously differentiable density.* Now

$$X_{t+1}(\beta) = a + \beta\{\lambda[X_t(\beta) - a]\} + \varepsilon_{t+1}, \quad (t = 0, \pm 1, \ldots). \quad (4.96)$$

It is convenient to define the associated family of processes $\{Y_t(\beta)\}$ by

$$Y_t(\beta) = \beta\{\lambda[X_t(\beta) - a]\}, \quad (t = 0, \pm 1, \ldots) \quad (4.97)$$

and then, defining $\eta_t = \varepsilon_t + a$ and $\Lambda(x) = \lambda(x) - a$, we have

$$X_{t+1}(\beta) = Y_t(\beta) + \eta_{t+1} \quad (4.98)$$

and

$$Y_{t+1}(\beta) = \beta\Lambda\{Y_t(\beta) + \eta_{t+1}\}, \quad (t = 0, \pm 1, \ldots). \quad (4.99)$$

By construction η_{t+1} is independent of $(Y_t(\beta), Y_{t-1}(\beta), \ldots)$. The method is then based on power expansions in β of the characteristic function, $\phi_{Y,m+1}(s, y; \beta)$, of $Y_{t+m+1}(\beta)$ given $Y_t(\beta)$. The characteristic function,

$\phi(s; \beta)$, of the stationary distribution of $\{X_t(\beta)\}$ is then given by

$$\phi(s; \beta) = \phi_Y(s; \beta)\phi_\eta(s) \tag{4.100}$$

where ϕ_η is the characteristic function of η_t and $\phi_Y(s; \beta)$ is $\phi_{Y,\infty}(s, y; \beta)$. Again, it seems difficult to assess the accuracy of the method.

4.2.4.2 Pemberton's method

Pemberton (1985) has proposed an iterative quadrature method for solving the integral equation

$$h(x) = \sum_{j=1}^{L} \int_{r_{j-1}}^{r_j} h(y)f_j(x - a_0^{(j)} - a_1^{(j)}y)\,dy \tag{4.101}$$

corresponding to the integral equation for the stationary density, h, of a SETAR $(L; 1, 1, \ldots, 1)$ model

$$X_t = a_0^{(j)} + a_1^{(j)}X_{t-1} + \varepsilon_t^{(j)}, \quad \text{if } X_{t-1} \in (r_{j-1}, r_j] \tag{4.102}$$

where $-\infty = r_0 < r_1 < \ldots < r_L = \infty$, $\{\varepsilon_t^{(j)}\}$ is a sequence of i.i.d. random variables each having a strictly positive density, f_j, and mean 0, and $\{\varepsilon_t^{(j)}\}$ and $\{\varepsilon_t^{(k)}\}$ are independent for $j \neq k$. (Conditions for ergodicity are given in Exercise 14.) His method is based on the iteration used for solving the integral equation (4.101) numerically:

$$h_{n+1}(x) = \lambda_n \sum_{j=1}^{L} \int_{r_{j-1}}^{r_j} h_n(y)f_j(x - a_0^{(j)} - a_1^{(j)}y)\,dy \tag{4.103}$$

with some suitable starting function, $h_0(x)$, normalized so that

$$\int_{-\infty}^{\infty} h_0(x)\,dx = 1.$$

The multiplying factor λ_n is a normalization constant, and is necessary because the numerical evaluation of the integrals requires a finite range of integration. It is reset after each iteration. Simpson's rule is used for the numerical integration. Pemberton (1985) has suggested the stopping rule: 10 iterations or agreement to at least seven figures with immediate predecessor. Convergence is not guaranteed and it seems difficult to assess the accuracy of the method. Figure 4.3 is taken from Pemberton (1985, p. 211).

4.2.4.3 Method based on the Chapman–Kolmogorov relation

The basic idea of this method is to evaluate the conditional distributions iteratively using a numerical quadrature. For simplicity of explanation, let $h(x_{t+m} \mid x_t)$ denote the conditional density (assumed to exist) of X_{t+m}

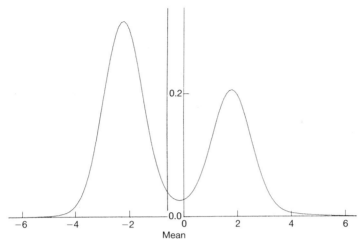

Fig. 4.3. Approximate marginal density of the SETAR $(3; 1, 1, 1)$ model

$$X_t = \begin{cases} -2 + 0.1X_{t-1} + \varepsilon_t & \text{if } X_{t-1} \leq -1 \\ 0.9X_{t-1} + \eta_t & \text{if } -1 < X_{t-1} \leq 1 \\ 2 - 0.1X_{t-1} + \varepsilon_t & \text{if } 1 < X_{t-1} \end{cases}$$

where $\varepsilon_t \sim \mathcal{N}(0, 0.5)$ and $\eta_t \sim \mathcal{N}(0, 5.0)$. The accuracy after ten iterations is only 2 figures. (Pemberton's method used)

given $x_t = x_t$, where $\{X_t\}$ follows the model

$$X_t = \lambda(X_{t-1}) + \varepsilon_t \tag{4.104}$$

where the ε_t are i.i.d. random variables with a known density f, mean zero, and variance σ^2. The model is assumed to be stationary but λ need not be smooth. From the Chapman–Kolmogorov relation, it holds that

$$h(x_{t+m} \mid x_t) = \int_{-\infty}^{\infty} h(x_{t+m} \mid x_{t+1})h(x_{t+1} \mid x_t) \, \mathrm{d}x_{t+1}. \tag{4.105}$$

Clearly

$$h(x_{t+1} \mid x_t) = f(x_{t+1} - \lambda(x_t)). \tag{4.106}$$

By stationarity, $h(x_{t+m} \mid x_t)$ tends to the stationary density, h, as $m \to \infty$. Starting with eqn (4.106), we may evaluate $h(x_{t+m} \mid x_t)$, $m = 2, 3, \ldots$ from eqn (4.105) using numerical integration. (Note that Pemberton's method may also be endowed with the Chapman–Kolmogorov interpretation.) We recommend the NAG subroutine D01BBF coupled with NAG subroutine D01BAX to generate at most 64 'weights' and 64 'abscissae' to be used in integration formulae of the Gaussian type. At each iteration (i.e. for each m), the function $h(x_{t+m} | x_t)$ is normalized to unit area. The stopping rule is agreement to 10^{-8} with the immediate previous iterate. Joint densities and moments can be handled in a similar manner. The method may also be extended to cope with higher-order dependence, that is

$$X_t = \lambda(X_{t-1}, \ldots, X_{t-m}) + \varepsilon_t \qquad (4.107)$$

although *computing time will increase* substantially. Again it is difficult to assess the accuracy of the method.

On the other hand, it is possible to reduce the computation generally by noting that (4.105) still holds if we replace the left-hand side by $h(x_{t+2m} | x_t)$, the integrand on the right-hand side by $h(x_{t+2m} | x_{t+m}) h(x_{t+m} | x_t)$, and dx_{t+1} by dx_{t+m}. Thus, instead of obtaining iterates $h(x_{t+m} | x_t)$, $m = 1, 2, 3, 4, \ldots$, we can 'accelerate' the iterates to $h(x_{t+2^m} | x_t)$, $m = 0, 1, 2, \ldots$. This method is analogous to the 'matrix-squaring' method in numerical linear algebra (see e.g. Wilkinson 1965). The advantage of the acceleration is that it takes $\log_2 n$ iterates to get the stationary density if the original scheme requires n iterates. Intermediate iterates $h(x_{t+2^m+j} | x_t)$, $j = 1, 2, \ldots, 2^{m+1} - 1$, can also be obtained more economically by using $h(x_{t+2^k} | x_t)$, $k = 0, 1, \ldots, m$, as the basic 'blocks'. The analogy with the matrix situation is quite apparent if we consider the numerical integration for eqn (4.105). Our experience suggests that the acceleration is marked if the transition matrix defined by $f(x_{t+1} | x_t)$, $x_{t+1} \in \{\xi_1, \xi_2, \ldots, \xi_N\}$, $x_t \in \{\xi_1, \xi_2, \ldots, \xi_N\}$, $\xi_1, \xi_2, \ldots, \xi_N$ being the abscissae used in the numerical integration, has two dominant eigenvalues which are close together in modulus. Tables 4.2 and 4.3 illustrate the point. Note that we may rescale each row of the transition matrix so that the row sums to unity. This may be realized by multiplying the i–jth entry by an appropriate weight generated by NAG routine D01BBF. In this case $\lambda_1 = 1$.

Table 4.2 Numerical evaluation of the stationary density of the AR(1) model $X_t = 0.5 X_{t-1} + \varepsilon_t$, $\varepsilon_t \sim \mathcal{N}(0, 1)$. ($N$ = number of abscissae used in the numerical integration, $|\lambda_1|$ = the largest eigenvalue in absolute value, $|\lambda_2|$ = the second largest eigenvalue in absolute value, run time 1 = run time without matrix squaring, run time 2 = run time with matrix squaring.)

N	$|\lambda_1/\lambda_2|$	Run time 1	Run time 2	Run time 2 / Run time 1
24	2.0	1.4	1.3	0.9
32	2.0	2.0	2.4	1.2
64	2.0	4.4	11.9	4.9

Table 4.3 Numerical evaluation of the stationary density of the SETAR $(2; 1, 1)$ model

$$X_t = \begin{cases} 1.5 - 0.9X_{t-1} + \varepsilon_t & \text{if } X_{t-1} \leq 0 \\ -0.4 - 0.6X_{t-1} + \varepsilon_t & \text{if } X_{t-1} > 0 \end{cases}$$

$\varepsilon_t \sim \mathcal{N}(0, 1)$

N	$|\lambda_1/\lambda_2|$	Run time 1	Run time 2	Run time 2 / Run time 1
24	1.02	76.9	1.2	0.02
32	1.02	85.0	2.5	0.03
64	1.02	160.0	20.9	0.13

Furthermore, it has been observed in the above experiments that

(1) the variance of ε_t and the number of points, N, do not affect the ratio of $|\lambda_1/\lambda_2|$ in the linear case; in the non-linear case, the variance of ε_t affects the ratio (c.f. (4) below);

(2) in the linear case, the run times with $\mathrm{var}(\varepsilon_t) = 0.01$ are approximately the same as those with $\mathrm{var}(\varepsilon_t) = 1$;

(3) in the non-linear case, when $\mathrm{var}(\varepsilon_t)$ is reduced to 0.01 the method without matrix squaring does not converge but the method with matrix squaring converges whether $\mathrm{var}(\varepsilon_t) = 1$ or 0.01 and the run times are similar;

(4) in the non-linear case with $\mathrm{var}(\varepsilon_t) = 0.01$, the ratio $|\lambda_1/\lambda_2|$ is approximately equal to 1.

As an illustration of the efficacy of the method based on the Chapman–Kolmogorov relation, we compare in Fig. 4.4 the approximate density by this method with the exact density (given by (4.71)) of the following model:

$$X_t = -\alpha |X_{t-1}| + \varepsilon_t \tag{4.108}$$

where the ε_t are i.i.d. $\mathcal{N}(0, 1)$. When $\alpha = 0.3$ the agreement is good to six decimal places. When $\alpha = 0.9$, the agreement is only good to four decimal places. Some deterioration is naturally expected because we are approaching the boundary of stationarity. Table 4.4 gives the first four moments.

As an illustration of the feasibility of the method for bivariate densities, we show in Fig. 4.5 approximate bivariate densities of (X_t, X_{t-1}) and (X_t, X_{t-2}) where $\{X_t\}$ is given by the SETAR $(2; 1, 1)$

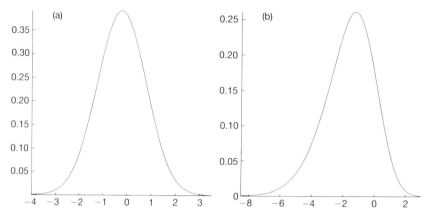

Fig. 4.4. (a) Stationary marginal density of model $X_t = -\alpha |X_{t-1}| + \varepsilon_t$, $\varepsilon_t \sim \mathcal{N}(0, 1)$, $\alpha = 0.3$. (b) $\alpha = 0.9$. In both cases, the agreement is so good that the approximate curve and the true curve practically coincide

model

$$X_t = \begin{cases} 1.5 - 0.9X_{t-1} + \varepsilon_t & \text{if } X_{t-1} \leq 0 \\ -0.4 - 0.6X_{t-1} + \varepsilon_t & \text{if } X_{t-1} > 0 \end{cases} \qquad (4.109)$$

where the ε_t are i.i.d. $\mathcal{N}(0, 1)$. Figure 4.6 gives the approximate conditional densities $h(x_t \mid x_0 = 1)$, $t = 1, 2, 3, 4, 5$, as well as $h(x_t)$, the stationary density.

Our experience suggests that this method works quite fast and is usually quite reliable. For example, for the calculation of the marginal density of model (4.108) the CPU time on the DEC VAX Cluster (one 8800 plus two 8200s) machine at the University of Kent at Canterbury, UK, was 1 second for $\alpha = 0.3$ and 1.5 seconds for $\alpha = 0.9$. The

Table 4.4 First four approximate moments (exact values in parentheses) of model $X_t = -\alpha |X_{t-1}| + \varepsilon_t$, $\varepsilon_t \sim \mathcal{N}(0, 1)$.

	$\alpha = 0.3$	$\alpha = 0.9$
Mean	$-0.250\,923$	$1.647\,593$
	$(-0.250\,923)$	$(1.647\,425)$
Variance	$1.035\,939$	$2.548\,593$
	$(1.035\,030)$	$(2.549\,147)$
Third central moment	$-6.782\,22 \times 10^{-3}$	$-1.919\,605$
	$(-6.781\,05 \times 10^{-3})$	$(-1.919\,023)$
Fourth central moment	$3.220\,583$	$21.572\,68$
	$(3.220\,629)$	$(21.580\,33)$

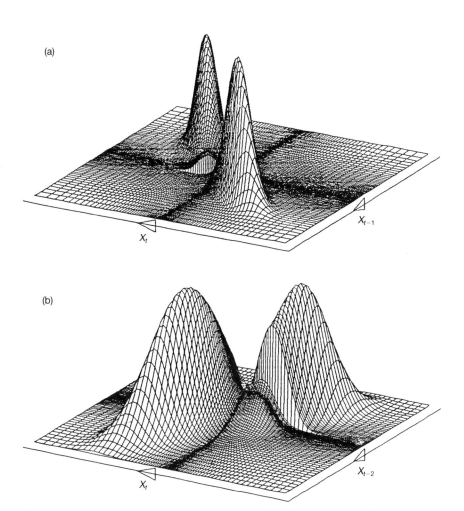

Fig. 4.5. (a) Stationary bivariate density of (X_t, X_{t-1}) of the SETAR $(2; 1, 1)$ model

$$X_t = \begin{cases} 1.5 - 0.9X_{t-1} + \varepsilon_t & \text{if } X_{t-1} \leq 0 \\ -0.4 - 0.6X_{t-1} + \varepsilon_t & \text{if } X_{t-1} > 0 \end{cases}$$

where $\varepsilon_t \sim \mathcal{N}(0, 1)$ (C–K method used). (b) Stationary bivariate density of (X_t, X_{t-2}) of the model in (a)

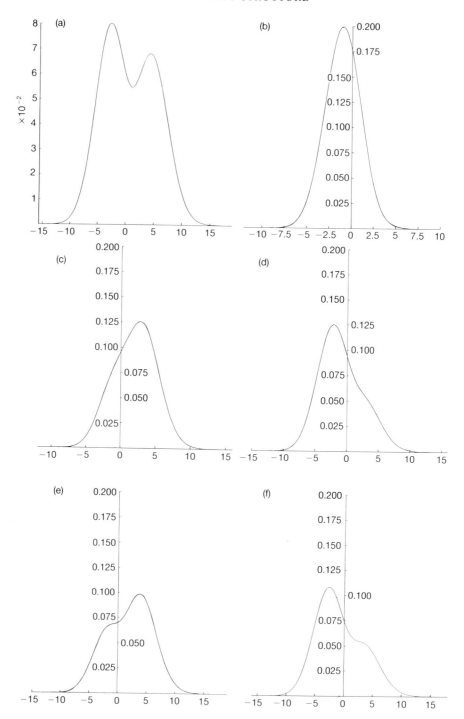

computational speed is such that it is feasible to compute the family of marginal densities of a low-order SETAR model indexed by the threshold parameter (see Fig. 4.7).

4.2.5 A SIMPLE MARKOVIAN BILINEAR MODEL

Consider the simple Markovian bilinear model

$$X_t = aX_{t-1} + b\varepsilon_t X_{t-1} + \varepsilon_t \qquad (4.110)$$

where $\varepsilon_t \sim \mathcal{N}(0, \sigma^2)$. Without loss of generality, we suppose that $\sigma^2 = 1$. Suppose that the model is stationary. As we have seen (cf Exercise 5), one sufficient condition for this is

$$a^2 + b^2 < 1. \qquad (4.11)$$

In this case X_t has the expansion

$$X_t = \sum_{j=0}^{\infty} \varepsilon_{t-j} \prod_{s=0}^{j-1} (a + b\varepsilon_{t-s}) \qquad (4.112)$$

where the infinite series is convergent almost surely. We denote this expansion of X_t by $X_t(b)$ so as to emphasize the dependence on the parameter b. It is not difficult to verify from (4.112) that

$$\mathrm{E}|X_t(b) - X_t(0)|^2 = \frac{b^2}{(1 - a^2 - b^2)(1 - a^2)} \to 0 \quad \text{as} \quad b \to 0 \qquad (4.113)$$

where the convergence is uniform for $0 < a^2 + b^2 < 1 - \delta$, $(\delta > 0)$. Note that $X_t(0)$ satisfies eqn (4.110) with $b = 0$, which implies that it is a stationary first-order autoregressive process, that is $X_t(0)$ satisfies

$$X_t(0) = aX_{t-1}(0) + \varepsilon_t \qquad (4.114)$$

from which it is clear that $X_t(0)$ is distributed as $\mathcal{N}(0, 1/(1 - a^2))$.

Theorem 4.5: Under condition (4.111), the bilinear process $\{X_t\}$ defined by (4.110) has a stationary distribution, the density, $f_b(x)$, of which possesses the following properties:

(1) $f_b(x)$ is everywhere continuous except at $x = -a/b$;
(2) $f_b(-a/b) = \infty$ and $f_b(x) \to \infty$ as $x \to -a/b$ $(b \neq 0)$;
(3) for $a \neq 0$, and for all $A > 0$, $f_b(x) \to f_0(x)$ uniformly for $|x| \leq A$, as $b \to 0$.

Fig. 4.6. (a) Stationary marginal density of X_t of the SETAR $(2; 1, 1)$ model in Fig. 4.5 (C–K method used). (b) $h(x_1 | x_0 = 1)$ (C–K method used); (c) $h(x_2 | x_0 = 1)$ (C–K method used); (d) $h(x_3 | x_0 = 1)$ (C–K method used); (e) $h(x_4 | x_0 = 1)$ (C–K method used); (f) $h(x_5 | x_0 = 1)$ (C–K method used)

(a)

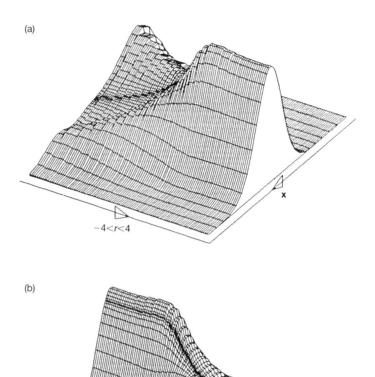

−4<r<4

(b)

−4<r<4

Fig. 4.7. A family of marginal densities of the following SETAR $(2; 1, 1)$ model indexed by the threshold parameter r:

$$X_t = \begin{cases} 0.7 - 0.5X_{t-1} + \varepsilon_t & \text{if } X_{t-1} \le r \\ -1.8 + 0.7X_{t-1} + \varepsilon_t & \text{if } X_{t-1} > r \end{cases}$$

where $\varepsilon_t \sim \mathcal{N}(0, 1)$. Note the 'bifurcation' from unimodality to bimodality as the parameter r crosses a critical value. There is a parallel 'bifurcation' from limit point to limit cycle for the skeleton

Proof. ¶ We prove (1) and (2) for $b > 0$ under condition (4.111). The process $\{X_t(b)\}$ has a stationary distribution, say $F_b(x)$, which, from (4.110) and for $b \geq 0$, satisfies

$$F_b(x) = P\{X_t(b) < x\}$$
$$= P\{aX_{t-1}(b) + [1 + bX_{t-1}(b)]\varepsilon_t < x\}$$
$$= \int \int_{as+(1+bs)\tau < x} \frac{1}{\sqrt{2\pi}} e^{-\tau^2/2} \, d\tau \, dF_b(s)$$
$$= \int_{-\infty}^{-1/b} \int_{(x-as)/(1+bs)}^{\infty} \frac{1}{\sqrt{2\pi}} \, d\tau \, dF_b(a)$$
$$+ \int_{-1/b}^{\infty} \int_{-\infty}^{(x-as)/(1+bs)} \frac{1}{\sqrt{2\pi}} e^{-\tau^2/2} \, d\tau \, dF_b(s).$$

Now, for all x such that $|x + a/b| \geq \delta > 0$, there exists a $k_\delta < \infty$ such that

$$|(1 + bs)^{-1} \exp\{ -\tfrac{1}{2}[(x - as)/(1 + bs)]^2\}| \leq K_\delta.$$

Therefore, by the bounded convergence theorem, for x bounded away from $-a/b$, we may differentiate under the integral sign and obtain

$$\frac{d}{dx} F_b(x) = - \int_{-\infty}^{-1/b} \frac{1}{\sqrt{2\pi}} \frac{1}{(1+bs)} \exp\left[-\frac{1}{2}\left(\frac{x - as}{1 + bs}\right)^2\right] dF_b(s)$$
$$+ \int_{-1/B}^{\infty} \frac{1}{\sqrt{2\pi}} \frac{1}{(1+bs)} \exp\left[-\frac{1}{2}\left(\frac{x - as}{1 + bs}\right)^2\right] dF_b(s)$$
$$= \frac{1}{\sqrt{2\pi}} \int_{-\infty}^{\infty} \frac{1}{|1 + bs|} \exp\left[-\frac{1}{2}\left(\frac{x - as}{1 + bs}\right)^2\right] dF_b(s) > 0. \quad (4.115)$$

Besides, we note trivially that $F_b(x)$ cannot have a discrete component at $x = -a/b$. For, suppose that

$$P[X_t = -a/b] > 0.$$

Then it follows from (4.110) that

$$P[\varepsilon_t = -a/b] > 0$$

which cannot be true. Thus, $F_b(x)$ is absolutely continuous with a positive density denoted by $f_b(x)$, which satisfies

$$f_b(x) = \frac{1}{\sqrt{2\pi}} \int_{-\infty}^{\infty} \frac{f_b(s)}{|1 + bs|} \exp\left[-\frac{1}{2}\left(\frac{x - as}{1 + bs}\right)^2\right] ds. \quad (4.116)$$

It is easy to see that (1) follows from (4.116).

For $b > 0$, (4.115) gives $f_b(-1/b) > 0$ which, together with (4.116), implies that (2) holds, that is $f_b(-a/b) = \infty$ and

$$f_b(x) \to \infty \quad \text{as} \quad x \to -a/b. \tag{4.117}$$

Next, we prove (3) for $a > 0$, $b > 0$. For $b = 0$, it follows from (4.114) that

$$f_0(x) = [(1 - a^2)/2\pi]^{1/2} \exp[-\tfrac{1}{2}x^2(1 - a^2)]. \tag{4.118}$$

For $a > 0$, $b > 0$, we have

$$|f_b(x) - f_0(x)| = \frac{1}{\sqrt{2\pi}} \int_{-\infty}^{\infty} \left\{ \frac{f_b(s)}{|1 + bs|} \exp\left[-\frac{1}{2}\left(\frac{x - as}{1 + bs}\right)^2\right] - f_0(s)e^{-1/2(x-as)^2} \right\} ds$$

$$= I_1 + I_2 + I_3 \tag{4.119}$$

where

$$I_1 = \frac{1}{\sqrt{2\pi}} \int_{-M}^{M} \left\{ \frac{1}{|1 + bs|} \exp\left[-\frac{1}{2}\left(\frac{x - as}{1 + bs}\right)^2\right] - e^{-1/2(x-as)^2} \right\} f_b(s)\, ds$$

$$I_2 = \frac{1}{\sqrt{2\pi}} \int_{-M}^{M} [f_b(s) - f_0(s)]e^{-1/2(x-as)^2}\, ds$$

$$I_3 = \frac{1}{\sqrt{2\pi}} \int_{|s| \geq M} \left\{ \frac{f_b(s)}{|1 + bs|} \exp\left[-\frac{1}{2}\left(\frac{x - as}{1 + bs}\right)^2\right] - f_0(s)e^{-1/2(x-as)^2} \right\} ds.$$

From (4.110) and (4.111) we have that

$$EX_t^2 = (1 - a^2 - b^2)^{-1} \to (1 - a^2)^{-1} \quad \text{as} \quad b \to 0.$$

Since $a > 0$, therefore $a/b \to \infty$ as $b \to 0$. Fix an $A > 0$. If $0 < b < \tfrac{1}{3}a/A$, then for all $x \in [-A, A]$, $|x + a/b| \geq 2A$, and so

$$\frac{1}{\sqrt{2\pi}} \frac{1}{|1 + bs|} \exp\left[-\frac{1}{2}\left(\frac{x - as}{1 + bs}\right)^2\right] \leq K_1 < \infty \quad \text{for all} \quad s \in (-\infty, \infty).$$

Here, K_1 can be chosen independently of b and x, for b and x in the range stated. For all $\varepsilon > 0$

$$|I_3| \leq K_1 \int_{|s| \geq M} f_b(s)\, ds + K_2 \int_{|s| \geq M} f_0(s)\, ds$$

$$\leq \frac{K_1}{M^2} E[X_t(b)]^2 + \frac{K_2}{M^2} E[X_t(0)]^2$$

$$\leq \frac{K_1}{M^2} \frac{1}{1 - a^2 - b^2} + \frac{K_2}{M^2} \frac{1}{1 - a^2}$$

$$\leq \varepsilon$$

for sufficiently large M.

On the other hand, (4.113) implies that $X_t(b)$ converges to $X_t(0)$ in mean square as $b \to 0$, and so the distribution function $F_b(x)$ of $X_t(b)$ converges pointwise to $F_0(x)$ of $X_t(0)$. Since $F_0(x)$ is continuous, then as $b \to 0$, $F_b(x) \to F_0(x)$ uniformly for $x \in [-A, A]$ and for all $A > 0$. Hence, for M fixed, as $b \to 0$,

$$|I_2| = \left| \frac{1}{\sqrt{2\pi}} \{ e^{-1/2(x-as)^2}[F_b(s) - F_0(s)] \}_{-M}^M \right.$$

$$\left. + \frac{1}{\sqrt{2\pi}} \int_{-M}^{M} [F_b(s) - F_0(s)](x - as) e^{-1/2(x-as)^2} \, ds \right|$$

$$\leq \frac{1}{\sqrt{2\pi}} \left(|F_b(M) - F_0(M) - F_b(-M) + F_0(-M)| + K_3 \sup_{|s| \leq M} |F_b(s) - F_0(s)| \right)$$

$$\to 0.$$

It is easy to see that as $b \to 0$

$$|I_1| \leq \frac{1}{\sqrt{2\pi}} \sup_{|s| \leq M} \left| \frac{1}{1+bs} \exp\left[-\frac{1}{2}\left(\frac{x-as}{1+bs} \right)^2 \right] - e^{-1/2(x-as)^2} \right| \int_{-M}^{M} f_b(s) \, ds \to 0.$$

Summarizing the above, we have proved that for all $x \in [-A, A]$,

$$\lim_{b \to 0} |f_b(x) - f_0(x)| \leq \lim_{b \to 0} |I_1| + \lim_{b \to 0} |I_2| + \lim_{b \to 0} |I_3| \leq \varepsilon.$$

By the arbitrariness of ε, it follows immediately that

$$\lim_{b \to 0} |f_b(x) - f_0(x)| = 0, \quad \forall |x| \leq A$$

where the convergence is uniform over all closed bounded intervals. This completes the proof of (3).

Finally, for the cases $a < 0$, $b < 0$ and $a < 0$, $b > 0$, and $a = 0$, the above argument also applies. □ ¶¶

The theorem shows that when $a \neq 0$ and b is sufficiently small, $f_b(x)$ has at least one local maximum point over the interval $[-1, 1]$ and this local maximum point is arbitrarily close to the origin as $b \to 0$. However, no matter how close b is to zero, $f_b(-a/b) = \infty$ for $b \neq 0$. Thus, for $a \neq 0$ and b sufficiently small, $f_b(x)$ has a local maximum point near the origin and the unique point of infinity at $-a/b$. However, a fairly extensive simulation study suggests that the point of infinity at $-a/b$ is a little 'elusive'. It does not seem to be clearly shown up even with a 10 000 point simulation. Figures 4.8 and 4.9 are typical frequency polygons based on 10 000 observations and with a 'bin' size of 0.2, the choice of which should presumably provide sufficient resolvability without undue

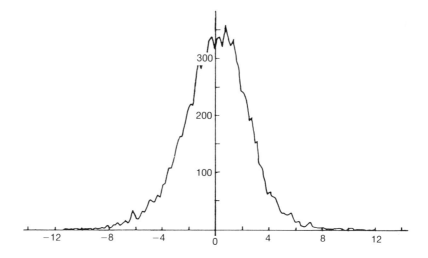

Fig. 4.8. Frequency polygon of $X_t = (-0.9 + 0.2\varepsilon_t)X_{t-1} + \varepsilon_t$, $\varepsilon_t \sim \mathcal{N}(0, 1)$

variability. This observation tends to suggest that the neighbourhood of $-a/b$ has a very small probability measure. In this connection, it may be noted that

$$f_b(-a/b \pm \varepsilon) = 0(\log \varepsilon^{-1}) \quad \text{as } \varepsilon \downarrow 0.$$

The result follows from eqn (4.116) on partitioning the range of

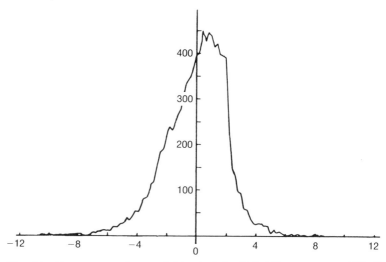

Fig. 4.9. Frequency polygon of $X_t = (-0.8 + 0.4\varepsilon_t)X_{t-1} + \varepsilon_t$, $\varepsilon_t \sim \mathcal{N}(0, 1)$

integration as follows:

$$\int_{-\infty}^{\infty} = \int_{-\infty}^{-B} + \int_{-B}^{-1/b} + \int_{-1/b}^{\infty}$$

and applying the mean value theorem.

A conjecture, which remains open, states that if $\{X_t\}$ follows a $BL(l, r, m, q)$ in the form (4.55) then X_t has a *unimodal* distribution under general conditions.

4.2.6 A 'CONVERSE' PROBLEM

There are essentially two types of problems which may be of interest. To see these, let us consider the simplest SETAR model first:

$$X_t = a^{(J_t)} X_{t-1} + \varepsilon_t \tag{4.120}$$

where $J_t = j$ if and only if $X_{t-1} \in R_j$ with $\{R_1, \ldots, R_j\}$ constituting a complete partition of $\mathbf{R}$. We assume stationarity. Let ϕ_Y denote the characteristic function of the random variable indicated by the subscript. From (4.120)

$$\phi_{X_t}(s) = \phi_{\varepsilon_t}(s) \sum_{j=1}^{J} \pi_j E[\exp\{a^{(j)} is X_{t-1}\} \mid J_t = j] \tag{4.121}$$

where $\pi_j = \Pr(J_t = j)$ independently of t by stationarity. For the stationary distributions

$$\phi_X(s) = \phi_\varepsilon(s) \sum_{j=1}^{J} \pi_j E[\exp\{a^{(j)} is X\} \mid X \in R_j] \tag{4.122}$$

where ϕ_X denotes the characteristic function of the stationary (marginal) distribution of X_t and ϕ_ε is that of ε_t.

Problem: Given $\phi_\varepsilon(s)$, find $\phi_X(s)$.

'Converse' problem: Given $\phi_X(s)$, find $\phi_\varepsilon(s)$.

We have discussed aspects of the Problem. Now we turn to the Converse Problem briefly, which is comparatively manageable. A related problem is when J_t is such that the conditional expectation in (4.122) may be replaced by the unconditional expectation; the solution is simpler then. For example, suppose that

$$\phi_X(s) = \lambda/(\lambda - is).$$

We may use (4.122) and deduce that

$$\phi_\varepsilon(s) = \lambda \Big/ \Big\{ (\lambda - is) \sum_{j=1}^{J} \pi_j [\lambda/(\lambda - a^{(j)} is)] \Big\} \tag{4.123}$$

where

$$\pi_j = \exp(-\lambda r_{j-1}) - \exp(-\lambda r_j) \qquad (4.124)$$

with $r_0(= 0) \leq r_1 \leq \ldots \leq r_{J-1} < r_J(= \infty)$ being the threshold parameters. Therefore,

$$\frac{1}{\phi_\varepsilon(s)} = \sum_{j=1}^{J} \frac{\pi_j}{[a^{(j)} + (1 - a^{(j)})\lambda/(\lambda - is)]}. \qquad (4.125)$$

That is, the characteristic function of ε_t is given by a harmonic mean of characteristic functions with respect to the weights $\pi_1, \pi_2, \ldots, \pi_J$. This result may be generalized to the case of general ϕ_X: the characteristic function of ε_t is given by the harmonic mean of $\phi_X(a^{(j)}s)/\phi_X(s)$, with respect to the π_j. Lawrance and Lewis (1980, 1985) and others have discussed this problem at length. Chan (1988a) has considered the problem for the NEAR(p) model. The primary interest here seems to be: find a distribution for the white noise compatible with a pre-specified *marginal* distribution of X_t.

4.2.7 RELATION WITH AUTOREGRESSION FUNCTION

Stationarity is assumed throughout.

Without solving the integral equation (4.64), can we say anything general about the solution? It is well known that a linear model driven by noise with a symmetric density has symmetric joint distribution. The next theorem addresses the non-linear autoregressive models.

Let $\mathbf{X}_t$ denote the column vector $(X_t, X_{t-1}, \ldots, X_{t-p+1})^T$. Let λ be a function from $\mathbf{R}^p$ to $\mathbf{R}$. We define the vector function $\boldsymbol{\lambda}$ by

$$\boldsymbol{\lambda}(\mathbf{X}_t) = (\lambda(X_t, X_{t-1}, \ldots, X_{t-p+1}), X_t, X_{t-1}, \ldots, X_{t-p+2})^T.$$

$\boldsymbol{\lambda}$ is referred to as the *regression function*. Consider the time series $\{\mathbf{X}_t: t = 0, \pm 1, \ldots\}$ which satisfies the equation

$$\mathbf{X}_t = \boldsymbol{\lambda}(\mathbf{X}_{t-1}) + \boldsymbol{\varepsilon}_t \qquad (4.126)$$

where $\boldsymbol{\varepsilon}_t = (\varepsilon_t, 0, \ldots, 0)^T$, is a p-dimensional column vector, with $\{\varepsilon_t: t = 0, \pm 1, \pm 2, \ldots\}$ a sequence of i.i.d. random variables. In the above set-up, $p \in \{1, 2, \ldots\}$, and the joint distributions of $\{X_t\}$ are assumed to be absolutely continuous. Also, $f(x_1, x_2, \ldots, x_k)$ is said to be a *symmetric probability density function about the origin* if it is a probability density function satisfying $f(x_1, x_2, \ldots, x_k) = f(-x_1, -x_2, \ldots, -x_k)$, all $x_1, x_2, \ldots, x_k$ and all $k \in \{1, 2, \ldots\}$.

Theorem 4.6: Let ε_t have a symmetric probability density function (p.d.f.) about the origin. Then all the finite stationary joint probability density functions of $X_{t_1}, X_{t_2}, \ldots, X_{t_k}$ are symmetric about the origin for all $t_1, t_2, \ldots, t_k$ and for $k = 1, 2, \ldots$, if and only if λ is a skew-symmetric function at points where the p.d.f. is positive, that is $-\lambda(\mathbf{x}) = \lambda(-\mathbf{x})$ for all $\mathbf{x}$ at which the (p-variate) p.d.f. of $(X_t, X_{t-1}, \ldots, X_{t-p+1})$ is positive.

¶ First we state the following lemma:

Lemma 4.1: Let the random variable $\mathbf{X}$ have an absolutely continuous distribution. The random variables $-\mathbf{X}$ and $\mathbf{X}$ have the same distribution if and only if $\mathbf{X}$ has a symmetric p.d.f. about the origin.

The proof is obvious and is therefore omitted.

Proof of theorem 4.6: Since ε_t has a symmetric p.d.f. about the origin, by the lemma $-\varepsilon_t$ and ε_t have the same p.d.f. Suppose that λ is skew symmetric at points where the p.d.f. is positive. Let $\mathbf{X}_{t-1}$ be one such point and let $\mathbf{Y}_{t-1} = -\mathbf{X}_{t-1}$. Then

$$\mathbf{Y}_t = -\lambda(-\mathbf{Y}_{t-1}) - \varepsilon_t = \lambda(\mathbf{Y}_{t-1}) - \varepsilon_t \qquad (4.127)$$

since λ is skew symmetric at $-\mathbf{Y}_{t-1}$ and eqn (4.127) holds for all such $\mathbf{X}_{t-1}$. Therefore $\{Y_t\}$ and $\{X_t\}$ have the same probabilistic structure. Since $\{X_t\}$ is stationary, $\{X_t\}$ and $\{Y_t\}$ have the same finite stationary joint p.d.f. which will be symmetric by lemma 4.1.

Conversely, suppose that all the finite stationary joint p.d.f.'s are symmetric about the origin. Now, the joint p.d.f. of $X_1, \ldots, X_p, X_{p+1}$ is given by the joint p.d.f. of $X_1, \ldots, X_p, \varepsilon_{p+1}$ and λ, that is in an obvious notation,

$$f_{(X_1, \ldots, X_p, X_{p+1})}(x_1, \ldots, x_p, x_{p+1})$$

$$= f_{(X_1, \ldots, X_p, \varepsilon_{p+1})}(x_1, \ldots, x_p, x_{p+1} - \lambda(x_p, \ldots, x_1))$$

$$= f_{(X_1, \ldots, X_p, \varepsilon_{p+1})}(-x_1, \ldots, -x_p, -x_{p+1} - \lambda(-x_p, \ldots, -x_1))$$

by the symmetry of the joint p.d.f. Also, by the independence of ε_{p+1} and $(X_1, \ldots, X_p)$ and the symmetry of the distribution of ε_{p+1} about the origin, it follows that

$$f_{\varepsilon_{p+1}}(x_{p+1} - \lambda(x_p, \ldots, x_1)) = f_{\varepsilon_{p+1}}(-x_{p+1} - \lambda(-x_p, \ldots, -x_1))$$

$$= f_{\varepsilon_{p+1}}(x_{p+1} + \lambda(-x_p, \ldots, -x_1))$$

for all $(x_p, x_{p-1}, \ldots, x_1)$ at which the joint p.d.f. of $X_p, X_{p-1}, \ldots, X_1$ is positive. Hence, at all such points

$$\lambda(-x_p, \ldots, -x_1) = -\lambda(x_p, \ldots, x_1),$$

which implies the skew symmetry of λ at such points. □

In particular, λ is skew symmetric if λ is a linear function without constant term.¶¶

A converse question for autoregressive models is this: if we know what the stationary *marginal* density is, can we infer something about the autoregression function? The following result due to C. Z. Wei (private communication, 1988) answers this question in the affirmative for the stationary first-order autoregressive model, that is let $\{X_t\}$ follow a stationary non-linear autoregressive model

$$X_t = \lambda(X_{t-1}) + \varepsilon_t \tag{4.128}$$

where $\{\varepsilon_t\}$ is a sequence of i.i.d. random variables with zero mean and $\lambda : \mathbf{R} \to \mathbf{R}$ is a measurable and differentiable function.

Theorem 4.7: If the stationary marginal distribution of X_t is Gaussian then λ is linear.

Proof. ¶ We recall *Cramer's theorem*, which states that if Y and Z are independent non-degenerate random variables, not necessarily identically distributed, and $Y + Z$ has a Gaussian distribution, then Y and Z are each Gaussian. (See e.g. Lukacs 1960, p. 173.) After suitable normalization, we only have to show that if $X \sim \mathcal{N}(0, 1)$ and $\lambda(X) \sim \mathcal{N}(0, 1)$ then $\lambda(x) = x$, $\forall x$, or $\lambda(x) = -x$, $\forall x$. The proof is in two steps.

First, λ is strictly monotone. If not, then by the continuity of λ, $\exists x \neq y$ s.t. $\lambda(x) = \lambda(y)$. Because λ is differentiable, $\exists z \in [x, y]$ s.t. $\lambda'(z) = 0$. Let $M(\delta)$ and $m(\delta)$ be the maximum and minimum respectively of λ on $[z - \delta, z + \delta]$. Then $M(\delta) - m(\delta) = o(\delta)$ as $\delta \to 0$. Let Φ denote the distribution of $\mathcal{N}(0, 1)$. We have

$$\begin{aligned}
\Phi(z + \delta) - \Phi(z - \delta) &= P[z - \delta \leq X \leq z + \delta] \\
&\leq P[m(\delta) \leq \lambda(X) \leq M(\delta)] \\
&= \Phi(M(\delta)) - \Phi(m(\delta)) \\
&= o(\delta).
\end{aligned}$$

This is a contradiction because

$$\lim_{\delta \to 0} [\Phi(z + \delta) - \Phi(z - \delta)]/\delta = 2\Phi'(z) > 0.$$

Next, by the first step we may assume that λ is strictly increasing (if not, we take $-\lambda$). Now for each $x \in \mathbf{R}$,

$$\begin{aligned}
\Phi(x) &= P[\lambda(X) \leq x] \\
&= P[X \leq \lambda^{-1}(x)] \\
&= \Phi(\lambda^{-1}(x)).
\end{aligned}$$

Since Φ is strictly increasing, $x = \lambda^{-1}(x)$. □¶¶

Results for higher-order AR or for multivariate $\{X_t\}$ are not available to our knowledge.

4.2.8 MOMENTS OF STATIONARY DISTRIBUTIONS

It is well known that moments need not exist for stationary* time series. The following theorem is a useful key for Markov chains on $\mathbf{R}^n$, which we state here but refer readers to Tweedie (1983) for a proof. First we need to introduce the concept of a *small set*.

Definition 4.2: A set C belonging to the σ-algebra of Borel sets of $\mathbf{R}^n$, $\mathbb{B}$, is called *small* if $\phi(C) > 0$ for some measure ϕ on $\mathbb{B}$ and for every $A \in \mathbb{B}$ with $\phi(A) > 0$, $\exists j$ s.t.

$$\inf_{\mathbf{x} \in C} \sum_{n=1}^{j} P^n(\mathbf{x}, A) > 0. \tag{4.129}$$

Roughly speaking, small sets play a similar role for the continuous state space, $\mathbf{R}^n$, as do individual states in the case of discrete state space, that is small sets 'discretize' the state space, $\mathbf{R}^n$. See Appendix 1 for a more abstract definition.

Theorem 4.8: Suppose that $\{\mathbf{X}_t\}$ is an ergodic Markov chain on $\mathbf{R}^n$ with limiting probability π, $\pi(\mathbf{R}^n) = 1$, and f is a non-negative $\mathbb{B}$-measurable function. Suppose for some small set A (w.r.t. π),

(1) f is bounded away from zero and infinity on A,

(2) $\sup \mathrm{E}[f(\mathbf{X}_t) \mid \mathbf{X}_{t-1} = \mathbf{x}] < \infty, \qquad \mathbf{x} \in A,$ $\tag{4.130}$

(3) $\exists \delta > 0$ s.t.

$$\mathrm{E}[f(\mathbf{X}_t) \mid \mathbf{X}_{t-1} = \mathbf{x}] \le (1 - \delta)f(\mathbf{x}), \qquad \mathbf{x} \notin A;$$

then

$$\int_{\mathbf{R}^n} f(\mathbf{x})\pi(\mathrm{d}\mathbf{x}) < \infty.$$

Moreover for some $\rho < 1$

$$\int_{\mathbf{R}^n} \pi(\mathrm{d}\mathbf{x}) \sup_{|h| \le f} |\mathrm{E}[h(\mathbf{X}_t)| \mathbf{X}_0 = \mathbf{x}] - \int_{\mathbf{R}^n} \pi(\mathrm{d}\mathbf{y})h(\mathbf{y})| = \mathrm{O}(\rho^t) \quad \text{as} \quad t \to \infty. \tag{4.131}$$

Besides determining whether the stationary probability has moments, the above theorem also gives us the rate of convergence of the (conditional) moments to their stationary values.

Let

$$\xi_t = (1, 0, \dots, 0)\mathbf{X}_t. \tag{4.132}$$

Then $\{\xi_t\}$ equipped with the marginal distribution of the first component of $\{\mathbf{X}_t\}$ is stationary.

---

* Recall that by *stationarity* we mean *strict stationarity* in this book.

Example 4.11: Consider the simple bilinear model

$$X_t = (a + b\varepsilon_t)X_{t-1} + \varepsilon_t \qquad (4.133)$$

where the ε_t are i.i.d. $\mathcal{N}(0, \sigma^2)$. Suppose that

$$K_1 = E\,|a + b\varepsilon_t| < 1 \qquad (4.134)$$

so that $\{X_t\}$ is stationary. (See e.g. Exercise 5.) Take

$$f(x) = 1 + |x| \qquad (4.135)$$

and as the required small set w.r.t. the stationary distribution,

$$A = \{x : f(x) = 1 + |x| \le (K_2 + 1 - K_1)/(K - K_1)\} \qquad (4.136)$$

where $K_2 = E\,|\varepsilon_t|$ and $K_1 < K < 1$. Condition (1) is immediate. Conditions (2 and 3) are implied by

$$E[f(X_t)\,|\,X_{t-1} = x] \le K_1 f(x) + K_2 + (1 - K_1) \le Kf(x), \quad \forall x \notin A$$
$$E[f(X_t)\,|\,X_{t-1} = x] \le 1 + |x| + E\,|\varepsilon_t|, \quad \forall x. \qquad (4.137)$$

Therefore, under condition (4.134), $E_\pi\,|X_t| < \infty$ w.r.t. the stationary distribution π. In general, provided

$$E\,|a + b\varepsilon_t|^k < 1 \qquad (4.138)$$

we have for large enough x and some $\delta > 0$,

$$E[|X_t|^k \mid X_{t-1}x] < (1 - \delta)\,|x|^k.$$

Expanding (4.138) we see that, in order for $\{X_t\}$ to have stationary moments of order k, it suffices that, for k even,

$$\sum_{n=0}^{k} \binom{k}{n} a^{k-n} b^n E(\varepsilon_t^n) < 1. \qquad (4.139)$$

For example, for $k = 4$, this reduces to

$$1 - a^4 - \sigma^2[6b^2 a^2 + 3b^2 \sigma^2] > 0. \qquad (4.140)$$

Let

$$M_{2k} = \left\{ (a, b) : \sum_{n=0}^{2k} \binom{2k}{n} a^{2k-n} b^n E(\varepsilon_t^n) < 1 \right\} \qquad (4.141)$$

Figure 4.10 shows that $M_2 \supset M_4 \supset M_6 \supset \dots$. This suggests that $\{X_t\}$ cannot possess moments of all orders. To prove this, we write μ_n for $E(X_1^n)$ and note the recurrence relation for the μ_n (which may be established by induction):

$$\mu_0 = 1$$
$$\mu_1 = 0$$
$$\mu_n = \sum_{s=0}^{[n/2]} \binom{n}{2s}(-\tfrac{1}{2})^s C_s a^{n-2s} \left[\sum_{j=0}^{2s} \binom{2s}{j} b^j \mu_{n-2s+j} \right], \qquad n = 2, 3, 4, \dots$$

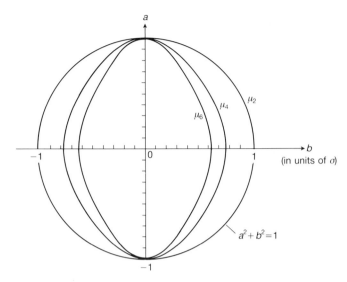

Fig. 4.10. Boundaries of regions inside which μ_{2k} exists ($k = 1, 2, 3$)

where

$$C_s = -2(2s - 1)C_{s-1}, \qquad s = 1, 2, \ldots$$
$$C_0 = 1.$$

Therefore, μ_{2n} exists only if $p_{2j}(a, b) < 1$, all $j = 1, 2, \ldots, n$, where

$$p_{2j}(a, b) = a^{2j} + \binom{2j}{2} 1 \cdot a^{2j-2}b^2 + \binom{2j}{4} 1 \cdot 3 a^{2j-4}b^4$$

$$+ \binom{2j}{6} 1 \cdot 3 \cdot 5 \cdot a^{2j-6}b^6 + \ldots + \binom{2j}{2j} 1 \cdot 3 \cdot 5 \ldots (2j + 1)b^{2j}.$$

Now

$$p_{2n}(a, b) \geq 1 \cdot 3 \cdot 5 \ldots (2n + 1)b^{2n}$$
$$\geq n! (2b^2)^n$$
$$\sim \sqrt{2\pi n} (n/B)^n$$

on using Stirling's formula and setting $B = e(2b^2)^{-1}$. Thus, for sufficiently large n, $p_{2n} \nless 1$. Therefore μ_{2n} does not exist for n sufficiently large. $\square$

For non-linear time series models, the existence of the kth order moment is one thing but the calculation of it is another and is usually quite tedious for $k > 2$ even if analytically feasible. (See e.g. Exercise 15.) However, if only the second-order moment is desired, there is quite a complete solution for the Markovian bilinear models discussed in Example 4.6.

Theorem 4.9; If $\{X_t\}$ is a stationary bilinear process defined by

$$X_t - \sum_{j=1}^{l} a_j X_{t-j} = \sum_{j=0}^{r} c_j \varepsilon_{t-j} + \sum_{i=1}^{q} \sum_{j=1}^{p} b_{ij} X_{t-i-j} \varepsilon_{t-i} \qquad (4.142)$$

where $c_0 = 1$, $\varepsilon_t \sim$ IID random variables with mean zero and variance σ^2, then its autocovariance function is the same as that of an ARMA model of order (l, s), $s = \max(r, q)$, with autoregressive coefficients $a_1, \ldots, a_l$ and moving average coefficients which are functions of the a_j, c_j, and b_{ij}.

Proof. Following the notations of Example 4.6, we may write (4.142) as

$$X_t = \mathbf{H}\xi_{t-1} + \varepsilon_t$$
$$\xi_t = \mathbf{A}\xi_{t-1} + \zeta_t \qquad (4.143)$$

where

$$\zeta_t = \mathbf{B}\xi_{t-1}\varepsilon_t + \mathbf{c}\varepsilon_t + \mathbf{d}(\varepsilon_t^2 - \sigma^2). \qquad (4.144)$$

Note that ε_t and components of ζ_t are uncorrelated with $X_{t-1}, X_{t-2}, \ldots$. Let H_t be the space of linear combinations of $X_t, X_{t-1}, \ldots$ and their limits in mean square. Let $\hat{Y}(s \mid H_t)$ denote the linear least-squares predictor of Y_s based on $X_t, X_{t-1}, \ldots$. If Y_s is a vector, then by $\hat{Y}(s \mid H_t)$ we mean the vector whose components are linear least-squares predictors in terms of $X_t, X_{t-1}, \ldots$ of the corresponding components of Y_s.

Now, from (4.143) we have

$$\hat{X}(t \mid H_{t-1}) = \mathbf{H}\hat{\xi}(t - 1 \mid H_{t-1})$$
$$\hat{\xi}(t \mid H_{t-1}) = \mathbf{A}\hat{\xi}(t - 1 \mid H_{t-1}). \qquad (4.145)$$

Put $\hat{\xi}_t = \hat{\xi}(t \mid H_t)$ and $\eta_t = X_t - \hat{X}(t \mid H_{t-1})$. Then

$$X_t = \mathbf{H}\hat{\xi}_{t-1} + \eta_t$$
$$\hat{\xi}_t = \mathbf{A}\hat{\xi}_{t-1} + \mathbf{Q}\eta_t \qquad (4.146)$$

where $\mathbf{Q}$ is a certain column vector in terms of the a_j, c_j, b_{ij}. The detailed form of $\mathbf{Q}$ may be computed using the Kalman filter method but is quite complicated. The first m components of $\mathbf{Q}$ are $0, 0, \ldots, 0, 1$. For, $\mathbf{Q}\eta_t = \hat{\xi}(t \mid H_t) - \hat{\xi}(t \mid H_{t-1})$ and $(\xi_t)_j = X_{t-m+j}$ for $j = 1, \ldots, m$ by construction. Therefore

$$(\mathbf{Q}\eta_t)_j = (\hat{\xi}(t \mid H_t))_j - (\hat{\xi}(t \mid H_{t-1}))_j = 0, \quad \text{if } j = 1, 2, \ldots, m - 1$$

and

$$(\mathbf{Q}\eta_t)_m = (\hat{\xi}(t \mid H_t))_m - (\hat{\xi}(t \mid H_{t-1}))_m = \eta_t.$$

Here $(\ )_m$ denotes the mth component. Let the last s components of $\mathbf{Q}$ be $a_1 + \beta_1, \ldots, a_s + \beta_s$, for some $\beta_1, \ldots, \beta_s$ which are functions of the a_j, c_j, and b_{ij}. Let $\mathbf{U}_t(j)$ denote the jth component of the vector $\mathbf{U}_t$. From the form of **H**, **A**, we have

$$X_t = \hat{\xi}_{t-1}(m+1) + \eta_t$$

$$\hat{\xi}_t(m+j) = a_j\hat{\xi}_{t-1}(m+1) + \hat{\xi}_{t-1}(m+j+1) + (a_j + \beta_j)\eta_t, \qquad 1 \le j < s$$

$$\hat{\xi}_t(n) = \sum_{j=s}^{n} a_j\hat{\xi}_{t-1}(n+1-j) + (a_s + \beta_s)\eta_t.$$

The above relations give

$$\xi_t(j) = X_{t-m+j}, \qquad j = 1, \dots, m$$

$$\xi_t(m+j) = a_j X_t + \xi_{t-1}(m+j+1) + \beta_j\eta_t, \qquad 1 \le j < s$$

$$\xi_t(n) = \sum_{j=s}^{n} a_j X_{t+s-j} + \beta_s\eta_t.$$

It then follows easily that

$$X_t = \sum_{j=1}^{n} a_j X_{t-j} + \eta_t + \sum_{j=1}^{s} \beta_j\eta_{t-j}. \qquad (4.147)$$

Since $s = \max(r, q)$ and $a_j = 0$ for $j > l$, and the η_t are uncorrelated, we have completed the proof. $\square$

There is again a strong connection between the stability of the skeleton and the existence of the moments of the clothed model. This time the moments of the driving (clothing) noise play an important role too.

Theorem 4.10: Under the conditions of Theorem 4.3 concerning the model

$$\mathbf{X}_{t+1} = \lambda(\mathbf{X}_t) + \boldsymbol{\varepsilon}_{t+1}$$

ε_t has kth absolute moment $\Rightarrow$ the stationary distribution of $\{\xi_t\}$ has finite kth absolute moment. (Recall eqn (4.132) for definition of ξ_t.]

Proof. Omitted, but see Chan and Tong (1985). $\square$

Example 4.12: Consider the SETAR $(2; 1, 1)$ model

$$X = \begin{cases} aX_{t-1} + \varepsilon_t \\ bX_{t-1} + \varepsilon_t \end{cases}$$

where $\varepsilon_t \sim$ IID. Suppose that $a < 1$, $b < 1$, and $ab < 1$ so that $\{X_t\}$ is stationary. Then on applying Theorem 4.10, $\mathrm{E}\,|\varepsilon_t|^k < \infty \Rightarrow \mathrm{E}\,|X_t|^k < \infty$ w.r.t. the stationary distribution. $\square$

4.2.9 HIGHER-ORDER SPECTRA

Suppose that X_t has moments of all orders. This implies that joint moments of all orders of $X_{t_1}, X_{t_2}, \dots, X_{t_k}$, for every $t_1, t_2, \dots, t_k \in \mathbf{Z}$

(not necessarily all distinct) and for every positive integer k, will also exist by stationarity and by the Cauchy–Schwarz inequality.

Definition 4.3: The kth order joint cumulant, $\operatorname{cum}(X_{t_1}, \ldots, X_{t_k})$, of $(X_{t_1}, \ldots, X_{t_k})$ is given by

$$\operatorname{cum}(X_{t_1}, \ldots, X_{t_k}) = \sum (-1)^{p-1}(p-1)! \left(\mathrm{E} \prod_{j \in v_1} X_{t_j} \right) \cdots \left(\mathrm{E} \prod_{j \in v_p} X_{t_j} \right)$$

(4.148)

where the summation extends over all partitions $(v_1, v_2, \ldots, v_p)$, $p = 1, \ldots, k$, of $(1, 2, \ldots, k)$.

We note that the joint cumulants of all orders certainly exist under the above assumed moment property. Also, if all the joint distributions of $\{X_t\}$ are symmetric about the origin, then all joint cumulants of odd orders vanish. We may interpret $\operatorname{cum}(X_{t_1}, \ldots, X_{t_k})$ as a measure of statistical dependence of $X_{t_1}, X_{t_2}, \ldots, X_{t_k}$. If some subset of $X_{t_1}, X_{t_2}, \ldots, X_{t_k}$ is statistically independent of the remainder, then $\operatorname{cum}(X_{t_1}, \ldots, X_{t_k})$ is identically zero. (See e.g. Brillinger 1965.)

Note that $\operatorname{cum}(X_{t_i}, X_{t_j})$ is just $\operatorname{cov}(X_{t_i}, X_{t_j})$. By stationarity, $\operatorname{cum}(X_{t+u_1}, X_{t+u_2}, \ldots, X_{t+u_{k-1}}, X_t)$ does not depend on t and we denote it by $\gamma(u_1, u_2, \ldots, u_{k-1})$, $(u_1, u_2, \ldots, u_{k-1} \in \mathbf{Z})$. Of course, $\gamma(u_1) \equiv \gamma_{u_1}$. Assume that

$$\sum_{-\infty}^{\infty} \cdots \sum_{-\infty}^{\infty} |\gamma(u_1, \ldots, u_{k-1})| < \infty$$

(4.149)

under which we may define the Fourier transforms

$h(\omega_1, \omega_2, \ldots, \omega_{k-1})$

$$= (2\pi)^{-k+1} \sum_{-\infty}^{\infty} \cdots \sum_{-\infty}^{\infty} \gamma(u_1, \ldots, u_{k-1}) \exp\left\{ -i \sum_{1}^{k-1} u_j \omega_j \right\}$$

(4.150)

which is called the (*non-normalized*) *cumulant spectral density function* of order k. When $k = 2$, this reduces to the (non-normalized) spectral density function. For $k > 2$, $h(\omega_1, \omega_2, \ldots, \omega_{k-1})$ is complex valued in general. (See e.g. Brillinger 1965.) The function $h(\omega_1, \omega_2)$ is also called a *bispectral density function*. Note that $(\omega_1, \omega_2, \ldots, \omega_{k-1})$, $(k > 2)$, do not have any physical interpretation.

4.2.10 APPROXIMATE MOMENTS

The approximate methods described in §§4.2.3 and 4.2.4 can be extended to the calculation of moments in a fairly obvious way. We give details of the method associated with §4.2.3 only, which is perhaps less straightforward than the others.

Taking expectations in (4.83b) gives

$$E(X_{t+1}^{(1)}) = bE(X_t^{(1)}) + E\{\Lambda(X_t^{(0)})\}$$

and therefore

$$E(X_t^{(1)}) = E\{\Lambda(X_t^{(0)})\}/(1-b)$$

where $E\{\Lambda(X_t^{(0)})\}$ is known. Other moments and joint moments of the time series $\{X_t^{(r)}\}$ can be derived in the same way and these lead to the following formulae:

$$E\{X_t(\beta)\} \approx E\{X_t^{(0)} + \beta X_t^{(1)} + \tfrac{1}{2}\beta^2 X_t^{(2)}\}$$

$$= E(X_t^{(0)}) + \beta E\{\Lambda(X_t^{(0)})\}/(1-b)$$

$$+ \beta^2 \sum_{r=0}^{\infty} b^r E[\Lambda^{(1)}(X_{t+1}^{(0)})\Lambda(X_{t-r}^{(0)})]/(1-b) \quad (4.151)$$

$$\text{var}\{X_t(\beta)\} \approx \text{var}\{X_t^{(0)} + \beta X_t^{(1)}\}$$

$$= \text{var}(X_t^{(0)}) + \frac{2\beta b}{1-b^2} \text{cov}[X_t^{(0)}, \Lambda(X_t^{(0)})]$$

$$+ \frac{\beta^2}{1-b^2} \sum_{r=-\infty}^{\infty} b^{|r|} \text{cov}[\Lambda(X_t^{(0)}), \Lambda(X_{t-r}^{(0)})], \quad (4.152)$$

and, for $k > 1$,

$$\text{cov}\{X_t(\beta), X_{t+k}(\beta)\} \approx \text{cov}\{X_t^{(0)} + \beta X_t^{(1)}, X_{t+k}^{(0)} + \beta X_{t+k}^{(1)}\}$$

$$= b^k \text{var}\{X_t^{(0)} + \beta X_t^{(1)}\}$$

$$+ \beta \sum_{r=0}^{k-1} b^{k-r-1} \text{cov}\{X_t^{(0)}, \Lambda(X_{t+r}^{(0)})\}$$

$$+ \frac{\beta^2}{1-b^2} \sum_{q=0}^{\infty} (b^{|q+1-k|} - b^{q+k+1})$$

$$\times \text{cov}\{\Lambda(X_{t+1}^{(0)}), \Lambda(X_{t-q}^{(0)})\}. \quad (4.153)$$

Table 4.5

Lag	Autocovariance	Lag	Autocovariance
0	2.218 93	7	0.25×10^{-2}
1	0.581 11	8	0.13×10^{-2}
2	0.043 84	9	0.29×10^{-3}
3	−0.0720	10	-0.6×10^{-4}
4	−0.0468	11	-0.1×10^{-3}
5	−0.0135	12	-0.2×10^{-4}
6	0.48×10^{-3}		

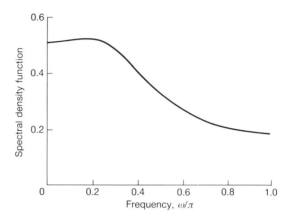

Fig. 4.11. Spectral density function of a SETAR $(3; 0, 1, 0)$ model (after Jones 1978)

Shown in Table 4.5 are the autocovariances of various lags of the model

$$X_t = \begin{cases} X_{t-1} + 0.5 + \varepsilon_t, & \text{if } -2 < X_{t-1} \le 1.5 \\ -1.5 + \varepsilon_t & \text{otherwise, } \varepsilon_t \sim \mathcal{N}(0, 1). \end{cases}$$

The spectral density function based on these autocovariances is shown in Fig. 4.11. Interestingly, it has a maximum at a *non-zero* frequency, in contrast with the case of a first-order *linear* AR model.

On the other hand, Table 4.4 illustrates the approach based on the Chapman–Kolmogorov relation, which may be extended to cover joint moments.

4.2.11 INDEX OF LINEARITY AND LAG REGRESSION

Let (X, Y) denote a two-dimensional random vector. Let f denote a (Baire) function of X s.t. $E\{f^2(X)\} < \infty$. We recall a result due to Brillinger (1966).

Theorem 4.11 (Brillinger's theorem): The squared correlation, r^2, between Y and $f(X)$ is maximized by choosing $f(X) = a + b E[Y \mid X]$, where a and b are constants.

Proof. Writing f for $f(X)$, we have

$$r^2 = \frac{[E\{Y - E(Y)\}\{f - E(f)\}]^2}{E\{Y - E(Y)\}^2 E\{f - E(f)\}^2}. \tag{4.154}$$

Now, on using iterated expectations,

$$\text{numerator} = (E[\{f - E(f)\}E\{Y - E(Y) \mid X\}])^2$$
$$\le E\{f - E(f)\}^2 E\{E(Y \mid X) - E(Y)\}^2$$

by the Cauchy–Schwarz's inequality. Substituting the numerator in eqn (4.154), we have

$$r^2 \leq \frac{E\{E(Y \mid X) - E(Y)\}^2}{E\{Y - E(Y)\}^2}$$

$$= \frac{\text{var}(E[Y \mid X])}{\text{var}(Y)}.$$

The upper bound is attained for $f(X) = a + bE[Y \mid X]$. $\square$

Let $\{X_t\}$ denote a stationary time series with $\gamma_0 = E(X_t^2) < \infty$ and autocorrelation function ρ_j, $j = 0, \pm 1, \ldots$. Now, the variance about the regression function $E(X_t \mid X_{t-j})$ is given by

$$E\{X_t - E(X_t \mid X_{t-j})\}^2 = \gamma_0 - \text{var}\{E(X_t \mid X_{t-j})\}. \qquad (4.155)$$

The best linear approximation of $E(X_t \mid X_{t-j})$, in the minimum mean square sense, is $\mu_x + \rho_j(X_{t-j} - \mu_x)$, where $\mu_x = EX_t$. The variance about this *linear* regression function is $\gamma_0 - \gamma_0\rho_j^2$. We have that

$$\gamma_0 - \gamma_0\rho_j^2 \geq \gamma_0 - \text{var}\{E(X_t \mid X_{t-j})\} \qquad (4.156)$$

because

$$0 \leq \gamma_0\rho_j^2/\text{var}\{E(X_t \mid X_{t-j})\} \leq 1. \qquad (4.157)$$

We call $\lim_{j \in \mathbf{Z}} [\gamma_0\rho_j^2/\text{var}\{E(X_t \mid X_{t-j})\}]$ the *second-order index of linearity*, $\mathcal{L}$. If var $\{E(X_t \mid X_{t-j})\} = 0$ for some j, $\mathcal{L}$ is defined to be 1. Clearly $0 \leq \mathcal{L} \leq 1$. It may be *roughly* interpreted as a *practical* measure of how close the generating mechanism of $\{X_t\}$ is linear. For, $\mathcal{L} = 1$ if $\{X_t\}$ is Gaussian and, on assuming an autoregressive model of order 1 with a differentiable autoregression function, the model is then linear. It may be worthwhile to study the properties of $\mathcal{L}$ more fully.

The above discussion also motivates us into studying *lag regressions*, that is $E[X_t \mid X_{t-j}]$, $j \in \mathbf{Z}$. Unfortunately, it is again usually very difficult to obtain closed-form analytic expressions for them and we commonly resort to numerical approximation of the types discussed in §4.2.10.

Under certain conditions, it is sometimes possible to obtain a 'quick-and-dirty' approximation of $E(X_t \mid X_{t-j})$ for $j = 1, 2, \ldots$, for a SETAR $(2; 2, 2)$ by exploiting the piecewise linearity. The technique is related to the second-order index of linearity. Under the assumption that $\rho_1^2 \text{var}(X_t)/\text{var}\{E(X_t \mid X_{t+i})\}$, say l_i, $(i = 1, -1)$, are close to unity, $E(X_t \mid X_{t+1} = x)$ is approximately linear in x. We may use this linear approximation as the basis of obtaining approximately $E(X_t \mid X_{t-j})$, $j = 1, 2, \ldots$. The essence of the technique is best explained by an example. Consider the following simple example of a SETAR $(2; 2, 2)$

fitted to the (log) Canadian lynx data of 1821–1919:

$$X_t = (0.62 + 1.25X_{t-1} - 0.43X_{t-2} + \varepsilon_t)I_{t-2}(3.25)$$
$$+ (2.25 + 1.52X_{t-1} - 1.24X_{t-2} + \varepsilon'_t)\{1 - I_{t-2}(3.25)\} \quad (4.158)$$

where $I_t(r)$ is an indicator variable defined by

$$I_t(r) = \begin{cases} 1 & \text{if } X_t \le r \\ 0 & \text{if } X_t > r. \end{cases} \quad (4.159)$$

$\{\varepsilon_t\}$ and $\{\varepsilon'_t\}$ are independent sequences of i.i.d. variables with $\mathcal{N}(0, 0.0381)$ and $\mathcal{N}(0, 0.0626)$ respectively. Now, from data, $l_{\pm 1}$ are close to unity. A fitted linear AR(2) to the same data leads to

$$E(X_t \mid X_{r \pm 1} = x) = 0.6 + 0.8x. \quad (4.160)$$

From model (4.158), we have

$$E(X_t \mid X_{t-1} = x) = \{0.62 + 1.25x - 0.43E(X_{t-2} \mid X_{t-1} = x)\}$$
$$\times P(X_{t-2} \le 3.25 \mid X_{t-1} = x)$$
$$+ \{2.25 + 1.52x - 1.24E(X_{t-2} \mid X_{t-1} = x)\}$$
$$\times P(X_{t-2} > 3.25 \mid X_{t-1} = x). \quad (4.161)$$

Since $\text{var}(\varepsilon_t)$ and $\text{var}(\varepsilon'_t)$ are quite small, then, for small x, eqn (4.161) gives

$$E(X_t \mid X_{t-1} = x) \doteq 0.62 + 1.25x - 0.43(0.6 + 0.8x)$$
$$= 0.36 + 0.91x. \quad (4.162)$$

Similarly, for large x, eqn (4.161) gives

$$E(X_t \mid X_{t-1} = x) \doteq 2.25 + 1.52x - 1.24(0.6 + 0.8x) = 1.51 + 0.53x. \quad (4.163)$$

On appealing to the continuity of $E(X_t \mid X_{t-1} = x)$ with respect to x, we may obtain

$$E(X_t \mid X_{t-1}) \doteq (0.36 + 0.91X_{t-1})I_{t-1}(3.03)$$
$$+ (1.51 + 0.53X_{t-1})\{1 - I_{t-1}(3.03)\}. \quad (4.164a)$$

It may be noted that over the dynamic range of the data, that is from 1.5 to 4.0, the piecewise linear regression function of (4.164a) and the straight-line regression (4.160) agree remarkably well.

Again, using model (4.158) we have that

$$E(X_t \mid X_{t-2}) = \{0.62 + 1.25E(X_{t-1} \mid X_{t-2}) - 0.43X_{t-2}\}I_{t-2}(3.25)$$
$$+ \{2.25 + 1.52E(X_{t-1} \mid X_{t-2}) - 1.24X_{t-2}\}\{1 - I_{t-2}(3.25)\}. \quad (4.165)$$

Using (4.164a) and a similar argument as used previously, we may deduce that

$$E(X_t \mid X_{t-2}) \doteq (1.08 + 0.71X_{t-2})I_{t-2}(3.04)$$
$$+ (4.54 - 0.43X_{t-2})\{1 - I_{t-2}(3.04)\}. \quad (4.164b)$$

Upon iteration, we may deduce that

$$E(X_t \mid X_{t-3}) \doteq (1.82 + 0.50X_{t-3})I_{t-3}(3.02)$$
$$+ (7.30 - 1.32X_{t-3})\{1 - I_{t-3}(3.02)\} \quad (4.164c)$$

and

$$E(X_t \mid X_{t-4}) \doteq (2.43 + 0.32X_{t-4})I_{t-4}(2.97)$$
$$+ (7.74 - 1.47X_{t-4})\{1 - I_{t-4}(2.97)\}. \quad (4.164d)$$

Of course, as the lags get larger, the quality of the approximation deteriorates. The 'quick-and-dirty' approximations given in (4.164a–d) all seem to agree quite well with the numerical approximations based on the Chapman–Kolmogorov relation (see Fig. 4.12).

4.2.12 PRE-ORDERING OF STATIONARY PROBABILITY MEASURES

For any two probability measures μ and v on **R**, we write $\mu \lhd v$ iff $\forall c > 0$, $\mu[-c, c] \geq v[-c, c]$, that is μ is more concentrated around the origin than v. The relation defined by $\lhd$ is called a *pre-order of measures on* **R**. It is transitive and reflexive.

Example 4.13: Let

$$T_g(x) = [0.2 - 0.2 \exp(-gx^2)]x. \quad (4.166)$$

Let π_g be the stationary distribution of the first-order EXPAR model

$$X_t = T_g(X_{t-1}) + \varepsilon_t, \quad (4.167)$$

where the ε_t are i.i.d. $\mathcal{N}(0, 1)$ random variables. It is clear that for $0 \leq g \leq g' \leq +\infty$, $|T_g(x)| \leq |T_{g'}(x)|$, $\forall x \in$ **R**. We now show that

$$\pi_g \lhd \pi_{g'} \quad \text{for} \quad 0 \leq g \leq g' \leq \infty. \quad (4.168)$$

¶ Let $\pi_{g,t}$ denote the conditional distribution of X_t given $X_0 = 0$. By stationarity $\pi_{g,t} \to \pi_g$ in distribution as $t \to \infty$. Because $\lhd$ is preserved under weak convergence, it suffices to show that

$$\pi_{g,t} \lhd \pi_{g',t}, \quad t \geq 0$$

for $0 \leq g \leq g' \leq \infty$. This may be proved by induction. Trivially,

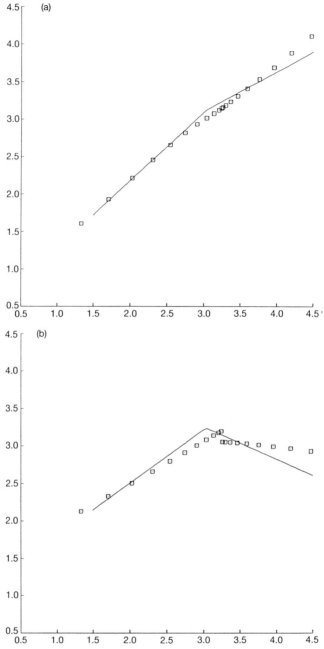

Fig. 4.12. Quick-and-dirty evaluation of lag regression in solid lines. C–K approximations in squares. The model is

$$X_t = \begin{cases} 0.62 + 1.25X_{t-1} - 0.43X_{t-2} + \varepsilon_t & \text{if } X_{t-2} \leq 3.25 \\ 2.25 + 1.52X_{t-1} - 1.24X_{t-2} + \varepsilon_t' & \text{if } X_{t-2} > 3.25 \end{cases}$$

where $\varepsilon_t \sim \mathcal{N}(0, 0.0381)$, $\varepsilon_t' \sim \mathcal{N}(0, 0.0626)$: (a) lag 1; (b) lag 2; (c) lag 3; (d) lag 4

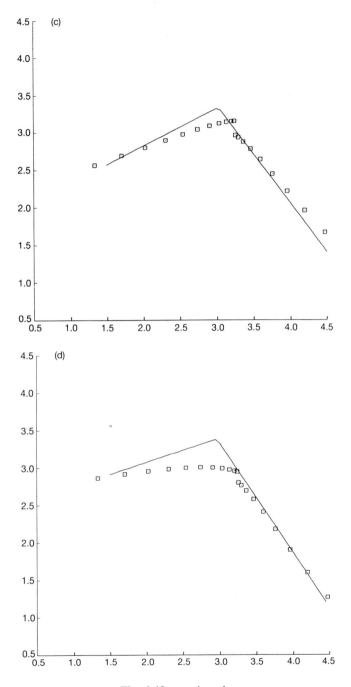

Fig. 4.12. continued

$\pi_{g,0} \lhd \pi_{g',0}$. Suppose that $\pi_{g,t} \lhd \pi_{g',t}$. Let ϕ denote the density function of $\mathcal{N}(0, 1)$ distribution. For any $c \geq 0$ and any a, we write $\Gamma = [-c, c]$ and $\Gamma - a = [-c - a, c - a]$. Then,

$$\pi_{g,t+1}(\Gamma) = \int_\Gamma \int_\mathbf{R} \phi(z - T_g(x))\pi_{g,t}(dx)\,dz$$

$$= \int_\mathbf{R} \int_\Gamma \phi(g - T_g(x))\,dz\pi_{g,t}(dx)$$

$$= \int_\mathbf{R} \int_{\Gamma - T_g(x)} \phi(z)\,dz\pi_{g,t}(dx)$$

$$\geq \int_\mathbf{R} \int_{\Gamma - T_{g'}(x)} \phi(z)\,dz\pi_{g,t}(dx)$$

$$= \int_\mathbf{R} \int_\Gamma \phi(z - T_{g'}(x))\,dz\pi_{g,t}(dx)$$

$$\geq \int_\mathbf{R} \int_\Gamma \phi(z - T_{g'}(x))\,dz\pi_{g',t}(dx)$$

$$= \pi_{g',t+1}(\Gamma).$$

The second equality is obtained by using Fubini's theorem. The first inequality follows from the symmetry and the unimodality of ϕ at 0. The last inequality follows from the inductive hypothesis and the positivity of the integral w.r.t. z. □ ¶¶

The above result may be further extended. First, for any two functions f and g, we say that $f \overset{a}{\leq} g$ iff $|f(x)| \leq |g(x)|$, $\forall x \in \mathbf{R}$. The relation $\overset{a}{\leq}$ defines a *pre-order of functions* on $\mathbf{R}$. Consider a family of stationary NLAR(1) models

$$X_t = T_\theta(X_{t-1}) + \varepsilon_t \tag{4.169}$$

where ε_t are i.i.d. random variables with zero mean and a symmetric and unimodal density. Let π_θ denote the stationary distribution of X_t when θ is the parameter. The general result may be stated in the form of the following theorem.

Theorem 4.12: Under the above set-up in (4.169), if $\theta_1 \leq \theta_2 \Rightarrow T_{\theta_1} \overset{a}{\leq} T_{\theta_2}$, then $\theta_1 \leq \theta_2 \Rightarrow \pi_{\theta_1} \lhd \pi_{\theta_2}$.

Proof. A slight modification of that given in Example 4.13 will do. Details are available in Högnäs (1986). □

Remark 4.6: It is fairly clear from the discussion in Example 4.13 that, for $T_g \overset{a}{\leq} T_{g'}$, if $\pi_{g',t} \to \pi_{g'}$ in distribution as $t \to \infty$ then $\pi_{g,t} \to \pi_g$ in distribution as $t \to \infty$. Thus, if model (4.167) with the skeleton defined by $T_{g'}$ is stationary then so is that with the skeleton defined by $T_g(\overset{a}{\leq} T_{g'})$, provided ε_t has a symmetric and unimodal density with zero mean. In this case, all absolute moments w.r.t. π_g are smaller than those w.r.t. $\pi_{g'}$.

4.2.13 CONVERGENCE OF STAR TO SETAR

An associated problem is the convergence of the STAR model to the SETAR model as the scale parameter tends to zero. Specifically, we consider the SETAR $(2, k, k)$ model

$$X_t = a_0 + \sum_{j=1}^{k} a_j X_{t-j} + \left(b_0 + \sum_{j=1}^{k} b_j X_{t-j}\right) I_r(X_{t-d}) + \varepsilon_t \quad (4.170)$$

of eqn (3.25) and the STAR$(2; k, k)$ model where $I_r(x)$ is replaced by $F((x-r)/\delta)$, F being the standard Gaussian distribution, namely

$$X_{t,\delta} = a_0 + \sum_{j=1}^{k} a_j X_{t-j} + \left(b_0 + \sum_{j=1}^{k} b_j X_{t-j}\right) F\left(\frac{X_{t-d}+r}{\delta}\right) + \varepsilon_t. \quad (4.171)$$

Theorem 4.13: Suppose that the distribution of ε_t is absolutely continuous with a bounded and uniformly continuous density function ϕ. Suppose that either (i) $k = 1$, $d = 1$, $a_1 < 1$, $a_1 + b_1 < 1$, and $a_1(a_1 + b_1) < 1$, or (ii) $\sup_{0 \leq \theta \leq 1} (\sum_{j=1}^{k} |a_j + \theta b_j|) < 1$ holds. Then, for each $\delta \geq 0$, the stationary distribution of $\{X_{t,\delta}\}$ is absolutely continuous with density function denoted by g_δ. Moreover, $g_\delta(y)$ is continuous in y, uniformly bounded, and equicontinuous over δ. Also, $g_\delta \to g_0$, the stationary density of $\{X_t\}$, everywhere as $\delta \to 0$.

(Note: $g_\delta(y)$ is equicontinuous over δ if to each $\varepsilon > 0 \exists \eta > 0$ s.t. $|y' - y''| < \eta \Rightarrow |g_\delta(y') - g_\delta(y'')| < \varepsilon \ \forall \delta$.)

¶ Proof: For simplicity, assume $k = 1$. Let μ_δ be the stationary distribution for $\{X_{t,\delta}\}$. Hence, for any measurable set K,

$$\mu_\delta(K) = \int_{\mathbb{R}} \int_{K} \phi(y - T_\delta(x)) \, dy \mu_\delta(dx)$$

$$\Rightarrow \mu_\delta(K) = \int_{K} \int_{\mathbb{R}} \phi(y - T_\delta(x)) \mu_\delta(dx) \, dy.$$

Here,

$$T_\delta(x) = a_0 + a_1 x + (b_0 + b_1 x) F\left(\frac{x-r}{\delta}\right).$$

Thus, μ_δ is absolutely continuous with density function

$$g_\delta(y) = \int_{\mathbf{R}} \phi(y - T_\delta(x))\mu_\delta(dx)$$

$$= \int_{\mathbf{R}} \phi(y - T_\delta(x))g_\delta(x)\,dx.$$

Therefore $g_\delta(.)$ is uniformly bounded over δ. As ϕ is uniformly continuous, $g_\delta(.)$ is equicontinuous over δ. Let δ_n be a sequence converging to zero. It follows from Theorem 3 of Feller (1966, p. 263) that there exists a subsequence δ_{n_k} (written as δ_k hereafter) such that g_{δ_k} converges to a continuous limit g. The convergence is uniform in every finite interval. Suppose $\exists \eta > 0$ s.t. $\forall \varepsilon > 0$ $\exists H > 0$ s.t.

$$1 \geq \int_{-H}^{H} g_\delta(y)\,dy \geq 1 - \varepsilon, \quad \forall 0 < \delta < \eta. \tag{4.172}$$

Then

$$1 \geq \int_{-H}^{H} g(y)\,dy = \lim_{k \to \infty} \int_{-H}^{H} g_{\delta_k}(y)\,dy \geq 1 - \varepsilon.$$

As $g(.)$ is non-negative and ε arbitrary,

$$\int g(y)\,dy = 1.$$

It may be similarly shown that

$$g(y) = \int \phi(y - T_0(x))g(y)\,dx.$$

It follows from the unicity of the stationary distribution of $\{X_{t,0}\}$ that $g = g_0$. As each sequence $\{\delta_n\}$ converging to zero has a subsequence δ_{n_k} such that $g_{\delta_{n_k}} \to g_0$ everywhere, therefore $g_\delta(.) \to g_0(.)$ everywhere as $\delta \to 0$.

It remains to prove (4.172). Under condition (i) of the theorem, $\exists 0 < \theta < 1$, $\alpha, \beta > 0$, $\eta > 0$, and

$$p(x) = \begin{cases} ax & x > 0 \\ \beta |x| & x \leq 0 \end{cases}$$

such that

$$p(T_\delta(x)) \leq \theta p(x)$$

uniformly for sufficiently large $|x|$ when $0 \leq \delta < \eta$. (Note that if $-1 < a_1$,

$a_1 + b_1 < 1$, then $p(x)$ may be chosen to be $|x|$.) Hence $\exists M > 0$ s.t.

$$p(T_\delta(x)) \leq \theta p(x) + M, \quad \forall x. \tag{4.173}$$

$p(.)$ may also be interpreted as follows:

$$p(x) = \inf\{\lambda \geq 0 : x \in \lambda(-\beta^{-1}, \alpha^{-1})\}$$

where $\lambda K = \{\lambda x : x \in K\}$, $K \subseteq \mathbf{R}$. As $(-\beta^{-1}, \alpha^{-1})$ is a convex set, $p(.)$ has the following properties:

(1) $\qquad\qquad p(cx) = cp(x), \qquad c > 0, \qquad x \in \mathbf{R}$

(2) $\qquad\qquad p(x + y) \leq p(x) + p(y), \qquad x, y \in \mathbf{R}.$

Thus

$$\begin{aligned}
p(X_{t+1,\delta}) &= p(T(X_{t,\delta}) + \varepsilon_{t+1}) \\
&\leq p(T_\delta(X_{t,\delta}) + p(\varepsilon_{t+1}) \\
&\leq \theta p(X_{t,\delta}) + M + p(\varepsilon_{t+1}). \tag{4.174}
\end{aligned}$$

Define $Y_{t+1} = \theta Y_t + \gamma_{t+1}$, where $\gamma_{t+1} = M + p(\varepsilon_{t+1})$. Then $\{Y_t\}$ has the unique stationary distribution which is the distribution of $\gamma_t + \theta\gamma_{t-1} + \theta^2\gamma_{t-2} + \ldots$ with $[M/(1-\theta), +\infty)$ as the state space. It is easily seen that Y_t and $X_{t,\delta}$ tend to their stationary distributions geometrically fast regardless of their starting distributions. Suppose $Y_0 = X_{0,\delta}$. It follows from (4.174) that, given the same ε_t, $p(X_{t,\delta}) \leq Y_t$. Hence

$$\int_{-H}^{H} g_\delta(x) \, dx \geq \Pr(Y_\infty \leq \min(p(H), p(-H)))$$

where Y_∞ denotes a random variable having the stationary distribution of Y_t. Evidently, the right-hand side of the inequality tends to unity as H tens to infinite; therefore (4.171) is established.

For the case where $k > 1$ and the condition (ii) of the theorem holds, we briefly mention some necessary changes to enable the above idea to go through. First, we appropriately augment the state vector so that the set-up becomes Markov. Next, we make use of the following invariant equation

$$\mu_\delta(K) = \int_{\mathbf{R}^m} P_\delta^m(y, K)\mu_\delta(dy)$$

and (2.2) of Chan and Tong (1985) to show that all of the reasonable properties of the invariant densities listed above still hold. Here, $P_z^m(y, K)$ is the mth step transition probability. Under condition (ii) a convex set may be found so as to define a $p(.)$ s.t. (4.173) holds. □¶¶

Remark 4.7: The Gaussian assumption for the function F in the STAR model (4.171) is not essential for the proof of the above theorem. In fact, it suffices to have any sufficiently smooth function with a derivative which has a rapidly decaying tail. The argument can also be extended to more than one threshold.

4.3 Predictor space and Markovian representation

A most fundamental concept in dynamical systems is the notion of a *state* (or a *state variable*). It is an abstract notion. Loosely speaking, it represents the most efficient condensation of information contained in the past and present about the future. Ingrained in the study is the assumption of 'finiteness' of the representation—this may be called the *hypothesis of finiteness*. It turns out that these ideas may be given a precise and *concrete* description in stochastic dynamical systems. The key is the introduction of an appropriate *predictor space*.

4.3.1 THE LINEAR CASE

The class of stationary ARMA models has an elegant and fundamental geometric characterization in terms of the concepts of a *predictor space* and a *Markovian representation* introduced by Akaike (1974a). These concepts are rooted in control systems theory. ¶ We describe the univariate specialization of his results. Without loss of generality, we consider the ARMA model of (1.7) and assume that $a_0 = 0$. A mean deletion will achieve this. Let Condition A of §1.3 hold. In Akaike's original discussion, Condition B is relaxed so that the ε_t are only assumed to be uncorrelated with zero mean and finite variance and are not necessarily Gaussian. We shall follow Akaike's relaxation in this section. Loosely speaking, we shall show that an ARMA model is a 'natural' choice if and only if the amount of information about the future that is extractable from the present and past data is, in some sense, *finite*. Under condition A, an ARMA(k, l) model for $\{X_t\}$ implies the linear representation

$$X_t = \sum_{s=0}^{\infty} W_s \varepsilon_{t-s} \qquad (4.175)$$

with $W_0 = 1$ and $\varepsilon_t = X_t - X_{t\,|\,t-1}$, where $X_{t\,|\,t-1}$ is the linear least-squares predictor of X_t in terms of $X_{t-1}, X_{t-2}, \dots$. The term ε_t is called the *innovation* at time t. Let $R(X_1, X_2, \dots)$ denote the closure, in the sense of mean square, of the linear space of finite linear combinations of the random variables $X_1, X_2, \dots$. It is called the space spanned by

$X_1, X_2, \ldots$. Now, $X_{t|t-1}$ is then a projection (in the mean-square sense) of X_t on $R(X_{t-1}, X_{t-2}, \ldots)$. Let $\varepsilon_{s|t}$ denote the projection of ε_s on $R(X_t, X_{t-1}, \ldots)$. Then, on using the ARMA model, with $a_0 = 0$ and $b_0 = 1$, $X_{t+i|t}$ satisfies the relation

$$X_{t+i|t} = \sum_{j=1}^{k} a_j X_{t+i-j|t} + \sum_{j=1}^{l} b_j \varepsilon_{t+i-j|t} \tag{4.176}$$

where $X_{t+h|t} = X_{t+h}$ for $h = 0, -1, \ldots$ and $\varepsilon_{t+h|t} = 0$ for $h = 1, 2, \ldots$. For $i \geq l + 1$,

$$X_{t+i|t} = \sum_{j=1}^{k} a_j X_{t+i-j|t}. \tag{4.177}$$

Thus, $X_{t+i|t}$ $(i = 0, 1, \ldots)$ can be expressed as linear transforms of $X_{t|t}$, $X_{t+1|t}, \ldots, X_{t+K-1|t}$, where $K = \max(k, l + 1)$, and

$$R(X_{t|t}, X_{t+1|t}, \ldots) = R(X_{t|t}, X_{t+1|t}, \ldots, X_{t+K-1|t}) \tag{4.178}$$

which implies that the linear space on the left of (4.178) (to be called the *predictor space*) is *finite-dimensional*. In particular, it holds that

$$X_{t+K|t} = \sum_{j=1}^{K} a_j X_{t+K-j|t} \tag{4.179}$$

where by definition $a_m = 0$ for $m = k + 1, k + 2, \ldots, K$. From (4.175),

$$X_{t+i+1|t+1} = X_{t+i+1|t} + W_i \varepsilon_{t+1}. \tag{4.180}$$

From (4.179) and (4.180), it follows that the vector $\mathbf{v}_t = (X_{t|t}, X_{t+1|t}, \ldots, X_{t+K-1|t})'$ admits a representation of the form

$$\mathbf{v}_{t+1} = \begin{bmatrix} 0 & 1 & 0 & \cdots & 0 \\ 0 & 0 & 1 & \cdots & 0 \\ \vdots & \vdots & \vdots & \cdots & \vdots \\ 0 & 0 & 0 & \cdots & 1 \\ a_K & a_{K-1} & a_{K-2} & \cdots & a_1 \end{bmatrix} \mathbf{v}_t + \begin{bmatrix} W_0 \\ W_1 \\ \vdots \\ W_{K-2} \\ W_{K-1} \end{bmatrix} \varepsilon_{t+1} \tag{4.181}$$

$$X_t = (1 \quad 0 \quad \cdots \quad 0)\mathbf{v}_t. \quad \P\P$$

The eqn (4.181) is called a *Markovian representation*. What we have just shown is that an ARMA model always has a Markovian representation. The vector $\mathbf{v}_t$ is called the *state vector at time* t; being a function of $X_t, X_{t-1}, \ldots$, it is an *observable* random vector at time t (the present) and represents the most efficient condensation of (linear) information from the present and past, such that the future evolution of the system can be completely described by the knowledge of the present state and the future input (i.e. $\varepsilon_{t+1}, \varepsilon_{t+2}, \ldots$). The dimension (namely K) of the state vector is *unique* and *minimal*. Beyond this, the state vector is not uniquely defined, since any basis of the predictor space will do. However, one basis is transformed to another by a non-singular transformation. Therefore, *the state vector is unique up to a non-singular transformation.*

Conversely, we may prove that a Markovian representation implies an ARMA representation. ¶ Specifically, suppose that the stationary Gaussian $\{X_t\}$ has a Markovian representation

$$\mathbf{v}_{t+1} = \mathbf{A}\mathbf{v}_t + \mathbf{B}\varepsilon_{t+1} \qquad X_t = \mathbf{C}\mathbf{v}_t \qquad (4.182)$$

where it is assumed that $\mathbf{v}_t$ is a $p \times 1$ state vector, $\mathbf{A}$ is a $p \times p$ matrix, $\mathbf{B}$ is a $p \times 1$ matrix, $\mathbf{C}$ is a $1 \times p$ matrix, and ε_t is the innovation of X_t, that is $X_t - X_{t\,|\,t-1}$. Writing the characteristic polynomial of $\mathbf{A}$ in the form

$$\det(\lambda\mathbf{I} - \mathbf{A}) = \lambda^p + \sum_{m=1}^{p} a_m \lambda^{p-m} \qquad (4.183)$$

we have, by the Cayley–Hamilton theorem (see e.g. Birkhoff and MacLane 1953, p. 320),

$$\mathbf{A}^p + \sum_{m=1}^{p} a_m \mathbf{A}^{p-m} = \mathbf{0}. \qquad (4.184)$$

From (4.182),

$$\mathbf{v}_{t+i} = \mathbf{A}^i \mathbf{v}_t + \mathbf{A}^{i-1}\mathbf{B}\varepsilon_{t+1} + \ldots + \mathbf{I}\mathbf{B}\varepsilon_{t+i}, \quad i = 1, 2, \ldots \qquad (4.185)$$

and it follows that

$$(0): \mathbf{v}_{t+p} = \mathbf{A}^p \mathbf{v}_t + \mathbf{A}^{p-1}\mathbf{B}\varepsilon_{t+1} + \mathbf{A}^{p-2}\mathbf{B}\varepsilon_{t+2} + \ldots + \mathbf{A}\mathbf{B}\varepsilon_{t+p-1} + \mathbf{I}\mathbf{B}\varepsilon_{t+p}$$

$$(1): \mathbf{v}_{v+p-1} = \mathbf{A}^{p-1}\mathbf{v}_t + \mathbf{A}^{p-2}\mathbf{B}\varepsilon_{t+1} + \mathbf{A}^{p-3}\mathbf{B}\varepsilon_{t+2} + \ldots + \mathbf{I}\mathbf{B}\varepsilon_{t+p-1}$$

$$\vdots$$

$$(p-1): \mathbf{v}_{t+1} = \mathbf{A}\mathbf{v}_t + \mathbf{I}\mathbf{B}\varepsilon_{t+1}$$

$$(p): \mathbf{v}_t = \mathbf{I}\mathbf{v}_t.$$

Premultiplying eqn (m) by $a_m\mathbf{C}$, $m = 0, 1, 2, \ldots, p$, $(a_0 = 1)$, and then adding, we have (on using (4.184))

$$X_{t+p} + a_1 X_{t+p-1} + \ldots + a_p X_t$$
$$= C_{p-1}\varepsilon_{t+1} + C_{p-2}\varepsilon_{t+2} + \ldots + C_1\varepsilon_{t+p-1} + \varepsilon_{t+p} \qquad (4.186)$$

where $C_i = \mathbf{C}(\mathbf{A}^i + a_1\mathbf{A}^{i-1} + \ldots + a_i\mathbf{I})\mathbf{B}$. Thus, every stationary time series with the Markovian representation (4.182) also has an ARMA representation (4.186). ¶¶

Thus, theoretically, there is not distinction between the Markovian and the ARMA representations of a stationary Gaussian time series. However, in practice it often seems a matter of convenience as to which representation is to be used.

Let $V_t = R(X_{t|t}, X_{t+1|t}, \ldots)$. It is called the *predictor space of a stationary time series* $\{X_t\}$ *at time t.* It has the intuitive interpretation as the totality of information extractable from the present and past data about the future. ¶ Clearly, from the above analysis, if $\{X_t\} \sim$ ARMA, V_t is finite-dimensional with a dimension independent of t by stationarity. Conversely, suppose that the dimension of V_t is $q < \infty$, which will be independent of t by stationarity. Let $\mathbf{v}_t$ be a $q \times 1$ vector whose components form a basis for V_t. By a similar argument, we may obtain $\mathbf{v}_{t+1}$. Let $\mathbf{A}\mathbf{v}_t$ denote the projection of $\mathbf{v}_{t+1}$ onto V_t, where $\mathbf{A}$ is a $q \times q$ matrix of constants independent of t by stationarity. Since components of $\mathbf{v}_{t+1}$ and $\mathbf{v}_t$ are elements of $R(X_{t+1}, X_t, X_{t-1}, \ldots,)$, say M_{t+1}, therefore we may write

$$\mathbf{v}_{t+1} = \mathbf{A}\mathbf{v}_t + \mathbf{W}_{t+1} \tag{4.187}$$

where the components of $\mathbf{W}_{t+1}$ are elements of M_{t+1}, whose projection onto M_t is zero, that is there is a $q \times 1$ vector $\mathbf{G}$ such that

$$\mathbf{W}_{t+1} = \mathbf{G}\varepsilon_{t+1} \tag{4.188}$$

where

$$\varepsilon_{t+1} = X_{t+1} - X_{t+1|t}. \tag{4.189}$$

Therefore eqn (4.187) becomes

$$\mathbf{v}_{t+1} = \mathbf{A}\mathbf{v}_t + \mathbf{G}\varepsilon_{t+1}. \tag{4.190}$$

Also, $X_t = X_{t|t} \in V_t$ implies that

$$X_t = \mathbf{H}\mathbf{v}_t. \quad ¶¶ \tag{4.191}$$

Hence, we have proved that the finiteness of the dimension of the predictor space V_t implies that $\{X_t\}$ admits a Markovian representation and thus, equivalently, an ARMA representation.

Summarizing the above results, we may conclude that *a stationary time series has a stationary ARMA representation if and only if its predictor space is finite-dimensional.*

4.3.2   THE BILINEAR CASE

This subsection may be skipped on first reading.

Let $\{X_t\}$ be a zero-mean (strictly) stationary time series with finite second-order moments. First, we need to extend the space $R(X_t, X_{t-1}, \ldots)$. Let H_t be the space of all square integrable random variables measurable w.r.t. the σ-algebra $\mathbb{B}_t$ generated by $X_t, X_{t-1}, \ldots$. Let $Y(s \mid H_t)$ denote the conditional expectation $E(Y_s \mid \mathbb{B}_t)$. It is the least-squares predictor of Y_s based on $X_t, X_{t-1}, \ldots$, that is it is that element of H_t which is the closest to Y_s in mean squares. If Y_s is a random (column) vector with components $Y_s(i)$, then $Y(s \mid H_t)$ is a random (column) vector with components $E(Y_s(i) \mid \mathbb{B}_t)$. Let $\mathcal{P}_t$ denote $R(X(t+1 \mid h_t), X(t+2 \mid H_t), \ldots)$, the closed subspace of H_t spanned by $X(t+1 \mid H_t), X(t+2 \mid H_t), \ldots$. We call $\mathcal{P}_t$ the predictor space. Note that unlike the linear case, it is technically more convenient to exclude $X(t \mid H_t)$, that is X_t, in the spanning set of $\mathcal{P}_t$.

We introduce assumptions A0, A1, and A2.

A0: The predictor space, $\mathcal{P}_t$, has finite dimension: Under this assumption we may let $\xi_t(1), \xi_t(2), \ldots, \xi_t(n)$ denote a basis of $\mathcal{P}_t$, where n is the dimension of $\mathcal{P}_t$. Let $\mathbf{\xi}_t = (\xi_t(1), \xi_t(2), \ldots, \xi_t(n))^T$. We have then

$$X(t \mid H_{t-1}) = \mathbf{H}\mathbf{\xi}_{t-1} \tag{4.192}$$

and

$$\mathbf{\xi}(t \mid H_{t-1}) = \mathbf{A}\mathbf{\xi}_{t-1} \tag{4.193}$$

for some row vector $\mathbf{H}$ and some matrix $\mathbf{A}$. Let

$$\varepsilon_t = X_t - X(t \mid H_{t-1}), \tag{4.194}$$

which is called the innovation. Unlike the linear case in general $\exists$ a column vector $\mathbf{Y}_{t-1}$ s.t.

$$\mathbf{\xi}_t - \mathbf{\xi}(t \mid H_{t-1}) = \varepsilon_t \mathbf{Y}_{t-1} \tag{4.195}$$

(cf. eqns (4.190) and (4.191)). Roughly speaking, we have lost the orthogonality of (4.175), which facilitates projection of a projection. Nevertheless, components of $\mathbf{\xi}_t - \mathbf{\xi}(t \mid H_{t-1})$ belong to the closed subspace, I_t, of H_t spanned by $X(t+k \mid H_t) - X(t+k \mid H_{t-1})$, $k = 1, 2, \ldots$. We call I_t the innovation space. All elements of I_t are uncorrelated with all elements of H_{t-1}.

A1: Each element of I_t can be expressed as

$$\varepsilon_t Y_{t-1}(i) + c\varepsilon_t + d(\varepsilon_t^2 - \sigma^2), \quad \text{some } i$$

where $Y_{t-1}(i)$ is the ith component of $\mathbf{Y}_{t-1}$ which spans some subspace I_{t-1}^0 of H_{t-1}, c and d are constants, and $\sigma^2 = E[\varepsilon_t^2 \mid \mathbb{B}_{t-1}]$, which is assumed constant.

A2: The space I_t^0 of assumption A1 is contained in $\mathcal{P}_t$: Note that the somewhat unexpected quadratic term $d\varepsilon_t^2$ in A1 turns out to be needed in a Markovian representation of the bilinear models. Subtracting $d\sigma^2$ from it ensures that elements of I_t have zero mean. Note also that each element of I_t as expressed in A1 is uncorrelated with those in H_{t-1} as required. Sometimes a weaker assumption than A2 is more useful. We list this in A2'.

A2': The space I_t^0 of assumption A1 is contained in the space $\mathcal{P}_t(m)$ for some $m \geq 0$, where $\mathcal{P}_t(m)$ denotes the space spanned by $\mathcal{P}_t$ and $X_t, \ldots, X_{t-m+1}$.

Definition 4.4: By a *bilinear Markovian representation* of a stationary time series $\{X_t\}$ we mean the representation

$$\xi_t = \mathbf{A}\xi_{t-1} + \mathbf{B}\xi_{t-1}\varepsilon_t + \mathbf{c}\varepsilon_t + \mathbf{d}(\varepsilon_t^2 - \sigma^2)$$
$$X_t = \mathbf{H}\xi_{t-1} + \varepsilon_t \tag{4.196}$$

where ξ_t is an n-dimensional column vector, $\mathbf{A}$ and $\mathbf{B}$ are $n \times n$ matrices, $\mathbf{c}$, $\mathbf{d}$, and $\mathbf{H}^T$ are n-dimensional column vectors, and $\{\varepsilon_t\}$ is a sequence of random variables s.t.

$$\mathrm{E}[\varepsilon_t \mid \xi_{t-1}, \xi_{t-2}, \ldots] = 0 \qquad \mathrm{E}[\varepsilon_t^2 \mid \xi_{t-1}, \xi_{t-2}, \ldots] = \sigma^2.$$

Theorem 4.14: If $\{X_t\}$ admits the bilinear Markovian representation (4.196) then it satisfies A0.

Proof. Trivial. □

Definition 4.5: A representation of $\{X_t\}$ of the form (4.196) is said to be *state invertible** if $\xi_t(j) \in H_t$ for each j. (This should not be confused with the notion of *invertibility* to be introduced in §5.4.)

Clearly for the linear case in the representation (4.181), elements of $\mathbf{v}_t \in H_t$.

Theorem 4.15: If $\{X_t\}$ admits the bilinear Markovian representation (4.196) which is state invertible then it satisfies A1.

Proof. By direct evaluation. □

Following the same arguments as the penultimate paragraph of §4.3.1, we may prove the following theorem.

Theorem 4.16: If a stationary time series $\{X_t\}$ satisfies assumptions A0, A1, and A2, then it admits a bilinear Markovian representation of the form (4.196) and ξ_t is then called a *state vector.·*

Remark 4.8: Owing to the technical requirements/restrictions of A1 and A2, Theorem 4.16 might appear to look not so elegant as the corresponding result in the linear case. However, no 'easy' characterization may be expected of the non-linear case! In a sense, the technical requirements of A1 and A2 merely focus on the specific type of non-linearity (in this case it is bilinearity) and this is necessary if we are to get anywhere. It is remarkable that the notion of a predictor space, which is after all only a *linear* notion because the predictor space is a linear space, still serves us well in a particular class of non-linear times series models. Normally we cannot expect to be as fortunate if we turn to some other types of non-linearity except in special circumstances (c.f. Exercise 20).

---

* Pham Dinh Tuan (1985) has used the term *invertible* for this.

Remark 4.9: The conclusion of Theorem 4.16 still holds if A2 is replaced by A2'.

Remark 4.10: Because $\{X_t\}$ admitting the bilinear representation (4.196) does not imply that it satisfies A2 or A2', therefore the class of time series admitting the bilinear Markovian representation (4.196) is larger than the class of time series satisfying assumptions A0, A1, and A2'.

Remark 4.11. Unlike the linear case, it is not guaranteed that the choice of the components of ξ_t as elements of a basis of $\mathscr{P}_t(m)$ would lead to a *minimal* state-invertible representation. However, under some technical conditions, n is the *minimal dimension*. Specifically, suppose that

$$\xi_t = \sum_{j=0}^{\infty} [\mathbf{A} + \mathbf{B}\varepsilon_t] \ldots [\mathbf{A} + \mathbf{B}\varepsilon_{t-j}][\mathbf{c}\varepsilon_{t-j} + \mathbf{d}\varepsilon_{t-j}^2 - \sigma^2]$$

in the mean squares sense and almost surely. Let $\mathbf{Q}_0 = 0$,

$$\mathbf{Q}_{k+1} = \mathbf{A}\mathbf{Q}_k\mathbf{A}^T + \mathbf{B}\mathbf{Q}_k\mathbf{B}^T\sigma^2 + \Sigma$$

define a convergent sequence, where Σ denotes the covariance matrix of $\mathbf{c}\varepsilon_t + \mathbf{d}\varepsilon_t^2$. Let $\mathbf{P}_k$ be defined by $\mathbf{P}_0 = 0$, $\mathbf{P}_{k+1} = \mathbf{A}^T\mathbf{P}_k\mathbf{A} + \mathbf{B}^T\mathbf{P}_k\mathbf{B}\sigma^2 + \mathbf{H}^T\mathbf{H}$, and $\mathbf{C}_k$ and $\mathbf{0}_k$ be respectively the matrices formed by the columns of $\mathbf{A}^{n_1}\mathbf{B}^{m_1}\ldots\mathbf{A}^{n_r}\mathbf{B}^{m_r}\Sigma$ and by the rows of $\mathbf{H}\mathbf{A}^{n_1}\mathbf{B}^{m_1}\ldots\mathbf{A}^{n_r}\mathbf{B}^{m_r}$, where $n_1, m_1, \ldots, n_r, m_r$ are non-negative integers with $\Sigma(n_i + m_i) \leq k$. Let the representation (4.196) be state invertible. Then it is minimal if and only if (B) and (C) hold, where (B) is one of the following equivalent conditions:

(B1) $\mathbf{Q}_k$ is non-singular for some $k \leq n$;

(B2): $\mathbf{C}_k$ is of rank n for some $k \leq n$;

and (C) is one of the following equivalent conditions:

(C1): $\mathbf{P}_k$ is non-singular for some $k \leq n$;

(C2): $\mathbf{0}_k$ is of rank n for some $k \leq n$.

Remark 4.12: In Example 4.6 we have seen how a Markovian bilinear model (sometimes also called a subdiagonal bilinear model) may be expressed in a bilinear Markovian representation of the form (4.196).

Remark 4.13: The general bilinear model (4.55) admits a Markovian representation but with a very high-dimensional state vector (Pham Dinh Tuan 1986).

4.3.3   THE GENERAL NON-LINEAR CASE

This is an uncharted area.

For many of the non-linear time series models, it is doubtful that the predictor space will remain *finite*-dimensional. For example, consider an

NLAR(1),

$$X_t = f(X_{t-1}) + \varepsilon_t \qquad (4.197)$$

$\varepsilon_t \sim \mathcal{N}(0, 1)$ say. It is inconceivable that $E[X_{t+j} \mid \mathbb{B}_t]$, where $\mathbb{B}_t$ is the σ-algebra generated by X_s, $s \leq t$, may be expressed as a *linear* combination of $E[X_{t+j-i} \mid \mathbb{B}_t]$, $i = 1, 2, \ldots K$, for some finite K (or even infinite K). However, intuitively it seems desirable to retain the finiteness hypothesis. We *speculate* or *conjecture* that one way out would be to remove the linearity of the predictor space by allowing $E[X_{t+j} \mid \mathbb{B}_t]$ to be expressible in terms of a continuous (not necessarily linear) function of some $\xi_t(1), \ldots, \xi_t(m)$, the 'coordinate functions', for some $m \leq \infty$. With luck, m may be finite.

4.4 Time reversibility

We have given the intuitive meaning of time reversibility in Chapter 1. In this section, we shall develop the idea more systematically.

4.4.1 DEFINITION

A formal definition for *time reversibility* of a stationary time series may be given as follows.

Definition 4.6: A stationary time series $\{X_t\}$ is *time reversible* if for every positive integer n, and every $t_1, t_2, \ldots, t_n \in \mathbf{Z}$, the vectors $(X_{t_1}, X_{t_2}, \ldots, X_{t_n})$ and $(X_{-t_1}, X_{-t_2}, \ldots, X_{-t_n})$ have the same joint distributions.

A stationary time series which is not time reversible is said to be *time irreversible*.

Let $\{X_t\}$ be a time series which is transformed instantaneously to another time series $\{Y_t\}$ by

$$Y_t = g(X_t), \quad \text{for each } t \qquad (4.198)$$

where g is a 1–1 function. Note that we may transform the time series $\{X_t\}$ which is stationary with marginal distribution H to another stationary time series $\{Y_t\}$ with a specified marginal distribution f if there exists a 1–1 function g satisfying

$$F(g(x)) = H(x), \qquad \forall x \in R.$$

Now, it is obvious that $\{Y_t\}$ is stationary and time reversible if and only if $\{X_t\}$ is stationary and time reversible. Thus, *it would be inappropriate to fit (Gaussian) ARMA models to time-irreversible data even after applying a 1–1 instantaneous transformation g*. The point is that whilst a 1–1 instantaneous transformation can often produce marginal distributions to our specification, this is not true with joint distributions.

Obviously a stationary linear Gaussian model is time reversible because the covariance functions of Gaussian distributions are symmetrical. In particular, a Gaussian ARMA model is time reversible. It would be interesting to study the converse.

4.4.2   CONVERSE RESULTS IN THE LINEAR CASE

We shall need the following theorem.

Theorem 4.17: Suppose that $\{X_t\}$ is a non-Gaussian, stationary*, zero-mean time series with the moment property. Suppose that the spectral density function of $\{X_t\}$ is positive almost everywhere. Then $\{X_t\}$ can have at most one mean square convergent bilateral linear representation of the form

$$X_t = \sum_{j=-\infty}^{\infty} c_j \varepsilon_{t-j} \qquad (4.199)$$

where $\{\varepsilon_t\}$ is a sequence of i.i.d. random variables with zero mean and possessing the moment property, ignoring changes of scale and shifts in the time origin of the sequence ε_t.

Proof. We prove by contradiction. Suppose that there is another mean square convergent representation

$$X_t = \sum_{j=-\infty}^{\infty} c_j' \varepsilon_{t-j}' \qquad (4.200)$$

essentially different from (4.199). By the assumption on the spectral density function of $\{X_t\}$, we can invert (4.200) and use (4.199) to obtain the representation

$$\varepsilon_t' = \sum_{j=-\infty}^{\infty} d_j \varepsilon_{t-j} \qquad (4.201)$$

where d_j is the coefficient of $\exp(-ij\omega)$ in the series expansion of the function $\Sigma\, c_j \exp(-ij\omega)/\Sigma c_j' \exp(-ij\omega)$. Because the function has constant squared modulus of $E(\varepsilon_t'^2)/E(\varepsilon_t^2)$, therefore $\Sigma\, |d_j|^2 < \infty$ and $\Sigma\, |d_j|^r < \infty$ for any $r \ge 3$. By assumption, (4.199) and (4.200) are essentially different. It follows that at least two coefficients in (4.201) are non-zero, that is

$$\sup_{-\infty < j < \infty} |d_j d_{j+h}| \ne 0 \qquad (4.202)$$

for some $h \ne 0$.

---

* As usual this means strictly stationary in this book.

From (4.201), using standard properties of cumulants (Brillinger 1975, p. 19), and using Parseval's formula, we calculate that

$$\text{cum}(\varepsilon_t', \underbrace{\varepsilon_{t+h}', \ldots, \varepsilon_{t+h}'}_{r-2 \text{ of them}}, \varepsilon_{t+m}')$$

$$= K_r \sum_{j=-\infty}^{\infty} d_j d_{j+h}^{r-2} d_{j+m}$$

$$= \frac{K_r}{2\pi} \int_{-\pi}^{\pi} \left(\sum_{j=-\infty}^{\infty} d_j d_{j+h}^{r-2} e^{ij\omega} \right)^* \left(\sum_{j=-\infty}^{\infty} d_{j+m} e^{ij\omega} \right) d\omega$$

$$= \frac{K_r}{2\pi} \int_{-\pi}^{\pi} e^{-im\omega} \left[\left(\sum_{j=-\infty}^{\infty} d_j d_{j+h}^{r-2} e^{ij\omega} \right)^* \left(\sum_{j=-\infty}^{\infty} d_j e^{ij\omega} \right) \right] d\omega \quad (4.203)$$

where the asterisk indicates the complex conjugate and K_r is the rth cumulant of ε_t. Since $\Sigma d_j \exp(ij\omega) \neq 0$ almost everywhere, it follows from (4.202) that the function in square brackets in (4.203) cannot be zero almost everywhere. As a result, for every $r \geq 3$, $\exists m$ s.t. the integral of (4.203) is not zero. However, for $r \geq 3$ and $h \neq 0$,

$$\text{cum}(\varepsilon_t', \underbrace{\varepsilon_{t+h}', \ldots, \varepsilon_{t+h}'}_{(r-2) \text{ of them}}, \varepsilon_{t+m}') = 0$$

for any choice of m because ε_t' and ε_{t+h}' are independent. Hence $K_r \equiv 0$ for $r \geq 3$, which implies by (4.199) that the rth cumulant of X_t is zero for all $r \geq 3$. This implies that $\{X_t\}$ must be Gaussian. This contradicts the hypothesis of the theorem. $\square$

This theorem enables us to show that a time-reversible non-Gaussian bilateral linear representation imposes symmetric or skew-symmetric constraints on the coefficients.

Corollary 4.1: Let $\{X_t\}$ be a time series satisfying the conditions of Theorem 4.17. If $\{X_t\}$ is time reversible, then there exists a $k < \infty$ and $s \in \{0, 1\}$ s.t.

$$c_{2k+j} = (-1)^s c_{2k-j}. \quad (4.204)$$

Proof. By time reversibility, we can write alternatively

$$X_t = \sum_{j=-\infty}^{\infty} c_j \varepsilon_{t+j}' = \sum_{j=-\infty}^{\infty} c_{-j} \varepsilon_{t-j}' \quad (4.205)$$

where $\{\varepsilon_t'\}$ is another copy of $\{\varepsilon_t\}$ Theorem 4.17 implies that (4.205) and (4.199) can only differ by a positive or negative change of scale and/or shift in the time origin. Since Σc_j^2 is proportional to var X_t, the only scale change permissible is a change of sign. The sequence

$(\ldots, c_{i+1}, c_i, c_{j-1}, \ldots)$ can be obtained from the original sequence $(\ldots, c_{j-1}, c_j, c_{j+1}, \ldots)$ by a shift in the time origin or by a shift and change of all signs. Thus, both sequences have to be (i) symmetric of the form $(\ldots, z, y, x, y, z, \ldots)$ or $(\ldots, y, x, x, y, \ldots)$, or (ii) skew-symmetric of the form $(\ldots, -y, -x, 0, x, y, \ldots)$ or $(\ldots, -y, -x, x, y, \ldots)$. $\square$

Corollary 4.2: Under the condition of Theorem 4.17 together with $c_0 = 1$, $c_j = 0$ for $j < 0$ or $j > q$, if $\{X_t\}$ is time reversible, then

$$c_q = -1 \qquad c_{q-i} = -c_i \quad (i = 1, \ldots, q-1)$$

or

$$c_q = 1 \qquad c_{q-i} = c_i \quad (i = 1, \ldots, q-1).$$

Proof. Obvious from Corollary 4.1. $\square$

Corollary 4.3: Let $\{X_t\}$ be given by the equation

$$X_t = \sum_{j=1}^{k} a_j X_{t-j} + \sum_{j=0}^{l} b_j \varepsilon_{t-j}, \qquad a_k \neq 0, \qquad b_l \neq 0 \qquad (4.206)$$

where $\{\varepsilon_t\}$ is a sequence of i.i.d. random variables with zero mean and has the moment property. Suppose that Condition A of Chapter 1 is satisfied and that the polynomials $z^k - \sum_{j=1}^{k} a_j z^{k-j}$ and $\sum_{j=0}^{l} b_j z^{l-j}$ have no common zeros. If $\{X_t\}$ is time reversible then ε_t has a Gaussian distribution.

Proof. Under Condition A of Chapter 1, $\{X_t\}$ is stationary and admits a unique mean square convergent linear representation of the form

$$X_t = \sum_{j=0}^{\infty} c_j \varepsilon_{t-j}, \quad c_0 = 1, \quad c_j > 0, \quad \text{for infinitely many } j > 0 \quad (4.207)$$

and the spectral density function of $\{X_t\}$ is positive almost everywhere. Therefore, either ε_t has a Gaussian distribution, or the c_j satisfy the constraints (4.204) which is impossible because $c_j > 0$ for infinitely many $j \geq 0$ and $c_{-j} = 0 \, \forall j > 0$. $\square$

4.4.3   REVERSING THE DIRECTION OF TIME

Let us consider the two MA(q) models

$$X_t = b_0 \varepsilon_t + b_1 \varepsilon_{t-1} + \ldots + b_q \varepsilon_{t-q} \qquad (4.208)$$

and

$$X_t^R = b_0 \varepsilon_t + b_1 \varepsilon_{t+1} + \ldots + b_q \varepsilon_{t+q} \qquad (4.209)$$

where $\{\varepsilon_t\}$ is the usual sequence of i.i.d. random variables. It is not difficult to verify that the joint distribution of $(X_t, X_{t+1}, \ldots, X_{t+r})$ and the joint distribution of $(X_{t+r}^{R}, X_{t+r-1}^{R}, \ldots, X_{t}^{R})$ are identical for any $r \geq 1$. Model (4.209) may be called *a reversed* model of model (4.208). However, an equivalent *reversed model* may be obtained by exploiting Corollary 4.2 to define

$$^{R}X_{t} = b_{0}\varepsilon_{t-q} + b_{1}\varepsilon_{t-q+1} + \ldots + b_{q}\varepsilon_{t}. \qquad (4.210)$$

Other examples of reversed time series models may be found in Lawrance (1987). Whittle (1963b), Box and Jenkins (1976), and Akaike (1973b), etc. were all aware of the facility afforded by reversed models in linear time series modelling.

4.4.4 THE NON-LINEAR CASE

The cumulant spectral density function of order k is useful for this case. If $\{X_{t}\}$ is stationary, $\text{cum}(X_{t+u_{1}}, X_{t+u_{2}}, \ldots, X_{t+u_{i-1}}, X_{t})$ does not depend on t and we may denote it by $\gamma(u_{1}, u_{2}, \ldots, u_{k-1})$, $(u_{1}, u_{2}, \ldots, u_{k-1} \in \mathbf{Z})$.

If $\{X_{t}\}$ is time reversible, then for every positive integer l,

$$\gamma(-u_{1}, -u_{2}, \ldots, -u_{l}) = \gamma(u_{1}, u_{2}, \ldots, u_{l}), (u_{1}, \ldots, u_{l} \in \mathbf{Z}) \quad (4.211)$$

and therefore the imaginary part of $h(\omega_{1}, \omega_{2}, \ldots, \omega_{l})$ is identically zero. For a stationary linear Gaussian model, cumulant spectral density functions of order $k \geq 3$ are all identically zero because the joint cumulants of order $k \geq 3$ are all zero. For a stationary time series all of whose joint distributions are symmetric about the origin, all odd-order cumulant spectral density functions are identically zero.

It would seem most unlikely that there will be many non-linear time series models which would satisfy (4.211). In other words, time irreversibility is the rule rather than the exception when it comes to non-linearity.

Example 4.14: (A simple bilinear model): Consider the bilinear model

$$X_{t} = \beta X_{t-k}\varepsilon_{t-k+m} + \varepsilon_{t}, \qquad k \geq 2, \quad 1 \leq m \leq k - 1 \qquad (4.212)$$

where $\{\varepsilon_{t}\}$ is a sequence of i.i.d. random variables with $\mathcal{N}(0, 1)$ distribution. Direct calculations verify that if $|\beta| < 1$, then

$$\text{E}X_{t} = 0, \quad \text{all } t$$

$$\text{E}(X_{t}X_{t-s}) = \begin{cases} 1/(1 - \beta^{2}) & \text{for } s = 0 \\ 0 & \text{for } s \neq 0 \end{cases}$$

$$\text{E}(X_{t}X_{t-s_{1}}X_{t-s_{2}}) = \begin{cases} \beta/(1 - \beta^{2}) & \text{if } s_{1} = k \text{ and } s_{2} = k - m \\ 0 & \text{otherwise} \end{cases}$$

and the bispectral density function

$$h(\omega_1, \omega_2) = \frac{1}{4\pi^2(1 - \beta^2)}[H(k, k - m) + H(-k, -m)$$

$$+ H(m, -k + m) + H(k - m, k) + H(-m, -k)$$

$$+ H(-k + m, m)] \qquad (4.213)$$

where

$$H(r, s) = \exp(ir\omega_1 + is\omega_2).$$

Clearly $\mathrm{Im}\, h(\omega_1, \omega_2) \neq 0.$ □

4.5   Invertibility

Consider the simple example of a BL model,

$$X_t = \varepsilon_r + \alpha\varepsilon_{t-1}X_{t-2} \qquad (4.214)$$

where $\varepsilon_t \sim \mathrm{IID}$. It would be natural to consider conditions on α which ensure that ε_t is measurable w.r.t. $\mathbb{B}_t$, the σ-algebra generated by X_s, $s \leq T$. More generally, given a non-linear model of the form

$$X_t = f(X_{t-j}, \varepsilon_{t-k}; j = 1, 2, \ldots, P \quad \text{and} \quad k = 0, 1, \ldots, Q) \quad (4.215)$$

it would be natural to consider conditions on f s.t. ε_t is measurable w.r.t. $\mathbb{B}_t$. The model is then said to be *invertible**. This is a natural generalization of the concept of invertibility of ARMA models. There is a duality between invertibility and stationarity. To see this, let $\mathbb{B}^{\varepsilon_t}$ denote the σ-algebra generated by ε_s, $s \geq t$. In the study of stationarity, we generally look for conditions on f s.t. X_t is $\mathbb{B}^{\varepsilon_t}$-measurable. We have seen the link between stationary and stability. It would be very interesting to explore a link between invertibility and a relevant concept in dynamical systems. As we are not aware of any clear link to date, we content ourselves with a few rudimentary remarks.

Remark 4.14: Sufficient conditions for invertibility are available in isolated cases only, principally for special cases of the BL models. Even these are often difficult to verify in a practical situation. References may be made to Granger and Andersen (1978), Quinn (1982) and Subba Rao and Gabr (1984), and Guegan and Pham Dinh Tuan (1987) whose sufficient condition may well lead to a link-up with dynamical systems. Specifically, let ϕ denote a vector norm which induces the *matrix norm*,

---

* C.f. Definition 4.5.

$\|.\|_\phi$, on a square matrix $\mathbf{K}$ by

$$\|\mathbf{K}\|_\phi = \sup_{\phi(\mathbf{x})\le 1} \phi(\mathbf{Kx}).$$

Their sufficient condition for the invertibility of the Markovian bilinear model (4.29) is that $\mathbf{B} = \mathbf{dH}$, and $E[\ln \|\mathbf{K}_t\|_\phi] < 0$, each t, where

$$\mathbf{K}_t = \mathbf{A} - \mathbf{cH} - \mathbf{dHX}_t.$$

Remark 4.15: Non-linear autoregressive models of the form

$$X_t = f(X_{t-1}, \ldots, X_{t-k}) + \varepsilon_t \tag{4.216}$$

where $\varepsilon_t \sim \text{IID}$, are invertible by definition.

Instead of giving rigorous proofs of what amounts to fairly isolated results, we give an example based on heuristics. Rigor may be supplied in the references quoted in Remark 4.14.

Example 4.15: Consider a simple bilinear model

$$X_t = \varepsilon_t + \alpha\varepsilon_{t-k}X_{t-l}, \quad (l > k) \tag{4.217}$$

where $\{\varepsilon_t\}$ is a sequence of i.i.d. random variables with zero mean and variance σ^2. Suppose that $\alpha^2\sigma^2 < 1$ so that the model is stationary. Now, write (4.217) in the form

$$X_t = (1 - \alpha X_{t-l}B^k)\varepsilon_t \tag{4.218}$$

where B is a shift operator on ε_t, that is

$$B^k\varepsilon_t = \varepsilon_{t-k}, \quad k = 0, \pm 1, \ldots.$$

Formally, from (4.218) we have

$$\varepsilon_t = A_t X_t \tag{4.219}$$

where the operator A_t is given by

$$A_t = 1 + \alpha(\ ) + \alpha^2(\ )(\ ) + \alpha^2(\ )(\ )(\ ) + \ldots \tag{4.220}$$

where

$$\begin{aligned}
(\ ) &= X_{t-l}B^k \\
(\ )(\ ) &= X_{t-l}X_{t-l-k}B^{2k} \\
(\ )(\ )(\ ) &= X_{t-l}X_{t-l-k}X_{t-l-2k}B^{3k}, \quad \text{etc.}
\end{aligned} \tag{4.221}$$

Note that following the same logic as in (4.221) we have

$$(1 - \alpha X_{t-1}B)A_t = 1.$$

The formal expansion (4.220) is valid provided

$$E(\alpha X_{t-1})^2 < 1 \tag{4.222}$$

by analogy with ordinary Taylor expansion. Now $EX_t = 0$, all t, and $\text{var}(X_t) = \sigma_X^2 = \sigma^2 + \alpha^2\sigma^2\sigma_X^2$, that is $\sigma_X^2 = \sigma^2/(1 - \alpha^2\sigma^2)$. Thus, from (4.222), we deduce the sufficient condition for invertibility $\alpha^2\sigma^2/(1 - \alpha^2\sigma^2) < 1$, that is $\alpha^2\sigma^2 < \frac{1}{2}$. $\square$

4.6   Catastrophe

Catastrophe theory is a branch of differential topology which studies the *sudden* appearance or disappearance of dynamical characteristics with smoothly changing parameters. The theory was developed by R. Thom. (See for example Poston and Stewart (1978) for an introduction.)

The applied side of catastrophe theory has a connection with probabilistic decision making, known as the theory of discontinuous decision processes by Smith *et al.* (1981). We discuss an application of this to the approximation of non-linear time series models.

The simplest dynamical system is linear. As we have seen in Chapter 2, this may be a locally valid model. As we gradually move over the state space, we expect the model to change gradually. As far as the modeller (i.e. the decision maker) is concerned, this gradual change over the state space is often not immediately discernible, but the modeller may act only after an accumulation of a sufficient amount of small changes. The action is then usually sudden. We may summarize the situation by saying that a *qualitatively different model is brought about by an accumulation of quantitative changes.*

For concreteness and simplicity of discussion, we address ourselves to the case

$$E(X_t \mid X_{t-1} = x) = \mu(x)x \qquad (4.223)$$

where μ is a 'smooth' function. Since a linear model has been found to be a generally acceptable first approximation we may start with the Bayesian *linear* model,

$$E(X_t \mid X_{t-1} = x) = \theta x \qquad (4.224)$$

where $\theta \sim \mathcal{N}(c, V)$. This model implies the belief that the expected approximating linear model is given by

$$E(X_t \mid X_{t-1} = x) = cx, \quad c \text{ a constant} \qquad (4.225)$$

and the size of V reflects our uncertainty about this belief. In order to quantify the closeness of the approximating model (4.224) to the 'true' model (4.223), we introduce the following *loss function, L,* which is commonly adopted in Bayesian decision theory, possibly because of its Bayesian robustness and mathematical convenience by being a conjugate to the Gaussian distribution. Thus,

$$L(\theta) = h\{1 - \exp[-\tfrac{1}{2}k^{-1}(\theta - \mu)^2]\}. \tag{4.226}$$

Here, and in subsequent discussion in this section, we suppress the
argument, x, of μ whenever this may be done without obscuring the
context. Of course, μ is the most desirable value of θ; k represents the
relative tolerance to differences between μ and θ, and h quantifies the
maximum loss. To decide whether (4.224) is an acceptable approximation
of (4.223) or not, we need to evaluate the expected loss of making a
decision. For this we let D denote the class of possible decisions. The
expected loss function, E_V, is defined by

$$E_V(\delta) = \int_{-\infty}^{\infty} L(\theta)\, dF_V(\theta \mid \delta), \qquad \delta \in D \tag{4.227}$$

where $F_V(\theta \mid \delta)$ denotes the distribution of θ given that the decision δ is
employed. As a consequence of Gaussian belief and conjugate Gaussian
loss, $F_V(\theta \mid \delta)$ is $\mathcal{N}(c + \delta, V)$, and we may write

$$E_V(\delta) = h\{1 - [k/(k + V)]^{1/2} \exp[-\tfrac{1}{2}(k + V)^{-1}(\delta - d)^2]\} \tag{4.228}$$

where $d = \mu - c$ represents the distance of the desired value of θ from the
expected value of θ. The minimizer of $E_V(\delta)$ with respect to $\delta \in D$ is
called the *Bayes decision*, which is denoted by δ^*. In Bayesian decision
theory, a decision is acceptable if and only if it is a Bayes decision. Two
important points emerge:

1.   If both k and V are unaffected by the decision δ, then $\delta^* = d$. This
implies that no approximation, linear or not, is acceptable, that is a
Bayes decision. Of course, in many practical situations it would be
unrealistic to assume that k and/or V are unaffected by δ. For example,
the variance V will generally be an increasing function of the degree of
change involved in taking a new decision.

2.   Suppose that $d > 0$ and

$$V(\delta) = \alpha + \beta \,|\delta|, \qquad \alpha, \beta > 0. \tag{4.229}$$

(Note that it can be arranged such that $d > 0$.) It is easily shown that the
Bayes decision $\delta^* \in [0, d]$ and that minimizing the expected loss $E_V(\delta)$ is
equivalent to minimizing the function

$$S(\delta) = \ln[k + V(\delta)] + (\delta - d)^2[k + V(\delta)]^{-1}. \tag{4.230}$$

Let us measure δ in units of $(k + V(0))^{1/2} = (k + \alpha)^{1/2}$ and define
$\gamma = \beta(k + \alpha)^{-1/2}$. For $\delta > 0$, $S'(\delta) = 0$ in a quadratic equation in δ and
the case $\delta = 0$ is examined separately. After some algebra, it is found

that the Bayes decision is

$$\delta^* = \begin{cases} 0 & \text{for } 0 < d < [(1 + \gamma^2)^{1/2} - 1]\gamma^{-1} \\ \frac{1}{2}\{[4(1 + \gamma d)^2 + \gamma^4]^{1/2} - (2 + \gamma^2)\}/\gamma & \text{otherwise.} \end{cases} \quad (4.231)$$

Returning to the original units, let

$$R_1 = \{x: 0 < \mu(x) - c < [(1 + \gamma^2)^{1/2} - 1]\beta\gamma^{-2}\}. \quad (4.232)$$

The above Bayes decision shows that $\forall x \in R_1$, the approximating *linear* model given by (4.225) is as true as the 'true' model. As soon as $x \notin R_1$, a different approximating model is *switched to*. Repeating the above arguments, we may obtain a partition $R_1 \cup R_2 \cup \ldots \cup R_l$ of the real line, such that over each R_i, $i = 1, 2, \ldots, l$, an approximating linear model is obtained. *The value of l is completely determined by α, β, and k.*

By allowing k to be a function of δ, for example

$$k(\delta) = (\pi + \rho |\delta|)^{-1}, \qquad \pi, \rho > 0 \quad (4.233)$$

a similar conclusion may be drawn. For many other possibilities, we refer readers to Smith *et al.* (1981).

4.7   Non-linear representation

Logically, this topic should have been discussed in Chapter 1. However, from the point of view of maximizing the degree of understanding it seems better placed here, that is after the display of an array of models unfamiliar to the traditional time series analysts and ideas not often described in detail in the traditional texts.

It is well known that any stationary time series $\{X_t\}$ with a purely continuous spectrum can be represented in the mean square convergent bilateral series

$$X_t = \sum_{u=-\infty}^{\infty} g_u \varepsilon_{t-u} \quad (4.234)$$

where $\{\varepsilon_t\}$ is a sequence of *uncorrelated* random variables (see e.g. Priestley 1981, Chapter 10). As the ε_t are only uncorrelated and not necessarily independent, there is still 'information left in the ε'. To see this, let us consider the so-called *polynomial representation*. Let $\{\varepsilon_t: t = 0, \pm 1, \ldots\}$ be a sequence of i.i.d. random variables with $\mathcal{N}(0, 1)$ distribution. A time series $\{X_t: t = 0, \pm 1, \ldots\}$ is said to admit a *polynomial representation* if it may be written in the form

$$X_t = \sum_p \sum_{i_1 \ldots i_p} a_{i_1 \ldots i_p} \prod_{v=1}^{p} \varepsilon_{t+i_v}. \quad (4.235)$$

Here, the summation over p is from 1 to $+\infty$ and the summations over the i_j are each from $-\infty$ to $+\infty$, and the convergence is in the almost sure sense. By virtue of the fact that the i_j extend over $(-\infty, \infty)$, the representation is *bilateral* or *two-sided*. If they extend only over $(0, \infty)$, then the representation is *one-sided*. Now, a deep theorem due to Nisio (1960) states that every stationary time series may be approximated in a certain sense by two-sided polynomial representations of the form (4.235). We quote his theorem without proof.

Theorem 4.18 (Nisio 1960): For any given stationary time series $\{X_t\}$ we can form a sequence of time series $\{Y_t^{(m)}\}$, $m = 1, 2, \ldots$, each admitting a polynomial representation such that

$$\lim_{m \to \infty} |\mathrm{E} \exp\{i\theta_{-n}X_{-n} + \ldots + i\theta_n X_n\}$$
$$\mathrm{E} \exp\{i\theta_{-n}Y_{-n}^{(m)} + \ldots + i\theta_n Y_n^{(m)}\}| = 0 \quad (4.236)$$

for any n and θ_j.

Henceforth, for simplicity, we shall say that $\{X_t\}$ admits a polynomial representation if the conclusion of Theorem 4.18 holds. If $p = 1$, we say that the representation is *linear* and $\{X_t\}$ is called a *linear time series*. If $p > 1$, $\{X_t\}$ is called a *non-linear time series*. We know that every stationary Gaussian time series $\{X_t\}$ admits a two-sided linear representation.

It is important to realize that all the above representations are two-sided and that the assumption of ε_t having a $\mathcal{N}(0, 1)$ distribution is not essential. The distribution could be uniform on $[0, 1]$, for example. The question of a *one-sided* representation, which is of fundamental importance to the structural side of prediction theory, is a very delicate one. For stationary Gaussian time series $\{X_t\}$ with a purely continuous spectrum whose density is positive almost everywhere, the existence of a one-sided representation is ensured provided the Paley–Wiener condition is satisfied, that is

$$\int_{-\pi}^{\pi} \ln f(\omega) \, d\omega > -\infty \quad (4.237)$$

where f is the spectral density function and provided that the associated ε_t is measurable w.r.t. $\mathbb{B}_t$, the σ-algebra generated by X_s, $s \leq t$. For general stationary time series, the situation is not completely resolved. Interested readers may refer to Rosenblatt (1971) for details.

To let readers taste the flavour of the area, we summarize some relevant results below without proof.

Let $\{X_t: t = 0, \pm 1, \ldots\}$ denote a stationary time series. Assume that it has the moment property; if not, we can always apply an instantaneous transform to achieve this. Let $\mathbb{B}_t$ denote the σ-algebra generated by X_s, $s \leq t$. Let H_t denote the Hilbert space of square integrable random variables measurable w.r.t. $\mathbb{B}_t$. Clearly $\ldots \subset \mathbb{B}_{t-1} \subset \mathbb{B}_t \subset \ldots$ and $\ldots \subset H_{t-1} \subset H_t \subset \ldots$. Let $\mathbb{B}_{-\infty} = \bigcap_t \mathbb{B}_t$. We call $\mathbb{B}_{-\infty}$ the *tail field*. Let $H_{-\infty} = \bigcap_t H_t$, which is called the *remote past*. If $\mathbb{B}_{-\infty}$ is the trivial σ-algebra consisting only of the empty set and the universal set, or equivalently, if $H_{-\infty}$ consists only of constant functions, then $\{X_t\}$ is said to be *purely non-deterministic* in the non-linear sense.

The programme initiated by Norbert Wiener in the 1950's was to find necessary and sufficient conditions for $\{X_t\}$ to admit a one-sided representation s.t. X_t is measurable w.r.t. the σ-algebra generated by ε_s, $s \le t$, where $\{\varepsilon_t\}$ is a sequence of i.i.d. random variables with, say, a uniform distribution on $[0, 1]$. The conjecture is that *a necessary and sufficient condition for a stationary time series $\{X_t\}$ to have a one-sided representation of the form $\{g(\ldots, \varepsilon_{t-1}, \varepsilon_t)\}$ is that $\{X_t\}$ has a trivial tail field*. The difficulty lies with the sufficiency, the necessity being a comparatively straightforward affair.

Bibliographical notes

Section 4.1: The idea of a skeleton was brought to bear in Chan and Tong (1985) although the term was formally coined in Tong (1987). The idea was given its full play in Chan (1986). The intimate triad of the deterministic Lyapunov function, the stochastic Lyapunov function, and the g-function orginated in Chan and Tong (1985) and culminated in Theorem 4.2 and Appendix 1, which are based on results in Chan (1986). In the Markov chain theory, the g-function idea seems to start with A. A. Markov (in the 1930s) and to reach its first sophisticated form in the hands of R. L. Tweedie (in the 1970s) via F. G. Foster (in the 1950s). Nummelin (1984) illustrates the degree of maturity of the idea. It seems to have developed independently of the idea of a Lyapunov function in dynamical systems. This is rather unfortunate because, for example Bertram and Sarachik, Khasminskii, Kats and Krasovskii, Kushner and others were already introducing many of the basic ideas in the late 1950s and early 1960s. Kushner (1971) is a remarkable contribution despite the sometimes irritating typographical errors. The triad is then used to streamline and systematize the study of ergodicity of various non-linear models. An early unexpected condition described in Example 4.4 was due to Petruccelli and Woolford (1984), which was generalized by Chan *et al.* in 1985. We have combined the Markovian representation of Pham Dinh Tuan (1985) and the proof of sufficiency of the spectral radius condition for the ergodicity of the random coefficient autoregressive models due to Feigin and Tweedie (1985) to streamline the proof of the sufficiency of the spectral radius condition for the ergodicity of the general Markovian bilinear models. Pham Dinh Tuan (1986) has given a complete discussion of the geometric ergodicity of the completely general bilinear model. Before the availability of the general result, special cases were obtained by Granger and Andersen (1978), Guegan (1981), Pham Dinh Tuan and Lanh Tat Tran (1981), Hannan (1982), Subba Rao (1981), Tong (1981), Quinn (1982), etc. Some of these are listed in the exercises. Pham Dinh Tuan (1985) gave a definitive study of the Markovian representation of model (4.28), sometimes (confusingly) called the subdiagonal bilinear model. He later (Pham Dinh Tuan 1986) extended the study to the completely general bilinear model. To date, this seems to be the only example of some generality in which a *finite*-dimensional state vector may be explicitly defined for a *non-linear* model in a sense acceptable in the dynamical systems approach. Pham Dinh Tuan's structural study was extended by Guegan (1987). For the completely general $BL(l, r, m, q)$ model, we have modified Liu and Brockwell (1988) to demonstrate heuristically the sufficiency of the spectral radius condition for stationarity. This reduces to the Bhaskara Rao–Subba Rao–Walker (1983) condition when $q = 1$. A sufficient condition for ergodicity of general RCA models was established by Nicholls and Quinn (1982), who extended the earlier work of Andel (1976) by using similar arguments but we have followed Feigin and Tweedie (1985) for streamlining purposes. Chan (1986, 1988a) addressed the ergodicity stationarity problem of NEAR(p) models directly. A direct approach can sometimes yield sharper results (see Exercise 10). A similar remark may be made about Milhøj (1985) in connection with GARCH models.

Necessary conditions for stationarity of non-linear models are available in some cases and they rely on different techniques for different cases. The approach (see Appendix 1) of Chan (1986) provides a more general methodology for non-linear autoregressive models. Some specific results are available in Nicholls and Quinn (1982), Petruccelli and Woolford (1984), Chan et al. (1985), Pham Dinh Tuan (1985), Chan (1988), etc. Tjøstheim (1989) is a recent extension of the drift criterion.

Section 4.2: The closed-form expressions (4.71) and (4.72) were first obtained by Andel et al. (1984) and Andel and Barton (1986). The streamline derivation here follows the general approach of Chan and Tong (1986b). D. A. Jones (1976) introduced the idea of perturbation into the numerical calculation of stationary distributions and moments of non-linear autoregressive models. Section 4.2.3 summarizes one of his methods. Our suggestion in §4.2.3 is based on continuous-time results discussed in Freidlin and Wentzill (1984). The method based on the Chapman–Kolmogorov relation seems to be first developed by Bellman et al. (1972) and results reported here are based on Moeanaddin and Tong (1989a). Section 4.2.5 is based on Wang *et al.* (1983). Section 4.2.7 is based on Pemberton and Tong (1981) and an unpublished result of C. Z. Wei. Theorem 4.8 is due to Tweedie (1983). We follow Tong (1981) and Feigin and Tweedie (1985) in Example 4.11, the conclusions of which were first obtained by Tong (1981). Theorem 4.9 is due to Pham Dinh Tuan (1985). Theorem 4.10 extends a similar result due to Chan and Tong (1985). We follow Brillinger (1965) for higher-order spectra. Section 4.2.10 is a continuation of §4.2.3. Section 4.2.11 is based on Tong (1983a). The ideas in §4.2.12 are not new and, in the non-linear autoregressive context, the first reference seems to be Högnäs (1986). Our discussion is slightly different and is based on the unpublished work of K. S. Chan. Section 4.2.13 is based on Chan and Tong (1986a).

Section 4.3: The concept of a predictor space was introduced by Akaike (1974a) for the Markovian representation of ARMA models, which gives a definitive geometric characterization of ARMA models. The concept was borrowed by Pham Dinh Tuan (1985) in a similar study of Markovian bilinear models. The speculation concerning general non-linear models was due to Tong (Tong and Lim 1980).

Section 4.4: We follow Brillinger and Rosenblatt (1967a,b) for the formal definition of time reversibility. An early and important result on reversibility and Gaussianity was due to Weiss (1975). We follow Hallin *et al.* (1988) to derive Corollary 4.1 by appealing to Theorem 4.17 due to Findley (1986). Corollaries 4.2 and 4.3 then reproduce in a simplified way the main part of Weiss's (1975) results. Lawrance (1987) discussed reversed models in time series which were motivated by time-reversibility considerations. Example 4.14 is due to Gabr (1988).

Section 4.6: We follow Tong (1982) in this section.

Exercises and complements

(1) Let
$$X_{t+1} = (\tfrac{1}{2} + \varepsilon_{t+1})X_t \qquad \varepsilon_t \sim \text{IID}(0, \tfrac{1}{2}).$$

Prove that $X_t \to 0$ in mean square and almost surely as $t \to \infty$.

(2) Let
$$X_t = [-0.9 - \exp(-X_{t-1}^2)]X_{t-2} + \varepsilon_t$$

$\varepsilon_t \sim \text{IID}(0, 1)$. Prove that $\{X_t\}$ is not stationary but as a Markov chain it is transient.

(Chan 1986)

(3) Let
$$X_t = \alpha X_{t-1} + \beta \varepsilon_t^2 X_{t-1} e^{-X_{t-1}^2} + \varepsilon_t$$

where the ε_t are i.i.d. $\mathcal{N}(0, 1)$ random variables. Prove that $|\alpha| < 1$ is sufficient for geometric ergodicity of $\{X_t\}$. Does the stationary distribution have moments of all orders?

(4) Prove that clothing the skeleton of Example 2.10 with $\mathcal{N}(0, 1)$ i.i.d. random variables gives a stationary time series. However, a similar clothing of the skeleton of Example 2.9 yields a non-stationary time series.

(Chan 1986)

(5) Prove that $\alpha^2 + \beta^2\sigma^2 < 1$ implies stationarity of the bilinear model

$$X_t = (\alpha + \beta\varepsilon_t)X_{t-1} + \varepsilon_t \qquad \varepsilon_t \sim \text{IID}(0, \sigma^2).$$

Prove that any one of the following conditions is also sufficient for stationarity:
(i) $\text{E}\,|\alpha + \beta\varepsilon_t| < 1$;
(ii) $\text{E}(\log|\alpha + \beta\varepsilon_t|) < 0$ provided $\text{E}\,|\log|x + \varepsilon_t|| < \infty \ \forall x \in \mathbf{R}$.

(Tong 1981; Quinn 1982)

(6) Prove that $\rho(\mathbf{A}^T\mathbf{A}) > 1$ for any companion matrix $\mathbf{A}$.

(Pemberton 1985)

(7) Construct a counter-example to show that ρ does not satisfy the triangular inequality, that is

$$\rho(\mathbf{A} + \mathbf{B}) \nleq \rho(\mathbf{A}) + \rho(\mathbf{B})$$

where $\mathbf{A}$ and $\mathbf{B}$ are both square matrices of the same dimension.

(8) Prove that $\sigma^2 b^2 < 1$ implies the stationarity of the bilinear model

$$X_t = bX_{t-2}\varepsilon_{t-1} + \varepsilon_t$$

where $\varepsilon_t \sim \text{IID}(0, \sigma^2)$.

(Guegan 1981)

(9) Prove that $a^2 + \sigma^2 b^2 < 1$ implies the stationarity of the bilinear model

$$X_t = aX_{t-1} + be_{t-1}X_{t-1} + e_t$$

where $e_t \sim \text{IID}(0, \sigma^2)$.

(Pham Dinh Tuan and Lanh Tat Tran 1981)

(10) Show that the NEAR(p) model may be expressed as the threshold model

$$X_t = \sum_{i=0}^{p} \beta_i^{(J_t)}X_{t-i} + \varepsilon_t$$

where
(i) $\varepsilon_t \sim \text{IID}$ and satisfies Condition A3 of §4.1.3;
(ii) $J_t \sim \text{IID}$ taking values $0, 1, 2, \ldots, p$ with probabilities $\alpha_0, \alpha_1, \ldots, \alpha_p$ ($\alpha_i \geq 0$ all i and $\sum_{i=0}^{p} \alpha_i = 1$);

(iii) $\{\varepsilon_t\}$ and $\{J_t\}$ are independent of each other;

(iv)

$$\beta_i^{(j)} = \begin{cases} \beta_j & \text{if } j = i \\ 0 & \text{otherwise} \end{cases}$$

$j = 0, 1, \ldots, p;$

(v) $\beta_0 = 0, \beta_1, \beta_2, \ldots, \beta_p$ are real constants satisfying $0 \le \beta_j \le 1$, for $j = 1, \ldots, p$.

Use the spectral radius condition of RCA models to obtain a sufficient condition for the ergodicity of the NEAR(p) model. Compare your condition with Chan's (1988a):

$$\sum_{j=1}^{p} \alpha_j \beta_j < 1.$$

(You may assume $\alpha_0 = 0$.)

(11) Consider an AR(1) model

$$X_t = aX_{t-1} + \varepsilon_t$$

where ε_t has a stable distribution of exponent θ, $(0 < \theta \le 2)$. Prove that if $|a| < 1$, then X_t also has a stable distribution of the same exponent.

(12) Verify eqns (4.71) and (4.72).

(13) Find the stationary density of model (4.65) when ε_t has the characteristic function $\exp(-|t|^{2/3})$.

(14) For any integer L, let

$$-\infty = r_0 < r_1 < \ldots < r_L = \infty$$

and define

$$X_t = a^{(k)} + b^{(k)} X_{t-1} + \varepsilon_t^{(k)}, \quad \text{if } X_{t-1} \in R_k$$

where $R_k \equiv (r_{k-1}, r_k]$, $1 \le k \le L$, and for each k, $\{\varepsilon_t^{(k)}\}$ is a sequence of i.i.d. random variables each having a strictly positive density $f_k(.)$ on $\mathbf{R}$ and mean 0. Further, $\{\varepsilon_t^{(k)}\}$ and $\{\varepsilon_t^{(j)}\}$ are independent for $j \ne k$. Prove that $\{X_t\}$ is ergodic if and only if one of the following conditions holds:

(i) $b^{(1)} < 1, \ b^{(L)} < 1, \ b^{(1)} b^{(L)} < 1;$
(ii) $b^{(1)} = 1, \ b^{(L)} < 1, \ a^{(1)} > 0;$
(iii) $b^{(1)} < 1, \ b^{(L)} = 1, \ a^{(L)} < 0;$
(iv) $b^{(1)} = 1, \ b^{(L)} = 1, \ a^{(L)} < 0 < a^{(1)};$
(v) $b^{(1)} b^{(L)} = 1, \ b^{(1)} < 1, \ a^{(L)} + b^{(L)} a^{(1)} > 0.$

(Chan et al. 1985)

(15) For model (4.133), under stationarity and existence of $\mu_n = E(|X_1|^n)$ verify that

$$\mu_n = \sum_{s=0}^{[n/2]} \binom{n}{2s}(-\tfrac{1}{2})^s C_s a^{n-2s} \left[\sum_{j=0}^{2s} \binom{2s}{j} b_j \mu_{n-2s+j}\right], \qquad n = 2, 3, \ldots$$

where

$$C_s = -2(2s - 1)C_{s-1}, \qquad s = 1, 2, \ldots$$
$$C_0 = 1.$$

(Tong 1981)

(16) Let $\{X_t\}$ follow the model

$$X_t = -\alpha |X_{t-1}| + \varepsilon_t, \qquad 0 < \alpha < 1$$

where the ε_t are i.i.d. random variables with $\mathcal{N}(0, 1)$ distribution. Verify that

$$EX_t = -\frac{\sqrt{2}}{\pi}\alpha(1 - \alpha^2)^{-1/2}$$

and

$$\operatorname{var} X_t = (1 - \alpha^2)^{-1}\left(1 - \frac{2\alpha^2}{\pi}\right).$$

Let μ_n denote the nth moment of a $\mathcal{N}(0, 1)$ random variable. Put

$$J_n = \int_{-\infty}^{\infty} x^n e^{-kx^2/2}\Phi(-x)\, dx, \qquad n = 0, 1, \ldots$$

where Φ is the distribution of $\mathcal{N}(0, 1)$, and

$$k = \alpha^{-2} - 1.$$

Verify that

$$J_n = \frac{n-1}{k}J_{n-2} - k^{-1}(k + 1)^{-n/2}\mu_{n-1}, \qquad n \geq 2$$

$$J_0 = [\pi/(2k)]^{1/2} \qquad J_1 = -k^{-1}(k + 1)^{-1/2} \qquad J_2 = k^{-1}J_0.$$

Let v_n denote the nth moment (about 0) of X_t. Verify that

$$v_n = \alpha^{-n-1}[2(1 - \alpha^2\pi)]^{1/2}J_n.$$

(Andel et al. 1984)

(17) Consider a special GARCH model

$$X_t^2 = \eta_t^2[\gamma + \phi(x_{t-1}^2 - \gamma)], \qquad \gamma > 0, \quad \phi \geq 0$$

where the η_t are i.i.d. $\mathcal{N}(0, 1)$ random variables. Using the drift criterion, verify that $\phi < 1$ is a sufficient condition for stationarity of $\{X_t\}$.

(18) Consider an ARCH model in the form

$$X_t^2 = \eta_t^2[\gamma + \phi_1(X_{t-1}^2 - \gamma) + \ldots + \phi_p(X_{t-p}^2 - \gamma)]$$

where the η_i are i.i.d. random variables with $\mathcal{N}(0, 1)$ distribution, $\gamma > 0$, $\phi_i \geq 0$ for all i. Use eqn (4.53) to obtain a sufficient condition for stationarity and compare this condition with the condition

$$\phi_1 + \ldots + \phi_p < 1.$$

(19) Consider an ARCH(p) model of the form in Exercise 18. Find a Markovian representation for $\{X_t^2\}$, by recognizing $\{X_t^2\}$ as a special case of a bilinear time series.

(20) Verify that an RCA model of order k has a predictor space of dimension k. Investigate the feasibility of a Markovian representation analogous to (4.196) for an RCA model.

(21) Prove that the bilinear model

$$X_t = aX_{t-1} + \varepsilon_t + b\varepsilon_{t-1}X_{t-1} \qquad \varepsilon_t \sim \mathcal{N}(0, \sigma^2)$$

is invertible if $|b| < \exp[-E \ln |X_t|]$. Using Jensen's inequality, show that this condition is implied by $b^2 E X_t^2 \leq 1$. Verify that the region of invertibility is defined by

$$\{(a, b): 2(1 + a)\lambda^4 + 2(1 - a)\lambda^2 - (1 - a)^2(1 + a) \leq 0, \lambda = b\sigma\}.$$

(Pham Dinh Tuan and Lanh Tat Tran 1981)

(22) Verify that the following non-linear moving-average model is not invertible:

$$X_t = \varepsilon_t + \alpha\varepsilon_{t-1}\varepsilon_{t-2}$$

where $\{\varepsilon_t\}$ is a sequence of i.i.d. random variables.

(Granger and Andersen 1978)

(23) Consider the SETAR model

$$X_t = \theta |X_{t-1}| + \varepsilon_t$$

$\theta \in (-1, 1)$. Let π_θ denote the stationary distribution of the model when θ is the parameter. Verify that

$$\theta_1 \leq \theta_2 \Rightarrow \pi_{\theta_1} \lhd \pi_{\theta_2}.$$

(24) Prove that a time-reversible MA(q) model satisfying the condition of Theorem 4.17 is not invertible.

(25) Consider the Markovian bilinear model (4.28). Suppose that it is stationary and $\mathbf{B} = \mathbf{dH}$. Let $\hat{\varepsilon}_t = X_t - \mathbf{H}\hat{\xi}_{t-1}$, where $\hat{\xi}_t$ is given by (4.28) with $\hat{\varepsilon}_t$ replacing ε_t.

Verify that

$$\hat{\boldsymbol{\xi}}_t = \mathbf{K}_t \hat{\boldsymbol{\xi}}_{t-1} + \mathbf{c} X_t + \mathbf{d} X_t^2 - \mathbf{d}\sigma^2$$

where

$$\mathbf{K}_t = \mathbf{A} - \mathbf{c}\mathbf{H} - \mathbf{B} X_t.$$

Check that

$$\hat{\boldsymbol{\xi}}_t - \boldsymbol{\xi}_t = \left(\prod_{j=1}^{t} \mathbf{K}_j\right)(\hat{\boldsymbol{\xi}}_0 - \boldsymbol{\xi}_0).$$

Suppose that $\mathrm{E}\ln\|\mathbf{K}_j\|_\phi < 0$, each j. Show that $\hat{\boldsymbol{\xi}}_t - \boldsymbol{\xi}_t \to \mathbf{0}$ a.s. (almost surely) and hence deduce that the model (4.28) is invertible.

(Guegan and Pham Dinh Tuan 1987)

(26) Consider a Markov-chain-driven threshold model

$$X_t = \theta_t X_{t-1} + \varepsilon_t, \qquad t = 0, \pm 1, \pm 2, \ldots$$

where $\{\theta_t\}$ is an irreducible and aperiodic Markov chain with states $1, 2, \ldots, k$, and $\varepsilon_t \sim \mathrm{IID}(0, \sigma^2)$ independent of $\{\theta_t\}$. Verify that

$$X_t = \sum_{j=0}^{\infty} \left(\prod_{i=0}^{j-1} \theta_{t-i}\right) \varepsilon_{t-j}$$

in the mean-square sense,

$$\mathrm{E} X_t = 0$$

and

$$\mathrm{cov}(X_t, X_{t+s}) = \sigma^2 \sum_{j=0}^{\infty} \mathrm{E}\left(\prod_{k=1}^{s} \theta_{t+k} \prod_{i=0}^{j-1} \theta_{t-i}^2\right)$$

where by convention

$$\prod_{k=1}^{s} \theta_{t+k} = 1 \quad \text{for} \quad s = 0$$

$$\prod_{i=0}^{j-1} \theta_{t-i}^2 = 1 \quad \text{for} \quad j = 0.$$

(Tyssedal and Tjøstheim 1988)

(27) Consider a doubly stochastic model

$$X_t = \phi_t X_{t-1} + \varepsilon_t, \qquad t = 0, \pm 1, \ldots$$

where $\varepsilon_t \sim \mathrm{IID}(0, \sigma^2)$ and $\{\phi_t\}$ is a time series independent of $\{\varepsilon_t\}$. Verify that there exists a time series $\{\beta_t : t = 0, \pm 1, \ldots\}$ with $\mathrm{var}\,\beta_t < \infty$ all t, s.t.

$$X_t = \sum_{j=-\infty}^{\infty} \beta_j \varepsilon_{t-j}$$

in the mean square sense iff

$$\sum_{n=1}^{\infty} \mathrm{E}\left(\prod_{i=0}^{n-1} \phi_{t-1}^2\right) < \infty, \quad \text{for all } t.$$

(Pourahamdi 1986)

Consider a stationary bilinear model

$$X_t = \beta X_{t-k'}\varepsilon_{t-j'} + \varepsilon_t, \qquad (k' \neq j')$$

where the ε_t are i.i.d. $\mathcal{N}(0, \sigma^2)$. Let

$$\mu_{k,j} = \mathrm{E}[(X_t - \mu)(X_{t-k} - \mu)(X_{t-j} - \mu)]$$

where

$$\mu = \mathrm{E}X_t.$$

Verify that $\mu_{k,j} = \mu_{j,k} = \mu_{-k,j-k} = \mu_{j-k,-k}$ for all j, k and $\mu_{k,-k} = \mu_{k,2k}$ for all k. Verify further that $\mu_{k,j}$ is non-zero when $(k = k', j = j')$ or $(k = j', j = k')$ and zero at all other points for which $k \geq 0$, $j \geq 0$.

(Kumar 1986)

(29) Consider the SETAR(2; 0, 0) model:

$$X_t = \begin{cases} \alpha + \varepsilon_t & \text{if } X_{t-1} \leq 0 \\ \beta + \varepsilon_t & \text{if } X_{t-1} > 0 \end{cases}$$

where $\varepsilon_t \sim \mathcal{N}(0, 1)$. Show that the stationary marginal density of X_t is a linear combination of Gaussian densities. Extend the result to a SETAR(k; 0, 0, . . . , 0) model.

(Private communication from J. Pemberton (1988)

(30) Suppose that $\{X_t\}$ is a ϕ-irreducible Markov chain on $(\mathbf{R}^k, \mathbb{B})$. Let μ denote a σ-finite non-trivial sub-invariant measure on $(\mathbf{R}^k, \mathbb{B})$ s.t.

$$\mu(A) \geq \int_{\mathbf{R}^k} \mu(\mathrm{d}y)P(y, A), \forall A \in \mathbb{B}.$$

Let $\mathbb{B}_\mu = \{A \in \mathbb{B}: 0 < \mu(A) < \infty\}$. Let g denote a non-negative measurable function on $\mathbf{R}^k$. Prove that the chain $\{X_t\}$ is positive recurrent if there exists an $\varepsilon > 0$, $\theta < \infty$, a positive integer m, and a set $K \in \mathbb{B}_\mu$ s.t.

$$\int_{\mathbf{R}^k} P^m(x, \mathrm{d}y)g(y) \leq g(x) - \varepsilon, \qquad x \in K^c$$

$$\int_{\mathbf{R}^k} P^m(x, \mathrm{d}y)g(y) \leq \theta, \qquad x \in K.$$

(Private communication from D. Tjøstheim (1988))

(31) Consider the set-up of Example 2.8. Suppose we clothe this skeleton by

$$\xi_t = \begin{cases} \mathbf{A}\xi_{t-1} + \begin{bmatrix} \varepsilon_t \\ 0 \end{bmatrix} & \text{if } X_{t-2} > 0 \\[2mm] \mathbf{B}\xi_{t-1} + \begin{bmatrix} \varepsilon_t \\ 0 \end{bmatrix} & \text{if } X_{t-2} \leq 0 \end{cases}$$

where $\{\varepsilon_t\}$ are independent random variables with $\mathcal{N}(0, 1)$ distribution. Prove that $\{\xi_t\}$ is an ergodic Markov chain on $\mathbf{R}^2$ if the eigenvalues of $A\mathbb{B}^2$ are all less than unity in modulus.

(32) Consider the first-order STAR model

$$X_t = c + \phi_2 X_{t-1} + [c' + (\phi_1 - \phi_2)X_{t-1}]F((X_{t-1} - r)/z) + \varepsilon_t$$

where F is the standard Gaussian distribution, $\varepsilon_t \sim$ IID satisfying Condition A3 of §4.1.3. As a Lyapunov function, use

$$V = \begin{cases} ax & x > 0 \\ -bx & x \leq 0 \end{cases}$$

where $a, b \in \mathbf{R}$ s.t. $a > 0$, $b > 0$, $1 > \phi_1 > -a/b$, $1 > \phi_2 > -b/a$, and verify that the model is ergodic if $\phi_1 < 1$, $\phi_2 < 1$, and $\phi_1\phi_2 < 1$.

(Chan and Tong 1986a)

(33) Consider a SETAR $(2; 0, 0)$ model

$$X_t = \begin{cases} 1 + \varepsilon_t & \text{if } X_{t-1} \leq 0 \\ -1 + \varepsilon_t & \text{if } X_{t-1} > 0 \end{cases}$$

where the ε_t are IID random variables with a uniform distribution on $[-1, 1]$. Let X_0 have a probability measure μ_0 with support $[-1, 1]$. Let U be as defined in eqn (4.11). Prove that $\omega(\mu_0) = \{\mu^{(1)}, \mu^{(2)}: U\mu^{(1)} = \mu^{(2)}, U\mu^{(2)} = \mu^{(1)}, \mu^{(1)} \neq \mu^{(2)}\}$ independent of μ_0.

(Modification of Tong 1983a, p. 109)

(34) Consider a SETARMA $(2; 1, 1, 1, 1)$ model

$$X_t = \begin{cases} aX_{t-1} + \varepsilon_t + b\varepsilon_{t-1} & \text{if } X_{t-1} \leq 0 \\ a'X_{t-1} + \varepsilon_t + b'\varepsilon_{t-1} & \text{if } X_{t-1} > 0 \end{cases}$$

where $\varepsilon_t \sim$ IID $\mathcal{N}(0, 1)$. Using the Lyapunov function approach, verify that $a < 1$, $a' < 1$, and $aa' < 1$ imply ergodicity of the model. [Hint: You may write the model in a suitable Markovian form first.]

(K. S. Chan and H. Tong, unpublished result)

(35) Consider the bilinear model (4.55). Suppose that $b_{ij} = 0$ for $j \neq p$ where $p \in \{1, 2, \ldots ,\}$. Let the model be written in the form of (4.56), with $\mathbf{B}_j = 0$, $j \neq p$. If $\mathbf{M} = (m_{ij})$, let $|M|$ denote the matrix $(|m_{ij}|)$. Let $\Gamma = \mathrm{E}\{|\mathbf{A} + \varepsilon_1 \mathbf{B}_p|\}$. Prove that if $\rho(\Gamma) < 1$ then the model is stationary. Compare this condition with $\rho(\mathbf{A} \otimes \mathbf{A} + \sigma^2 \mathbf{B}_p \otimes \mathbf{B}_p) < 1$.

(Liu 1989)

5
Statistical aspects

Dim and dark,
Yet within it is an essence.
This essence is quite genuine
And within it is something that can be tested.

Ch. XXI Lao Tzu

5.1 Introduction

We have been looking at the ensemble properties, that is properties pertaining to the collection of all realizations/sample paths. Under ergodicity/stationarity, these properties will tell us about the long-run behaviour of each realization. Now, we are going to study the 'inverse problem' of inferring something about the ensemble properties from one, or more precisely part of one, single realization. This falls within the domain of statistical inference. Before performing any formal statistical procedure, it is always good practice to examine the data graphically.

5.2 Graphical methods for initial data analysis

A number of graphical methods have been in routine use in time series modelling. For example, time series data plots, sample autocorrelation function plots, sample partial autocorrelation function plots, sample spectral density functions, histograms, plots of differenced data, plots of instantaneously transformed data, etc., have been used as standard practice. These are very valuable tools whether our primary interests are linear modelling or not. We shall therefore assume that our readers are familiar with these techniques and will include them in their basic toolkits for non-linear modelling. What will be described in this section is a collection of extra tools which we have found useful and would recommend to the readers for addition to their tool kits.

Let $x_1, x_2, \ldots, x_N$ denote the observed sample.

Fig. 5.1. Reverse data plot of Fig. 1.4

5.2.1 REVERSE DATA PLOTS

These are plots going backward in time, that is time plots with the time axis reversed.

Comparing Fig. 5.1 with Fig. 1.4, we can quickly detect the time irreversibility of the data. Experimenting with several vertical scales while keeping the same horizontal scale can often aid visual detection of interesting features (see e.g. Cleveland and McGill 1987).

5.2.2 DIRECTED SCATTER DIAGRAMS

These are diagrams of (x_t, x_{t-j}), $j = \pm 1, \pm 2, \ldots, \pm p$, say, with adjacent points, that is (x_t, x_{t-j}) and (x_{t+1}, x_{t+1-j}), linked by straight lines.

These are the discrete-time analogues of the phase diagrams (phase planes) described in Chapter 2. A cyclical pheomenon analogous to that of a limit cycle is discernible in Fig. 5.2. These plots were included in the time series toolkit no later than 1980. (See e.g. Tong 1980*a*; Tong and Lim 1980, p. 285.) Interestingly, a similar idea was introduced into the analysis of chaos by physicists around the same time under the name of *delay maps* (see e.g. Packard *et al.* 1980; Takens 1981), j playing the role of a time delay.

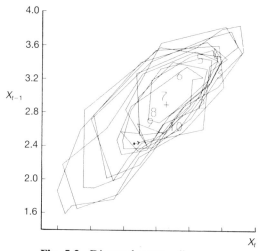

Fig. 5.2. Directed scatter diagram

In fact, Yule (1927, p. 277) gave (undirected) scatter plots of $(x_t, x_{t+1} + x_{t-1})$ for the Wolf sunspot numbers*.

5.2.3 BIVARIATE HISTOGRAMS

These can give useful visual indication of the non-normality of the data.

Figure 5.3 clearly shows non-normality in the form of an 'L'-shaped base and apparent bimodality. Formal tests for bimodality may be incorporated. An example will be given in §7.2.3.

5.2.4 LAGGED REGRESSION

Non-parametric estimates of regression functions of X_t on X_{t+j}, $(j = 1, 2, \ldots, p$, say) provide valuable information about the non-linearity of the time series. Let $m_j(x)$ denote $\mathrm{E}(X_t \mid X_{t+j} = x)$. The index of linearity introduced in §4.2.11 suggests that estimate of these $m_j(x)$, denoted by $\hat{m}_j(x)$, may be useful for the identification of the delay parameter. We shall illustrate this point later. We now describe the so-called kernel methods of obtaining a non-parametric estimate of $m_j(x)$. Let $\{\delta_N(z)\}$ be a sequence of non-negative functions of z, of total area unity. (These are also called smoothing functions of windows.) As $N \to \infty$, $\delta_N(z)$ is to tend to the Dirac delta function. Such a sequence may be realized by introducing a fixed function $k(z) \geq 0$, $\int k(z)\, dz = 1$ and a B_N so that the family is $\{B_N^{-1}k(z/B_N)\}$, that is $\delta_N(z) = B_N^{-1}k(z/B_N)$, with $B_N \to 0$ as $N \to \infty$. For convenience, we further require $\int zk(z)\, dz = 0$. Given the observations $\{x_1, x_2, \ldots, x_N\}$, a kernel estimate of $m_j(x)$ may be given

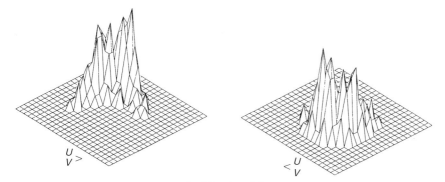

Fig. 5..3. Bivariate histogram

* Incidentally, Yule was probably responsible for wrongly attributing the series to Wolfer: see Izenman (1983).

for $j = 1, 2, \ldots, p \ (\ll N)$:

$$\hat{m}_{j,N}(x) = \sum_{t=1}^{N-j} x_t \delta_N(x - x_{t+j}) \Big/ \sum_{t=1}^{N-j} \delta_N(x - x_{t+j}) \qquad (5.1a)$$

and

$$\hat{m}_{-j,N}(x) = \sum_{t=j+1}^{N} x_t \delta_N(x - x_{t-j}) \Big/ \sum_{t=j+1}^{N} \delta_N(x - x_{t-j}). \qquad (5.1b)$$

The second subscript, namely N, emphasizes the dependence of the estimate on the sample size. A simple form of $k(z)$ is given by

$$k(z) = \begin{cases} 1 - |z| & \text{for } |z| \le 1 \\ 0 & \text{otherwise.} \end{cases}$$

Of course, other specific forms may be used (cf. windows in spectral analysis; see e.g. Priestley 1981; Brockwell and Davis 1987). Sampling properties of $\hat{m}_{\pm j,N}(x)$ are given by Robinson (1983) following earlier

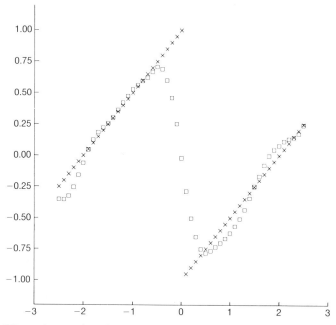

Fig. 5.4. Discontinuous function

$$X_t = \begin{cases} 0.5X_{t-1} + 1 + \varepsilon_t & \text{if } X_{t-1} \le 0 \\ 0.5X_{t-1} - 1 + \varepsilon_t & \text{if } X_{t-1} > 0 \end{cases}$$

$\varepsilon_t \sim \mathcal{N}(0, 1)$: X, true values; $\square$, fitted values; sample size 1000

works by Watson (1964) and Rosenblatt (1969). For example, under geometric ergodicity of $\{X_t\}$, smoothness of $m_1(x)$ and $NB_N \to 0$ as $N \to \infty$, Robinson (op. cit.) has shown that $(NB)^{1/2}[\hat{m}_{1,N}(x) - m_1(x)]$ converges in distribution to $\mathcal{N}(0, kV(x)/h(x))$ where $k = \int k^2(z)\,dz$, $V(x) = \text{Var}[X_t \mid X_{t-1} = x]$ and $h(x)$ is the stationary marginal density of X_t (assumed to exist). Azzalini *et al.* (1989) have discussed the use of cross-validation to determine B_N. Figure 1.6 clearly reveals nonlinearity in the conditional mean of the data. In practice, estimates corresponding to the two ends of the horizontal axis generally tend to exhibit greater sampling fluctuations. Moreover, the method 'smooths' over discontinuity points as illustrated by Figs 5.4 and 5.5.

It is also sometimes useful to go beyond the one-dimensional lagged regression into, for example, the two-dimensional case such as $E(X_t \mid X_{t-j} = x, X_{t-k} = y)$, etc. as in Fig. 5.6. Another generalization is to regress X_t on an explanatory variable, say Z_t as in Fig. 1.7

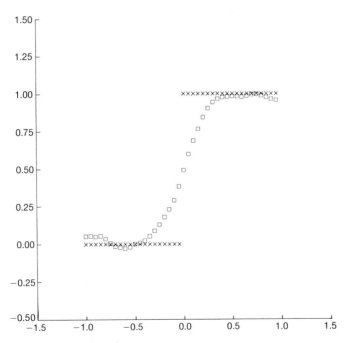

Fig. 5.5. Discontinuous function

$$X_t = \begin{cases} \varepsilon_t & \text{if } X_{t-1} \le 0 \\ 1 + \varepsilon_t & \text{if } X_{t-1} > 0 \end{cases}$$

$\varepsilon_t \sim \mathcal{N}(0, 1)$. X, true values; $\square$, fitted values; sample size 1000

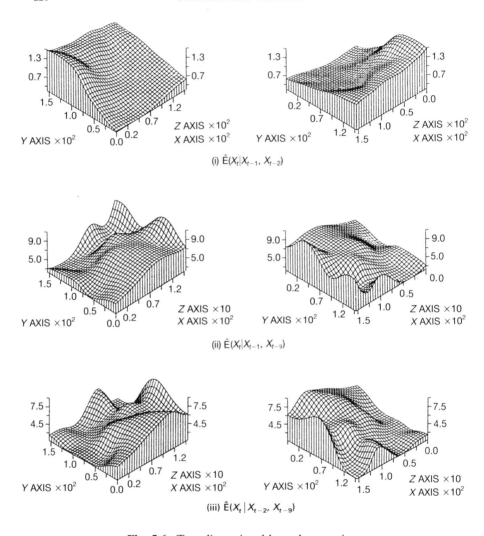

Fig. 5.6. Two-dimensional lagged regression

Conditional variances, that is $\text{var}(X_t \mid X_s)$, may be constructed in a similar way and these are very informative too (Fig. 5.7).

The use of $\text{E}(X_t \mid X_s)$ and $\text{var}(X_t \mid X_s)$ may be motivated by the formalization introduced at the end of §3.2.

5.25   SAMPLE BISPECTRA

We have commented that the simple spectral density function and sample second-order sample moments are always included in a time series

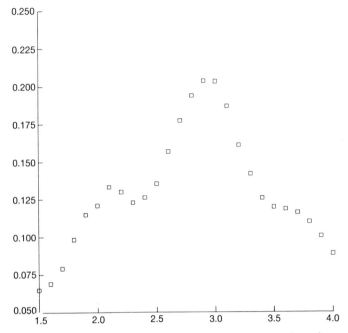

Fig. 5.7. Conditional variance (non-parameteric estimate)

analyst's basic toolkit. A natural addition of a similar type is the sample bispectral density function, which is just the double Fourier transform of sample third-order moments, appropriately smoothed, because as we have seen in Chapter 4 (§§4.2.9 and 4.4.4) the theoretical (i.e. population) bispectral density function is the double Fourier transform of the third-order moments. Brillinger (1965) and Subba Rao and Gabr (1984) may be consulted for further details.

As we have commented there, it would aid revealing non-normality and time irreversibility. Figure 5.8 suggests that the data are non-normal and Fig. 5.9 suggests that the data are time irreversible.

5.3 Tests for Linearity

Formal tests for linearity may be used to complement the informal graphical methods. These tests may be developed in either the frequency domain or the time domain. In the former, a natural approach is to utilize higher-order spectra. In the latter, tests may be constructed within parametric models.

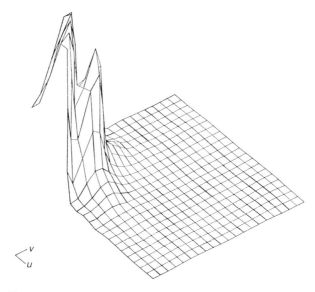

Fig. 5.8. Modulus of a sample bispectral density function

ω_2	0.00	0.05	0.10	0.15	0.20	0.25	0.30	0.35	0.40	0.45	0.50	0.55	0.60	0.65
1.00	−0.00													
0.95	−0.00	−0.62	−1.28											
0.90	0.00	0.33	−1.08	−1.63	−1.96									
0.85	−0.00	1.22	0.37	−1.43	−1.95	−2.37	−2.88							
0.80	−0.00	1.27	0.98	−0.91	−1.78	−2.35	−2.89	2.80	2.26					
0.75	−0.00	1.15	1.29	−1.05	−1.65	−2.19	−2.86	2.78	2.22	1.71	0.97			
0.70	−0.00	1.02	1.59	2.83	−2.12	−2.20	−2.78	2.74	2.15	1.58	0.85	0.52	0.58	
0.65	−0.00	0.84	1.66	2.49	−3.09	−2.73	−2.92	2.67	2.10	1.61	0.92	0.50	0.58	0.58
0.60	−0.00	0.72	1.49	2.26	2.79	3.07	3.07	2.60	2.05	1.74	1.52	1.30	0.73	
0.55	−3.14	1.22	1.50	1.77	2.30	2.77	2.88	2.60	2.02	1.71	1.70	1.99		
0.50	−3.14	2.50	1.83	1.67	1.67	2.05	2.56	2.54	2.07	1.62	1.55			
0.45	−3.14	2.87	2.09	1.80	1.69	1.68	1.97	2.31	2.19	1.81				
0.40	−3.14	2.71	2.06	1.82	1.75	1.75	1.84	2.11	2.24					
0.35	−3.14	1.78	1.65	1.62	1.62	1.68	1.82	1.99						
0.30	−3.14	2.38	1.60	1.54	1.50	1.50	1.63							
0.25	−3.14	2.91	1.96	1.60	1.53	1.48								
0.20	−3.14	2.96	2.57	1.83	1.60									
0.15	3.14	2.91	2.77	2.42										
0.10	3.14	2.89	2.79											
0.05	3.14	2.99												
0.00	0.00													

ω_1

Fig. 5.9. Argument of a sample bispectral density function

There are now about a dozen such tests available in the literature. Consideration of space, experience, and idiosyncrasy dictate that these tests will be described in varying degrees of detail. Missing details can be recovered in the references cited.

These tests may be grouped into two categories: (i) Portmanteau tests, (ii) tests with specific alternatives. The first three approaches to be described below belong to (i); the others belong to (ii).

5.3.1 BISPECTRAL APPROACH

This approach is included mainly for historical reasons as it is probably the earliest test in the time series literature which specifically addresses the problem of testing for linearity. Accordingly, our description will be brief. The original form of the test is due to Subba Rao and Gabr (1980), which has been improved by Hinich (1982).

Suppose that the time series $\{X_t\}$ has the *linear* representation (in mean square)

$$X_t = \sum_{s=0}^{\infty} h_s \varepsilon_{t-s} \qquad (5.2)$$

where the ε_t are i.i.d. random variables with zero mean and finite variance and h_s is square summable. It is a simple exercise to check that for all $k \geq 2$ and for all $\omega_1, \omega_2, \ldots, \omega_k$, $(-\pi \leq \omega_i \leq \pi)$, the linear representation (5.2) implies the constancy of the ratios $|h_k(\omega_1, \ldots, \omega_k)|^2$ $\{h(\omega_1) \ldots h(\omega_k) h(\omega_1 + \ldots + \omega_k)\}^{-1}$, where h_k is the (non-normalized) cumulant spectral density function of order $k+1$ and $h \equiv h_1$. It is clearly not practical to check the constancy of all ratios. As a *first* step, we may check the constancy of the ratio with $k = 2$, that is the 'scaled' bispectral density. Further, if ε_t is Gaussian, the ratio (with $k = 2$) is identically zero.

Given $X_1, \ldots, X_N$, the above discussion naturally suggests a test statistic of the form

$$\hat{S} = \sum_{\omega_1} \sum_{\omega_2} \frac{|\hat{h}_2(\omega_1, \omega_2)|^2}{\hat{h}(\omega_1)\hat{h}(\omega_2)\hat{h}(\omega_1 + \omega_2)}$$

where the spectral functions are replaced by their (smoothed) sample estimates and the double summation is over a suitable grid of points. The asymptotic distribution is χ^2 under either the hypothesis (5.2) or the hypothesis (5.2) together with ε_t Gaussian.

Chan and Tong (1986b) have reported difficulties facing users of the original Subba Rao–Gabr test in that great care is needed in designing the smoothing of the spectral estimates. Slightly different smoothing parameters can result in vastly different $\hat{S}$ values. Subba Rao and Gabr

(1984) have given listings of their FORTRAN computer program for implementing the test. An alternative program was developed by Professor Doug Patterson incorporating Hinich's modification. Ashley *et al.* (1986) and Brockett *et al.* (1988) have discussed more recent developments in the area.

The advantage of the approach is that no specific parametric model is assumed. In this sense, it is *non-parametric*. However, further thought will reveal that the smoothing operation in spectral estimates actually *parametrizes* the approach. This can lead to problems because often great care is needed and no stable results are assured, if the Subba Rao–Gabr program is adopted (see e.g. Chan and Tong 1986*b*). Hinich's improvement is valuable, which stabilizes the results and renders it less sensitive to outliers. However, our experience shows that (i) it is demanding on sample size; (ii) it lacks power generally. In particular, it will not be able to detect non-linear autoregression with a skew-symmetric skeleton and symmetrically distributed noise, that is

$$X_t = f(X_{t-1}, \dots, X_{t-k}) + \varepsilon_t$$

where ε_t has a symmetric distribution and $f(x_1, \dots, x_k) = -f(-x_1, \dots, -x_k)$.

5.3.2 APPROACH BASED ON EXAMINING SQUARES OF TIME SERIES DATA

The tests to be described in this subsection are of the diagnostic type. The approach is motivated by the result which states that if $\{X_t\}$ is a stationary Gaussian time series then

$$\rho_\tau(X_t^2) = \{\rho_\tau(X_t)\}^2, \quad \text{all } \tau \tag{5.3}$$

where

$$\rho_\tau(Z_t) = \text{corr}(Z_{t+\tau}, Z_t). \tag{5.4}$$

Granger and Andersen (1978) have suggested that departures from this result tend to indicate the possibility of non-linearity. Maravall (1983) has considered the use of $\rho_\tau(\hat{\varepsilon}_t^2)$, where the $\hat{\varepsilon}_t^2$ are the fitted residuals. Later, McLeod and Li (1983) proposed a portmanteau test for linearity along these lines. Specifically, let $\{\hat{\varepsilon}_1, \hat{\varepsilon}_2, \dots, \hat{\varepsilon}_N\}$ be the fitted residuals from an ARMA model. Let r_k denote the sample autocorrelation of the squared residuals, that is

$$r_k = \sum_{j=1}^{N-k} (\hat{\varepsilon}_j^2 - \hat{\sigma}^2)(\hat{\varepsilon}_{j+k}^2 - \hat{\sigma}^2) \Big/ \sum_{j=1}^{N} (\hat{\varepsilon}_j^2 - \hat{\sigma}^2)^2$$

where

$$\hat{\sigma}^2 = \sum_{j=1}^{N} \hat{\varepsilon}_j^2 / N.$$

Analogous to the Ljung–Box portmanteau statistic, McLeod and Li proposed the portmanteau statistic

$$Q = N(N+2) \sum_{k=1}^{m} r_k^2 / (N-k) \qquad (5.5)$$

to detect model mis-specification within the ARMA family and, owing to the fact that squared residuals are used, the Q statistic might have some use in detecting non-linearity, possibly in the direction of bilinearity. The asymptotic null distribution is χ_m^2 if the true innovations are independent. However, it is not clear if it is possible to distinguish between non-linearity and model mis-specification when a significant result is found. As an alternative, Lawrence and Lewis (1985) have suggested examining the cross-covariances between $\{\hat{\varepsilon}_t\}$ and $\{\hat{\varepsilon}_t^2\}$. These should be zero for linear models.

The above tests are probably more appropriate at the post-model-fitting stage. Comparative studies by Davies and Petruccelli (1985) and by Luukkonen *et al.* (1988b) suggest that the McLeod and Li test is of value when testing linearity against ARCH-type alternatives but is otherwise inferior to the other time domain tests.

5.3.3 APPROACH BASED ON TUKEY'S ONE-DEGREE-OF-FREEDOM TEST FOR NON-ADDITIVITY

Let us consider testing

$$H_0 : X_t = a_0 + \sum_{j=0}^{M} a_j X_{t-j} + \varepsilon_t \qquad (5.6)$$

where $\{\varepsilon_t\}$ are i.i.d. random variables with zero mean, variance σ^2, and finite fourth moment. Under the usual root condition of the AR operator, X_t admits a linear representation. We may compare this with a linear regression. We may similarly compare the general non-linear expansion of a stationary time series discussed in §4.7 with polynomial regressions. Exploiting the analogy, Keenan (1985) has constructed a test of H_0 employing mechanics similar to Tukey's one-degree-of freedom test for non-additivity. The test runs as follows. Let $(X_1, \ldots, X_N)$ denote the observations.

1. Regress X_t on $\{1, X_{t-1}, \ldots, X_{t-M}\}$, M being a large but fixed positive integer; calculate the fitted values $\{\hat{X}_t\}$, the fitted residuals, $\{\hat{e}_t\}$, for $t = M+1, \ldots, N$, and the residual sum of squares, $\sum \hat{e}_t^2$, which is to be denoted RSS.

2. Regress $\hat{X}_t^2$ on $\{1, X_{t-1}, \ldots, X_{t-M}\}$ and calculate the fitted residuals, $\{\hat{\xi}_t\}$, for $t = M + 1, \ldots, N$.

3. Regress $(\hat{e}_{M+1}, \ldots, \hat{e}_N)$ on $(\hat{\xi}_{M+1}, \ldots, \hat{\xi}_N)$; obtain

$$\eta = \eta_0 \left(\sum_{t=M+1}^{N} \hat{\xi}_t^2 \right)^{1/2}$$

where η_0 is the regression coefficient, and form the test statistic

$$F = \frac{\eta^2(N - 2M - 2)}{\text{RSS} - \eta^2}.$$

Theorem 5.1: Under H_0 the asymptotic distribution of F is an F distribution with degrees of freedom $1, N - 2M - 2$.

Proof. It suffices to prove that η is asymptotically $\mathcal{N}(0, \sigma^2)$. The rest follows from standard arguments in linear model theory in statistics.

Define $\mathbf{Z}_t$ and Θ by

$$\mathbf{Z}_t = (1, X_{t-1}, \ldots, X_{t-M}) \qquad \Theta^T = (a_0, a_1, \ldots, a_M).$$

Then model (5.6) may be written in the matrix form

$$\begin{bmatrix} X_{M+1} \\ \vdots \\ X_N \end{bmatrix} = \begin{bmatrix} \mathbf{Z}_{M+1} \\ \vdots \\ \mathbf{Z}_N \end{bmatrix} \Theta + \begin{bmatrix} \varepsilon_{M+1} \\ \vdots \\ \varepsilon_N \end{bmatrix}.$$

Define $\mathbf{A}_N$ and $\mathbf{V}_N$ by

$$\mathbf{A}_N = (N - M)^{-1} \sum_{t=M+1}^{N} \mathbf{Z}_t^T \mathbf{Z}_t \qquad \mathbf{V}_N = (N - M)^{-1} \sum_{t=M+1}^{N} \mathbf{Z}_t^T X_t.$$

The least-squares estimate of Θ is

$$\hat{\Theta} = \mathbf{A}_N^{-1} \mathbf{V}_N.$$

Clearly for $t = M + 1, \ldots, N$,

$$\hat{X}_t = \mathbf{Z}_t \hat{\Theta} \tag{5.7}$$

and

$$\hat{e}_t = X_t - \hat{X}_t = \mathbf{Z}_t(\Theta - \hat{\Theta}) + \varepsilon_t. \tag{5.8}$$

From step 2,

$$\hat{\xi}_t = \hat{X}_t^2 - \mathbf{Z}_t \mathbf{A}_N^{-1} \mathbf{Q}_N \tag{5.9}$$

where

$$\mathbf{Q}_N = (N - M)^{-1} \sum_{t=M+1}^{N} \mathbf{Z}_t^T \hat{X}_t^2$$

$$= (N - M)^{-1} \sum_{t=M+1}^{N} \mathbf{Z}_t^T \hat{\Theta}^T \mathbf{Z}_t^T \mathbf{Z}_t \hat{\Theta}. \tag{5.10}$$

Standard theory of autoregressive model inference gives

$$\hat{\Theta} - \Theta = o_p(1) \tag{5.11}$$

and

$$\mathbf{A}_N^{-1}\mathbf{V}_N - \mathbf{A}^{-1}\mathbf{V} = o_p(1) \tag{5.12}$$

where $\mathbf{A}$ and $\mathbf{V}$ are limits in probability of $\mathbf{A}_N$ and $\mathbf{V}_N$ respectively. Let $\mathbf{Q}$ be the column vector whose first component is

$$a_0^2 + 2a_0\mu \sum_{j=1}^{M} a_j + \sum_{i=1}^{M}\sum_{j=1}^{M} a_i a_j \, \text{cov}(X_i, X_j)$$

and whose kth component, for $2 \le k \le M+1$, is

$$a_0^2 + 2a_0 \sum_{j=1}^{M} a_j \, \text{cov}(X_j, X_k) + \sum_{i=1}^{M}\sum_{j=1}^{M} a_i a_j \mathrm{E}[(X_i - \mu)(X_j - \mu)(X_k - \mu)]$$

where $\mu = \mathrm{E}X_t$.

By (5.11), $(\mathbf{Q}_N - \mathbf{Q})$ is also $o_p(1)$. The numerator of η is

$$N^{-1/2} \sum_{t=M+1}^{N} \hat{e}_t \hat{\xi}_t \tag{5.13}$$

and substituting (5.7), (5.8), and (5.9) in (5.13), we have

$$\text{numerator of } \eta = N^{-1/2} \sum_{t=M+1}^{N} \varepsilon_t(\Theta^T \mathbf{Z}_t^T \mathbf{Z}_t \Theta - \mathbf{Z}_t \mathbf{A}^{-1}\mathbf{Q}) + o_p(1). \tag{5.14}$$

Because the summands in (5.14) form a stationary and ergodic martingale difference sequence with constant variance $\sigma^2\delta$, where $\delta = \mathrm{E}\{(\Theta^T \mathbf{Z}_t^T \mathbf{Z}_t \Theta - \mathbf{Z}_t \mathbf{A}^{-1}\mathbf{Q})^2\}$, the martingale central limit theorem (Appendix 1) implies that the numerator is asymptotically $\mathcal{N}(0, \sigma^2\delta)$. The denominator of η is $N^{-1/2}(\sum_{t=M+1}^{N} \hat{\xi}_t^2)^{1/2}$. Now, on using (5.7) and (5.9),

$$N^{-1} \sum_{t=M+1}^{N} \hat{\xi}_t^2 = N^{-1} \sum_{t=M+1}^{N} (\Theta^T \mathbf{Z}_t^T \mathbf{Z}_t \Theta - \mathbf{Z}_t \mathbf{A}^{-1}\mathbf{Q})^2 + o_p(1)$$

$$= \delta + o_p(1)$$

because $\{X_t\}$ is stationary and ergodic. Hence η is asymptotically $\mathcal{N}(0, \sigma)$. $\square$

Tsay (1986) later improved Keenan's procedure so as to increase its power. The improved version goes as follows:

(T1) Regress X_t on $\{1, X_{t-1}, \ldots, X_{t-M}\}$ and calculate the fitted residuals $\{\hat{e}_{M+1}, \ldots, \hat{e}_N\}$. The regression model will be denoted by

$$X_t = \mathbf{W}_t \mathbf{A}^T + e_t \tag{5.15}$$

where $\mathbf{W}_t = (1, X_{t-1}, \ldots, X_{t-M})$ and $\mathbf{A} = (a_0, \ldots, a_M)$. We denote $\mathbf{W}_t \mathbf{A}^T$ by $\hat{X}_t$.

(T2) Let $\mathbf{Z}_t$ denote the $m = \frac{1}{2}M(M+1)$-dimensional row vector obtained from the symmetric matrix $\mathbf{U}_t^T\mathbf{U}_t$, where $\mathbf{U}_t = (\hat{X}_{t-1}, \ldots, \hat{X}_{t-M})$, by the usual column stacking operation but using only those elements on or below the main diagonal of each column. Regress the *vector* $\mathbf{Z}_t$ on $\{1, X_{t-1}, \ldots, X_{t-M}\}$ and obtain the fitted residual vectors $\{\hat{\boldsymbol{\xi}}_{M+1}, \ldots, \hat{\boldsymbol{\xi}}_N\}$. Here, instead of a univariate regression, a multivariate regression is used, that is

$$\mathbf{Z}_t = \mathbf{W}_t\mathbf{H} + \boldsymbol{\xi}_t. \tag{5.16}$$

(T3) Regress $(\hat{e}_{M+1}, \ldots, \hat{e}_N)$ on $(\hat{\boldsymbol{\xi}}_{M+1}, \ldots, \hat{\boldsymbol{\xi}}_N)$. That is, fit

$$\hat{e}_t = \hat{\boldsymbol{\xi}}_t\boldsymbol{\beta} + a_t \qquad (t = M+1, \ldots, N). \tag{5.17}$$

Let $\bar{F}$ be the F ratio of the mean square of regression to the mean square of error. That is,

$$\bar{F} = \frac{(\sum \hat{\boldsymbol{\xi}}_t\hat{e}_t)(\sum \hat{\boldsymbol{\xi}}_t^T\hat{\boldsymbol{\xi}}_t)^{-1}(\sum \hat{\boldsymbol{\xi}}_t^T\hat{e}_t)(N - M - m - 1)}{m \sum \hat{a}_t^2} \tag{5.18}$$

where the summations extend from $M+1$ to N and $\hat{a}_t$ is the fitted residual of (5.17). Tsay (1986) proved that, under H_0, the asymptotic distribution of $\bar{F}$ is an F distribution with degrees of freedom $\frac{1}{2}M(M+1)$, $N - \frac{1}{2}M(M+3) - 1$.

Tsay (1986) considered a further modification of $\bar{F}$ in order to cope with contemporaneous non-linearity such as the presence of $\varepsilon_t\varepsilon_{t-1}$ in the expansion of X_t. He has also considered $H_0 : X_t \sim \text{ARMA}(p, q)$.

The advantages of the approach are

(1) it is easy to implement involving little subjective choice of parameters, M being the only one;

(2) it is quick;

(3) it seems to give stable results generally.

The disadvantages of the approach are

(1') it is probably powerless in detecting *odd* power expansions of the form

$$H_1' : X_t = \sum a_j\varepsilon_{t-j} + \sum\sum\sum a_{jkl}\varepsilon_{t-j}\varepsilon_{t-k}\varepsilon_{t-l}, \text{ etc.} \tag{5.19}$$

because the approach is implicitly testing H_0 in the direction of

$$H_1 : X_t = \sum a_j\varepsilon_{t-j} + \sum\sum a_{jk}\varepsilon_{t-j}\varepsilon_{t-k} \tag{5.20}$$

although the alternative hypothesis has never been spelt out in

Keenan (1985) or Tsay (1986). However, see Chan and Tong (1986b).*

(2') It is of questionable value when the true non-linear model requires very large lags in the power expansion for any moderate degree of accuracy, for example a SETAR model.

5.3.4 LAGRANGE MULTIPLIER APPROACH

In none of the above tests is the non-linear alternative clearly stated. They therefore belong to the category of portmanteau tests. We now turn our attention to tests with clearly stated alternatives. The null hypothesis is naturally a linear model of some description which is, for convenience, a sub-class of the non-linear models specified under the general hypothesis, that is we envisage a nested situation. We may proceed in any one of the three variants of the likelihood approach, namely the likelihood ratio test, the Wald test, and the Lagrange multiplier (LM) test. An elementary but instructive exposition is given by Buse (1982). Saikkonen and Luukkonen (1988) and Luukkonen et al. (1988a,b) are relevant references. The Lagrange multiplier variant is the most convenient for our purpose because, at this stage, we may not wish to embark on the more time-consuming estimation of a non-linear alternative. In circles outside econometrics and present-day time series analysis, the Lagrange multiplier test is usually known as the score test. The latter name predates the former.

Symbolically, we may express the LM test statistic by

$$\text{LM} = S(\hat{\boldsymbol{\theta}}_{H_0})^T I(\hat{\boldsymbol{\theta}}_{H_0})^{-1} S(\hat{\boldsymbol{\theta}}_{H_0}) \tag{5.21}$$

where S denotes the column vector of first derivatives of the log likelihood (i.e. the score statistics for $\boldsymbol{\theta}$), I denotes Fisher's information matrix, and $\hat{\boldsymbol{\theta}}_{H_0}$ denotes the restricted maximum likelihood estimate of $\boldsymbol{\theta}$, the parameter vector, under the null hypothesis, H_0. In the presence of nuisance parameters, say $\mathbf{v}$, we need to modify the expression (5.21). Specifically, let $\boldsymbol{\theta}$ denote the vector of parameters of interest and $\mathbf{v}$ the vector of nuisance parameters. Under the null hypothesis $H_0 : \boldsymbol{\theta} = \boldsymbol{\theta}_0$, let the constraint maximum likelihood estimate of $\mathbf{v}$ be denoted by $\hat{\mathbf{v}}_0$. Let the vector of score statistics for $\boldsymbol{\theta}$ evaluated at $\boldsymbol{\theta}_0$ be denoted by $S(\boldsymbol{\theta}_0, \hat{\mathbf{v}}_0)$. The information matrix, $\mathbf{I}(\boldsymbol{\theta}, \mathbf{v})$, may be partitioned according to the partition of the vector $(\boldsymbol{\theta}, \mathbf{v})$:

$$\mathbf{I}(\boldsymbol{\theta}, \mathbf{v}) = \begin{bmatrix} \mathbf{I}_{11} & \mathbf{I}_{12} \\ \mathbf{I}_{12}^T & \mathbf{I}_{22} \end{bmatrix}.$$

---

*Chan and Tong (1986b, p. 221) have inadvertently mis-stated H_0. The analysis of the paper is not affected.

The LM test statistic for H_0 is given by

$$LM = S(\theta_0, \hat{v}_0)^T \{I_{11} - I_{12}I_{22}^{-1}I_{12}^T\}^{-1} S(\theta_0, \hat{v}_0) \qquad (5.22)$$

where all I_{ij} are calculated at $(\theta, \hat{v}_0)$.

5.3.4.1 General formulation We assume that all the 'innovations', the ε_t, are i.i.d. random variables with a $\mathcal{N}(0, \sigma^2)$ distribution. Suppose we observe $X_1, \ldots, X_N$. The unknown parameters may be estimated by maximizing the (conditional) log likelihood conditional on $X_0, X_{-1}, \ldots, X_{-p+1}$, where p is an appropriate positive constant to be defined. The null hypothesis H_0 always takes the form

$$H_0 : X_t + a_1 X_{t-1} + \ldots + a_p X_{t-p} = \mu + \varepsilon_t \qquad (5.23)$$

where $\varepsilon_t \sim \mathcal{N}(0, \sigma^2)$, $a_p \neq 0$, and the zeros of the polynomial $a(z) = z^p + a_1 z^{p-1} + \ldots + a_p$ lie inside the unit circle. Let $\hat{\mu}$, $\hat{a}_j$ be the (conditional) maximum likelihood estimates (MLE) under H_0 of μ and a_j respectively. Define

$$\hat{\varepsilon}_t = X_t + \hat{a}_1 X_{t-1} + \ldots + \hat{a}_p X_{t-p} - \hat{\mu}, \qquad t = 1, \ldots, N \qquad (5.24)$$

and the MLE of σ^2 under H_0 is

$$\hat{\sigma}^2 = N^{-1} \sum_{t=1}^{N} \hat{\varepsilon}_t^2.$$

5.3.4.2 The general model is bilinear We consider the general hypothesis

$$H_{BL} : X_t + a_1 X_{t-1} + \ldots + a_p X_{t-p} = \mu + \varepsilon_t + \sum_{i=1}^{m} \sum_{j=1}^{k} c_{ij} \varepsilon_{t-i} X_{t-j} \quad (k \leq p + 1).$$
$$(5.25)$$

H_0 is therefore equivalent to $H_{BL0} : c_{ij} = 0$, $i = 1, \ldots, m$; $j = 1, \ldots, k$. The log likelihood under H_{BL} is (on ignoring constant terms)

$$L = -\frac{N}{2} \ln \sigma^2 - \frac{1}{2} \sigma^{-2} \sum_{t=1}^{N} \varepsilon_t^2. \qquad (5.26)$$

Here,

$$\theta = (c_{11}, \ldots, c_{1k}, \ldots, c_{m1}, \ldots, c_{mk})$$

and

$$v = (a_1, a_2, \ldots, a_p, \mu).$$

Now,

$$\frac{\partial \varepsilon_t}{\partial c_{ij}} = -\varepsilon_{t-i} X_{t-j}, \quad (i = 1, \ldots, m; j = 1, \ldots, k) \tag{5.27}$$

$$\frac{\partial \varepsilon_t}{\partial \mu} = 1 \tag{5.28}$$

$$\frac{\partial \varepsilon_t}{\partial a_j} = X_{t-j}, \quad (j = 1, \ldots, m). \tag{5.29}$$

After some tedious algebra (which the reader may try as an exercise), the LM test statistic for H_{BL0} is given by

$$\mathrm{LM(BL)} = \hat{\sigma}^{-2} \left(\sum_{t=1}^{N} \mathbf{Z}_{1t} \hat{\varepsilon}_t \right)^T (\mathbf{M}_{11} - \mathbf{M}_{10} \mathbf{M}_{00}^{-1} \mathbf{M}_{01})^{-1} \left(\sum_{t=1}^{N} \mathbf{Z}_{1t} \hat{\varepsilon}_t \right) \tag{5.30}$$

where

$$\mathbf{M}_{i0} = \mathbf{M}_{0i}^T = \sum_{t=1}^{N} \mathbf{Z}_{it} \mathbf{Z}_{0t}^T, \quad i = 0, 1$$

$$\mathbf{M}_{11} = \sum_{t=1}^{N} \mathbf{Z}_{1t} \mathbf{Z}_{1t}^T$$

$$\mathbf{Z}_{0t} = (-1, X_{t-1}, \ldots, X_{t-p})^T$$

$$\mathbf{Z}_{1t} = (\hat{\varepsilon}_{t-1} X_{t-1}, \hat{\varepsilon}_{t-1} X_{t-2}, \ldots, \hat{\varepsilon}_{t-m} X_{t-k})^T.$$

The LM(BL) test statistic may be identified with N times the so-called R^2 statistic (R^2 = coefficient of determination) in the artificial regression of $\hat{\varepsilon}_t$ on $\hat{\varepsilon}_{t-j} X_{t-l}$ $(j = 1, \ldots, n; l = 1, \ldots, k)$. Using the standard LM test theory, under H_{BL0} as $N \to \infty$,

$$\mathrm{LM(BL)} \rightsquigarrow \chi_{mk}^2$$

Here $\rightsquigarrow$ denotes the convergence in distribution.

5.3.4.3 Keenan's test revisited

We consider the general model which is a special type of EXPAR model

$$H_{\mathrm{KT}} : X_t + a_1 X_{t-1} + \ldots + a_p X_{t-p} + \exp\left[\eta \left(\sum_{j=1}^{p} a_j X_{t-j} \right)^2 \right] = \mu + \varepsilon_t \tag{5.31}$$

where $p > 0$. H_0 is then equivalent to

$$H_{\mathrm{KT0}} : \eta = 0.$$

Following similar arguments as in §5.3.4.2, we may derive the LM test of H_{KT0}, which may be identified with N times the R^2 statistic of the artificial regression of $\hat{\varepsilon}_t$ on $\partial \varepsilon_t / \partial \eta$ evaluated under H_{KT0}, that is $(\hat{X}_t - \hat{\mu})^2$, where

$\hat{X}_t = X_t - \hat{\varepsilon}_t$, or equivalently the artificial regression of $\hat{\varepsilon}_t$ on $\hat{X}_t^2$ after an appropriate reparametrization of the regressors. Thus, $NR^2 = \eta^2/\hat{\sigma}^2$ with η as defined in Keenan's test described in §5.3.3. This establishes the asymptotic equivalence of Keenan's test and the LM test here.

5.3.4.4 General remarks Tsay's test may be similarly given an LM test interpretation. We need only consider the more general EXPAR model

$$H_{TS}: X_t + a_1 X_{t-1} + \ldots + a_p X_{t-p} + \exp\left(\sum_{i=1}^{p}\sum_{j=1}^{p} d_{ij} X_{t-i} X_{t-j}\right) = \mu + \varepsilon_{t_1}$$

(5.32)

and the null hypothesis

$$H_{TS0}: d_{ij} = 0, \quad (i = 1, \ldots, p; j = 1, \ldots, p).$$

McLeod and Li's test also has an LM test interpretation. One appropriate general hypothesis for this is

$$H_{ML}: \begin{cases} X_t + a_1 X_{t-1} + \ldots + a_p X_{t-p} = \mu + e_t \\ e_t = \sqrt{(h_t)}\varepsilon_t \text{ where } \varepsilon_t \text{ are i.i.d. } \mathcal{N}(0, 1) \text{ and} \\ h_t = \sigma^2 + \alpha_1 e_{t-1}^2 + \ldots + \alpha_q e_{t-q}^2. \end{cases}$$

(5.33)

In this case the null hypothesis is

$$H_{ML0}: \alpha_1 = \ldots = \alpha_q = 0.$$

Naturally, other models may be entertained as the general hypothesis, for example a STAR model, leading to the test statistic LM(STAR). Luukkonen et al. (1988a) has studied the asymptotic relative efficiency of the tests and highlighted the role played by the intercept, μ, in the statistical inference of non-linear time series models. It is intuitively clear that if any one of the time domain tests for linearity is applied, with μ set at zero, to data which have not been mean deleted, then the test is 'biased' against linearity in the sense that linearity may be rejected not because of non-linearity but because of a non-zero mean. On the other hand, with μ not set at zero and with the data mean-deleted, power may be lost unless the parameters of the non-linear model have been constrained to give zero mean.

5.3.4.5 An example from economic business cycles It is our view that if the notion of a *business cycle* is to be taken seriously it must be related to a non-linear economic system, not unlike a limit cycle in a dynamical system. There is some evidence to suggest that a business cycle may indeed be identified with a limit cycle. As an illustration, we have extracted analysis by Luukkonen and Teräsvirta (1988) of quarterly, seasonally unadjusted logarithmic indices of industrial production from 13 OECD countries (1960(i)–1986(iv)) in Table 5.1. The data have been seasonally

Table 5.1. p values of various linearity tests using quarterly, seasonally unadjusted logarithmic indices of industrial production from 13 OECD countries, 1960(i)–1986(iv)

Country	AR order $\hat{p}$	LM(STAR)	Test statistic LM(BL) $m = k = 1$	LM(BL) $m = k = 2$	McLeod–Li
Austria	5	0.048	0.020	0.096	0.046
Belgium	5	0.054	0.024	0.044	0.0002
Canada	5	0.138	0.266	0.096	0.889
FR Germany	4	0.027	0.514	0.544	0.998
Finland	1	0.891	0.459	0.927	0.720
	(4)	(0.717)	(0.880)	(0.653)	(0.873)
France	5	0.109	0.381	0.553	0.019
Italy	5	0.124	0.986	0.987	0.013
Japan	5	0.033	0.889	0.227	0.001
The Netherlands	1	0.197	0.255	0.436	0.004
	(5)	(0.676)	(0.650)	(0.632)	(0.049)
Norway	5	0.046	0.463	0.724	0.022
Sweden	4	0.998	0.820	0.934	0.989
	(5)	(0.584)	(0.932)	(0.974)	(0.945)
United Kingdom	5	0.140	0.332	0.818	0.521
	(7)	(0.278)	(0.372)	(0.808)	(0.286)
United States	2	0.033	0.201	0.110	0.082
	(6)	(0.017)	(0.170)	(0.092)	(0.061)

Note: The figures in parentheses are related to tests in which the AR model has been selected by using AIC. If there are no values in parentheses, BIC and AIC yield the same AR model. (AIC and BIC are discussed in §5.4.)

differenced by applying the filter $1 - B^4$, B being the usual back-shift operator.

Among the different directions of the alternatives of the tests listed in the above table, LM(STAR) is the only one connected with a limit cycle by virtue of the fact that the skeleton specified under this alternative hypothesis is a general STAR model. Luukkonen and Teräsvirta (1988) have argued that among these series, the W. German series shows evidence of possible 'cyclical asymmetry' in its business cycle. In our language, the series shows evidence of possible limit cycle behaviour in its skeleton. The possibility of a chaotic skeleton should not be ruled out (cf. §7.2.7 and Brock and Sayers 1988).

5.3.5 THE UNSMOOTH CASES

5.3.5.1 The non-standard problem So far we have not discussed tests for threshold autoregressions. This is due to the fact that the problem is non-standard.

Let us have the same observation set-up as in §5.3.4.1. Let the general model be a SETAR model, that is

$$H_{TAR} : X_t + \theta_0 + \theta_1 X_{t-1} + \ldots + \theta_p X_{t-p}$$
$$+ I(X_{t-d} \leq r)(\phi_0 + \phi_1 X_{t-1} + \ldots + \phi_q X_{t-q}) = \varepsilon_t \quad (5.34)$$

where d, p, and q are known non-negative integers, $0 \leq q \leq p$, the ε_t are i.i.d. $\mathcal{N}(0, \sigma^2)$ random variables, $r \in \mathbf{R}$ is the threshold parameter, and

$$I(x \leq r) = \begin{cases} 1 & \text{if } x \leq r \\ 0 & \text{otherwise.} \end{cases}$$

We shall abbreviate $I(X_{t-d} \leq r)$ to I_{t-d} if r is understood in the context. The null hypothesis is

$$H_0 : \phi_0 = \phi_1 = \ldots = \phi_q = 0.$$

For each r fixed, the likelihood ratio statistic is

$$\lambda_r = \{\hat{\sigma}^2_{(NL,r)} / \hat{\sigma}^2_{(L)}\}^{1/2N} \quad (5.35)$$

where $\hat{\sigma}^2_{(NL,r)}$ is the usual average residual sum of squares under H_{TAR} for r fixed and $\hat{\sigma}^2_{(L)}$ is that under H_0.

If r is known, then under H_0, $-2 \ln \lambda_r$ is asymptotically χ^2_{q+1}. If r is unknown, the likelihood ratio statistic becomes

$$\lambda' = \{\hat{\sigma}^2_{(NL,\hat{r})} / \hat{\sigma}^2_{(L)}\}^{1/2N} \quad (5.36)$$

where $\hat{r}$ is the maximum likelihood estimate of r. Unfortunately, under H_0, the asymptotic distribution of $-2 \ln \lambda'$ is no longer χ^2 because *the nuisance parameter r is absent under H_0*. This is a non-standard situation for which standard theory does not hold. Effectively, $-2 \ln \lambda'$ involves the maximum of a stochastic process of χ^2 random variables *which are dependent*. Of course, we could always obtain an empirical null distribution by appealing to the Monte Carlo method. (See e.g. Chan and Tong 1986b.) For a recent survey of non-standard problems, see for example Smith (1989).

5.3.5.2 The Gaussian process approach

(A) The LM test

First, let us consider the LM test approach. Using similar arguments as in §5.3.4.2 and the same notation as in §5.3.4, we can easily verify that the LM(TAR, r) test statistic *for each fixed r* may be identified with N times the R^2 in the artificial regression of $\hat{\varepsilon}_t$ on $\partial \varepsilon_t / \partial \phi_k$ ($k = 0, \ldots, q$) evaluated under H_0, that is the 'regressors' are I_{t-d}, $I_{t-d} X_{t-k}$ ($k = 0, \ldots, q$).

Let $Z_{0t} = (1, X_{t-1}, \ldots, X_{t-p})^T$ and $Z_{1t} = (I_{t-d}, I_{t-d}, X_{t-1}, \ldots,$ $I_{t-d}X_{t-q})'$. Then it follows that (see Exercise 4) for each fixed r

$$\text{LM(TAR}, r) = \hat{\sigma}^{-2}\left(\sum_{t=1}^{N} Z_{1t}\hat{\varepsilon}_t\right)^T (M_{11} - M_{10}M_{00}^{-1}M_{01})^{-1}\left(\sum_{t=1}^{N} Z_{1t}\hat{\varepsilon}_t\right) \quad (5.37)$$

where

$$M_{i0} = M_{0i}^T = \sum_{t=1}^{N} Z_{it}Z_{0t}^T, \qquad i = 0, 1$$

$$M_{11} = \sum_{t=1}^{N} Z_{1t}Z_{1t}^T.$$

Let $\xrightarrow{P}$ denote convergence in probability.

Suppose that the SETAR model is ergodic and stationary so that

(1) $(1/N)M_{11} \xrightarrow{P} EZ_{1t}Z_{1t}^T = \Sigma_r$ say, a symmetric matrix, where

$$\Sigma_r \atop (q+1)\times(q+1) = \begin{bmatrix} EI_{t-d} & EI_{t-d}X_{t-1} \ldots EI_{t-d}X_{t-1} \\ EI_{t-d}X_{t-1} & \\ \vdots & S_r \\ EI_{t-d}X_{t-q} & \end{bmatrix} \quad (5.38)$$

$$S_r = (E(I_{t-d}X_{t-i}X_{t-j}));$$

(2) $(1/N)M_{10} \xrightarrow{P} EZ_{1t}Z_{0t}^T = \Lambda_r$ say, where

$$\Lambda_r \atop (q+1)\times(p+1) = \begin{bmatrix} EI_{t-d} & EI_{t-d}X_{t-1} \ldots EI_{t-d}X_{t-p} \\ EI_{t-d}X_{t-1} & \\ \vdots & L_r \\ EI_{t-d}X_{t-q} & \end{bmatrix} \quad (5.39)$$

$$L_r = (E(I_{t-d}X_{t-i}X_{t-j}));$$

(3) $(1/N)M_{00} \xrightarrow{P} EZ_{0t}Z_{0t}^T = \Sigma$, say, a symmetric matrix, where

$$\Sigma = \begin{bmatrix} 1 & EX_{t-1} \ldots EX_{t-p} \\ EX_{t-1} & \\ \vdots & S \\ EX_{t-p} & \end{bmatrix} \quad (5.40)$$

$$S = (E(X_{t-i}X_{t-j}));$$

(4) $\hat{\sigma}^2 \xrightarrow{P} \sigma^2$.

Note that if $p = q$, then $\Sigma_r = \Lambda_r$.

Let

$$Y_r = \sigma^{-1} N^{-1/2} \sum_{t=1}^{n} Z_{1t} \hat{\varepsilon}_t \tag{5.41}$$

where the dependence on r is from Z_{1t} through $I_{t-d}(X_t \le r)$. Since r is unknown, it is natural to construct the test statistics $\mathrm{LM(TAR)} = \sup_{r \in \mathbf{R}} \mathrm{LM(TAR}, r)$, which has asymptotically the same distribution as $-2 \ln \lambda'$ under H_0. To find the asymptotic distribution of $\mathrm{LM(TAR)}$, we need to study the distribution of

$$\sup_{r \in \mathbf{R}} Y_r^T (\Sigma_r - \Lambda_r \Sigma^{-1} \Lambda_r^T)^{-1} Y_r. \tag{5.42}$$

Now, $\{Y_r; r \in \mathbf{R}\}$ is a continuous parameter stochastic process. Instead of pursuing this approach further, which is, in a sense, approximate because of the fact that the Taylor expansion of the log likelihood has been used, we shall describe a more direct approach in (B) below.

(B) The added regressors

The threshold model under consideration may be defined by

$$X_t - \theta_0 - \theta_1 X_{t-1} - \ldots - \theta_p X_{t-p}$$
$$- I(X_{t-d} \le r)(\phi_0 + \phi_1 X_{t-1} + \ldots + \phi_q X_{t-q}) = \varepsilon_t \tag{5.43}$$

where the ε_t are independent i.i.d. $\mathcal{N}(0, \sigma^2)$ random variables ($0 < \sigma^2 < \infty$), ε_t is independent of past $X_{t-1}, X_{t-2}, \ldots$, and I is the indicator function with r being the threshold parameter. The non-negative integers p, q, and d are assumed known, and are such that $0 \le q \le p$.

It is also assumed that the threshold parameter r belongs to a known bounded subset $\bar{R}$ of $\mathbf{R}$. In general, $\bar{R}$ is in the form of a finite interval. More about the choice of $\bar{R}$ will be given later. Also, the time series $\{X_t\}$ is assumed to be stationary and all roots of the characteristic equation

$$x^p - \theta_1 x^{p-1} \ldots - \theta_p = 0$$

lie inside the unit circle. For convenience, d is assumed to be less than, or equal to, p. This is not always essential as we will see later. In general, the case with $d > p$ can be handled but the results do not appear to be as practically useful. Given observations $X_0, X_1, X_2, \ldots, X_n$, consider testing the null hypothesis

$$H_0: \phi_0 = \phi_1 = \ldots = \phi_q = 0. \tag{5.44}$$

(1) The set-up   Let $\mathbf{x}$ denote the column vector $(X_p, X_{p+1}, \ldots, X_N)'$.

Let $\mathbf{X}$ and $\mathbf{Y}_r$ denote the matrices

$$\mathbf{X} = \begin{bmatrix} 1 & X_{p-1} & \cdots & X_0 \\ 1 & X_p & \cdots & X_1 \\ \vdots & \vdots & \cdots & \vdots \\ 1 & X_{N-1} & \cdots & X_{N-p} \end{bmatrix} \qquad (5.45)$$

and

$$\mathbf{Y}_r = \begin{bmatrix} I_r(X_{p-d}) & X_{p-1}I_r(X_{p-d}) & \cdots & X_{p-q}I_r(X_{p-d}) \\ \vdots & \vdots & \cdots & \vdots \\ I_r(X_{N-d}) & X_{N-1}I_r(X_{N-d}) & \cdots & X_{N-q}I_r(X_{N-q}) \end{bmatrix} \qquad (5.46)$$

where we have abbreviated the indicator functions $I(X_{t-d} \leq r)$ by $I_r(X_{t-d})$. We sometimes denote $\mathbf{Y}_r$ as given by (5.46) by $\mathbf{Y}_r(x-0)$ or simply $\mathbf{Y}_r(x)$ so that $\mathbf{Y}_r(x-c)$ will be given by (5.46) with X_j replaced by $X_j - c$, for any real c. Now, let $\mathbf{W}$ be a matrix with linearly independent column vectors $W_1, W_2, \ldots, W_n$. We may defined the *projection matrix* (also sometimes called the *hat matrix*), P_W, by

$$P_W = \mathbf{W}(\mathbf{W}'\mathbf{W})^{-1}\mathbf{W}' \qquad (5.47)$$

which projects vectors of compatible dimension on to the column space of $\mathbf{W}$. We may now proceed to construct the (conditional) likelihood ratio test (LRT) as follows:

1. Regress X_t on $1, X_{t-1}, \ldots, X_{t-p}$ and denote the vector of residuals $(I - P_X)\mathbf{x}$ by $\boldsymbol{\eta}$.

2. Regress $\mathbf{Y}_r$ on $\mathbf{X}$, that is, project column vectors of $\mathbf{Y}_r$ onto the column space of $\mathbf{X}$ and obtain the residual (matrix) $(I - P_X)\mathbf{Y}_r$, say $\mathbf{W}_r$.

3. Regress $\boldsymbol{\eta}$ on $\mathbf{W}_r$, that is project $\boldsymbol{\eta}$ onto the column space of $\mathbf{W}_r$. The projection is $P_{W_r}\boldsymbol{\eta}$. Let $Q(r)$ denote the Euclidean norm of the projection, that is

$$Q(r) = \|P_{W_r}\boldsymbol{\eta}\|^2$$

$$= \text{RSS}_{AR} - \text{RSS}_{TAR(r)} \qquad (5.48)$$

where RSS_{AR} = residual sum of squares of the best-fitting $AR(p)$ model and $\text{RSS}_{TAR(r)}$ = residual sum of squares of the best-fitting threshold autoregressive model of order p with threshold fixed at r, which is of the form specified in (5.43), that is with $p - q$ constraints on a full SETAR $(2; p, p)$ model with homogeneous noise. Clearly,

$$\mathbf{W}_r = (I - P_X)\mathbf{Y}_r$$
$$= \mathbf{Y}_r - \mathbf{X}(\mathbf{X}'\mathbf{X})^{-1}\mathbf{X}'\mathbf{Y}_r \tag{5.49}$$
$$P_{W_r} = \mathbf{W}_r(\mathbf{W}_r'\mathbf{W}_r)^{-1}\mathbf{W}_r'$$
$$= (\mathbf{Y}_r - \mathbf{X}(\mathbf{X}'\mathbf{X})^{-1}\mathbf{X}'\mathbf{Y}_r)(\mathbf{Y}_r'\mathbf{Y}_r - \mathbf{Y}_r'\mathbf{X}(\mathbf{X}'\mathbf{X})^{-1}\mathbf{X}'\mathbf{Y}_r)^{-1}$$
$$\times (\mathbf{Y}_r' - \mathbf{Y}_r'\mathbf{X}(\mathbf{X}'\mathbf{X})^{-1}\mathbf{X}') \tag{5.50}$$

and

$$Q(r) = \|P_{W_r}\boldsymbol{\eta}\|^2$$
$$= \boldsymbol{\eta}' P_{W_r}\boldsymbol{\eta} \tag{5.51}$$

because P_{W_r} is a projection matrix, that is idempotent. Let $\hat{\sigma}^2 = \inf_{r \in \mathbf{R}} \mathrm{RSS}_{\mathrm{TAR}(r)}/n$, where $n = N - p + 1$ is the effective sample size.

Now, the likelihood ratio test (LRT) is based on the statistic λ:

$$\lambda = \sup_{r \in \mathbf{R}} Q(r)/\hat{\sigma}^2. \tag{5.52}$$

It is clear that λ is a monotone function of the likelihood ratio statistic.

(II) The asymptotic null distribution   We now discuss the asymptotic null distribution of λ. Our discussions in this section and the next are partly heuristic. A rigorous demonstration of these and related results, under more general assumptions on ε_t, is given in Chan (1988b). In these two sections, the null hypothesis is assumed to hold.

Under H_0,

$$\mathbf{x} = \boldsymbol{\varepsilon} + \mathbf{X}\boldsymbol{\Theta} \tag{5.53}$$

where $\boldsymbol{\varepsilon} = (\varepsilon_p, \varepsilon_{p+1}, \ldots, \varepsilon_N)'$ and $\boldsymbol{\Theta} = (\theta_0, \theta_1, \ldots, \theta_p)'$. Therefore,

$$\boldsymbol{\eta} = \boldsymbol{\varepsilon} + \{\mathbf{X}\boldsymbol{\Theta} - P_X\mathbf{x}\}, \tag{5.54}$$

where the braced vector lies in the column space of $\mathbf{X}$. By virtue of the fact that the columns of $\mathbf{W}_r$ are orthogonal to the column space of $\mathbf{X}$, we have

$$\|P_{W_r}, \boldsymbol{\eta}\|^2 = \|P_{W_r}\boldsymbol{\varepsilon}\|^2.$$

On using (5.50), this reduces to

$$\|P_{W_r}\boldsymbol{\eta}\|^2 = (n^{1/2}T_r')(\mathbf{Y}_r'\mathbf{Y}_r - \mathbf{Y}_r'\mathbf{X}(\mathbf{X}'\mathbf{X})^{-1}\mathbf{X}'\mathbf{Y}_r)^{-1}(n^{1/2}T_r) \tag{5.55}$$

where

$$T_r = n^{-1/2}(\mathbf{Y}_r' - \mathbf{Y}_r'\mathbf{X}(\mathbf{X}'\mathbf{X})^{-1}\mathbf{X}')\boldsymbol{\varepsilon} \tag{5.56}$$

that is

$$Q(r) = T_r' \left(\frac{\mathbf{Y}_r'\mathbf{Y}_r}{n} - \frac{\mathbf{Y}_r'\mathbf{X}}{n} \left(\frac{\mathbf{X}'\mathbf{X}}{n} \right)^{-1} \frac{\mathbf{X}'\mathbf{Y}_r}{n} \right)^{-1} T_r. \qquad (5.57)$$

In what follows all expectations will be taken under the true model specified by the null hypothesis. For convenience, the true parameters are also denoted by $\theta_0, \theta_1, \ldots, \theta_p$, and σ^2. Thus, these symbols serve both as dummy variables and the true parameters. However, which quantities they represent will be clear from the context. Let

$$\Sigma_r = \begin{bmatrix} EI_r(X_{t-d}) & EI_r(X_{t-d})X_{t-1} \ldots EI_r(X_{t-d})X_{t-q} \\ EI_r(X_{t-d})X_{t-1} & \\ \vdots & S_r \\ EI_r(X_{t-d})X_{t-q} & \end{bmatrix} \qquad (5.58)$$

$$S_r = (E(I_r(X_{t-d})X_{t-i}X_{t-j})) \qquad (5.59)$$

$$\Lambda_r = \begin{bmatrix} EI_r(X_{t-d}) & EI_r(X_{t-d})X_{t-1} \ldots EI_r(X_{t-d})X_{t-p} \\ EI_r(X_{t-d})X_{t-1} & \\ \vdots & L_r \\ EI_r(X_{t-d})X_{t-q} & \end{bmatrix} \qquad (5.60)$$

$$L_r = (E(I_r(X_{t-d})X_{t-i}X_{t-j})) \qquad (5.61)$$

$$\Sigma = \begin{bmatrix} 1 & EX_{t-1} \ldots EX_{t-p} \\ EX_{t-1} & \\ \vdots & S \\ EX_{t-p} & \end{bmatrix} \qquad (5.62)$$

$$S = (E(X_{t-i}X_{t-j})). \qquad (5.63)$$

Now, by ergodicity it holds that as $N \to \infty$

$$\left(\frac{\mathbf{X}'\mathbf{X}}{n} \right)^{-1} \to \Sigma^{-1} \text{ in probability} \qquad (5.64)$$

and, uniformly for $-\infty < -b \le r \le b < \infty$, b being any positive number,

$$\frac{\mathbf{Y}_r'\mathbf{X}_r}{n} \to \Lambda_r \text{ in probability} \qquad (5.65)$$

and

$$\frac{\mathbf{Y}_r'\mathbf{Y}_r}{n} \to \Sigma_r \text{ in probability.} \qquad (5.66)$$

Also, it is shown in Chan (1988b) that $\hat{\sigma}^2$ is a consistent estimator of σ^2

and that $\Sigma_r - \Lambda_r \Sigma^{-1} \Lambda_r'$ is positive definite. Thus, the asymptotic null distribution of λ is given by that of

$$\sup_{r \in \mathbf{R}} \left(\frac{T_r}{\sigma}\right)' (\Sigma_r - \Lambda_r \Sigma^{-1} \Lambda_r')^{-1} \left(\frac{T_r}{\sigma}\right). \tag{5.67}$$

(III) The process $\{T_r\}$ $\{T_r : r \in \mathbf{R}\}$ is a real parameter $(q+1)$-dimensional vector stochastic process. Now, from (5.56), (5.64), and (5.65), uniformly for $-b \leq r \leq b$,

$$T_r = n^{-1/2} \mathbf{Y}_r' \boldsymbol{\varepsilon} - n^{-1/2} \Lambda_r \Sigma^{-1} \mathbf{X}' \boldsymbol{\varepsilon} + o_p(1). \tag{5.68}$$

Applying the Cramer–Wold device (see e.g. Brockwell and Davis 1987, p. 197) and a martingale central limit theorem, we get for each r that

$$T_r \text{ tends to } \mathcal{N}(0, \sigma^2(\Sigma_r - \Lambda_r \Sigma^{-1} \Lambda_r')) \text{ in distribution} \tag{5.69}$$

with (T_r, T_s) converging in distribution to the joint normal distribution with

$$\text{covariance} = \sigma^2(\Sigma_{\min(r,s)} - \Lambda_r \Sigma^{-1} \Lambda_s'). \tag{5.70}$$

Hence, $\{T_r\}$ is asymptotically a $(q+1)$-dimensional Gaussian process indexed by the threshold parameter $r \in \mathbf{R}$. (Some rigour is omitted here. Chan (1988*b*) gives the detail.)

To summarize, we have derived the following basic result.

Basic result: *The asymptotic null distribution of the LRT statistic λ is the same as the distribution of $\sup_{r \in \mathbf{R}} \xi_r'(\Sigma_r - \Lambda_r \Sigma^{-1} \Lambda_r')^{-1} \xi_r$, where $\{\xi_r : r \in \mathbf{R}\}$ is a $(q+1)$-dimensional Gaussian process with zero-mean function and covariance kernel $\Sigma_{\min(r, s)} - \Lambda_r \Sigma^{-1} \Lambda_s'$.*

Trivially, for each fixed r, $\xi_r'(\Sigma_r - \Lambda_r \Sigma^{-1} \Lambda_r')^{-1} \xi_r \to \chi_{q+1}^2$ in distribution.

(IV) Special cases

1. The general hypothesis is

$$X_t - \theta_0 - \phi_0 I(X_{t-d} \leq r) = \varepsilon_t \tag{5.71}$$

and the null hypothesis is $H_0 : \phi_0 = 0$. In this case

$$\Sigma_r = \Lambda_r = \mathrm{E}[I(X_{t-d}) \leq r)] \tag{5.72}$$

and $\Sigma = 1$. Define $s : \mathbf{R} \to [0, 1]$ by

$$s(r) = \mathrm{E}[I(X_{t-d} \leq r)]. \tag{5.73}$$

Then

$$\Sigma_r - \Lambda_r \Sigma^{-1} \Lambda_r' = s(r) - s(r)^2. \tag{5.74}$$

Let $\rho:[0, 1]\rightarrow \mathbf{R}$ denote the inverse of s, that is

$$\rho\circ s = \text{identity map} \quad \text{and} \quad s\circ\rho = \text{identity map}. \quad (5.75)$$

Abusing the notation of s, we define

$$B_s = \xi_{\rho(s)}. \quad (5.76)$$

Here, $\{B_s : 0\leq s\leq 1\}$ is a one-dimensional Brownian bridge. In this case the asymptotic null distribution of the LRT statistic λ reduces to that of

$$\sup_s B_s^2/(s - s^2) \quad (5.77)$$

where s ranges over a suitable subset of $[0, 1]$, namely $\bar{S}_1$, the image of $\bar{R}$ under the mapping s.

2. The general hypothesis is

$$X_t - \theta_d X_{t-d} - \phi_d X_{t-d}I(X_{t-d}\leq r) = \varepsilon_t \quad (5.78)$$

and the null hypothesis is $H_0 : \phi_d = 0$. In this case

$$\Sigma_r = \Lambda_r = \mathrm{E}[X_{t-d}^2 I(X_{t-d}\leq r)] \quad (5.79)$$

and

$$\Sigma = \mathrm{E}(X_{t-d}^2). \quad (5.80)$$

Define $s:\mathbf{R}\rightarrow [0, 1]$ by

$$s(r) = \mathrm{E}[X_{t-d}^2 I(X_{t-d}\leq r)]/\sigma_X^2 \quad (5.81)$$

where $\sigma_X^2 = \text{var } X_t$. Then

$$\Sigma_r - \Lambda_r\Sigma^{-1}\Lambda_r' = \sigma_X^2(s(r) - s(r)^2). \quad (5.82)$$

Let

$$B_s = \xi_{\rho(s)}/\sigma_X. $$

Again, $\{B_s : 0\leq s\leq 1\}$ is one-dimensional Brownian bridge, which leads to the same reduction for the asymptotic null distribution of the LRT statistic λ as in Case 1.

3. Let $p\geq 2$; the general hypothesis is

$$X_t - \theta_1 X_{t-1} -\ldots - \theta_p X_{t-p} - I(X_{t-d}\leq r)(\phi_1 X_{t-1} +\ldots + \phi_p X_{t-p}) = \varepsilon_t. \quad (5.83)$$

In this case, $\Lambda_r = \Sigma_r = (\mathrm{E}(X_{t-i}X_{t-j}I(X_{t-d}\leq r)))$, and $\Sigma = (\mathrm{E}(X_{t-i}X_{t-j}))$. Write

$$\Sigma = \begin{bmatrix} \Sigma_{11} & \Sigma_{12} \\ \Sigma_{21} & \Sigma_{22} \end{bmatrix} \quad (5.84)$$

where Σ_{11} is $(p-1) \times (p-1)$. Under $H_0 : \phi_1 = \ldots = \phi_p = 0$, $\Sigma_{22} = EX_t^2 = \sigma_X^2$. We shall henceforth in this case assume that $d = p$. As we shall see, this will be without loss of any generality as far as the asymptotic null distribution of the LRT statistic is concerned.

Lemma 5.1: Under H_0,

$$\Sigma_r = \Lambda_r = \begin{bmatrix} \Sigma_{11.2} & \begin{matrix} 0 \\ \vdots \\ 0 \end{matrix} \\ \hline 0 \ldots 0 & 0 \end{bmatrix} s_1 + \begin{bmatrix} \Sigma_{12}\Sigma_{22}^{-1}\Sigma_{21} & \Sigma_{12} \\ \hline \Sigma_{21} & \Sigma_{22} \end{bmatrix} s_2 \qquad (5.85)$$

where

$$s_1 = s_1(r) = E(I(X_t \le r))$$

$$s_2 = s_2(r) = E(X_t^2 I(X_t \le r)/\sigma_X^2)$$

and

$$\Sigma_{11.2} = \Sigma_{11} - \Sigma_{12}\Sigma_{22}^{-1}\Sigma_{21}.$$

Proof. Let $U = (X_{t-1}, \ldots, X_{t-p+1})'$, $V = X_{t-p}$. Then, under H_0,

$$\binom{U}{V} \sim \mathcal{N}(0, \Sigma)$$

and $U \sim \mathcal{N}(\Sigma_{12}\Sigma_{22}^{-1}v, \Sigma_{11.2})$ conditional on $V = v$.

Now, for $i \ne p$ and $j \ne p$,

$$E[X_{t-i}X_{t-j}I(X_{t-p} \le r)] = E[I(X_{t-p} \le r)E(X_{t-i}X_{t-j} \mid X_{t-p})]$$

where

$$E[X_{t-i}X_{t-j} \mid X_{t-p}] = E[X_{t-i} \mid X_{t-p}]E[X_{t-j} \mid X_{t-p}] + \text{cov}[X_{t-i}, X_{t-j} \mid X_{t-p}].$$

For $i \ne p$, $j = p$,

$$E[X_{t-i}X_{t-p}I(X_{t-p} \le r)] = E[I(X_{t-p} \le r)X_{t-p}E(X_{t-i} \mid X_{t-p})].$$

After some routine but tedious algebra, we get the decomposition of Σ_r as given in the lemma. $\square$

Remark 5.1: Equation (5.85) may be rewritten as

$$\Sigma_r = \begin{bmatrix} \Sigma_{11.2} & \begin{matrix} 0 \\ \vdots \\ 0 \end{matrix} \\ \hline 0 \ldots 0 & 0 \end{bmatrix} (s_1 - s_2) + \Sigma s_2. \qquad (5.86)$$

Lemma 5.2: There exists a non-singular P such that $P\Sigma_r P' = \text{diag}(s_1, s_1, \ldots, s_1, s_2)$ and $P\Sigma P' = I$.

Proof. Let

$$W = \Sigma_{11}^{-1/2}\Sigma_{12}\Sigma_{22}^{-1/2}$$

and $\Delta = \|W\|$. The set $\{X_i, 0 \le i < \infty\}$ generates a vector space with the inner product of X_i and X_j given by $E(X_iX_j)$. Now, $\Delta^2 = \Sigma_{22}^{-1}\Sigma_{21}\Sigma_{11}^{-1}\Sigma_{12}$. Using the notation adopted in the previous proof, $\Sigma_{22}^{1/2}\Delta$ is the length of the projection of V on the space spanned by the components of U. Under H_0, $\{X_t\}$ is not purely deterministic and therefore $0 \le \Delta < 1$. Define

$$P_1 = \begin{bmatrix} \Sigma_{11}^{-1/2} & \begin{matrix} 0 \\ \vdots \\ 0 \end{matrix} \\ \hline 0 \ldots 0 & \Sigma_{22}^{-1/2} \end{bmatrix} \qquad P_2 = \begin{bmatrix} & & 0 \\ T & & \vdots \\ & & 0 \\ & & -\Delta \\ \hline 0 \ldots 0 & & 1 \end{bmatrix}$$

where T is a $(p-1) \times (p-1)$ orthogonal matrix such that

$$TW = \Delta \begin{bmatrix} 0 \\ \vdots \\ 0 \\ 1 \end{bmatrix}$$

and

$$P_3 = \mathrm{diag}(\underbrace{1, 1, \ldots, 1}_{p-2}, (1-\Delta^2)^{-1/2}, 1).$$

Let $P = P_3P_2P_1$. Then

$$\begin{aligned} P\Sigma P' &= P_3P_2P_1\Sigma P_1'P_2'P_3' \\ &= P_3P_2 \begin{bmatrix} I & \Sigma_{11}^{-1/2}\Sigma_{12}\Sigma_{22}^{-1/2} \\ \Sigma_{22}^{-1/2}\Sigma_{21}\Sigma_{11}^{-1/2} & 1 \end{bmatrix} P_2'P_3' \\ &= P_3 \begin{bmatrix} I - \Delta^2 Z & \begin{matrix} 0 \\ \vdots \\ 0 \end{matrix} \\ \hline 0 \ldots 0 & 1 \end{bmatrix} P_3' \\ &= I. \end{aligned}$$

In the above, Z denotes the matrix with 1 in the final diagonal element and 0 everywhere else. Now, from (5.86),

$$\begin{aligned} P\Sigma_r P' &= P \begin{bmatrix} \Sigma_{11.2} & \begin{matrix} 0 \\ \vdots \\ 0 \end{matrix} \\ \hline 0 \ldots 0 & 1 \end{bmatrix} P'(s_1 - s_2) + P\Sigma P' s_2 \\ &= (s_1 - s_2)\,\mathrm{diag}(1, \ldots, 1, 0) + s_2\,\mathrm{diag}(1, 1, \ldots, 1) \\ &= \mathrm{diag}(s_1, s_1, \ldots, s_1, s_2). \quad \square \end{aligned}$$

Now,

$$\sup_{r\in\mathbf{R}} \xi_r'(\Sigma_r - \Lambda_r\Sigma^{-1}\Lambda_r')\xi_r = \sup_{r\in\mathbf{R}} \xi_r'P'(P(\Sigma_r - \Lambda_r\Sigma^{-1}\Lambda_r')P')^{-1}P\xi_r.$$

However,

$$P\xi_r = (B_s^{(1)}, B_{s_1}^{(2)}, \ldots, B_{s_1}^{(p-1)}, B_{s_2}^{(p)})'$$

where s_1 and s_2 are functions of r as defined in Lemma 5.1 and $\{B_{s_1}^{(i)}: 0 \le s_1 \le 1\}$, $i = 1, \ldots, p-1$, and $\{B_{s_2}^{(p)}: 0 \le s_2 \le 1\}$ are independent Brownian bridges. Therefore, the desired asymptotic null distribution of the LRT statistic is given by that of

$$\sup_{r\in\mathbf{R}} \left\{ \frac{(B_{s_1}^{(1)})^2}{s_1 - s_1^2} + \ldots + \frac{(B_{s_1}^{(p-1)})^2}{s_1 - s_1^2} + \frac{(B_{s_2}^{(p)})^2}{s_2 - s_2^2} \right\}$$

that is

$$\sup_s \left\{ \frac{(B_s^{(1)})^2}{s - s^2} + \ldots + \frac{(B_s^{(p-1)})^2}{s - s^2} + \frac{(B_{s_2(s)}^{(p)})^2}{s_2(s) - (s_2(s))^2} \right\} \tag{5.87}$$

where s_1 and s_2 are functions of r as defined in Lemma 5.1, s_2 may be considered a function of s_1, and s ranges over a suitable subset of $[0, 1]$. The stochastic process within the braces is related to the so-called Bessel process.

4. The general hypothesis is

$$X_t - \theta_0 - \theta_1 X_{t-1} - \ldots - \theta_p X_{t-p}$$
$$- I_r(X_{t-d})(\phi_0 + \phi_1 + X_{t-1} + \ldots + \phi_p X_{t-p}) = \varepsilon_t \tag{5.88}$$

and the null hypothesis is $H_0: \phi_i = 0$, $i = 0, \ldots, p$.

In this case, $\Sigma_r = \Lambda_r$ and is defined in (5.58). It is clear that $I_r(X_t) = I_{r-c}(X_t - c)$ for any real constant c. Therefore, the column space of $\mathbf{Y}_r(x) = $ column space of $\mathbf{Y}_{r-\mu}(x - \mu)$ where $\mu = EX_t$ and may be unknown. Moreover, the column space of $\mathbf{X} = $ column space of $\mathbf{X} - \mu\mathbf{1}$ where $\mathbf{1}$ denotes the matrix with all entries equal to one, and $(I - P_X)\mathbf{x} = (I - P_{X-\mu\mathbf{1}})(\mathbf{x} - (\mu, \mu, \ldots, \mu)')$. Thus, in the calculation of the covariance kernel of the Gaussian process, we may set $\mu = 0$ without loss of generality. Again, as in Case 3, without loss of generality, let $d = p$.

Then it can be readily seen that

$$\Sigma = \begin{bmatrix} 1 & 0\ldots0 \\ 0 & \\ \vdots & S \\ 0 & \end{bmatrix} \tag{5.89}$$

where $S = (E(X_{t-i}X_{t-j}))$ is $p \times p$. Partition S as

$$S = \begin{bmatrix} S_{11} & S_{12} \\ S_{21} & S_{22} \end{bmatrix} \tag{5.90}$$

where S_{11} is $(p-1) \times (p-1)$. Define $s_3 = E(X_t I_r(X_t))/\sigma_X$ and $u' = s_3(S_{21}S_{22}^{-1/2}, S_{22}^{1/2})$. Then it can be shown, as in Lemma 5.1, that

$$\Sigma_r = \Lambda_r = \begin{bmatrix} s_1 & u' \\ u & S_r \end{bmatrix} \tag{5.91}$$

and $S_r = E(X_{t-i}X_{t-j}I_t(X_{t-p}))$ is $p \times p$.

Let G be the $(p+1) \times (p+1)$ matrix which, when premultiplied to another matrix, say, A, permutes the second and the last rows of A. Let

$$Q = G \begin{bmatrix} 1 & 0 \dots 0 \\ 0 & \\ \vdots & P \\ 0 & \end{bmatrix} \tag{5.92}$$

where P is the matrix constructed in the proof of Lemma 5.2. Then it can be verified that $Q\Sigma Q' = I$ and

$$Q\Sigma_r Q' = \begin{bmatrix} s_1 & s_3 & & & \\ s_3 & s_2 & & & \\ & & s_1 & & \\ & & & \ddots & \\ & & & & s_1 \end{bmatrix} \tag{5.93}$$

where s_1 and s_2 are as in Case 3 and all other entries are zero. Thus, $Q\xi_r$ is a Gaussian process, whose last $p-1$ components are independent Brownian bridges and independent of the first two components, which are correlated between themselves. Nonetheless, it follows from the above derivation that the asymptotic null distribution of λ only depends on p, $\tilde{R}$, μ, and σ_X.

5. The general hypothesis is

$$X_t - \theta_0 - \theta_1 X_{t-1} - \dots - \theta_p X_{t-p} - I_r(X_{t-d})\phi_d X_{t-d} = \varepsilon_t \tag{5.94}$$

and the null hypothesis is $H_0: \phi_d = 0$. As in the previous case, d can be taken as p with no loss of generality. Again as in Case 4, we may set $\mu = 0$ without loss of generality. In this case

$$\Sigma_r = E(X_t^2 I_r(X_t)) = s_2\sigma_X^2 \tag{5.95}$$

and, arguing as in Lemma 5.1,

$$\Lambda_r = (s_3(r)\sigma_X, s_2(r)\Sigma_{21}, s_2(r)\Sigma_{22}) \tag{5.96}$$

Σ_{21} and Σ_{22} being as in Case 3 and s_3 being as in Case 4. Then, it is not difficult to see that the asymptotic null distribution of λ is the same as the distribution

$$\sup_{\tilde{R}} \left(\frac{\xi_r}{\sigma_X}\right)\{s_2(r) - (s_2(r)^2 + s_3(r)^2)\}^{-1}\left(\frac{\xi_r}{\sigma_X}\right) \tag{5.97}$$

where ξ_r/σ_X is a one-dimensional Gaussian process with zero-mean function and covariance kernel equal to $s_2(\min(r, r')) - s_2(r)s_2(r') - s_3(r)s_3(r')$. Thus, the asymptotic null distribution of λ only depends on $\tilde{R}$, μ, and σ_X.

Remark 5.2: Note that

(a) $E[X_t I_r(X_t)] = -E[X_t(1 - I_r(X_t))]$ so   that $(E[X_t I_r(X_t)])^2 = E[X_t I_r(X_t)]E[-X_t(1 - I_r(X_t))]$;

(b) $\sigma_X^4(s_2(r) - s_2(r)^2) = E[X_t^2 I_r(X_t)]E[X_t^2(1 - I_r(X_t))]$.

Then simple algebra involving the Cauchy–Schwarz inequality establishes the positivity of the covariance kernel in (5.97).

Remark 5.3: If θ_0 is known *a priori* to be zero so that the intercept term is discarded from (5.94), then s_3 will vanish from (5.97) and hence ξ_r/σ_X becomes a Brownian bridge.

(V) Tabulation of the first passage probability associated with the one-dimensional Brownian bridge We consider the specific case of the distribution of

$$\sup_{s \in \tilde{S}} B_s^2/(s - s^2) \tag{5.98}$$

where $\{B_s : 0 \leq s \leq 1\}$ is a one-dimensional Brownian bridge and $\tilde{S}$ is a closed sub-interval of $(0, 1)$. The most convenient way to evaluate this is to convert the problem into one related to the Ornstein–Uhlenbeck (O–U) process $\{U(t) : t \in \mathbf{R}\}$ by recalling the well-known characterization

$$B_s = W(s) - sW(1) \tag{5.99}$$

and Doob's transformation

$$U(T) = e^{-t}W(e^{2t}) \tag{5.100}$$

where $\{W(t) : t \in \mathbf{R}\}$ is the Wiener process. Thus, the 'time' t in $U(t)$ is related to the 'time' s in B_s by

$$s = \frac{e^{2t}}{1 + e^{2t}}. \tag{5.101}$$

(See e.g. Anderson and Darling 1952.)

The above conversion enables us to exploit the extensive tables compiled for the O–U process. Table 5.2 gives percentage points for the distribution of (5.98).

To use the table, we simply note that by definition (Anderson and

Table 5.2. Three percentage points (α values) of the $b_2(z, \alpha)$ function of Anderson and Darling (1952)

z	p		
	99%	95%	90%
2.0	5.239×10^{-3}	9.320×10^{-2}	2.745×10^{-1}
2.1	7.971×10^{-3}	1.286×10^{-1}	3.638×10^{-1}
2.2	1.196×10^{-2}	1.770×10^{-1}	4.806×10^{-1}
2.3	1.799×10^{-2}	2.426×10^{-1}	6.327×10^{-1}
2.4	2.707×10^{-2}	3.312×10^{-1}	8.306×10^{-1}
2.5	4.074×10^{-1}	4.499×10^{-1}	1.088
2.6	6.115×10^{-2}	6.084×10^{-1}	1.423
2.7	9.131×10^{-2}	8.195×10^{-1}	1.863
2.8	1.353×10^{-1}	1.101	2.441
2.9	1.988×10^{-1}	1.476	3.209
3.0	2.892×10^{-1}	1.979	4.236
3.1	4.167×10^{-1}	2.658	5.625
3.2	5.956×10^{-1}	3.585	7.519
3.3	8.457×10^{-1}	4.859	1.013×10
3.4	1.196	6.631	1.376×10
3.5	1.688	9.119	1.886×10
3.6	2.385	1.265×10	2.610×10
3.7	3.382	1.771×10	3.649×10
3.8	4.823	2.503×10	5.152×10
3.9	6.927	3.574×10	7.351×10
4.0	1.003×10	5.156×10	1.060×10^2
4.1	1.466×10	7.517×10	1.545×10^2
4.2	2.164×10	1.108×10^2	2.276×10^2
4.3	3.226×10	1.649×10^2	3.389×10^2
4.4	4.859×10	2.482×10^2	5.100×10^2
4.5	7.394×10	3.776×10^2	7.758×10^2

Darling 1952)

$$b_2(z, \alpha) = \Pr[|U(t)| \le z; 0 \le t \le \alpha]$$
$$= \Pr[|U(t)| \le z; -\tfrac{1}{2}\alpha \le t \le \tfrac{1}{2}\alpha].$$

Using (5.99)–(5.101), we have (by $B_s/(s-s^2)^{1/2}$ and $U(t)$ having common covariance)

$$b_2(z, \alpha) = \Pr\left[\frac{B_s^2}{s-s^2} \le z^2; \frac{e^{-\alpha}}{1+e^{-\alpha}} \le s \le \frac{e^{\alpha}}{1+e^{\alpha}}\right]. \qquad (5.102)$$

As an illustration, the α value for $z = 2.8$ and under the 95% column is 1.101. This gives

$$\Pr\left[\frac{B_s^2}{s-s^2} \le 2.8^2; \frac{e^{-1.101}}{1+e^{-1.101}} \le s \le \frac{e^{1.101}}{1+e^{1.101}}\right] = 95\%$$

that is

$$\Pr\left[\frac{B_s^2}{s-s^2} \le 7.84; 0.2496 \le s \le 0.7504\right] = 95\%. \qquad (5.103)$$

Note that an uncritical use of asymptotics would refer the test statistic of Case 1 to χ_1^2, the 5% point of which is 3.84 and is wide off the mark. The value of 7.84 in (5.103) is close to the 5% point of χ_3^2. In a different context, Hinkley (1969) has commented on a similar observation based on simulation results. An explanation of the 'χ_3^2 phenomenon' in our case lies with the fact that from Dirkse (1975), for $z \to \infty$,

$$\Pr[|U(T)| > z; 0 \le t \le] \sim \sqrt{(2/\pi)}e^{-z^2/2}\left(\alpha z - \frac{\alpha}{z} + \frac{1}{z}\right), \qquad (5.104)$$

which may be compared with $(z \to \infty)$

$$\Pr[\chi_3^2 > z^2] \sim \sqrt{(2/\pi)}e^{-z^2/2}\left(z + \frac{1}{z}\right) \qquad (5.105)$$

The implicit assumption in (5.104) of $z \gg \alpha$ implies a practical bound on α and thus s. Indeed, $b_2(z, \infty) = 0, \forall |z| < \infty$.

Thus, the tests as outlined in Cases 1, 2, and Remark 5.2 of Case 5 can be carried out and the critical values looked up from the previous table with $\tilde{S}$ being the image of $\bar{R}$ under the mapping defined in (5.73), (5.81), and (5.81) respectively. We illustrate the method with one example from the chaotic time series area, which is attracting enormous attention outside statistics.

Example 5.1: Consider a chaotic time series generated by the well-known logistic map $f : [0, 1] \to [0, 1]$ where

$$f(x) = 4x(1-x).$$

After a change of origin, we may consider the model

$$x_t = g(x_{t-1}), \quad (t = 0, 1, 2, \ldots)$$

where

$$g(x) = 0.5 - 4x^2.$$

Clearly $g : [-\frac{1}{2}, \frac{1}{2}] \to [-\frac{1}{2}, \frac{1}{2}]$. On choosing $x_0 = \pi - 3$, the realization cannot be distinguished from a realization of a stochastic process. We may apply the result of Case 2 and use $0.25 \le s \le 0.75$ and eqn (5.103); the test statistic λ, based on $x_{1001}, \ldots, x_{1100}$, takes the value 67.24, which is substantially greater than the 5% point of 7.84. A similar conclusion holds for all other randomly selected x_0 with which we have experimented. Below is a listing of the λ values (arranged in ascending order) for the 10 experiments:

$$25.64, 41.44, 44.19, 44.97, 63.32, 65.50, 65.88, 66.89, 67.24, 91.23.$$

(VI) Discussion It is clear from the derivation in Case 1 that the asymptotic null distribution of λ does not depend on the exact null distribution of X_t. For Cases 2, 3, 4, and 5, the same is true up to μ and σ_X. However, analytic expressions may be hard to obtain. Monte Carlo studies may be carried out to obtain approximate critical values for the various tests outlined in these latter cases. For example, based on Monte Carlo results with $0.25 \le s \le 0.75$, we suggest 12.6 as the nominal 5% point for the case $p = 1 = d$, and 15.6 as the 5% point for $p = 2$, $d = 1$ or 2. The non-standard problem studied here obviously has many points of contact, for example change-point problems (e.g. Hinkley 1969; Feder 1975), Kolmogorov–Smirnov tests (e.g. Durbin 1971), repeated significance tests on accumulated data (e.g. Armitage *et al.* 1969; Siegmund 1977), over-parametrization problems of ARMA processes (Veres 1988), etc. In our case, it is fortunate that percentage points may be tabulated in certain special cases. Note that Case 1, is a test for a mixture of the two normal distributions with unequal means but equal variance (cf. Titterington 1988).

5.3.5.3 The Ordered Autoregression Approach Consider a
SETAR($l; p, \ldots, p$) model with delay parameter d and thresholds $-\infty = r_0 < r_1 < \ldots < r_l = \infty$,

$$X_t = b_0^{(j)} + \sum_{i=1}^{p} b_i^{(j)} X^{t-i} + \varepsilon_t, \quad r_{j-1} < X_{t-d} \le r_j \qquad (5.106)$$

where $t = \max\{D + 1, p + 1\}, \ldots, N$ and $\{\varepsilon_t\}$ is a sequence of i.i.d. random variables with mean zero and variance $\sigma^2 < \infty$. It is more convenient to rewrite the model (5.106) in terms of an ordered autoregression.

Let $X_1, \ldots, X_n$ denote the data set. Let $h = \max\{1, p + 1 - d\}$ and $X_{(i)}$ denote the ith smallest observation among $X_h, \ldots, X_{N-d}$, $i = 1, 2, \ldots, N - d - h + 1$. Suppose $m_0 = 0$, $m_l = N$, and m are such that $X_{(m_j)} \le X_{(m_j+1)}$. Let $X_{(i)+j}$ denote X_{s+j} if $X_{(i)} = X_s$. Model (5.106) may be rewritten as

$$X_{(i)+d} = b_0^{(j)} + \sum_{v=1}^{p} b_v^{(j)} X_{(i)+d-v} + \varepsilon_{(i)+d} \tag{5.107}$$

$i = m_{j-1} + 1, \ldots, m_j$, $j = 1, \ldots, l$. Under the null hypothesis H_0, $b_i^{(j)} = b_i^{(1)}$ for *all* j and for *each* i, that is model (5.106) is linear, we can write the ordered autoregression (5.107) as

$$\mathbf{Y} = \mathbf{X}\mathbf{b} + \boldsymbol{\varepsilon} \tag{5.108}$$

where $\mathbf{Y}$ is a column vector containing components $X_{(i)+d}$, $i = 1, \ldots, N - d - h + 1$, $\mathbf{X}$ is an $(N - d - h + 1) \times (p + 1)$ design matrix, and $\mathbf{b}$ is a column vector of unknown parameters $b_0^{(1)}, b_1^{(1)}, \ldots, b_p^{(1)}$; $\boldsymbol{\varepsilon}$ is a column vector of noise terms.

Let r_{min} denote a positive integer much less than $\mathbf{N}$. For each $r \ge r_{min}$, and $AR(p)$ (p is the fixed order) model of the form (5.108) is fitted to a *truncated* column vector consisting of the first r components of $\mathbf{Y}$. Let z_{r+1} denote the standardized prediction error (also called the standardized *predictive residual*) of using this fitted model to predict $X_{(r+1)+d}$. The standardization is realized by division by the variance estimate at each step. We compute z_{r+1}, successively for $r = r_{min}, r_{min} + 1, \ldots, N - d - h$. Petruccelli and Davies (1986a) form the CUSUMS

$$\mathbf{Z}_r = \sum_{i=r_{min}+1}^{r} z_i, \qquad r = r_{min} + 1, \ldots, N - d - h + 1$$

and from them they construct the P statistic,

$$P = \max_{r_{min}+1 \le r \le N+r_{min}} |Z_r|/\sqrt{N}.$$

Under H_0, Petruccelli and Davies (1986a) have suggested the following asymptotic distribution for P:

$$\Pr\{P < t\} \to \frac{4}{\pi} \sum_{k=0}^{\infty} (-1)^k (2k + 1)^{-1} \exp[-(2k + 1)^2 \pi^2 / (8t^2)].$$

Note that there is a connection between this distribution and the asymptotic distributions associated with the first passage probability of a Brownian bridge discussed in §5.3.5.2. We do not pursue this further but refer readers to Shorack and Wellner (1986).

It is clear that the CUSUMS can be constructed with the X data arranged in descending order too. We refer to this arrangement as a D-ordered autoregression and the previous one as an I-ordered autoregression.

More recently, Petruccelli (1987) has improved the test and a *reverse* CUSUM test results. Let

$$W_r = \sum_{i=1}^{r} z_{N^*+r_{mn}+1-i}, \qquad r = 1, 2, \ldots, N^*,$$

where $N^* = N - d - h + 1 - r_{min}$.

In order to provide greater sensitivity to deviations in W_r for small r, he has used boundaries of the form $ar + b$, and H_0 is rejected if $|W_r| > ar + b$ for some r, $1 \le r \le N^*$.

For a level α test, he has suggested that choosing

$$b = \tfrac{1}{2}(-(N^*/2)\ln(\alpha/2))^{1/2} \quad \text{and} \quad a = 2(-\ln(\alpha/2)/2N^*)^{1/2}$$

gives satisfactory results. Again, this has a connection with the results in §5.3.5.2.

Tsay (1989) has considered an alternative way of using the one-step-ahead forecast errors to construct a test for linearity within the SETAR class. He suggests the following regression model in lieu of (5.108):

$$\zeta = \tilde{X}\beta + \tilde{\varepsilon} \tag{5.109}$$

where ζ is the vector with components z_i, $i = r_{min} + 1, \ldots, N^* + r_{min}$, and $\tilde{X}$ is the matrix X of (5.108) with the first r_{min} rows deleted. The usual F test statistic, say $\hat{F}$, is computed for testing $H_0: \beta = 0$. Under H_0, Tsay (1989) has shown that $\hat{F}$ is asymptotically F_{v_1, v_2} where $v_1 = p + 1$, $v_2 = N^* - p - 1$.

Moeanaddin and Tong (1988) have conducted a comparative study of the likelihood ratio test and the CUSUM test.

Numerical illustrations of some of the tests described in §5.3.5 will be given in Chapter 7.

5.3.6 PARTIALLY OBSERVED DATA

In practice, the time series may not be fully observed for various reasons. For example, the stock exchange closes at weekends and public holidays, making it impossible to have complete daily share price index data. Rather interestingly, it seems that daily share price indices have been analysed as if they were complete in the literature!

5.3.6.1 State space formulation To test for linearity with partially observed data, we describe how the ordered autoregression approach may be adapted. For simplicity, we assume that the 'intercepts' are absent. The necessary modification when they are present is quite straightforward.

We may recast model (5.106) under $H_0: b_i^{(j)} = a_i$, all j, into the state space form as follows:

System equation:

$$
\begin{bmatrix} X_{(i)+d} \\ X_{(i)+d-1} \\ \vdots \\ X_{(i)+d-p+1} \end{bmatrix} = \begin{bmatrix} a_1 & \cdots & & a_p \\ 1 & 0 & & 0 \\ & & \ddots & \vdots \\ 0 & & \cdots & 1 & 0 \end{bmatrix} \begin{bmatrix} X_{(i)+d-1} \\ X_{(i)+d-2} \\ \vdots \\ X_{(i)+d-p} \end{bmatrix} + \begin{bmatrix} \sigma \\ 0 \\ \vdots \\ 0 \end{bmatrix} u_{(i)+d} \quad (5.110)
$$

where the $u_{(i)+d}$ are i.i.d. standard normal random variables, and

$$
\text{Observed equation: } Y_{(i)+d} = (1 \quad \cdots \quad 0) \begin{bmatrix} X_{(i)+d} \\ \vdots \\ X_{(i)+d-p+1} \end{bmatrix}. \quad (5.111)
$$

In matrix notation, eqns (5.110) and (5.111) can be written as

$$
\mathbf{X}_{(i)+d} = \mathbf{F}\mathbf{X}_{(i)+d-1} + \mathbf{G}u_{(i)+d} \qquad Y_{(i)+d} = \mathbf{H}\mathbf{X}_{(i)+d}
$$

where $\mathbf{X}_{(i)+d}$ is a $p \times 1$ column vector representing the state of the process at time $(i) + d$, $\mathbf{F}$ is a $p \times p$ state transition matrix defining how the process progresses from the time point $(i) + d - 1$ to the next time point $(i) + d$, $u_{(i)+d}$ is the random input to the state equation at time $(i) + d$, $\mathbf{G}$ is a $p \times 1$ matrix defining how the random inputs are propagated into the state, $\mathbf{H}$ is a $1 \times p$ observation matrix defining linear combinations of the state that are observed at time $(i) + d$, and $Y_{(i)+d}$ is the observation at time $(i) + d$.

Note that here $\mathbf{F}$, $\mathbf{G}$, and $\mathbf{H}$ are time invariant for the stationary linear AR(p) process and the observational error has not been included.

Let $\mathbf{X}_{(i)+d-1|(i)+d-1}$ denote the 'estimate' of the state at time $(i) + d - 1$ given observations up to time $(i) + d - 1$ and $\mathbf{P}_{(i)+d-1|(i)+d-1}$ denote the covariance matrix of the estimate. Similarly, let $\mathbf{X}_{(i)+d|(i)+d-1}$ denote the 'estimate' of the state at time $(i) + d$ given observations up to time $(i) + d - 1$ and $\mathbf{P}_{(i)+d|(i)+d-1}$ denote the covariance matrix of the corresponding estimate. We consider two separate cases.

(A) Full observation

If the time series is fully observed, then for each observed $Y_{(i)}$, $(i = 1, \ldots, r; r = r_{min}, \ldots, n - d - h + 1)$, the following algorithm evaluates $-2 \ln$ likelihood.

Step (Ai):   Calculate a one-step prediction

$$\mathbf{X}_{(i)+d\,|\,(i)+d-1} = \mathbf{F}\mathbf{X}_{(i)+d-1\,|\,(i)+d-1}.$$

Step (Aii):   Calculate the covariance matrix of this prediction

$$\mathbf{P}_{(i)+d\,|\,(i)+d-1} = \mathbf{F}\mathbf{P}_{(i)+d-1\,|\,(i)+d-1}\mathbf{F}' + \mathbf{G}\mathbf{G}'.$$

Step (Aiii):   Predict the next observation

$$Y_{(i)+d\,|\,(i)+d-1} = \mathbf{H}\mathbf{X}_{(i)+d\,|\,(i)+d-1}.$$

Step (Aiv):   Calculate the innovation

$$I_{(i)+d} = Y_{(i)+d} - Y_{(i)+d\,|\,(i)+d-1}.$$

Step (Av):   Calculate the innovation variance

$$V_{(i)+d} = \mathbf{H}\mathbf{P}_{(i)+d\,|\,(i)+d-1}\mathbf{H}'.$$

Step (Avi):   Contributions to $-2\ln$ likelihood is

$$(I^2_{(i)+d}/V_{(i)+d}) + \ln V_{(i)+d}.$$

Step (Avii):   Calculate the Kalman gain matrix

$$\mathbf{K}_{(i)+d} = \mathbf{P}_{(i)+d\,|\,(i)+d-1}\mathbf{H}'/V_{(i)+d}.$$

Step (Aviii):   Update the estimate of the state vector

$$\mathbf{X}_{(i)+d\,|\,(i)+d} = \mathbf{X}_{(i)+d\,|\,(i)+d-1} + \mathbf{K}_{(i)+d}I_{(i)+d}.$$

Step (Aix):   Update the estimate of the state covariance matrix

$$\mathbf{P}_{(i)+d\,|\,(i)+d} = \mathbf{P}_{(i)+d\,|\,(i)+d-1} - \mathbf{K}_{(i)+d}\mathbf{H}\mathbf{P}_{(i)+d\,|\,(i)+d-1}.$$

Then a non-linear optimization search procedure is applied to find the minimum of $-2\ln$ likelihood which gives the maximum likelihood estimates of the parameters $\hat{a}_1, \ldots, \hat{a}_p, \hat{\sigma}^2$.

(B) Partial observations

Let # denote the number of missing observations. Then for each observed $Y_{(i)}$, $i = 1, \ldots, r$; $(r = r_{min}, \ldots, n - d - h - \# + 1)$,

(1) if $Y_{(i)+d}$ is available but not yet processed, we follow steps (Ai)–(Aix) with no change;

(2) if $Y_{(i)+d}, Y_{(i)+d+1}, \ldots, Y_{(i)+d+k_i-2}$ are missing and $Y_{(i)+d+k_i-1}$ is available but not yet processed, the following Steps (Bi)–(B(iv) are run $k_i - 1$ times with $i = 0, 1, \ldots, k_i - 2$ respectively:

Step (Bi):   Calculate a one-step prediction

$$\mathbf{X}_{(i)+d+j\,|\,(i)+d+j-1} = \mathbf{F}\mathbf{X}_{(i)+d+j-1\,|\,(i)+d+j-1}.$$

Step (Bii):   Calculate the covariance matrix of this prediction

$$\mathbf{P}_{(i)+d+j\,|\,(i)+d+j-1} = \mathbf{FP}_{(i)+d+j-1\,|\,(i)+d+j-1}\mathbf{F'} + \mathbf{GG'}.$$

Step (Biii):   Update the estimate of the state vector

$$\mathbf{X}_{(i)+d+j\,|\,(i)+d+j} = \mathbf{X}_{(i)+d+j\,|\,(i)+d+j-1}.$$

Step (Biv):   Update the estimate of the state covariance matrix

$$\mathbf{P}_{(i)+d+j\,|\,(i)+d+j} = \mathbf{P}_{(i)+d+j\,|\,(i)+d+j-1}.$$

For the observed $Y_{(i)+d+k_i-1}$, we follow steps (Ai)–(Aix) with d replaced by $d + k_i - 1$.

In this way we may obtain $-2\ln$ likelihood from the available observations and hence maximum likelihood estimates of the parameters.

After the unknown parameters have been estimated, we may proceed to calculate the predictive residuals as follows:

1. If $Y_{(r+1)+d}$ is available, the one-step-ahead standardized prediction error $z_{(r+1)}$ $(r = r_{\min}, \ldots, n - d - h - \#)$, can be found by running step (Ai) to step (Av); this gives the one-step-ahead prediction error in step (Aiv) and its variance in step (Av).

2. If $Y_{(r+1)+d}$, $Y_{(r+1)+d+1}, \ldots, Y_{(r+1)+d+k_{r+1}-2}$ are missing and $Y_{(r+1)+d+k_{r+1}-1}$ is available for processing, steps (Bi) to B(iv) are run $k_{r+1} - 1$ times. For the (k_{r+1})th time, steps (Ai) to (Av) are run which give the k_{r+1}-step-ahead prediction error in step (Aiv) and its variance in step (Av).

It is well known that for a linear time series $\{Y_{(i)}\}$, the prediction error of a linear least-squares k_{r+1}-step-ahead prediction is a linear combination of $(k_{r+1} - 1)$ prediction errors of one-step-ahead linear least squares prediction, say $I_{(r+1)+d}, I_{(r+1)+d+1}, \ldots, I_{(r+1)+d+k_{r+1}-2}$, (see e.g. Anderson and Moore 1979, p. 112), where $I_j = Y_j - \hat{Y}_j$, $\hat{Y}_j$ being the linear least-squares prediction made at time $j - 1$ for Y_j. For a linear Gaussian time series $\{Y_{(i)}\}$, $I_{(r+1)+j}$ is Gaussian and orthogonal to past observations $Y_{(r+1)+j-1}, Y_{(r+1)+j-2}, \ldots$. Thus the k_{r+1}-step-ahead standardized prediction errors are i.i.d. and normally distributed with mean 0 and variance 1, and each error is orthogonal to the corresponding past lagged Y values. Therefore, we may adapt the Petruccelli–Davies (PD) test and the Tsay test from the fully observed case to the partially observed case, provided we standardize the forecast errors. Tong and Yeung (1988a) have given results of a Monte Carlo study on models listed in Table 5.3.

Some conclusions based on 100 replications of sample size 100 can be

Table 5.3. Models

Model 1:	Threshold autogregressive model

$$x_t = a_1 x_{t-1} + \varepsilon_t \quad \text{if } x_{t-1} \leq 0.0$$
$$= a_2 x_{t-1} + \varepsilon_t \quad \text{if } x_{t-1} > 0.0 \qquad \varepsilon_t \sim \mathcal{N}(0, 1)$$

Model 2: Bilinear model A (non-linear term is $\varepsilon_t x_{t-1}$)
$$x_t = (\phi + \beta \varepsilon_t) x_{t-1} + \varepsilon_t \qquad \varepsilon_t \sim \mathcal{N}(0, 1)$$

Model 3: Bilinear model B (non-linear term is $\varepsilon_{t-1} x_{t-1}$)
$$x_t = (\phi + \beta \varepsilon_{t-1}) x_{t-1} + \varepsilon_t \qquad \varepsilon_t \sim \mathcal{N}(0, 1)$$

Model 4: EXPAR(1) model
$$x_t = [a - b \exp(c x_{t-1}^2)] x_{t-1} + \varepsilon_t \qquad \varepsilon_t \sim \mathcal{N}(0, 1)$$

Model 5: Linear MA(1) model
$$x_t = \varepsilon_t + c \varepsilon_{t-1} \qquad \varepsilon_t \sim \mathcal{N}(0, 1)$$

Model 6: Non-linear MA(1) model
$$x_t = \varepsilon_t + a \varepsilon_{t-1} + b \varepsilon_{t-1}^2 \qquad \varepsilon_t \sim \mathcal{N}(0, 1)$$

drawn from the results:

(1) For fully observed time series:

(a) The powers of the tests do not appear to be affected by methods of estimation of unknown parameters be they based on least squares (LS) or Kalman Filter (KF). This is true for both I-ordered and D-ordered autoregressions.

(b) Both the PD and Tsay tests seem to perform well. Neither test is uniformly more powerful. In practice, we recommend running both tests.

(c) Results of the tests using I-ordered autoregression complement quite well those using D-ordered autoregression. In practice, we recommend carrying out both I-ordered and D-ordered autoregressions.

(2) For partially observed time series:

(a) The points mentioned in 1(b)–(c) also apply.

(b) The power of the tests generally decreases as the proportion of missing values increases for both sampling methods. This is as expected intuitively.

(c) Tests with periodically sampled time series tend to have a higher power than those with binomially sampled time series in detecting non-linearity with the same proportion of missing values.

5.3.6.2 Applications to real data We now apply the tests to three sets of daily closing stock price data: IBM (first part, i.e. Series B of Box and

Jenkins 1976, p. 527), IBM (second part, i.e. Series B of Box and Jenkins 1976, p. 526), and the Hang Seng index which is compiled from 33 major stocks of Hong Kong and acts as an indicator of the Hong Kong market situation. In all cases, $p = d = 1$ and $r_{min} = 11$.

Commonly, stock price data are treated as fully observed time series for analysis. Here we shall additionally treat them as partially observed because typically a stock market is closed during weekends and holidays.

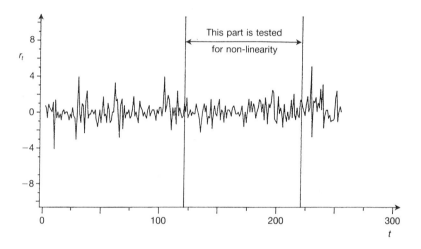

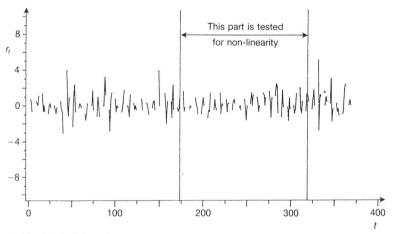

Fig. 5.10. IBM daily closing relative stock price (29 June 1959–30 June 1960), referred to as IBM (Part I): (upper figure is for fully observed case; lower figure is for partially observed case

Hence we shall test the data twice for non-linearity, treating them first as if they were fully observed and then as partially observed. Furthermore, we consider only the daily relative change in price, $r_t = (p_t - p_{t-1})/p_{t-1}$, where p_t denote the stock price at time t. The $\{r_t\}$ series for the three sets of real data are plotted in Figs 5.10–5.12, the partially observed series being represented by broken lines. Informal data analyses suggest that the data are non-stationary and in each case we select a 'stationary'

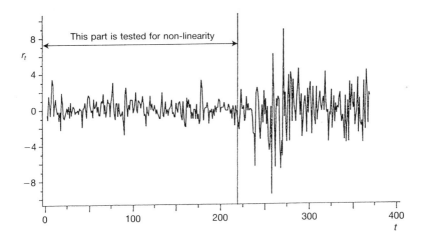

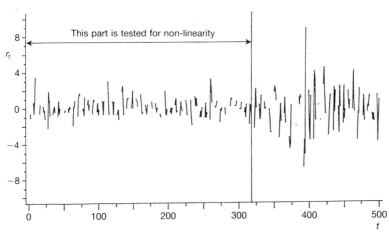

Fig. 5.11. IBM daily closing relative stock price (17 May 1961–2 November 1962), referred to as IBM (Part II): (upper figure is for fully observed case; lower figure is for partially observed case

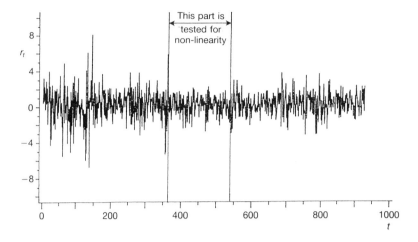

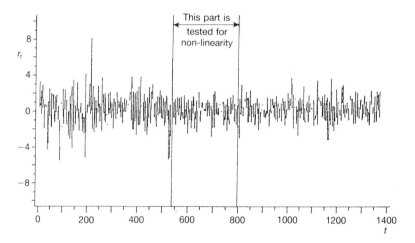

Fig. 5.12. Hang Seng relative index (1 January 1984–30 September 1987): upper figure is for fully observed case; lower figure is for partially observed case

section for investigation. The selected sections are indicated in the figures and listed in Appendix 3 and they correspond to:

(1) IBM (Part I) covering the period 18 December 1959–12 May 1960;
(2) IBM (Part II) covering the period 18 May 1961–30 March 1962;
(3) Hang Seng index covering the period 20 June 1985–7 March 1986.

The IBM data are listed in Brown (1962, Table C5 pp. 422–5, with dates

Table 5.4(a). Results of tests applied to real data with full observations (I = I-ordered autoregression, D = D-ordered autoregression)

Data	IBM (Part I)				IBM (Part II)				Hang Seng index			
	I		D		I		D		I		D	
	LS	KF	LS	KF	LS	KF	LS	KF	LS	KF	LS	KF
n	100	100	100	100	217	217	217	217	176	176	176	176
n_1, n_2	57, 43	57, 43	43, 57	43, 57	117, 100	117, 100	100, 117	100, 217	85, 91	85, 91	91, 85	91, 85
$\hat{a}$ (initial)	−0.0018	−0.0018	−0.0817	−0.0817	−0.1621	−0.1621	0.3382	0.3382	−0.0794	−0.0794	0.1157	0.1157
$\hat{a}$ (final)	−0.0009	−0.0009	−0.0009	−0.0009	0.2100	0.2100	0.2100	0.2100	0.0741	0.0741	0.0741	0.0741
$\hat{\sigma}$ (initial)	0.9024	0.8604	1.1231	1.0709	1.7826	1.6996	1.1947	1.1391	1.2360	1.1785	0.9489	0.9048
$\hat{\sigma}$ (final)	0.9326	0.9279	0.9326	0.9279	0.9408	0.9386	0.9408	0.9386	1.0203	1.0174	1.0203	1.0174
P	0.9953	0.9938	0.9878	0.9828	0.0534	0.0504	0.2671	0.2664	0.5418	0.5212	0.9709	0.9714
T	0.9014	0.9014	0.6703	0.6703	0.0002	0.0002	0.0138	0.0138	0.3124	0.3124	0.6715	0.6715
(P, T)	L, L	L, L	L, L	L, L	NL, NL	NL, NL	L, NL	L, NL	L, L	L, L	L, L	L, L
Runs test	0.3779				0.0057				0.4034			

Table 5.4(b). Results of tests applied to real data with partial observations (I = I-ordered autoregression, D = D-ordered autoregression)

Data	IBM (Part I)		IBM (Part II)		Hang Seng index	
	I	D	I	D	I	D
n	79	79	168	168	136	136
n_1, n_2	42, 37	37, 42	89, 79	79, 89	67, 69	69, 67
$\hat{a}$ (initial)	-0.1849	-0.0304	-0.4142	0.3710	-0.1596	0.2949
$\hat{a}$ (final)	-0.0275	-0.0275	0.1855	0.1855	0.0376	0.0376
$\hat{\sigma}$ (initial)	0.8125	1.0587	1.3209	0.8858	0.9272	0.9078
$\hat{\sigma}$ (final)	0.9178	0.9178	0.9182	0.9182	1.0299	1.0299
P	0.3469	0.7551	0.0352	0.2245	0.8470	0.0946
T	0.1563	0.5765	0.0072	0.0022	0.8496	0.0156
P, T	L, L	L, L	NL, NL	L, NL	L, L	NL, NL

given so that the observation pattern may be checked). The Hang Seng indices are collected from standard sources such as the Hong Kong stock exchange. The data are mean-deleted and tested for non-linearity. The results are summarized in Table 5.4 and plotted in Figs 5.13 and 5.14. When we examine the p values of the PD (row P) and Tsay (row T) tests using both orderings in the autoregression, we notice that the test suggest strongly that IBM (Part I) is linear. Rather interestingly, the tests strongly suggest that IBM (Part II) is non-linear and there is marginal evidence to suggest that the Hang Seng index might also be non-linear. A two-tailed runs test for randomness is also applied to the three sets of data. It is interesting to note that it also suggests randomness for IBM (Part I) and non-randomness for IBM (Part II), but randomness for the Hang Seng index. It would therefore seem prudent not to read too much into the marginal evidence of non-linearity for the Hang Seng index at this stage. However, it is interesting to notice the closing date effects on the IBM (Part I) and the Hang Seng index by comparing

(1) Fig. 5.13(a) with Fig. 5.14(a),

(2) Fig. 5.13(f) with Fig. 5.14(f),

(3) Column I of IBM (Part I) in Table 5.4(a) with that in Table 5.4(b), and

(4) Column I of the Hang Seng index in Table 5.4(a) with that in Table 5.4(b). The closing date effects seem particularly strong with the Hang Sent index, which might be due to (a) the more volatile and speculative nature of the Hong Kong equity market, and (b) the tradition of the local Chinese population, for example heavy sellings before the Chinese New Year holidays, etc.

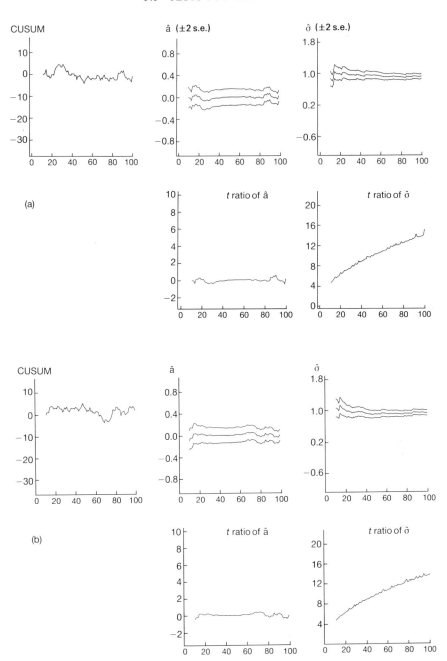

Fig. 5.13. (a) IBM (Part I) fully observed (CUSUM and I-ordered autoregression); (b) IBM (Part I) fully observed (CUSUM and D-ordered autoregression).

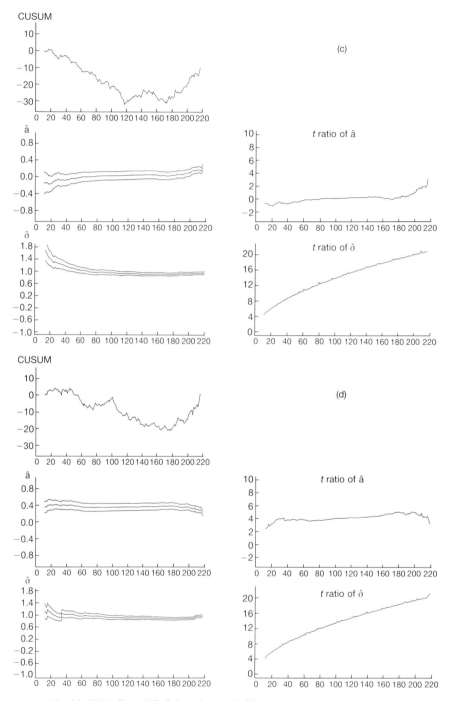

Fig. 5.13. (c) IBM (Part II) fully observed (CUSUM and I-ordered autoregression); (d) IBM (Part II) fully observed (CUSUM and D-ordered autoregression).

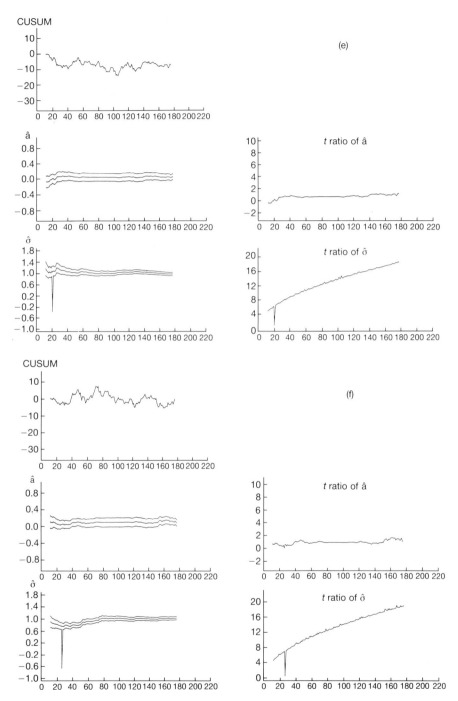

Fig. 5.13. (e) Hang Seng fully observed (CUSUM and I-ordered autoregression);
(f) Hang Seng fully observed (CUSUM and D-ordered autoregression)

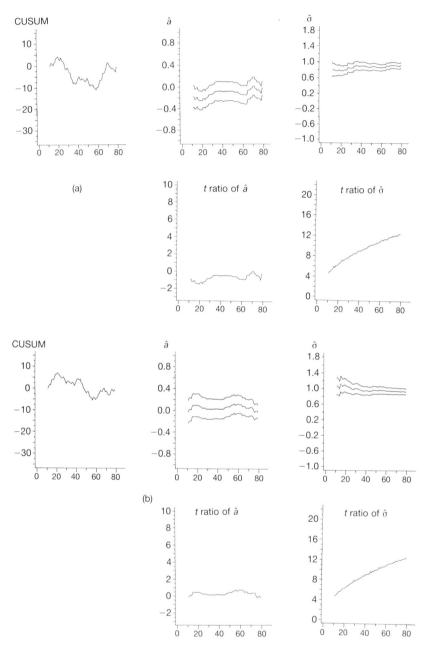

Fig. 5.14. (a) IBM (Part I) partially observed (CUSUM and I-ordered auto-regression); (b) IBM (Part I) partially observed (CUSUM and D-ordered autoregression).

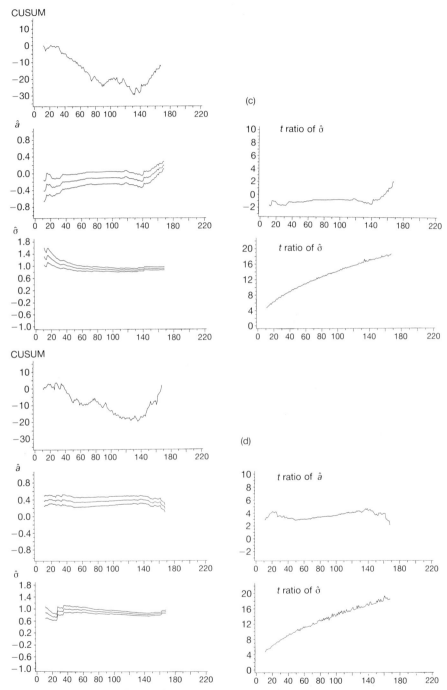

Fig. 5.14. (c) IBM (Part II) partially observed (CUSUM and I-ordered autoregression); (d) IBM (Part II) partially observed (CUSUM and D-ordered autoregression).

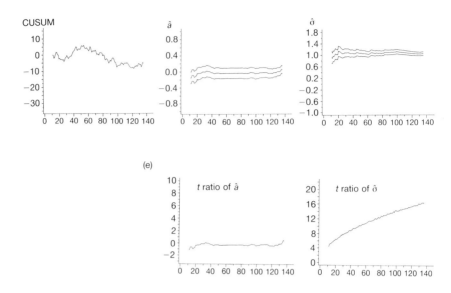

(e)

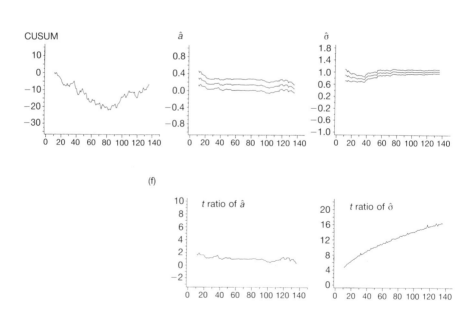

(f)

Fig. 5.14. (e) Hang Seng partially observed (CUSUM and I-ordered autoregression); (f) Hang Seng partially observed (CUSUM and D-ordered autoregression)

The CUSUM, the estimates of the lag 1 AR coefficient $\hat{a}$ and the noise standard deviation $\hat{\sigma}$ (with 2-σ lines) and the t ratios of the estimates over the observations processed are given in Figs 5.13 and 5.14. Table 5.4 gives the number (n_1) of observations processed before crossing the zero value and the number (n_2) of observations processed after crossing the zero value, and the initial and final estimates of a and σ. The row headed by the initial P gives the p values of the PD statistic. Similarly, the row headed by the initial T gives the p values of the Tsay statistic. The row headed by P, T gives the conclusions (at 10% level) of the PD test and the Tsay test respectively. For IBM (Part II) data, there is a change in CUSUM when the observation crosses over the value 0.0, that is around $r_{(118)} = 0.0990$ ($r_{(117)} = -0.0722$) in Fig. 5.13(c), $r_{(101)} = -0.0772$ ($r_{(100)} = 0.0990$) in Fig. 5.13(d), $r_{(90)} = 0.0698$ ($r_{(89)} = -0.1014$) in Fig. 5.14(c), and $r_{(80)} = -0.1014$ ($r_{(79)} = 0.0698$) in Fig. 5.14(d). Also there is an obvious change in estimates of $\hat{a}$, for instance, -0.1621 to 0.2100 for the fully observed case and -0.4142 to 0.1855 for the partially observed case using I-ordered autoregression. It might be possible that IBM (Part II) data obey a SETAR-type model in which different linear dynamics are obtained depending on whether the price change is positive or not. It would appear that the Hang Seng index exhibits a similar but weaker tendency.

The different behaviour between the IBM (Part I) data for the period December 18, 1959–May 12, 1960 and the IBM (Part II) data for the period May 18, 1961–Mar 30, 1962 might be related to the change in presidency in the USA on January 20, 1961. During Eisenhower's eight years in office (1953–1961), things were at peace and the Dow Jones Industrial average (DJIA) moved relatively steadily from 288 to over 630 (634.17) until he left office at the age of 70 on Jan 20, 1961. After the youthful J. F. Kennedy took office at the age of 43, numerous political changes took place which affected the basic economic structure of the country.

5.3.7 IRREGULARLY SPACED DATA

In practice, irregularly sampled data frequently occur. Now we shall extend the tests to irregularly spaced time series where observations can occur at any time points. Although the irregularly spaced case may be approximately reduced to the equally spaced case with missing observations by dividing the time axis into small equally spaced intervals in each of which there is, at most, a single observation, this procedure may produce an equally spaced data set in which most of the observations are missing. Moreover, as irregularly spaced data often imply that it is an underlying continuous-time process which is being sampled, it is more realistic and natural to consider a continuous-time model and use continuous-time state space representations. However, it is possible to derive from the continuous-time state space representations the corresponding discrete-time state space representatives at the observation times. Hence, the discrete-time Kalman filter can still be used. Then, as in the partially observed case, we again consider both increasingly ordered (abbreviated I-ordered) and decreasingly ordered (abbreviated D-ordered) autoregression, Petruccelli and Davies's (1986a), abbreviated PD, and Tsay's (1989) test statistics in testing for non-linearity in irregularity space time series.

5.3.7.1 Tests for non-linearity in irregularly spaced time series
Consider the following continuous-time SETAR model of order p with thresholds $-\infty = r_0 < r_1 < \ldots < r_l = \infty$

$$y^{(p)}(t) + a_{j,p-1}y^{(p-1)}(t) + \ldots + a_{j,0}y(t) = \varepsilon_j(t), \qquad r_{j-1} < y(t) \le r_j \quad (5.112)$$

where $y^{(i)}(t)$ denotes the ith derivarive of $y(t)$ with respect to time t and $\varepsilon_j(t)$ is a continuous-time Gaussian white noise with instantaneous variance σ_j^2. Clearly, some rigour has been sacrificed for the sake of convenience in (5.112). To restore rigour, we only need to replace $\varepsilon_j(t)$ by $dW_j(t)$, where $\{W_j(t)\}$ is a Wiener process, together with the routine changes on the left-hand side of (5.112).

Note that here (i) the usual difference equation formulation used for discrete-time processes is replaced by a differential equation and (ii) we do not consider the delay term.

Suppose we have n observations $y(t_1), y(t_2), \ldots, y(t_n)$ taken at n arbitrary time points $t_1 < t_2 < \ldots < t_n$, which may be equally or unequally spaced. Let $y_{(i)}$ be the ith smallest observation among $y(t_1), y(t_2), \ldots, y(t_{n-1})$, $i = 1, \ldots, n-1$. Also let $m = 0$, $m_l = n$, and suppose that m_j, $j = 1, \ldots, l-1$, are such that $y_{(m_j)} < r_j \le y_{(m_j+1)}$. Then model (5.112) may be written as

$$y_{(i)}^{(p)} + a_{j,p-1}y_{(i)}^{(p-1)} + \ldots + a_{j,0}y_{(i)} = \varepsilon_{j,(i)} \qquad (5.113)$$

$i = m_{j-1} + 1, \ldots, m_j$, $j = 1, \ldots, l$. Such an I-ordered autoregression effectively divides the model (5.112) into the respective autoregressions in the l regimes defined by the thresholds.

If we assume that model (5.112) is linear (i.e. $a_{1,K} = a_{2,K} = \ldots = a_{l,K} = a_K$, $K = 0, \ldots, p-1$; $\sigma_1^2 = \sigma_2^2 = \ldots = \sigma_l^2 = \sigma^2$), then the I-ordered autoregression (5.113) can be cast in the following state space form with system equation:

$$
\frac{d}{dt}
\begin{bmatrix}
X_{(i)} \\
X_{(i)}^{(1)} \\
\vdots \\
X_{(i)}^{(p-1)}
\end{bmatrix}
=
\begin{bmatrix}
0 & 1 & 0 & \cdot & \cdot & 0 \\
0 & 0 & 1 & 0 & \cdot & 0 \\
\vdots & \vdots & \vdots & \vdots & \vdots & \vdots \\
-a_0 & -a_1 & -a_2 & -a_3 & \cdot & -a_{p-1}
\end{bmatrix}
\begin{bmatrix}
X_{(i)} \\
X_{(i)}^{(1)} \\
\vdots \\
X_{(i)}^{(p-1)}
\end{bmatrix}
+
\begin{bmatrix}
0 \\
\vdots \\
\sigma
\end{bmatrix}
w_{(i)}
$$

$$(5.114)$$

where $w_{(i)}$ is a continuous-time Gaussian white noise with instantaneous variance equal to 1 and the observation equation

$$
y_{(i)} = (1 \quad 0 \quad \cdots \quad 0)
\begin{pmatrix}
X_{(i)} \\
X_{(i)}^{(1)} \\
\vdots \\
X_{(i)}^{(p-1)}
\end{pmatrix},
\quad i = 1, \ldots, n-1. \qquad (5.115)
$$

In matrix notation, eqns (5.114) and (5.115) can be written as

$$\frac{d}{dt} \mathbf{X}_{(i)} = \mathbf{F} \mathbf{X}_{(i)} + \mathbf{G} \mathbf{w}_{(i)} \qquad (5.116)$$

$$y_{(i)} = \mathbf{H} \mathbf{X}_{(i)} \qquad (5.117)$$

where $\mathbf{X}_{(i)}$ is a $p \times 1$ column vector representing the state of the process at time $t_{(i)}$, $\mathbf{F}$ is a $p \times p$ system dynamics matrix, $\mathbf{w}_{(i)}$ is the random input to the state equation at $t_{(i)}$, $\mathbf{G}$ is a $p \times 1$ column vector defining how the random inputs are propagated into the state, $\mathbf{H}$ is a $1 \times p$ observation matrix defining linear combinations of the states that are observed at time $t_{(i)}$ and $y_{(i)}$ is the observation at time $t_{(i)}$.

Note that here $\mathbf{F}$, $\mathbf{G}$, and $\mathbf{H}$ are time invariant and the observational error has not been included. The solution of eqn (5.116) over a finite time step δ_i from time $t_{(i)}$ is

$$\mathbf{X}_{(i)+1} = \phi(\delta_i) \mathbf{X}_{(i)} + \mathbf{G}_{(i)} \qquad (5.118)$$

where $\delta_i = t_{(i)+1} - t_{(i)}$ is the length time step, $\phi(\delta_i) = \exp(\mathbf{F}\delta_i)$ is the state transition matrix defining how the process progresses from the time point $t_{(i)}$ to the time point $t_{(i)+1}$, and

$$\mathbf{G}_{(i)} = \int_0^{\delta_i} \exp[\mathbf{F}(\delta_i - t)] \mathbf{G} \mathbf{w}_{(i)} \, dt$$

is the driven response due to the presence of the white noise input during the $(t_{(i)}, t_{(i)+1})$ interval. Clearly eqns (5.117) and (5.118) are in a form where the discrete-time Kalman filter can be used to obtain maximum likelihood estimates of the parameters. The state transition matrix may be written as an exponential series

$$\phi(\delta_i) = \exp(\mathbf{F}\delta_i) = \mathbf{I} + \sum_{k=1}^{\infty} \frac{(\mathbf{F}\delta_i)^k}{k!} \tag{5.119}$$

where $\mathbf{I}$ is the identity matrix. Instead of evaluating $\phi(\delta_i)$ by matrix addition and matrix multiplication operations, we may use the eigenvalues and the eigenvectors of the matrix $\mathbf{F}$.

Assuming distinct eigenvalues, $\mathbf{F} = \mathbf{U}\mathbf{\Lambda}\mathbf{U}^{-1}$, where $\mathbf{\Lambda}$ is a diagonal matrix of the eigenvalues λ_k of $\mathbf{F}$, and $\mathbf{U}$ is a $p \times p$ matrix, the columns of which are the right eigenvectors of $\mathbf{F}$. Since $\mathbf{F}$ is not symmetric, $\mathbf{\Lambda}$ and $\mathbf{U}$ are complex.

Multiplying eqn (5.116) by $\mathbf{U}^{-1}$, we get

$$\mathbf{U}^{-1}\frac{\mathrm{d}}{\mathrm{d}t}\mathbf{X}_{(i)} = \mathbf{U}^{-1}\mathbf{F}\mathbf{X}_{(i)} + \mathbf{U}^{-1}\mathbf{G}\mathbf{w}_{(i)}. \tag{5.120}$$

Define the transformed state vector

$$\mathbf{Z}_{(i)} = \mathbf{U}^{-1}\mathbf{X}_{(i)}. \tag{5.121}$$

The state space representation in (5.116) and (5.117) can be written in terms of the transformed state as

$$\frac{\mathrm{d}}{\mathrm{d}t}\mathbf{Z}_{(i)} = \mathbf{\Lambda}\mathbf{Z}_{(i)} + \mathbf{C}\mathbf{w}_{(i)} \tag{5.122}$$

$$y_{(i)} = \mathbf{D}\mathbf{Z}_{(i)} \tag{5.123}$$

where $\mathbf{C} = \mathbf{U}^{-1}\mathbf{G}$, $\mathbf{D} = \mathbf{H}\mathbf{U}$.

As $\mathbf{\Lambda}$ is a diagonal matrix, the solution of (5.122) over a finite step δ_i from time $t_{(i)}$ to time $t_{(i)+1}$ is

$$\mathbf{Z}_{(i)+1} = \phi(\delta_i)\mathbf{Z}_{(i)} + \mathbf{W}_{(i)} \tag{5.124}$$

where

$$\phi(\delta_i) = \mathrm{e}^{\mathbf{\Lambda}\delta_i} = \begin{Bmatrix} \mathrm{e}^{\lambda_1\delta_i} & \mathrm{e}^{\lambda_2\delta_i} & & 0 \\ & & \ddots & \\ 0 & & & \mathrm{e}^{\lambda_p\delta_i} \end{Bmatrix} \tag{5.125}$$

is the transformed state transition matrix and

$$\mathbf{W}_{(i)} = \int_0^{\delta_i} \exp[\mathbf{\Lambda}(\delta_i - t)]\mathbf{C}\mathbf{w}_{(i)}\, \mathrm{d}t$$

is the driven response for the transformed state.

The covariance matrix of $\mathbf{W}_{(i)}$ is

$$\boldsymbol{\theta}(\delta_i) = \int_0^{\delta_i} \exp[\boldsymbol{\Lambda}(\delta_i - t)]\mathbf{CC}^* \exp[\boldsymbol{\Lambda}^*(\delta_i - t)]\, dt \qquad (5.126)$$

where the asterisk denotes the complex conjugate transpose.

An element of $\boldsymbol{\theta}(\delta_i)$ is

$$\theta_{jk}(\delta_i) = \frac{L_{jk}\{\exp[(\lambda_j + \bar{\lambda}_k)\delta_i] - 1\}}{\lambda_j + \bar{\lambda}_k}, \qquad \lambda_j + \bar{\lambda}_k \neq 0$$

$$= L_{jk}\delta_i, \qquad\qquad\qquad \lambda_j + \bar{\lambda}_k = 0 \qquad (5.127)$$

where L_{jk} is an element of $\mathbf{L} = \mathbf{CC}^*$ and the bar over λ_k denotes the complex conjugate. Similarly, (5.123) and (5.124) are in the form where the discrete-time Kalman filter can be used.

Let $\mathbf{Z}_{(i)+1\,|\,(i)}$ denote the estimate of the transformed state vector at observation time $t_{(i)+1}$ given observations up to time $t_{(i)}$ and $\mathbf{P}_{(i)+1\,|\,(i)}$ the covariance matrix of the estimate. Similarly, let $\mathbf{Z}_{(i)+1\,|\,(i)+1}$ denote the estimate of the state at time $t_{(i)+1}$ given observations up to time $t_{(i)+1}$ and $\mathbf{P}_{(i)+1\,|\,(i)+1}$ the covariance matrix of the corresponding estimate.

For each observed $y_{(i)}$, $i = 1, \ldots, r$; $r = r_{\min}, \ldots, n - 1$, the following algorithm is executed to evaluate the $-2\ln$ likelihood.

Step (1): Calculate the length of the time step and one-step prediction, that is

$$\delta_i = t_{(i)+1} - t_{(i)}$$
$$\mathbf{Z}_{(i)+1\,|\,(i)} = \phi(\delta_1)\mathbf{Z}_{(i)}$$

where $\phi(\delta_i)$ is defined in eqn (5.125).

Step (2): Calculate the covariance matrix of this prediction

$$\mathbf{P}_{(i)+1\,|\,(i)} = \phi(\delta_i)\mathbf{P}_{(i)\,|\,(i)}\phi^*(\delta_i) + \boldsymbol{\theta}(\delta_i)$$

where $\boldsymbol{\theta}(\delta_i)$ is defined in eqn (5.126).

Step (3): Predict the next observation

$$y_{(i)+1\,|\,(i)} = \mathbf{D}\mathbf{Z}_{(i)+1\,|\,(i)}.$$

Step (4): Calculate the innovation

$$I_{(i)} = y_{(i)+1} - y_{(i)+1\,|\,(i)}.$$

Step (5): Calculate the innovation variance

$$V_{(i)} = \mathbf{D}\mathbf{P}_{(i)+1\,|\,(i)}\mathbf{D}^*.$$

Step (6): Calculate the contribution to $-2\ln$ likelihood for this step

$$I_{(i)}^2 V_{(i)}^{-1} + \ln V_{(i)}.$$

Step (7): Calculate the Kalman gain matrix

$$\mathbf{K}_{(i)} = \mathbf{P}_{(i)+1\,|\,(i)} \mathbf{D}^* \mathbf{V}_{(i)}^{-1}.$$

Step (8): Update the estimate of the state vector

$$\mathbf{Z}_{(i)+1\,|\,(i)+1} = \mathbf{Z}_{(i)+1\,|\,(i)} + \mathbf{K}_{(i)} I_{(i)}.$$

Step (9): Update the estimate of the state covariance matrix

$$\mathbf{P}_{(i)+1\,|\,(i)+1} = \mathbf{P}_{(i)+1\,|\,(i)} - \mathbf{K}_{(i)} \mathbf{D} \mathbf{P}_{(i)+1\,|\,(i)}.$$

Then a non-linear optimization search procedure is applied to find the maximum likelihood estimates of the parameters $a_0, a_1, \ldots, a_p$, and σ^2.

After the unknown model parameters have been estimated, the one-step-ahead standardized prediction error

$$e_{(r+1)} = \frac{I_{(r+1)}}{\sqrt{V_{(r+1)}}}, \qquad r = r_{min}, r_{min} + 1, \ldots, n - 1$$

can be found by running the first five steps of the algorithm, which give the one-step-ahead prediction error in step (4) and its variance in step (5).

For a linear Gaussian time series $y_{(i)}$, the one-step-ahead prediction error is Gaussian and orthogonal to its past observations. Thus the one-step-ahead standardized prediction error is i.i.d. and normally distributed with mean 0 and variance 1, and each error is orthogonal to the corresponding past lagged y values. Therefore, we can conduct the PD and Tsay test for non-linearity as in the partially observed case.

5.3.7.2   Applications to real irregularly spaced data

(A) Medical Data

In Jones (1984), pp. 179–80), Appendix I contains a set of 99 observations on two variables: DNA binding (DB) and serum complement (SC) from a patient with systematic lupus erythematosis, whereas Appendix II contains a set of 55 observations on three variables: white blood cell count (WBC), platelet count (PLC), and hematocrit (HCT) from a patient receiving a bone marrow transplant. The first data set is taken over a 9 year period whereas the second data set is recorded up to 91 post-transplant days. (These data are listed in Appendix 3 of this book.)

Although five variables are available, we study only the SC of Appendix I and the HCT of Appendix II. Their plots are given in Figs 5.15 and 5.16 respectively. From Jones's study (1984, pp. 168, 172), the observational error variance of these two variables is not significant. The unit of time is taken as 10 days. The data are mean-deleted and tested for

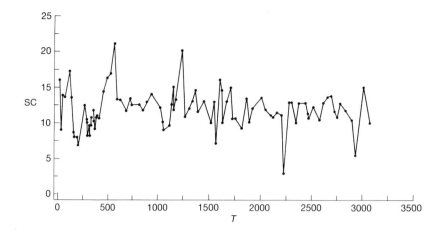

Fig. 5.15. Time plot of SC data

non-linearity. The p values of the PD and Tsay tests are shown in Table 5.5 and suggest that SC tends to be linear and HCT shows marginal evidence of non-linearity.

(B) Respiration data

The experimental set-up involves a person riding a computer-controlled cycle ergometer with a known time-varying load which is a first-order autoregressive process. The data are collected over a period of 10

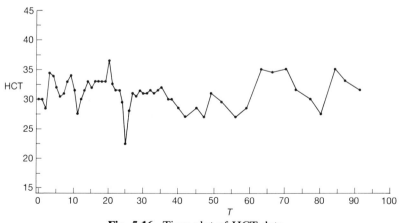

Fig. 5.16. Time plot of HCT data

Table 5.5. Results (p values) of the tests to medical data (I = I-ordered autoregression, D = D-ordered autoregression)

Data	SC		HCT	
	I	D	I	D
n	97	97	54	54
PD	0.5939	0.9394	0.4391	0.1213
Tsay	0.5959	0.4038	0.0949	0.4400

minutes on four variables: work load (WORK), total volume of inspired and expired flows (VENT), and O_2 and CO_2 breathed out.

A square root transformation is used on O_2 and CO_2 data. The plots for the four variables are given in Figs 5.17–5.20. The plots of VENT, $\sqrt{O_2}$, and $\sqrt{CO_2}$ seem to suggest some transient behaviour of the subject during the first 100 seconds of the experiment. Also outliers are observed; it is suggested that these may be caused by the subject taking a shallow breath or swallowing, which temporarily affects the gas exchange (Jones 1984, p. 175). So the initial data points and the outliers are omitted in our test for non-linearity.

The unit of time is taken as 10 seconds. The data are mean-deleted and ordered according to their own values for testing. The p values of the PD

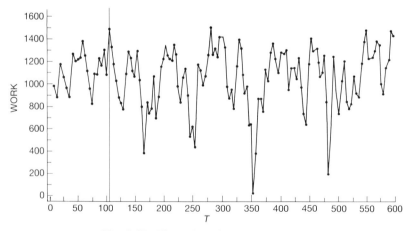

Fig. 5.17. Time plot of work load data

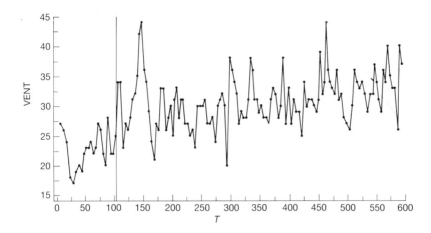

Fig. 5.18. Time plot of VENT data

and Tsay tests are shown in Table 5.6. Next, the data are ordered according to the values of work load and tested again. The p values of the tests are shown in Table 5.7 and the CUSUMs are plotted in Fig. 5.21. It is interesting to note that the p values in Table 5.7 tend to be smaller than those in Table 5.6. On taking everything together, we may argue that work load seems to affect the respiration physiology. Also there is a 'turning point' in the CUSUMs for the three respiration variables around a work

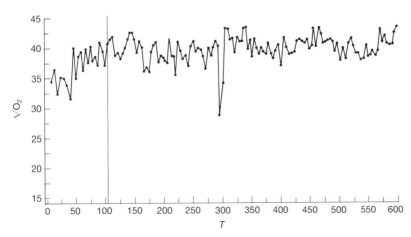

Fig. 5.19. Time plot of $\sqrt{O_2}$ data

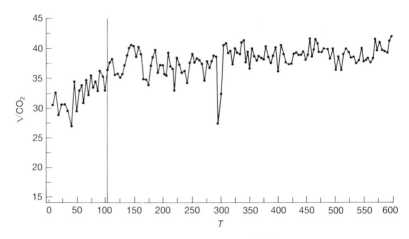

Fig. 5.20. Time plot of $\sqrt{CO_2}$ data

Table 5.6. Results (p values) of the tests applied to respiration data where threshold variable is $y(t)$ itself (I = I-ordered autoregression, D = D-ordered autoregression)

Data	VENT		$\sqrt{O_2}$		$\sqrt{CO_2}$	
	I	D	I	D	I	D
n	119	119	119	119	119	119
PD	0.6388	0.8391	0.4739	0.7785	0.9276	0.8971
Tsay	0.2874	0.9942	0.1004	0.3264	0.7092	0.8539

Table 5.7. Results (p-values) of the tests applied to respiration data where the threshold variable is work load (I = I-ordered autoregression, D = D-ordered autoregression)

Data	VENT		$\sqrt{O_2}$		$\sqrt{CO_2}$	
	I	D	I	D	I	D
n	119	119	119	119	119	119
PD	0.2655	0.6466	0.1718	0.4209	0.2132	0.3679
Tsay	0.0938	0.1749	0.6161	0.2280	0.5077	0.3959

VENT (I-ordered autoregression)

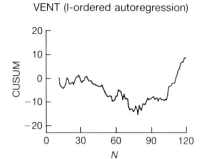

VENT (D-ordered autoregression)

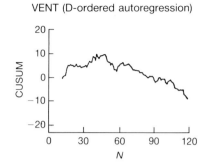

$\sqrt{O_2}$ (I-ordered autoregression)

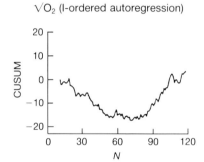

$\sqrt{O_2}$ (D-ordered autoregression)

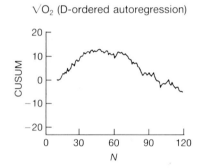

$\sqrt{CO_2}$ (I-ordered autoregression)

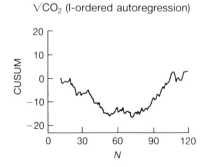

$\sqrt{CO_2}$ (D-ordered autoregression)

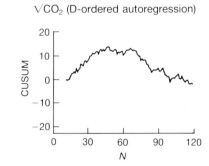

Fig. 5.21. CUSUM for respiratory data

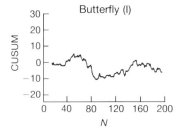 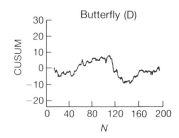

Fig. 5.22. CUSUM for log DO content in Butterfly Beach, Hong Kong. (I = I-ordered autoregression; D = D-ordered autoregression)

load of 1154 (which corresponds to $N = 70$ in I-ordered autoregression and $N = 49$ in D-ordered autoregression).

(C) Hong Kong beach water quality data

In the past few years (1980–85), samples of seawater from Hong Kong beaches were taken one to three times a month, which are not equally spaced. On each sampling occasion, the physical, chemical, and bacteriological characteristics of the water were analysed and the water quality determined. Now our tests are limited to dissolved oxygen content in 10^{-5} mg per litre (DO) which is a chemical characteristic and acts as an indicator of bacterial activities. Moreover, only four beaches were studied, namely Butterfly, Anglers, Repulse Bay, and Shek 0. The log transformation is used on the DO data and the CUSUM plots are given in Figs 5.22 –5.25 respectively.

The unit of time is taken as 10 days. The data are mean-deleted and tested. The results of the tests are given in Table 5.8.

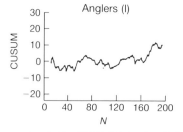 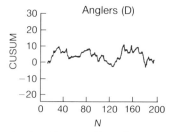

Fig. 5.23. CUSUM for log DO content in Anglers Beach, Hong Kong

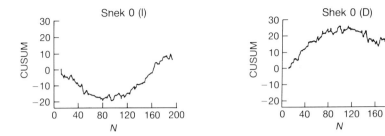

Fig. 5.24. CUSUM for log DO content in Shek 0 Beach, Hong Kong

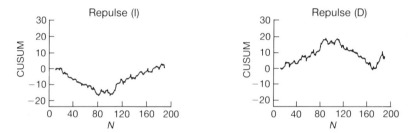

Fig. 5.25. CUSUM for log DO content in Repulse Bay Beach, Hong Kong

Table 5.8. Results (p values) of tests applied to DO content of Hong Kong beaches (I = I-ordered autoregression, D = D-ordered autoregression)

Data	Butterfly		Anglers		Shek 0		Repulse	
	I	D	I	D	I	D	I	D
n	192	192	193	193	192	192	188	188
PD	0.8159	0.9259	0.7383	0.7870	0.2703	0.1005	0.3876	0.2980
Tsay	0.6465	0.7169	0.2665	0.4991	0.0101	0.0612	0.1153	0.6361

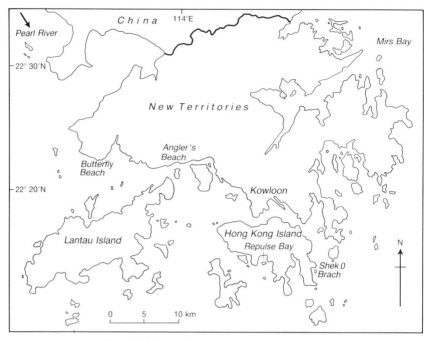

Fig. 5.26. Location of Hong Kong beaches

It is interesting to note that the p values of Butterfly and Anglers data are similar and they both suggest linearity, whereas the p values of Repulse Bay and Shek 0 are similar but both suggest some nonlinearity.

The similarity of the p values (excluding 0.6361) might be due to the geographical location of the beaches. As shown in Fig. 5.26, the beaches in each pair are close to each other and so similar water quality behaviour could be expected. Moreover, the water qualities of Butterfly and Anglers beaches are both classified as grossly polluted and *are closed to public use*. On the other hand, the water quality of Repulse Bay and Shek 0 are classified as moderately polluted and *are popular beaches for swimming,* usually extremely crowded. It seems plausible that the apparent non-linearity of the water qualities of the latter beaches is a reflection of the fact that in moderately polluted beaches the condition switches between the aerobic state and the anaerobic state. In polluted beaches the condition is always anaerobic.

5.3.8 CONCLUDING REMARKS

In any real situation, a wise time series analyst will always start with graphical analyses before entertaining any formal ones, because the former might suggest the possible direction of non-linearity. For example, if the lag regression suggests piecewise linearity, then tests described in §5.3.5 may be appropriate. Even then, it seems prudent to conduct more than one test. Our experience suggests that in general four or five different tests are not uncommon since most of them are very fast anyway. The area of formal tests is still undergoing fairly intensive development. It is hoped that before long a more comprehensive guidance will be available to users. An alternative approach which we have not discussed is the Bayesian analysis of threshold switching models (see e.g. Pole and Smith 1985).

5.4 Model selection

5.4.1 INTRODUCTION

A fundamental difficulty in statistical analysis is the choice of an appropriate model. This is particularly pronounced in time series analysis. The book by Box and Jenkins (1970) has been successful in popularizing linear time series models through the formulation of an iterative process of model building, consisting of the stages of identification, estimation, and diagnostic checking. This approach is commonly referred to as the *Box–Jenkins approach*. It seems that the general philosophy of this approach is to allow modellers a fair degree of flexibility in exercising their *subjective* judgement as to which one of several candidate models they may adopt. The approach has been popular and, in the hands of experienced time series analysts, many successful results have been reported. Their emphasis on diagnostic checking is particularly relevant in the present context.

5.4.2 AKAIKE's APPROACH

An alternative view is adopted by Akaike. At a fundamental level the approach seeks objective expressions for the subjective judgement mentioned earlier. The problem of model identification is then converted into an optimization problem with respect to a specified criterion over a pre-selected family of models. Currently, there are quite a number of alternative criteria proposed. We do not propose to give a survey of this growing area—a separate monograph would be needed for this purpose—but merely mention Akaike (1977, 1979, 1985), Atkinson (1978), Bhansali and Downham (1977), Dawid (1984), Gooijer et al. (1985), Hannan (1980), Hannan and Quinn (1979), Rissanen (1987), Schwarz

(1978), Smith and Spiegelhalter (1980), Stone (1977, 1979), Tong (1976), Wallace and Freeman (1987). In what follows in this subsection, we describe the approach developed by Akaike in some detail. Limitation of both space and our practical experience has dictated this choice.

The fundamental concept used by Akaike in a series of papers is based on that of entropy introduced by Boltzmann (1877) in thermodynamics. The following statistical characterization of entropy is due to Akaike (1978a).

Consider a distribution $(q_1, q_2, \ldots, q_k)$ with $q_i > 0$ $(i = 1, \ldots, k)$, and $q_1 + q_2 + \ldots + q_k = 1$. Suppose that N independent drawings are made from the distribution and that the resulting frequency distribution is given by $(N_1, N_2, \ldots, N_k)$, where $N_1 + N_2 + \ldots + N_k = N$. Then the probability of getting this same $(N_1, N_2, \ldots, N_k)$ by sampling from $(q_1, \ldots, q_k)$ is given by

$$W = \frac{N!}{N_1! \ldots N_k!} q_1^{N_1} q_2^{N_2} \ldots a_k^{N_k}. \tag{5.128}$$

Taking logarithms and using the asymptotic equality $\ln N! = N \ln N - N$, we get the asymptotic equality

$$\ln W = -N \sum_{i=1}^{q} \frac{N_i}{N} \ln\left(\frac{N_i}{Nq_i}\right).$$

Putting $p_i = N_i/N$, we get

$$\ln W = -N \sum_{i=1}^{q} p_i \ln(p_i/q_i)$$

$$= NB(p; q) \tag{5.129}$$

where $B(p; q)$ is the entropy of the distribution $\{p_i\}$ with respect to the distribution $\{q_i\}$.

The historical probabilistic interpretation of thermodynamic entropy by Boltzmann (1877) may be symbolized by

$$S = k \ln W \tag{5.130}$$

where S denotes the thermodynamic entropy and k is a constant. The analogy between S and $B(p; q)$ is now made obvious by (5.129) and (5.130). The former equation suggests the interpretation of the entropy $B(p; q)$ as the logarithm of the probability of getting the distribution $\{p_i\}$, which in the limit as $N \to \infty$ is the *true distribution*, by sampling from the assumed, that is *hypothetical distribution* $\{q_i\}$. In Akaike's approach, the primary distribution, q, is always hypothetical while the secondary distribution, p, is factual. The approach emphasizes the different roles played by the primary and the secondary distributions. The relation between the two distributions is *not* symmetrical. The existence of a true distribution is, of course, a deep philosophical issue, which we do not pursue here. Interested readers may wish to consult Akaike (1985) and the discussions of the papers by Rissanen (1987) and Wallace and Freeman (1987) as *hors-d'oeuvre*.

The above discussion may be extended to more general distributions. Suppose then f and g are the probability density functions of the true and the hypothetical distributions respectively, and f_N is the probability density function estimate based on the conceptual random sampling of N observations from g. This is based on Sanov's result (1961) which justifies the definition of

$$B(f;g) = -\int f(z) \ln(f(z)/g(z)) \, dz$$

as $\lim_{\varepsilon \downarrow 0} \lim_{N \to \infty} N^{-1} \ln \Pr(\sup_x |f_N(x) - f(x)| < \varepsilon)$. Note that $B(f;g) = 0$ if and only if $f \equiv g$ and that $B(f;g) \leq 0$. Akaike has argued that $-B(f;g)$ may be used as a measure of discrepancy between f and g.

Suppose that the data set $\mathbf{x}$ of N of observations is given. Akaike suggests that the purpose of statistical analysis of $\mathbf{x}$ is the prediction of future observations $\mathbf{y}$ whose distribution is identical to that for the elements of $\mathbf{x}$. The prediction is realized by specifying a distribution $g(\mathbf{y} \mid \mathbf{x})$, the predictive distribution of $\mathbf{y}$, as a function of the available data $\mathbf{x}$. Assume that the true distribution of $\mathbf{y}$ is given by $f(\mathbf{y})$. The goodness of $g(\mathbf{y} \mid \mathbf{x})$ as an estimate of $f(\mathbf{y})$ is measured by the entropy of $f(\mathbf{y})$, with respect to $g(\mathbf{y} \mid \mathbf{x})$, that is

$$B\{f(\cdot); g(\cdot \mid \mathbf{x})\} = -\int \left(\frac{f(\mathbf{y})}{g(\mathbf{y} \mid \mathbf{x})}\right) \ln\left(\frac{f(\mathbf{y})}{g(\mathbf{y} \mid \mathbf{x})}\right) g(\mathbf{y} \mid \mathbf{x}) \, d\mathbf{y}$$

$$= \int f(\mathbf{y}) \ln g(\mathbf{y} \mid \mathbf{x}) \, d\mathbf{y} - \int f(\mathbf{y}) \ln f(\mathbf{y}) \, d\mathbf{y}$$

$$= E_y \ln g(\mathbf{y} \mid \mathbf{x}) - \text{constant} \tag{5.131}$$

where E_y denotes the expectation with respect to the distribution of $\mathbf{y}$. For convenience, we have temporarily abandoned the convention of using upper case $\mathbf{y}$ to denote a random vector. The ambiguity of the lower case $\mathbf{y}$ should not cause any problems. Thus the entropy is equivalent to the expected log likelihood of $g(\mathbf{y} \mid \mathbf{x})$, (the 'data-dependent model') with respect to a 'future' observation $\mathbf{y}$, apart from a constant. The goodness of the estimation procedure specified by $g(\mathbf{y} \mid \mathbf{x})$ is measured by $E_x E_y \ln g(\mathbf{y} \mid \mathbf{x})$ which is the average over $\mathbf{x}$ of the expected log likelihood of the model $g(\mathbf{y} \mid \mathbf{x})$ w.r.t. a future observation $\mathbf{y}$. The problem is how to measure $E_x E_y \ln g(\mathbf{y} \mid \mathbf{x})$. Suppose that $\mathbf{x}$ and $\mathbf{y}$ are independent. If $g(\cdot \mid \mathbf{x}) = g(\cdot \mid \boldsymbol{\theta})$, that is a distribution specified by a *fixed* parameter vector $\mathbf{\theta}$, then $\ln g(\mathbf{x} \mid \mathbf{x}) = \ln g(\mathbf{x} \mid \mathbf{\theta})$, which is exactly the classical definition of the log likelihood of the model specified by $g(\cdot \mid \mathbf{\theta})$, conventionally called the log likelihood of the parameter $\mathbf{\theta}$. In this case, only *one* model is entertained and obviously,

$$E_x \ln g(\mathbf{x} \mid \mathbf{\theta}) = E_x E_y \ln g(\mathbf{y} \mid \mathbf{x}). \tag{5.132}$$

This equation may be interpreted as a justification of the conventional maximum likelihood estimation procedure.

However, for a general $g(\cdot \mid \mathbf{x})$,

$$E_x \ln g(\mathbf{x} \mid \mathbf{x}) \neq E_x E_y \ln g(\mathbf{y} \mid \mathbf{x}). \tag{5.133}$$

Akaike (1978a) proposes that the *log likelihood of the data-dependent model* $g(\cdot \mid \mathbf{x})$, as distinct from the log likelihood of the parameter $\mathbf{\theta}$, be defined by

$$l\{g(\cdot \mid \mathbf{x})\} = \ln g(\mathbf{x} \mid \mathbf{x}) + C \tag{5.134}$$

where C is a constant correction term such that

$$E_x l\{g(\cdot \mid \mathbf{x})\} = E_x E_y \ln g(\mathbf{y} \mid \mathbf{x}). \tag{5.135}$$

The introduction of $l\{g(\cdot \mid \mathbf{x})\}$ is, of course, motivated by the prospect of a family of possible models. For the definition (5.134) to be operational, *the constant C must be a constant for the members of that family.* One way to realize this is by parametrization, that is by restricting $g(\mathbf{y} \mid \mathbf{x})$ to be of the form $g(\mathbf{y} \mid \mathbf{\theta}(\mathbf{x}))$.

Specifically, let $g_m(\mathbf{y} \mid_m \mathbf{\theta}(\mathbf{x}))$, $m = 1, 2, \ldots, M$, denote M competing models. For simplicity of notation, we shall write $g(\mathbf{y} \mid_m \mathbf{\theta}(\mathbf{x}))$ for $g_m(\mathbf{y} \mid_m \mathbf{\theta}(\mathbf{x}))$.

Basic assumption: *We assume that the true distribution (i.e. true model), $f(\mathbf{y})$, belongs to each of these M models.*

Under this assumption, we may use the standard likelihood theory to obtain the constant C. We write $g(\mathbf{y} \mid \mathbf{\theta}_0)$ for $f(\mathbf{y})$. The usual regularity conditions are now assumed to hold. Let $_m\hat{\mathbf{\theta}}(\mathbf{x})$ denote the maximum likelihood estimate of $_m\mathbf{\theta}(\mathbf{x})$, that is

$$g(\mathbf{x} \mid_m \hat{\mathbf{\theta}}(\mathbf{x})) = \max_{_m\mathbf{\theta}(\mathbf{x})} g(\mathbf{x} \mid_m \mathbf{\theta}(\mathbf{x})). \tag{5.136}$$

1. As $N \to \infty$, the likelihood ratio statistic $2 \ln g(\mathbf{x} \mid_m \hat{\mathbf{\theta}}(\mathbf{x})) - 2 \ln g(\mathbf{x} \mid \mathbf{\theta}_0)$ has the asymptotic χ_r^2 distribution, where $r = \dim {}_m\mathbf{\theta}(\mathbf{x})$.

2. Next, by expanding $\ln g(\mathbf{y} \mid_m \hat{\mathbf{\theta}}(\mathbf{x}))$ in the neighbourhood of $\ln g(\mathbf{y} \mid \mathbf{\theta}_0)$, we have

$$2 \ln g(\mathbf{y} \mid \mathbf{\theta}_0) - 2 \ln g(\mathbf{y} \mid_m \hat{\mathbf{\theta}}(\mathbf{x}))$$
$$= 2 \ln g(\mathbf{y} \mid \mathbf{\theta}_0) - 2[\ln g(\mathbf{y} \mid \mathbf{\theta}_0) + \tfrac{1}{2}(_m\hat{\mathbf{\theta}}(\mathbf{x}) - \mathbf{\theta}_0)^T D_\theta^2(\mathbf{\theta}_0)(_m\hat{\mathbf{\theta}}(\mathbf{x}) - \mathbf{\theta}_0)$$
$$+ \text{terms of higher order in } (_m\hat{\mathbf{\theta}}(\mathbf{x}) - \theta_0)]$$

where $D_\theta^2(\theta_0)$ denotes the matrix of second derivatives of $\ln g(y \mid \theta)$ with respect to the components of θ and evaluated at θ_0. Ignoring the higher-order terms, we may write

$$2 \ln g(y \mid \theta_0) - 2 \ln g(y \mid {}_m\hat{\theta}(x))$$
$$= \{{}_m\hat{\theta}(x) - \theta_0\}^T \{-D_\theta^2(\theta_0)\} \{{}_m\hat{\theta}(x) - \theta_0\}. \quad (5.137)$$

Now, the property of the best asymptotic normality of ${}_m\hat{\theta}(x)$ implies that

$$\sqrt{N} \{{}_m\hat{\theta}(x) - \theta_0\} \rightsquigarrow \mathcal{N}(0, I_{\theta_0}^{-1}) \qquad (5.138)$$

where $\rightsquigarrow$ denotes the convergence in distribution and $I_{\theta_0} = -(1/N)E_y\{D_\theta^2(\theta_0)\}$. From (5.137) and (5.138),

$$2E_y\{\ln g(y \mid \theta_0)\} - 2E_y\{\ln (y \mid {}_m\hat{\theta}(x))\}$$
$$= N\{{}_m\hat{\theta}(x) - \theta_0\}^T I_{\theta_0}\{{}_m\hat{\theta}(x) - \theta_0\} \rightsquigarrow \chi_r^2, \quad \text{as} \quad N \to \infty. \quad (5.139)$$

Combining the results of (1) and (2) above, we have shown that

$$2E_x[\ln g(x \mid {}_m\hat{\theta}(x)) - \ln g(x \mid \theta_0)] = r \qquad (5.140)$$

and

$$2E_x E_y[\ln g(y \mid \theta_0) - \ln g(y \mid_m \hat{\theta}(x))] = r \qquad (5.141)$$

from which it follows that

$$C = -r. \qquad (5.142)$$

Akaike (1978a) has proposed that the model which maximizes $\ln g(x \mid {}_m\hat{\theta}(x)) - r$ over $m = 1, 2, \ldots, M$, should be adopted. We here have a direct extension of the idea of maximum likelihood estimation of *parameters* to the maximum likelihood estimation of *models*. We may note that the maximization of the log likelihood $\ln g(x \mid {}_m\hat{\theta}(x)) - r$ is a maximization of the entropy $B\{g(\cdot \theta_0); g(\cdot {}_m\hat{\theta}(x))\}$. The basic principle underlying the above procedure is therefore that of *entropy maximization*, which is the basis of Akaike's approach to model identification (see Akaike 1977).

In practice, the problem of maximization of $\ln g(x \mid {}_m\hat{\theta}(x)) - r$ is more commonly replaced by the equivalent problem of minimization of $-2 \ln g(x \mid {}_m\hat{\theta}(x)) + 2r$, expressed generically by

$$\text{AIC}(m) = -2 \ln(\text{maximized likelihood})$$
$$+ 2 \text{ (no. of independently adjusted parameters)}. \quad (5.143)$$

The minimizer of AIC(m), over $m = 1, 2, \ldots, M$, is then called the minimum AIC estimate (MAICE). The notation AIC stems from the paper Akaike (1973a) and we may consider it an abbreviation of *Akaike's information criterion* in honour of its creator.

When the true model $f(\mathbf{y})$ does not belong to the $g(\mathbf{x} \mid {}_m\boldsymbol{\theta}(\mathbf{x}))$, the asymptotic χ^2 distributions in (1) and (2) are not necessarily obtained. (See e.g. Kent 1982.) Thus, in this case, $C \neq -r$. Consequently, $\ln g(\mathbf{x} \mid {}_m\hat{\boldsymbol{\theta}}(\mathbf{x})) - r$ is not necessarily the log likelihood of the model $g(\mathbf{x} \mid {}_m\boldsymbol{\theta}(\mathbf{x}))$. However, in Akaike's papers on the subject (see, in particular, Akaike 1974b, section VII), it seems implicit that the MAICE procedure is still considered practically useful because in the first term on the right-hand side of (5.143), the maximized likelihood is a measure of the goodness of fit of the assumed model. If $g(\mathbf{x} \mid {}_m\boldsymbol{\theta}(\mathbf{x}))$ is 'very far from' $f(\mathbf{y})$, then presumably the likelihood content of the former about the latter must be rather low. Roughly speaking, the first and second terms on the right-hand side of (5.143) may be interpreted as measures of the badness of fit and the complexity of the model respectively. A MAICE model may be considered the result of an optimal compromise with respect to an explict loss function, between these two measures, that is a realization of Occam's razor. Although procedures such as MAICE have been found to be reasonably successful in a fairly large number of practical applications, it is fair to note that these methodologies, just like many others in statistical inference, are not universally accepted by statisticians. Readers may refer to Tong (1977b), Bhansali (1978), Akaike (1978b,c), Stone (1979), Shibata (1980), Cox (1981), Newbold (1981), Stone (1982), Larimore (1983) and Rissanen (1987) for some information on the divergence of opinions.

So far the discussion applies to independent observations only. However, the basic results of (1) and (2) above may be extended to Markov-dependent observations. Tong (1975) has discussed the extension to a discrete-time Markov chain with a finite state space. For the case of a discrete-time Markov chain on the real line, we may appeal to the standard martingale theory (see e.g. Billingsley 1961; Hall and Heyde 1980). We now *outline* the general argument. Let $\{\mathbf{x}_k \colon k = 1, 2, \ldots, N + 1\}$ denote a set of Markov-dependent observations. Now by the Markov property the joint probability density function (assumed to exist) of $\mathbf{x}_1, \ldots, \mathbf{x}_{N+1}$ is given by

$$f(\mathbf{x}_1, \ldots, \mathbf{x}_{N+1}) = f(\mathbf{x}_1)f(\mathbf{x}_2 \mid \mathbf{x}_1)f(\mathbf{x}_3 \mid \mathbf{x}_2) \ldots f(\mathbf{x}_{N+1} \mid \mathbf{x}_N) \quad (5.144)$$

where $f(\mathbf{x}_i \mid \mathbf{x}_{i-1})$ denotes the conditional probability density function of $\mathbf{x}_i$ given $\mathbf{x}_{i-1}$. Let the densities have the parameter $\boldsymbol{\theta}$. Let $L_N(\mathbf{x}; \boldsymbol{\theta})$ and $L(\mathbf{x}_i \mid \mathbf{x}_{i-1}; \boldsymbol{\theta})$ denote the log likelihood of the parameter $\boldsymbol{\theta}$ given the observations $\mathbf{x}_1, \ldots, \mathbf{x}_{N+1}$ and $\ln f(\mathbf{x}_i \mid \mathbf{x}_{i-1}; \boldsymbol{\theta})$ respectively. Then (5.144) gives

$$L_N(\mathbf{x}; \boldsymbol{\theta}) = \sum_{k=1}^{N} L(\mathbf{x}_{k+1} \mid \mathbf{x}_k; \boldsymbol{\theta}) + \ln f(\mathbf{x}_1; \boldsymbol{\theta}). \quad (5.145)$$

The last term on the right-hand side of (5.145) is the transient term which, for large n, may be omitted.

Let $\hat{\boldsymbol{\theta}}$ denote the maximum estimate of $\boldsymbol{\theta}$, that is $\hat{\boldsymbol{\theta}}$ satisfies the equation

$$D_\theta L_N(\mathbf{x}; \hat{\boldsymbol{\theta}}) = D_\theta L_N(\mathbf{x}; \boldsymbol{\theta}) \big|_{\hat{\theta}} = \mathbf{0} \qquad (5.146)$$

where D_θ denotes the (vector) operator of first derivatives with respect to the components of $\boldsymbol{\theta}$. The usual Taylor expansion of $D_\theta L_N(\mathbf{x}; \hat{\boldsymbol{\theta}})$ about $\boldsymbol{\theta}_0$, the true parameter, gives, under the usual regularity conditions pertinent to the theory of maximum likelihood estimation,

$$\mathbf{0} = D_\theta L_N(\mathbf{x}; \hat{\boldsymbol{\theta}}) = D_\theta L_N(\mathbf{x}: \boldsymbol{\theta}_0) + D_\theta^2 L_N(\mathbf{x}; \boldsymbol{\theta}_0)(\hat{\boldsymbol{\theta}} - \boldsymbol{\theta}_0)$$
$$+ \text{ terms of higher order in } (\hat{\boldsymbol{\theta}} - \boldsymbol{\theta}_0) \qquad (5.147)$$

where D_θ^2 is the matrix of second derivatives with respect to the components of $\boldsymbol{\theta}$. Thus, ignoring the higher-order terms, we have the well-known result

$$\sqrt{N}\,(\hat{\boldsymbol{\theta}} - \boldsymbol{\theta}_0) = -\left(\frac{1}{N} D_\theta^2 L_N(\mathbf{x}; \boldsymbol{\theta}_0)\right)^{-1}\left(\frac{1}{\sqrt{N}} D_\theta L_N(\mathbf{x}; \boldsymbol{\theta}_0)\right). \quad (5.148)$$

Now, $\{D_\theta L_N(\mathbf{x}; \boldsymbol{\theta}) : N = 1, 2, \dots \}$ is a *martingale, for*

$$\mathrm{E}\{D_\theta L_{N+1}(\mathbf{x}; \boldsymbol{\theta}) \mid D_\theta L_N(\mathbf{x}; \boldsymbol{\theta}), D_\theta L_{N-1}(\mathbf{x}; \boldsymbol{\theta}), \dots \} = D_\theta L_N(\mathbf{x}; \boldsymbol{\theta}). \quad (5.149)$$

This follows from the fact that the left-hand side of (5.149) is equal to the sum $D_\theta L_N(\mathbf{x}; \boldsymbol{\theta}) + \mathrm{E}\{D_\theta L(\mathbf{x}_{N+2} \mid \mathbf{x}_{N+1}; \boldsymbol{\theta})\}$ where the second summand vanishes because, under the usual regularity justifying differentiation under the integral sign,

$$\int f(\mathbf{x}_{N+2} \mid \mathbf{x}_{N+1}; \boldsymbol{\theta})\, \mathrm{d}\mathbf{x}_{N+2} = 1$$

$$\Rightarrow \int \{D_\theta L(\mathbf{x}_{N+2} \mid \mathbf{x}_{N+1}; \boldsymbol{\theta})\} f(\mathbf{x}_{N+2} \mid \mathbf{x}_{N+1}; \boldsymbol{\theta})\, \mathrm{d}\mathbf{x}_{N+2} = 0.$$

Suppose that $\{\mathbf{x}_1, \mathbf{x}_2, \dots \}$ is such that as $N \to \infty$

$$\frac{1}{N} D_\theta^2 L_N(\mathbf{x}; \boldsymbol{\theta}_0) \to \mathrm{V}$$

a constant matrix, in probability. (This simply requires that the ergodicity and stationary of $\{\mathbf{x}_1, \mathbf{x}_2, \dots \}$ is obtained.) On applying the martingale central limit theorem (see Appendix 2) to $\{\mathrm{V}^{-1}(1/N^{1/2})D_\theta L_N(\mathbf{x}; \boldsymbol{\theta}_0) : N = 1, 2, \dots \}$,

$$\sqrt{N}\,(\hat{\boldsymbol{\theta}} - \boldsymbol{\theta}_0) \rightsquigarrow \mathcal{N}(0, \mathrm{V}^{-1}\mathbf{W}\mathrm{V}^{-1}) \quad \text{as} \quad N \to \infty \qquad (5.150)$$

where **W** is almost everywhere equal to

$$\lim_{N\to\infty} \frac{1}{N} \sum_{k=1}^{N} \mathrm{E}[\{D_\theta L(\mathbf{x}_{k+1} \mid \mathbf{x}_k; \boldsymbol{\theta}_0)\}\{D_\theta L(\mathbf{x}_{k+1} \mid \mathbf{x}_k; \boldsymbol{\theta}_0)\}^T \mid \mathbf{x}_k, \mathbf{x}_{k-1}, \ldots, \mathbf{x}_1].$$

Equation (5.150) is an extension of (5.138). The χ^2 distribution of the likelihood ratio statistic may be extended in a similar way.

For a rigorous exposition in the linear autoregressive moving-average case see Findley (1983) and Bhansali (1986).

5.4.3 A FEW CAUTIONARY REMARKS

We have suggested that a *preliminary* model identification may be based on MAICE. Just as is the case with other statistical tools, common sense should prevail. With experience and common sense, we have found MAICE quite serviceable. However, in view of its increasing popularity, readers might find it helpful if we draw their attention to the following points, which might not be sufficiently widely known.

1. The likelihood in (5.143) refers to the *exact* likelihood. In practice, the exact likelihood is often avoided either because it is computationally expensive or theoretically very complicated. Practically, it is then often the case that ε_t is assumed Gaussian and that only a conditional likelihood is used, for example conditional on some initial observations $x_1, x_2, \ldots, x_Q$, say. In this case, the exact AIC(k) is replaced by an approximate AIC(k) based on $n(=N-Q)$ observations. This approximation is presumably quite adequate for the purpose of searching for a model within the *same* class of models using the *same* method of estimation based on the *same* numerical algorithm, because the effect of the approximation is then relatively *uniform throughout the class*. Our experience now suggests that the said approximation is not necessarily acceptable as a means of comparison if we deviate from the above conditions because the uniformity may no longer hold. We must also bear in mind the basic assumption underlying the statistics (5.143). This suggests that there may be reservations against its use for comparison *between* classes. Moreover, the results of Shibata (1980, 1981) suggest the possible loss of 'optimality' of MAICE when the number of candidate models is too 'large' relative to the sample size. Indeed the method becomes unreliable in such circumstances because of the increased sensitivity to sampling fluctuations. The situation here seems to mimic that of using a large number of two-sample t tests in a multi-sample situation. Akaike (1985) has warned against the mechanistic enumeration of AIC of all possible models. He has emphasized that the selection of the basic set of models must represent the particular way of looking at the data by the researcher.

2. In the literature, AIC has sometimes been equated with a test statistic. (See for example Söderström (1977) together with Akaike's comments on it (Akaike 1978*d*). It turns out that it is only a coincidence if the two different approaches yield the same conclusion. Akaike (1978*d*) has given typical examples where the two approaches lead to drastically different conclusions.

3. We should be more cautious if several local minima of heights differing only very slightly are observed in the AIC plot. One possible way out of this difficulty is by considering a 'combined' model based on the 'likelihoods' supplied by these local minima (Akaike 1978*a*).

4. AIC(k) is apt to take a rather low value for a k near the maximum order entertained when in fact the model corresponding to this choice of k might well turn out to be the worst model (Shimizu 1978). This is related to the fact that MAICE of orders are not consistent (Shibata 1976). Our own practice is to discard models of exceptionally high orders. The subjectivity of the choice of the maximum order should be borne constantly in mind too. It is as well to bear in mind the 'ideal' shape of the AIC plot (Fig. 5.27).

5. Diagnostic checks are indispensable, especially for non-linear time series modelling, because the number of candidate models is generally larger in the non-linear cases than in the linear cases. We argue that every parametric specification of a time series model is coloured by some subjective judgement. The initial graphical explorations help towards forming a better informed subjective judgement. Whether the specifica-

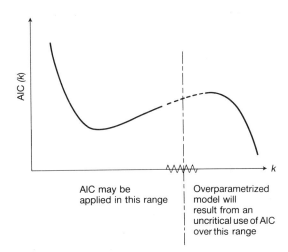

Fig. 5.27. AIC(k) vs k

tion conforms to the objective reality can be examined through diagnostic examinations. This part of the exercise requires substantial statistical common sense, and considerable experience. AIC is basically a *global* measure of goodness of fit, and as such it cannot be expected to pinpoint some of the *finer* details which might be of particular interest for a particular problem.

We shall describe some diagnostic checks in §5.6.

5.4.4 SOME OTHER APPROACHES TO MODEL SELECTION

In a sense, it is probably true to say that Akaike's (1974b)* very influential paper signalled a shift of the paradigm of statistical thinking, a movement which is still going on. Since then, an 'industry' of model selection has flourished. We briefly comment on a few representative developments without giving the technical details. Most of the developments, like Akaike's, go beyond the time series context.

(A) Cross-validation approach

The available data are divided into two (not necessarily equal) subsets. The first subset is used for the estimation of the parameters in the models to be used for prediction and the second subset for the testing or checking of the result of estimation. An excellent account of the method is given by Stone (1974). In systems engineering, a similar technique, which has been quite widely used by engineers for a while, is the so-called *group method of data handling* (GMDH) developed by Ivakhnenko (1971).

The cross-validation method also emphasizes the predictive aspect of model selection. The similarity between MAICE and the cross-validation was first pointed out by Tong (1976). Stone (1977) gives a proof of the asymptotic equivalence of the two procedures under certain general conditions.

(B) Prequential approach

Another prediction-oriented approach is the *prequential approach* of Dawid (1984). Assessment of sequential probability forecast performance for future observations forms the basis of the method. This method differs from Akaike's approach in that it does not stipulate any 'conceptual sampling' from the hypothetical distribution and it explicitly

---

* The Institute for Scientific Information spotted this paper as one of the most frequently cited papers in the area of engineering, technology, and applied science (Akaike 1981).

exploits the sequential nature of real modelling. In practical terms, it means only 'real-time' predictions of the data actually being collected are considered. Under certain general conditions, this approach leads asymptotically to the replacement of the 'penalty term' in eqn (5.143) by $(\ln N \times (\text{number of independently adjusted parameters})$, where N is the sample size.

(C) Bayesian approach

Jeffreys (1936) has used a Bayesian argument to conclude that, in inference, the maximum log likelihood $\ln p(\mathbf{x}^N \mid \hat{\boldsymbol{\theta}}_N)$ should be penalized by a term $\frac{1}{2} d \ln N$, where $\mathbf{x}^N$ denotes the data vector at hand, that is $x_1, \ldots, x_N$, and $\hat{\boldsymbol{\theta}}_N$ denotes the maximum likelihood estimate based on $\mathbf{x}^N$ of the underlying probability law parameterized by $\boldsymbol{\theta} \in \mathbf{R}^d$. This result underlies the arguments used by Schwarz (1978) and Akaike (1977, 1985) to arrive at the criteria carrying the acronym, BIC, which replaces the multiplier 2 in eqn (5.143) by $\ln N$.

(D) Parzen's approach

In 1974, Parzen proposed the *criterion autoregressive tranfer function* (*CAT*), which is also prediction based. Specifically, CAT is designed for selecting an AR model of appropriate order. The starting point is the assumption that the true model is AR(∞) with (non-normalized) spectral density function $h(\omega)$. Given time series data of finite duration (say sample size $= N$), an AR(m) model is adopted if its spectral density function $\hat{h}_m(\omega)$ with the associated autoregressive parameters estimated from the Yule–Walker equations minimizes the 'integrated relative mean square error', that is

$$\frac{1}{2\pi} \int_{-\pi}^{\pi} \mathrm{E} \left| \frac{\hat{h}_m(\omega) - h(\omega)}{h(\omega)} \right|^2 \mathrm{d}\omega$$

which is approximately equal to

$$1 - \frac{\sigma_\infty^2}{\sigma_m^2} + \frac{m}{N}$$

where σ_m^2 is the mean square prediction error of one-step-ahead prediction based on the best (i.e. in the minimum mean square sense) approximating AR(m), and

$$\ln \sigma_\infty^2 = \frac{1}{2\pi} \int_{-\pi}^{\pi} \ln(2\pi h(\omega)) \, \mathrm{d}\omega.$$

This then motivates the following criterion. Let $m = 0, 1, \ldots, L$ (a pre-fixed integer) and

$$\text{CAT}(m) = 1 - \frac{\hat{\sigma}_{\infty}^2}{\bar{\sigma}_m^2} + \frac{m}{N} \qquad (5.151)$$

where $\hat{\sigma}_{\infty}^2$ is an estimate of the one-step-ahead prediction error variance, σ_{∞}^2. The term $\bar{\sigma}_m^2$ is given by $(N - m)^{-1}$ times the residual sum of squares when an AR(m) model is fitted. The order estimate, $\hat{m}$, is the minimizer of CAT(m) over m. Tong (1979) has shown that CAT and AIC are locally equivalent in the sense that approximately

$$\text{CAT}(m) - \text{CAT}(m - 1) \propto \text{AIC}(m) - \text{AIC}(m - 1).$$

(E) Hannan–Quinn's approach

The Bayesian approach is partly motivated by the emphasis of consistency of the estimate of the dimension of the parameter space *which is assumed fixed and finite*. It may be argued that this assumption is often not practically important or realistic. However, suppose that we do accept the assumption. Then what BIC does is to increase the penalty (by using the multiplier $\ln N$) with the sample size so as to achieve consistent estimates. For finite sample size, BIC has the tendency of underestimating the dimension whilst the MAICE tends to overestimate the dimension. Now, it is still possible to achieve consistency even with a slower rate of increase of the penalty, thereby reducing the underestimation just mentioned. This consideration has motivated Hannan and Quinn's approach (1979), which replaces the multiplier 2 of eqn (5.143) by $2c \ln \ln N$, c being a constant greater than 1.

(F) Coding theoretic approach

In this recent approach the basic task of modelling is conceived to be the most efficient transmission of a sequence of data via some code. The efficiency is measured by the code lengths used. In concrete applications of the approach to problems similar to those considered so far in this section it shares many common features with the prequential approach. In particular, the multiplier $\ln N$ emerges in several cases. Details are given in Rissanen (1987) and Wallace and Freeman (1987).

5.5 Estimation

There are mainly two methods of parameter estimation which have been used in the literature of non-linear time series analysis, namely the maximum likelihood method and the conditional least-squares method. When these two methods are intractable, the method of moments may be used. Owing to the vast variety of non-linear models, it is probably to be expected that the sampling properties of the parameter estimates are quite diverse. As a result, although it is possible to describe some general framework, it is often the case that useful results will emerge only after each concrete case is analysed in depth. We describe first some general results in §§5.5.1 and 5.5.2. Specific cases will be described in later subsections.

5.5.1 ASYMPTOTIC PROPERTIES OF MAXIMUM LIKELIHOOD ESTIMATORS

There is a considerable literature on the maximum likelihood estimation of parameters of stationary ergodic Markov chains. An early systematic account is Billingsley (1961) and more recent references are Basawa and Prakasa Rao (1980) and Hall and Heyde (1980). We *sketch* the main results here and refer readers to the references just cited for further detail.

Let $X^N = (X_1, X_2, \ldots, X_N)$ denote a sample of N consecutive observations from the time series $\{X_t : t \in \mathbf{Z}\}$. Assume that X^N has a probability density $P_N(x_1, \ldots, x_N)$, which depends on $\theta \in \Theta$, an open subset of $\mathbf{R}^p$. For easy exposition, we only consider the case $p = 1$, noting that the result may be extended to the case of general p. Let $L_N(\theta)$ denote the log likelihood, that is $\ln P_N(X_1, \ldots, X_N; \theta)$. We assume that (i) $L_N(\theta)$ is differentiable w.r.t. θ, (ii) $E_\theta(dL_N(\theta)/d\theta)^2 < \infty$ for each N, where E_θ denotes the expectation w.r.t. P_N with θ being the parameter, and (iii) $\int P_N(x_1, \ldots, x_N; \theta) \, dx^N$ can be differentiated twice w.r.t. θ under the integral sign. Let $L_0(\theta) \equiv 0$ and write $u_i(\bar{\theta}) = d[L_i(\theta) - L_{i-1}(\theta)]/d\theta$ evaluated at $\bar{\theta}$. Clearly

$$\frac{d}{d\theta} L_N(\bar{\theta}) = \sum_{i=1}^{N} u_i(\bar{\theta}).$$

Consider the Taylor expansion of $(d/d\theta)L_N(\bar{\theta})$:

$$\frac{d}{d\theta} L_N(\bar{\theta}) = \sum_{i=1}^{N} u_i(\theta) - (\bar{\theta} - \theta)I_N(\theta) + (\bar{\theta} - \theta)(J_N(\theta_N^*) + I_N(\theta)) \quad (5.152)$$

where $\theta_N^* = \theta + \gamma(\bar{\theta} - \theta)$, γ is a function of (X^N, θ), and $|\gamma| < 1$. Here, $I_N(\theta) = \sum_{i=1}^{N} E_\theta(u_i^2(\theta) \mid \mathbb{B}_{i-1})$, with $\mathbb{B}_k$ being the σ-algebra generated by X_s, $1 \le s \le k$ and $\mathbb{B}_0$ being the trivial σ-algebra:

$$J_N(\theta) = \sum_{i=1}^{N} \frac{du_i(\theta)}{d\theta}.$$

Note that $E_\theta[u_i \,|\, \mathbb{B}_{i-1}] = 0$, almost surely (or more briefly a.s.) and $\{dL_i(\theta)/d\theta, \mathbb{B}_i, i \geq 1\}$ is a square integrable martingale—that is $\{u_i, \mathbb{B}_i, i \geq 1\}$ is a square integrable *martingale difference sequence*. There, *the quantity $I_N(\theta)$ plays the role of Fisher information* and expresses the (conditional) information of the data on θ. Suppose that $I_N(\theta) \to \infty$ a.s. as $N \to \infty$. Then using a strong law of large numbers for the mixingales (see Appendix 2), we have, as $N \to \infty$

$$[I_N(\theta)]^{-1} \sum_{i=1}^{N} u_i(\theta) \to 0, \quad \text{a.s.} \tag{5.153}$$

because

$$\sum_{N=1}^{\infty} [I_N(\theta)]^{-2} E_\theta[u_N^2(\theta) \,|\, \mathbb{B}_{N-1}] < \infty, \quad \text{a.s.}$$

Let $\hat{\theta}_N$ denote a root of the likelihood equation

$$\frac{d}{d\theta} L_N(\theta) = 0.$$

Then from (5.152) we have

$$[I_N(\theta)]^{-1} \sum_{i=1}^{N} u_i(\theta) = (\hat{\theta}_N - \theta)\left[1 - \left(\frac{J_N(\theta_N^*) + I_N(\theta)}{I_N(\theta)}\right)\right]. \tag{5.154}$$

Therefore, we have sketched a proof of the following theorem.

Theorem 5.2: If $I_N(\theta) \to \infty$, a.s. and

$$\limsup_{N \to \infty} [I_N(\theta)]^{-1} \,|\, J_N(\theta_N^*) + I_N(\theta)| < 1, \quad \text{a.s.} \tag{5.155}$$

then $\hat{\theta}_N \to \theta$, a.s., that is $\hat{\theta}_n$ is strongly consistent for θ.
    From (5.154), we can see that if

$$[I_N(\theta)]^{-1/2} \sum_{i=1}^{N} u_i(\theta) \rightsquigarrow \mathcal{N}(0, 1) \tag{5.156}$$

and $J_N(\theta)/I_N(\theta) \to -1$ in probability as $N \to \infty$ uniformly on compact subsets of Θ, then

$$[I_N(\theta)]^{1/2}(\hat{\theta}_N - \theta) \rightsquigarrow \mathcal{N}(0, 1). \tag{5.157}$$

In turns out that conditions for (5.156) to hold are quite mild and we state them as follows.

Assumption 1: As $N \to \infty$, $I_N(\theta) \to \infty$, a.s., $I_N(\theta)/E_\theta I_N(\theta) \to \eta^2(\theta)$ in probability for some random variable η ($\neq 0$ a.s.), and $J_N(\theta)/I_N(\theta) \to -1$ in probability, uniformly on compact subsets of Θ.

Assumption 2: For $\delta > 0$, suppose that $|\theta_N - \theta| \leq \delta/(E_\theta I_N(\theta))^{.1/2}$ Then

(1) $E_{\theta_N} I_N(\theta_N) = E_\theta I_N(\theta)(1 + o(1))$ as $N \to \infty$;

(2) $I_N(\theta_N) = I_N(\theta)(1 + o(1))$ a.s. as $N \to \infty$;

(3) $J_N(\theta_N) = J_N(\theta) + o(I_N(\theta))$ a.s. as $N \to \infty$.

Thus we have sketched the proof of the following theorem.

Theorem 5.3: Under Assumptions 1 and 2 above, as $N \to \infty$

$$[I_N(\theta)]^{1/2}(\hat{\theta}_N - \theta) \rightsquigarrow \mathcal{N}(0, 1).$$

The maximum likelihood estimate $\hat{\theta}_N$ enjoys certain optimality properties. Let $S_N = S_N(X_1, \ldots, X_N)$ be any consistent estimate of θ for which $[I_N(\theta)]^{1/2}(S_N - \theta) \rightsquigarrow \mathcal{N}(0, \gamma^2(\theta))$ where $\gamma(\theta)$ is bounded and continuous in θ. Then it may be shown that, under suitable regularity conditions, $\gamma^2(\theta) \geq 1$. We refer interested readers to, for example, Hall and Heyde (1980, Chapter 6) for further detail.

It is not difficult to see that, for the case $p > 1$, we may define $u_i(\boldsymbol{\theta})$ by the column vector of first partial derivatives of $L_i(\boldsymbol{\theta}) - L_{i-1}(\boldsymbol{\theta})$ and $I_N(\boldsymbol{\theta})$ by $\sum_{i=1}^{N} E_\theta(u_i(\boldsymbol{\theta}) u_i^T(\boldsymbol{\theta}) | \mathbb{B}_{i-1})$. The above results may then be generalized in an obvious way (cf. §5.5.2).

Example 5.2 (NLAR(1)): Consider the model

$$X_t = \lambda(X_{t-1}; \theta) + \varepsilon_t, \qquad t = 1, 2, \ldots, N \qquad (5.158)$$

with $\{\varepsilon_1, \varepsilon_2, \ldots, \varepsilon_N\}$ independent of X_0 and independent amongst themselves with a common density $N(0, 1)$. Suppose that the NLAR(1) consideration is stationary. Conditional on X_0, the log likelihood function is (for $N \geq 1$)

$$L_N(\theta) = -\frac{N}{2} \ln(2\pi) - \frac{1}{2} \sum_{j=1}^{N} [X_j - \lambda(X_{j-1}; \theta)]^2. \qquad (5.159)$$

(Note that the condition on X_0 does not affect the large sample results.) We set $L_0(\theta) = 0$. Therefore

$$u_i(\theta) = \varepsilon_i \frac{d\lambda(X_{i-1}, \theta)}{d\theta}, \qquad i = 1, \ldots, N \qquad (5.160)$$

if λ is differentiable w.r.t. θ. Indeed we assume that λ is almost surely twice differentiable w.r.t. θ. Clearly

$$\frac{dL_N(\theta)}{d\theta} = \sum_{i=1}^{N} u_i(\theta)$$

$$E[u_i(\theta) \,|\, \mathbb{B}_{i-1}] = \frac{d\lambda(X_{i-1}; \theta)}{d\theta} E(\varepsilon_i) = 0, \quad \text{a.s.} \qquad (5.161)$$

$$I_N(\theta) = \sum_{i=1}^{N} \left(\frac{d\lambda(X_{i-1}; \theta)}{d\theta}\right)^2$$

which tends to ∞ a.s. as $N \to \infty$ for a variety of λ, for example λ s.t. $E[d\lambda/d\theta]^2 > 0$. Other parts of Assumptions 1 and 2 may be shown to hold for these λ. Then, for large N, we have approximately the result

$$\hat{\theta} - \theta \approx \mathcal{N}(0, (N E[d\lambda(X_1; \theta/d\theta]^2)^{-1}) \qquad (5.162)$$

where $\hat{\theta}$ satisfies the likelihood equation

$$\sum_{j=1}^{N} [X_j - \lambda(X_{j-1}; \hat{\theta})] \frac{d\lambda(X_{j-1}; \hat{\theta})}{d\theta} = 0. \qquad (5.163)$$

In particular, when $\lambda(x; \theta)$ is linear in the parameter θ, that is $\lambda(x; \theta) = \theta \chi(x)$ say, then

$$\hat{\theta} = \left(\sum_{j=1}^{N} X_j \chi(X_{j-1}) \right) / \sum_{j=1}^{N} \{\chi(X_j)\}^2 \qquad (5.164)$$

and

$$\text{var } \hat{\theta} \approx \frac{1}{N E[\chi^2(X_1)]}. \qquad (5.165)$$

$\square$

5.5.2   CONDITIONAL LEAST SQUARES

We continue to employ the notation of §5.5.1 and once again only a *sketch* of the basic ideas is presented. Further detail is given in Klimko and Nelson (1978) and Hall and Heyde (1980).

Suppose that $E|X_t| < \infty$, $t = 1, 2, \ldots$. We may estimate $\boldsymbol{\theta}$ by minimizing the 'residual sum of squares' (or equivalently the sum of squares of the innovations)

$$Q_N(\boldsymbol{\theta}) = \sum_{j=1}^{N} [X_j - E_\theta(X_j \mid \mathbb{B}_{j-1})]^2 \qquad (5.166)$$

w.r.t. $\boldsymbol{\theta}$. The estimates, $\hat{\boldsymbol{\theta}}_N$, are given by the solutions of the system of algebraic equations

$$\frac{\partial Q_N(\boldsymbol{\theta})}{\partial \theta_i} = 0, \qquad i = 1, \ldots, p \qquad (5.167)$$

where the partial derivatives are assumed to exist. In fact we assume that $E_\theta(X_j \mid \mathbb{B}_{j-1})$ is almost surely twice differentiable w.r.t. $\boldsymbol{\theta}$ in some neighbourhood S of $\boldsymbol{\theta}_0$, the true parameter. We may consider a Taylor series expansion in a neighbourhood of $\boldsymbol{\theta}_0$ within S. We let it be understood that henceforth all neighbourhoods are contained in S. First, we give some heuristics. Let $D_\theta Q_N(\boldsymbol{\theta}_0)$ denote the column vector of first partial derivatives of $Q_N(\boldsymbol{\theta})$ evaluated at $\boldsymbol{\theta}_0$. Let $D_\theta^2 Q_N(\boldsymbol{\theta}^*)$ denote the matrix of second partial derivatives evaluated at $\boldsymbol{\theta}^*$:

$$Q_N(\boldsymbol{\theta}) = Q_N(\boldsymbol{\theta}_0) + (\boldsymbol{\theta} - \boldsymbol{\theta}_0)^T D_\theta Q_n(\boldsymbol{\theta}_0) + \tfrac{1}{2}(\boldsymbol{\theta} - \boldsymbol{\theta}_0)^T D_\theta^2 Q_N(\boldsymbol{\theta}^*)(\boldsymbol{\theta} - \boldsymbol{\theta}_0)$$

$$= Q_N(\boldsymbol{\theta}_0) + (\boldsymbol{\theta} - \boldsymbol{\theta}_0)^T D_\theta Q_N(\boldsymbol{\theta}_0) + \tfrac{1}{2}(\boldsymbol{\theta} - \boldsymbol{\theta}_0)^T V_N(\boldsymbol{\theta} - \boldsymbol{\theta}_0)$$

$$+ \tfrac{1}{2}(\boldsymbol{\theta} - \boldsymbol{\theta}_0)^T T_N(\boldsymbol{\theta}^*)(\boldsymbol{\theta} - \boldsymbol{\theta}_0) \tag{5.168}$$

where V_n is the $p \times p$ matrix of second partial derivatives of $Q_N(\boldsymbol{\theta})$ evaluated at $\boldsymbol{\theta}_0$ and

$$T_N(\boldsymbol{\theta}^*) = D_\theta^2 Q_N(\boldsymbol{\theta}^*) - V_N. \tag{5.169}$$

Specifically, for $1 \le i \le p$, $1 \le j \le p$,

$$\left(\frac{1}{2N} V_N\right)_{ij} = \sum_{k=1}^{N} \left[\frac{1}{N}\left(\frac{\partial}{\partial\theta_i} E_\theta(X_k \mid \mathbb{B}_{k-1})\right)\left(\frac{\partial}{\partial\theta_j} E_\theta(X_k \mid \mathbb{B}_{k-1})\right) \right.$$

$$\left. - \frac{1}{N}\left(\frac{\partial^2}{\partial\theta_i\,\partial\theta_j} E_\theta(X_k \mid \mathbb{B}_{k-1})\right)(X_k - E_{\theta_0}(X_k \mid \mathbb{B}_{k-1})) \right] \tag{5.170}$$

where all the partial derivatives are evaluated at $\boldsymbol{\theta}_0$. Under appropriate conditions, the second summand tends to 0 almost surely for each i, j, on appealing to the strong law of large numbers of mixingales (Appendix 2), and the first summand tends to a positive definite $p \times p$ matrix V almost surely, on appealing to ergodicity (which we assumed). Provided T_N is small in an appropriate sense, it follows from (5.168) that $\hat{\boldsymbol{\theta}}_N$ is a strongly consistent estimator of $\boldsymbol{\theta}_0$. The result may be given formally in the following theorem due to Klimko and Nelson (1978).

Theorem 5.4 (Klimko and Nelson): Assume that (i) $\lim_{N\to\infty} \sup_{\delta\to 0}(|T_N(\boldsymbol{\theta}^*)_{ij}|/N\delta) < \infty$ almost surely (a.s.), $1 \le i \le p$, $1 \le j \le p$; (ii) $(2N)^{-1} V_N \to V$ a.s., where V is a positive definite symmetric $p \times p$ matrix of constants; (iii) $N^{-1} D_\theta Q_N(\boldsymbol{\theta}_0) \to 0$ component-wise a.s. Then, there exists a sequence of estimators $\{\hat{\boldsymbol{\theta}}_N\}$ s.t. $\hat{\boldsymbol{\theta}}_N \to \boldsymbol{\theta}_0$ a.s., and for any $\varepsilon > 0$ there exists an event E with $P(E) > 1 - \varepsilon$ and an N_0 such that on E, for $N > N_0$, $\hat{\boldsymbol{\theta}}_N$ satisfies the (conditional) least-squares equations (5.167) and Q_N attains a relative minimum at $\hat{\boldsymbol{\theta}}_N$.

Proof. ¶ First we recall *Egorov's theorem*: If $X_N \to X$ a.s. on (Ω, A, P) and X is a.s. finite, then $\forall \varepsilon > 0$, there exists a set A_ε with $P(A_\varepsilon) \ge 1 - \varepsilon$ s.t. $X_N \to X$ uniformly on A_ε. (See e.g. Neveu 1965, p. 49.)

Given $\varepsilon > 0$, it follows from conditions (i)–(iii) of the theorem and from Egorov's theorem that there exists an event E with $P(E) > 1 - \varepsilon$, a positive $\delta^* < \delta$, an $M > 0$, and an N_0 s.t. on E, $\forall N > N_0$ and $\forall \boldsymbol{\theta} \in S_{\delta^*}$, the open sphere of radius δ^* centred at $\boldsymbol{\theta}_0$, the following conclusions hold:

(1) $|(\boldsymbol{\theta} - \boldsymbol{\theta}_0)^T D_\theta Q_N(\boldsymbol{\theta}_0)] < N\delta^3$;

(2) $\exists \Delta > 0$ s.t. the minimum eigenvalue of $(2N)^{-1}V_N > \Delta$;

(3) $\frac{1}{2}(\boldsymbol{\theta} - \boldsymbol{\theta}_0)^T T_N(\boldsymbol{\theta}^*)(\boldsymbol{\theta} - \boldsymbol{\theta}_0) < NM\sigma^3$.

From (5.168), we have $\forall \boldsymbol{\theta} \in \partial S_{\delta^*}$ (the boundary of S_{δ^*}),

$$Q_N(\boldsymbol{\theta}) \geq Q_N(\boldsymbol{\theta}_0) + N\delta^2(\Delta - \delta - M\delta).$$

Now, $\Delta - \delta - M\delta$ can be made positive by initially choosing δ sufficiently small. Therefore, the minimizer $\hat{\boldsymbol{\theta}}_N$ of $Q_N(\boldsymbol{\theta})$ must be in S_{δ^*}, at which point the least-squares equations (5.167) hold.

Next, set $\varepsilon_k = 2^{-k}$ and $\delta_k = k^{-1}$, $k = 1, 2, \ldots$ to determine a sequence of events $\{E_k\}$ and an increasing sequence $\{N_k\}$ s.t. the equations (5.167) have a solution on E_k for any $N > N_k$. For $N_k < N \leq N_{k+1}$, define $\hat{\boldsymbol{\theta}}_N$ on E_k to be a solution of (5.167) within δ_k of $\boldsymbol{\theta}_0$ and at which Q_N attains a relative minimum, and define $\hat{\boldsymbol{\theta}}_N$ to be zero outside E_k. Then $\hat{\boldsymbol{\theta}}_N \to \boldsymbol{\theta}_0$ on $\bigcup_n \bigcap_{k \geq n} E_k$ which has probability 1 since

$$P\left(\bigcup_n \bigcap_{k \geq n} E_k\right) = 1 - P\left(\bigcap_n \bigcup_{k \geq n} E_k^c\right)$$

$$= 1 - \lim_{n > \infty} P\left(\bigcup_{k \geq n} E_k^c\right)$$

$$\geq 1 - \lim_{n \to \infty} \sum_{k=n}^{\infty} P(E_k^c)$$

$$= 1 - \lim_{n \to \infty} \sum_{k=n}^{\infty} 2^{-k}$$

$$= 1. \quad \square \; \P\P$$

Now, expanding $N^{-1/2}D_\theta Q(\hat{\boldsymbol{\theta}}_N)$ about $\boldsymbol{\theta}_0$, we have

$$\mathbf{0} = N^{-1/2}D_\theta Q(\hat{\boldsymbol{\theta}}_N)$$
$$= N^{-1/2}D_\theta Q(\boldsymbol{\theta}_0) + N^{-1}(V_N + T_N(\boldsymbol{\theta}^*))N^{1/2}(\hat{\boldsymbol{\theta}}_N - \boldsymbol{\theta}_0). \qquad (5.171)$$

Since $N^{-1}(V_N + T_N(\boldsymbol{\theta}^*)) \to 2V$ a.s., the limiting distribution of $N^{1/2}(\hat{\boldsymbol{\theta}}_N - \boldsymbol{\theta}_0)$ is the same as that of $-(2V)^{-1}N^{-1/2}D_\theta Q(\boldsymbol{\theta}_0)$. If we assume that $\frac{1}{2}N^{-1/2}D_\theta Q(\boldsymbol{\theta}_0)$ converges to $\mathcal{N}(0, W)$ in distribution as $N \to \infty$, where W is a $p \times p$ positive definite matrix, then

$$N^{1/2}(\hat{\boldsymbol{\theta}}_N - \boldsymbol{\theta}_0) \text{ converges to } \mathcal{N}(0, V^{-1}WV^{-1}) \qquad (5.172)$$

in distribution as $N \to \infty$. Thus, we have sketched a proof of the following theorem.

Theorem 5.5 (Klimko and Nelson): Suppose that the conditions of Theorem 5.4 hold and, in addition, $\frac{1}{2}N^{-1/2}D_\theta Q(\theta_0)$ converges to $\mathcal{N}(0, W)$ in distribution as $N \to \infty$, where W is a $p \times p$ positive definite matrix. Then $N^{1/2}(\hat{\theta}_N - \theta_0)$ tends to $\mathcal{N}(0, V^{-1}WV^{-1})$ in distribution as $N \to \infty$.

In fact, Klimko and Nelson (1978) have established that, under quite mild conditions, for any non-zero vector c of constants

$$\limsup_{N \to \infty} \frac{N^{1/2}c^T(\hat{\theta}_N - \theta_0)}{(2\sigma^2 \ln \ln N)^{1/2}} = 1 \quad \text{a.s.} \tag{5.173}$$

where

$$\sigma^2 = c^T V^{-1} W V^{-1} c.$$

This gives the rates of convergence for $N^{-1/2}(\hat{\theta}_n - \theta_0)$.

Example 5.3 (NLAR(1) revisited): We consider the same set-up as in Example 5.2 but with θ_0 denoting the true parameter. Clearly

$$Q_N(\theta) = \sum_{j=1}^{N} [X_j - \lambda(X_{j-1}; \theta)]^2$$

and the conditional least-squares estimate $\hat{\theta}_n$ satisfies the same equation as the maximum likelihood equation, namely (5.163). It can also be easily checked that $V = W$. Therefore, subject to λ being s.t. the conditions of Theorems 5.4 and 5.5 are satisfied,

$$N^{1/2}(\hat{\theta}_N - \theta_0) \text{ tends to } \mathcal{N}(0, (E[d\lambda(X_1; \theta_0)/d\theta]^2)^{-1}).$$

So far our examples have all been given in very general terms. However, as soon as λ is specified, we can set about checking if all the assumptions of Theorems 5.4 and 5.5 are satisfied. The next example gives an illustration.

Example 5.4 (STAR): Let $X_1, X_2, \ldots, X_N$ be a sample record from a STAR model of order p:

$$X_t = a_0 + a_1 X_{t-1} + \ldots + a_p X_{t-p}$$

$$+ (b_0 + b_1 X_{t-1} + \ldots + b_p X_{t-p})F\left(\frac{X_{t-d} - r}{z}\right) + \varepsilon_t \tag{5.174}$$

where $\{\varepsilon_t\}$ is a sequence of i.i.d. random variables with zero mean and finite variance σ^2. For concreteness we assume that F is the standard normal distribution, although this assumption is not essential (see Chapter 3).

Let

$$\theta = (a_0, a_1, \ldots, a_p, b_0, \ldots, b_p, r, z)'.$$

Then, the natural space for θ is $\Omega = \bigcup_{i=1}^{p+1} \Omega_i$, where

$$\Omega_i = \underbrace{\mathbf{R} \times \ldots \times \mathbf{R} \times \overset{i\text{th}}{\mathbf{R}} \times \ldots \times (\mathbf{R}\backslash\{0\})}_{p+1} \times \underbrace{\ldots \times \mathbf{R} \times \mathbf{R}}_{p+1} \times \mathbf{R}^+$$

$$\mathbf{R}^+ = \{x : x > 0 \quad \text{and} \quad x \in \mathbf{R}\}$$

and $\mathbf{R}$ the totality of real numbers.

Let θ_0 be the true parameter. Given a set of observations X_t, $t = 1, 2, \ldots, N$, we estimate θ_0 by minimizing the conditional sum of squares

$$Q_N(\theta) = \sum_{t=m}^{N-1} [X_{t+1} - g(\theta, \mathbb{B}_t)]^2 \tag{5.175}$$

where $m = \max(d, p)$, $g(\theta, \mathbb{B}_t) = E_\theta(X_{t+1} \mid \mathbb{B}_t)$, and $\mathbb{B}_t$ is the σ-algebra generated by $X_1, \ldots, X_t$.

Let $\hat{\theta}$ be such that $Q_N(\hat{\theta}) = \min_\theta Q_N(\theta)$. The variance of ε_t, σ^2, is estimated by

$$\hat{\sigma}_N^2 = \frac{Q_N(\hat{\theta})}{N}.$$

From now on, we assume that $\{X_t\}$ is ergodic and the stationary distribution of X_t possesses finite second moment unless stated otherwise. We are going to prove the following result, which is technically the most demanding one to check among all the assumptions in Theorems 5.4 and 5.5 for the present example.

Let $V = E_{\theta_0}(\partial g(\theta_0, \mathbb{B}_m)/\partial \theta_i \cdot \partial g(\theta_0, \mathbb{B}_m)/\partial \theta_j)$. Then V is positive definite. (It then follows that, subject to the other assumptions in Theorems 5.4 and 5.5, there exists a sequence of estimators $\hat{\theta}_N$ s.t. $\hat{\theta}_N \to \theta_0$ a.s., and for $\varepsilon > 0$ there is an event E with $P(E) > 1 - \varepsilon$ and n_0 s.t. on E, for $N > n_0$, Q_N attains a relative minimum at $\hat{\theta}_N$. Also, $N^{1/2}(\hat{\theta}_N - \theta_0) \rightsquigarrow \mathcal{N}(0, \sigma^2 V^{-1})$, and $\hat{\sigma}_N^2 \to \sigma^2$ a.s.

¶ **Proof:** First we note that $W = \sigma^2 V$. As V is clearly non-negative definite, to prove that V is positive definite, it only remains to prove that for

$$\beta = (\tilde{a}_0, \tilde{a}_1, \ldots, \tilde{a}_p, \bar{b}_0, \bar{b}_1, \ldots, \bar{b}_p, \tilde{r}, \tilde{z})' \in \mathbf{R}^{2p+4}$$
$$\beta' V \beta = 0 \Rightarrow \beta = 0.$$

For simplicity, denote $F(X_{m+1-d} - r/z)$ by F and its derivative, $f(X_{m+1-d} - r/z)$, by f. We note the following facts:

(i) $F \to 0$ as $X_{m+1-d} \to -\infty$

(ii) $F \to 1$ as $X_{m+1-d} \to \infty$

(iii) $X_{m+1-d}^k F \to 0$ as $X_{m+1-d} \to \infty$, $k \geq 0$

(iv) $X_{m+1-d}^k f \to 0$ as $X_{m+1-d} \to \pm\infty$, $k \geq 0$.

$$\tag{5.176}$$

(i) and (ii) are trivial; (iii) and (iv) may be verified by using the L'Hopital rule. Let

$$h = \bar{a}_0 + \bar{b}_0 F + \sum \bar{a}_i X_{m+1-i} + \left(\sum \bar{b}_i X_{m+1-i}\right) F$$
$$- \left(b_0 + \sum b_i X_{m+1-i}\right) \cdot f \cdot \left[\frac{\bar{r}}{z} + \bar{z}\left(\frac{X_{m+1-d} - r}{z^2}\right)\right]$$

(all summations range form $i = 1$ to p). Then

$$\beta' V \beta = E_{\theta_0}(h^2|_{\theta=\theta_0}).$$

That is $\beta' V \beta$ is the average of h^2 at $\theta = \theta_0$ over the true distribution indexed by θ_0. For convenience, we shall write the above expression as $\beta' V \beta = E(h^2)$. Suppose

$$0 = \beta' V \beta = E(h^2) = E(E(h^2 \mid X_m, \ldots, X_1)).$$

Let $\varepsilon > 0$. Treating X_{m+1-d} as variable and keeping the other X_j as constants, it follows from (5.176) that when X_{m+1-d} is sufficiently large negatively,

$$E(h^2 \mid X_m, \ldots, X_{m+1-d}, \ldots, X_1) \geq w^2 - 2\,|w\varepsilon| \qquad (5.177)$$

where $w = (\sum \bar{a}_i X_{m+1-i} + \bar{a}_0)$.

To be explicit, if $X_{m+1-d} \leq \psi_1^{(\varepsilon)}(X_m, \ldots, \hat{X}_{m+1-d}, \ldots, X_1)$, then (5.177) holds. Here, $\hat{X}$ indicates that X is deleted.

$\psi_1^{(\varepsilon)}(X_m, \ldots, \hat{X}_{m+1-d}, \ldots, X_1)$ is a complicated function of $X_m, \ldots, X_1$ with X_{m+1-d} deleted. It may be chosen to be measurable. Consider $(\bar{a}_0 + \sum \bar{a}_i X_{m+1-i})^2$. Let $K > 0$.

If $\bar{a}_j \neq 0$ for some $j \geq 1$, it is easily seen that there exists a measurable function $\psi_2^{(K)}(X_m, \ldots, \hat{X}_{m+1-j}, \ldots, X_1)$ such that

$$\left(\bar{a}_0 + \sum \bar{a}_i X_{m+1-i}\right)^2 > K \quad \text{if} \quad |X_{m+1-j}| \geq \psi_2^{(K)}(X_m, \ldots, \hat{X}_{m+1-j}, \ldots, X_1).$$

For simplicity, we shall not indicate the dependence of $\psi_1^{(\varepsilon)}$ and $\psi_2^{(K)}$ on the relevant variables explicitly but write $\psi_1^{(\varepsilon)}$ and $\psi_2^{(K)}$ instead. Suppose $\bar{a}_i \neq 0$. There are two cases:

Case (i): $\bar{a}_{i_0} \neq 0$ for some $i_0 > 1$;

Case (ii): $\bar{a}_i = 0 \; \forall i \geq 1$ and $\bar{a} \neq 0$.

In Case (i), if $\bar{a}_{m+1-d} \neq 0$, we choose $i_0 = m + 1 - d$. Fix $K > 0$. Let

$$S = \{(X_m, \ldots, X_1) : X_{m+1-d} \leq \psi_1^{(K/4)}, X_{i_0} \leq \psi_2^{(K)}\}$$

in Case (i). Otherwise,

$$S = \{(X_m, \ldots, X_1) : X_{m+1-d} \leq \psi_1^{|\bar{a}_0|/K}\}$$

S is easily seen to be of positive Lebesgue measure.

It is clear that $E(h^2 \mid X_m, \ldots, X_1) > 0$ over S in either case. Therefore, all the $\bar{a}_j$ are zero, for otherwise $\beta' V \beta = E(Eh^2 \mid X_m, \ldots, X_1) > 0$. Similar argument yields that $\beta = 0$. The argument makes use of the properties of the density function of $X_1, \ldots, X_m$ being positive everywhere, which can be readily verified. This completes the proof.

Moreover, we can assess the rate of convergence. Let $C \in \mathbf{R}^{2p+4}$. We note that

$$\sum_{t=m}^{N-1} \sum_i (\partial g(\theta_0, B_t)/\partial \theta_i) \varepsilon_{t+1}$$

is a stationary, ergodic, and square integrable martingale difference sequence. Then on appealing to Corollary 2.2 in Klimko and Nelson (1978) we can establish the rate as described in eqn (5.173). □ ¶¶

Results described so far in §§ 5.5.1 and 5.5.2 would enable us to obtain estimates of the unknown parameters and their sampling properties for (i) non-linear autoregressive models with smooth regression function (cf Exercises 6 and 7), (ii) random coefficient AR models (cf Exercise 8), (iii) NEAR models (cf Exercise 9), and (iv) others. However, unsmooth models, like SETAR models, require more individual attention, and we turn to these in the next subsection. Further, models for which the invertibility conditions will have a crucial part to play in their estimation will receive special attention in §5.5.4.

5.5.3 THRESHOLD AUTOREGRESSIVE MODELS

Before any formal discussion, let us look at Fig. 5.28, which gives the (*conditional*) *sum of squared errors* (*SSE*) of a simple $(2; 1, 1)$ model. The many ridges are typical and are the results of the 'discontinuity' of the model due to the structural parameter, r, that is the threshold parameter. They suggest that it is unlikely that $\hat{r}$, the conditional least-squares estimate of r, will be asymptotically normal because w.r.t. r the SSE is a step function with jumps at the observations and thus *attains its global minimum over at least a half open interval*. It is therefore to be expected that the SSE will have an esoteric structure over r.

The theory of §§5.5.1 and 5.5.2 is sufficient to show straightforwardly that conditional on the *structural parameters*, namely the threshold parameters and the delay parameters, being known, the autoregressive parameter estimates of a SETAR model, that is the conditional least-squates estimates (CLS) of the $a_i^{(j)}$ in the notation of §3.3.1.1, will be asymptotically normal. (Readers are encouraged to prove this as an exercise.) This is expected by analogy with the case of linear AR models. As far as the estimation of the structural parameters is concerned,

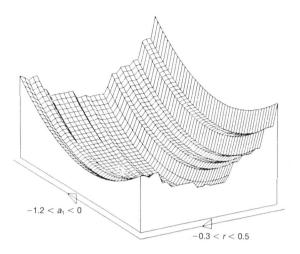

Fig. 5.28. Conditional sum of squared errors as a function of a_1 and r in a SETAR $(2; 1, 1)$ model of the form

$$X_t = \begin{cases} a_0 + a_1 X_{t-1} + \varepsilon_t & \text{if } X_{t-1} \leq r \\ b_0 + b_1 X_{t-1} + \varepsilon_t & \text{if } X_{t-1} > r \end{cases}$$

where 100 observations have been generated using $a_0 = 0.7$, $a_1 = -0.5$, $b_0 = -1.8$, $b_1 = 0.7$, and $r = 0$

simulation results of Tong (1978) and Li (1988) suggest that the CLS/maximum likelihood estimates enjoy good properties.

We shall quote without proof three theorems due to Chan (1988c). As the proofs are very technical and lengthy, involving the use of a Skorohod metric and a compound Poisson process defined on a function space of continuous functions on the real line, we shall only sketch the basic ideas after stating the theorems. For details, interested readers may refer to Chan (1988c). Although the results will be stated for the two-regime case, some of them can be generalized to the m-regime case $(m > 2)$ without difficulty when m is known.

Let us therefore consider the two-regime SETAR model

$$X_t = \begin{cases} a_{011} + a_{010} X_{t-1} + \ldots + a_{01p} X_{t-p} + \sigma_{01} \varepsilon_t & \text{if } X_{t-d_0} \leq r_0 \\ a_{020} + a_{021} X_{t-1} + \ldots + a_{02p} X_{t-p} + \sigma_{02} \varepsilon_t & \text{if } X_{t-d_0} > r_0. \end{cases} \quad (5.178)$$

Suppose that we have observations $\{X_0, X_1, \ldots, X_N\}$ from (5.178) and we use the method of conditional least squares to estimate the *true* parameter $\boldsymbol{\theta}_0 = (\mathbf{A}'_{01}, \mathbf{A}'_{02}, r_0, d_0)'$ where $\mathbf{A}_{0i} = (a_{0i0}, \ldots, a_{0ip})'$, $i = 1, 2$. It is assumed throughout that $\mathbf{A}_{01}$ and $\mathbf{A}_{02}$ are distinct and that there is a known *a priori* upper bound for p and d. Without loss of generality, let $d_0 \leq p$ and p be known. Let $\boldsymbol{\theta} = (\mathbf{A}_1', \mathbf{A}_2', r, d)'$ denote a vector in $\mathbf{R}^{2p+3} \times \{1, 2, \ldots, p\}$. Define the (conditional) sum of squares

$$L_N(\boldsymbol{\theta}) = \sum_{t=p}^{N} [X_t - \mathbb{E}_\theta(X_t \mid \mathbb{B}_{t-1})]^2 \tag{5.179}$$

where $\mathbb{B}_t$ is the σ-algebra generated by $X_0, X_1, \ldots, X_t$, $\mathbb{E}_\theta(. \mid .)$ is the conditional expectation assuming that $\boldsymbol{\theta}$ is the true parameter. Let the CLS estimate of $\boldsymbol{\theta}_0$ be denoted by $\hat{\boldsymbol{\theta}}_N = (\hat{\mathbf{A}}_{1N}', \hat{\mathbf{A}}_{2N}', \hat{r}_N, \hat{d}_N)'$, where $\hat{r}_N = \hat{r}_N(\hat{d}_N)$ and $\hat{\mathbf{A}}_{iN}(\hat{r}_N, \hat{d}_N)$, $i = 1, 2$, that is the CLS search w.r.t. $(\mathbf{A}_1', \mathbf{A}_2', r, d)$ is over d last and r second last. Let $X_{(0)} \leq X_{(1)} \leq \ldots \leq X_{(N)}$ denote the order statistics of the sample. Given $\hat{\boldsymbol{\theta}}_N$, $L_N(\hat{\boldsymbol{\theta}}_N)$ can be decomposed into the sum of two non-negative parts, the 'sum of squared errors of the lower regime' $L_{1N}(\hat{\boldsymbol{\theta}}_N)$, and the 'sum of squared errors of the upper regime' $L_{2N}(\hat{\boldsymbol{\theta}}_N)$, namely,

$$L_N(\hat{\boldsymbol{\theta}}_N) = L_{1N}(\hat{\boldsymbol{\theta}}_N) + L_{2N}(\hat{\boldsymbol{\theta}}_N) \tag{5.180}$$

where

$$L_{1N}(\hat{\boldsymbol{\theta}}_N) = \sum_{X_{(i)-d} \leq \hat{r}_N} [X_{(j)} - \mathbb{E}_{\hat{\theta}_N}(X_{(j)} \mid \mathbb{B}_{(j)-1})]^2 \tag{5.181}$$

$$L_{2N}(\hat{\boldsymbol{\theta}}_N) = L_N(\hat{\boldsymbol{\theta}}_N) - L_{1N}(\hat{\boldsymbol{\theta}}_N) \tag{5.182}$$

and the usual care is taken to ensure that only those j will be included in the summation for which $X_{(j)} \in \{X_p, \ldots, X_N\}$. The CLS estimates of σ_{0i}^2, $i = 1, 2$, are

$$\hat{\sigma}_{iN}^2 = L_{iN}(\hat{\boldsymbol{\theta}}_N)/N_i \tag{5.183}$$

where

$$N_1 = \sum_{t=p}^{N} I(X_{t-\hat{d}_N} \leq \hat{r}_N) \qquad N_2 = N - p - N_1 + 1 \tag{5.184}$$

I denoting the indicator function. Note that $\hat{d}_N \leq p$ by design. Chapter 7 summarizes an implementation of the CLS algorithm. (Details are given in Tong 1983a.)

Theorem 5.6 (Chan 1988c): Suppose that $\{X_t\}$ is stationary (ergodic)* having finite second moments and that the stationary distribution of $(X_1, X_2, \ldots, X_p)'$ admits a density which is positive everywhere. Then $\hat{\boldsymbol{\theta}}_N$ is strongly consistent, that is as $N \to \infty$ $\hat{\boldsymbol{\theta}}_N \to \boldsymbol{\theta}_0$ almost surely, and so are $\hat{\sigma}_{1N}$ and $\hat{\sigma}_{2N}$.

The almost sure convergence of $\hat{\boldsymbol{\theta}}_N$ to $\boldsymbol{\theta}_0$ implies that $\hat{d}_N = d_0$ for all

* Recall our convention of assigning the stationary distribution assured by ergodicity to X_0.

sufficiently large N with probability 1. Thus, *as far as asymptotics are concerned, we may assume that d_0 is known.* Henceforth, without loss of generality, we drop d_0 from $\boldsymbol{\theta}_0$ and $\hat{d}_N$ from $\hat{\boldsymbol{\theta}}_N$.

First we need some regularity conditions:

(C1) $\{X_t\}$ is geometrically ergodic with a unique invariant measure $\pi(.)$;

(C2) ε_t is absolutely continuous and f, its probability density function, is positive everywhere and uniformly continuous. Also $E(\varepsilon_n^4) < \infty$;

(C3) $\{X_t\}$ is stationary with its marginal pdf denoted by $\pi(.)$. Also, $E(X_t^4) < \infty$;

(C4) The autoregression function is discontinuous, i.e. $\exists Z^* = (1, z_{p-1}, \ldots, z_0)'$ s.t. $(\mathbf{A}_{01} - \mathbf{A}_{02})Z^* \neq \mathbf{0}$ and $z_{p-d} = r_0$.

Theorem 5.7 (Chan 1988c): Under Conditions (C1)–(C4):

(1) $\hat{r}_N = r_0 + o_p(1/N)$;

(2) if $\mathbf{A}_0 = (\mathbf{A}_{01}', \mathbf{A}_{02}')'$ and $\hat{\mathbf{A}}_N = (\hat{\mathbf{A}}_{1N}', \hat{\mathbf{A}}_{2N}')'$, then $N^{1/2}(\hat{\mathbf{A}}_N - \mathbf{A}_0)$ is asymptotically distributed as $\mathcal{N}(\mathbf{0}, \Sigma)$, where Σ is the same as that given for the case when r_0 is known.

The significance of Theorem 5.7 is the $(1/N)$ consistency of $\hat{r}_N$. This is clearly an advantage. Part (2) of the results is as expected by analogy with the case of linear AR models.

Before the next theorem, we need some more terminology. Define, for $-\infty < z < \infty$,

$$\bar{L}_N(z) = L_N(\mathbf{A}_{1N}(r + z/N), \mathbf{A}_{2N}(r + z/N), r + z/N)$$
$$- L_N(\mathbf{A}_{1N}(r), \mathbf{A}_{2N}(r), r). \tag{5.185}$$

$\bar{L}_N$ is a technical device which enables us to examine the L_N function with an 'increasingly powerful magnifying glass' as N increases. Let ζ and η be two random variables and ϕ_ζ and ϕ_η their respective characteristic functions. Let $\gamma > 0$. A stochastic process $\{X(t):t \in R\}$ is called a *Compound Poisson process with parameters γ, ζ and η*, denoted by $CPP(\gamma, \zeta, \eta)$, if

(i) $X(0) = 0$ a.s.,

(ii) $\{X(t):t \geq 0\}$ is independent of $\{X(t):t < 0\}$,

(iii) for any $\tau > 0$, $s \geq 0$, $X(s + \tau) - X(s)$ is independent of $\{X(t):0 \leq t \leq s\}$ and $E[\exp\{iu[X(s + \tau) - X(s)]\}] = \exp\{\tau\gamma[\phi_\eta(u) - 1]\}$,

(iv) for any $\tau < 0$, $s \leq 0$, $X(s + \tau) - X(s)$ is independent of $\{X(t): s \leq t \leq 0\}$ and $E[\exp\{iu[X(s + \tau) - X(s)]\}] = \exp\{-\tau\gamma[\phi_\zeta(u) - 1]\}$. Essentially, almost surely each realisation of a CPP(γ, ζ, η) starts from 0 at $t = 0$, has jumps occurring with an average interarrival time of γ, and ζ is the jump size on the left of 0 and η that on the right of 0 (see Fig. 5.28). Let $\mathcal{L}(.)$ denote the distribution of the random variable inside the parentheses.

Theorem 5.8 (Chan 1988c): Let δ denote $(1, r_0)(\mathbf{A}_{02} - \mathbf{A}_{01})/2$. Let $p = d_0 = 1$. Under Conditions (C1)–(C4), $\bar{L}_n$ converges weakly to a CCP (ρ, ζ, η) where

$$\rho = \pi(r_0) \qquad \mathcal{L}(\zeta) = \mathcal{L}(-4\delta\sigma_1\varepsilon_0 + 4\delta^2) \qquad \mathcal{L}(\eta) = \mathcal{L}(4\delta\sigma_2\varepsilon_2\varepsilon_0 + 4\delta^2).$$

The CCP(ρ, ζ, η) attains its global minimum at a unique finite random interval $[M_-, M_+)$ almost surely. Furthermore, $N(\hat{r}_N - r_0)$ converges in distribution to $\mathcal{L}(M_-)$ and $N(\hat{r}_N - r_0)$ is asymptotically independent of $N^{1/2}(\hat{\mathbf{A}}_N - \mathbf{A}_0)$. Finally, the conclusions remain true under (C1)–(C4) for general p and d_0 but the associated CCP has to be appropriately modified.

In Chan's proof, it is shown that $M_+ - M_-$ is exponentially distributed with mean $1/\rho > 0$. One practical import of Theorem 5.8 is that we may assign approximate standard errors to $\hat{\mathbf{A}}_n$ as if r_0 were equal to $\hat{r}_N$, for sufficiently large sample size.

Questions concerning a continuous SETAR model and the tabulation of $\mathcal{L}(M_-)$ are currently under investigation.

The complete and rigorous proof of the above theorems is rather involved. Here, instead, we outline how the compound Poisson process and the $1/N$ rate of convergence arise in the estimation of the threshold parameter. We refer the reader to Chan (1988c) for the complete proof. For simplicity, consider a simple SETAR model:

$$X = \begin{cases} a_{010} + a_{011}X_{t-1} + \varepsilon_t & \text{if } X_{t-1} \leq r_0 \\ a_{020} + a_{021}X_{t-1} + \varepsilon_t & \text{otherwise.} \end{cases}$$

We assume that the conditions of the theorems hold and that the a are known but r_0 is unknown. The conditional least-squares estimate, $\hat{r}_N$, for r_0 is defined to be the infimum of all r which minimizes the conditional sum of squares globally. The conditional sum of squares is given by

$$L_N(r) = \sum [X_t - g_1(X_{t-1})I(X_{t-1} \leq r) - g_2(X_{t-1})I(X_{t-1} > r)]^2$$

where $g_1(x) = a_{010} + a_{011}x$, $g_2(x) = a_{020} + a_{021}x$, and the summation is over $1 \leq t \leq N$. We now normalize $L_N(r)$ so that it is asymptotically a compound Poisson process. Define

$$\tilde{L}_N(r) = L_N\left(r_0 + \frac{r}{N}\right) - L_N(r_0).$$

For $r \geq 0$, when N is large,

$$\tilde{L}_N(r) = 2\sum \{\varepsilon_t[g_2(X_{t-1}) - g_1(X_{t-1})]$$

$$+ [g_2(X_{t-1}) - g_1(X_{t-1})]^2\}I\left(r_0 < X_{t-1} \leq r_0 + \frac{r}{N}\right)$$

$$\doteq \sum 4(\delta\varepsilon_t + \delta^2)I\left(r_0 < X_{t-1} \leq r_0 + \frac{r}{N}\right)$$

where $2\delta = g_2(r_0) - g_1(r_0)(> 0)$. A similar expression for $r < 0$ can be obtained. Each realization of $\tilde{L}_N(r)$, $r \in \mathbf{R}$, is a step function with variable jump sizes. For $r_2 > r_1 \geq 0$, the expected number of non-zero summands in $\tilde{L}_N(r_2) - \tilde{L}_N(r_1)$ is asymptotically $\pi(r_0)(r_2 - r_1)$. The marginal distribution of the jump size is the same as that of $4(\delta\varepsilon_1 + \delta^2)$. Thus, it is conceivable that $\{\tilde{L}_N(r), r \geq 0\}$ converges in distribution to a compound Poisson process with rate $\pi(r_0)$. Similarly, $\{\tilde{L}_N(r), r < 0\}$ converges to another compound Poisson process independent of the previous one but with the same rate. Denote the limiting process by $\{\tilde{L}(r), -\infty < r < \infty\}$. A typical realization is as shown in Fig. 5.29.

By considering the values of $\tilde{L}(r)$, $r \geq 0$, at the points of discontinuity, we have a random walk $\{S_m^{(2)}\}$, where m denotes the mth discontinuity point and $S_m^{(2)} = \zeta_1 + \zeta_2 + \ldots + \zeta_m$ with the ζ_i independent and identi-

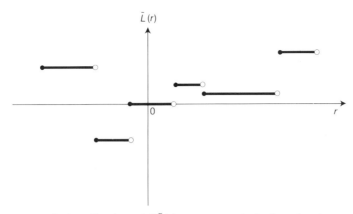

Fig. 5.29. A typical realization of $\{\tilde{L}(r): -\infty < r < \infty\}$. Left end points are open and right end points are closed

cally distributed as $4(\delta\varepsilon_1 + \delta^2)$. $\{S_m^{(2)}\}$ may be called the right random walk. Similarly, we have a left random walk $\{S_m^{(1)}\}$, which describes the transition of the values of $\bar{L}(r)$ at points of discontinuity on the negative r axis. $\{S_m^{(1)}\}$ is independent of $\{S_m^{(2)}\}$ and its summands, η_i, have the marginal distribution of $4(-\delta\varepsilon_1 + \delta^2)$. Since $E(\zeta_i) > 0$ and $E(\eta_i) > 0$, both $\{S_m^{(1)}\}$ and $\{S_m^{(2)}\}$ diverge to $+\infty$ a.s. As ε_1 has a continuous distribution, $\bar{L}(r)$ attains its global minimum at a unique random interval $[M_-, M_+)$ a.s. Thus, $N(\hat{r}_N - r_0)$ converges in distribution to M_-. This shows that $\hat{r}_N = r_0 + o_p(1/N)$. $\square$

5.5.4 BILINEAR MODELS

Given consecutive observations from a bilinear model

$$X_t - \sum_{i=1}^{p} a_i X_{t-i} = \alpha + \sum_{i=1}^{q} c_i \varepsilon_{t-i} + \sum_{j=1}^{r} \sum_{k=1}^{s} b_{jk} X_{t-j} \varepsilon_{t-k} + \varepsilon_t \quad (5.186)$$

where $\varepsilon_t \sim \text{IID}(0, \sigma^2)$, we may estimate the unknown parameters $(\alpha, a_i, b_{jk}, c_i, \sigma^2)$ by one of the above two methods. Of course, for the maximum likelihood method, we need the distribution of ε_t. If $\varepsilon_t \sim \mathcal{N}(0, \sigma^2)$, then the two methods yield essentially the same estimates. The implementation of either scheme of estimation is fairly standard, it being a matter of numerical optimization. (See e.g. Subba Rao and Gabr 1984.) However, we should remark that *an essential assumption is invertibility*. Unfortunately this condition cannot be verified easily. In practice, it means that a diagnostic/post-fitting examination of the Q_N function or its equivalent assumes greater importance. The initial value problem is also a related aspect. We return to these issues in §5.5.6.

5.5.4.1 Markovian representation of a diagonal model and its invertibility We shall study the sampling properties of the estimates. To date, the study is complete for the consistency study in the case of the diagonal bilinear models in which $b_{jk} = 0$ for $j \neq k$ and $\alpha = 0$ and we discuss this case now. First, we rewrite the model in a Markovian representation as discussed in Example 4.6 with minor changes of notation. We set $p = \max(p, q, r, s)$ and we write b_i for b_{jj}. Then

$$\begin{aligned}
\boldsymbol{\xi}_t &= (\mathbf{A} + \mathbf{B}\varepsilon_t)\boldsymbol{\xi}_{t-1} + \mathbf{c}\varepsilon_t + \mathbf{d}(\varepsilon_t^2 - \sigma^2) \\
X_t &= \mathbf{H}\boldsymbol{\xi}_{t-1} + \varepsilon_t
\end{aligned} \quad (5.187)$$

where ξ_t is a p-vector and

$$
\mathbf{A} = \begin{bmatrix} a_1 & 1 & 0 & \cdots & 0 \\ a_2 & 0 & 1 & \cdots & 0 \\ \vdots & & & & 1 \\ a_p & 0 & 0 & \cdots & 0 \end{bmatrix}
\qquad
\mathbf{B} = \begin{bmatrix} b_1 & 0 & \cdots & 0 \\ \vdots & & & \vdots \\ b_p & 0 & \cdots & 0 \end{bmatrix}
$$

$$
\mathbf{c} = \begin{bmatrix} a_1 + c_1 \\ \vdots \\ a_p + c_p \end{bmatrix}
\qquad
\mathbf{d} = \begin{bmatrix} b_1 \\ \vdots \\ b_p \end{bmatrix}
\qquad
\mathbf{H} = [1 \quad 0 \quad \cdots \quad 0].
$$

By convention, $c_j = 0$ if $j > q$, $b_{jk} = 0$ if $j > r$ or $k > s$. Note that diagonality implies the important relation

$$\mathbf{B} = \mathbf{dH}. \tag{5.188}$$

The converse is not true. Note that the Markovian representation (5.187) is unique only up to a similarity transformation in the sense that for any non-singular $p \times p$ matrix $\mathbf{T}$ if we replace $(\mathbf{A}, \mathbf{c}, \mathbf{d}, \mathbf{H})$ by $(\mathbf{TAT}^{-1}, \mathbf{Tc}, \mathbf{Td}, \mathbf{HT}^{-1})$, then eqn (5.187) holds with ξ_t replaced by $\mathbf{T}^{-1}\xi_t$. This poses identifiability problems for the estimation of parameters of the Markovian representation. To circumvent the problem, Guegan and Pham Dinh Tuan (1988) have suggested taking $\theta = (a_1, \ldots, a_p, c_1, \ldots, c_p, b_1, \ldots, b_p)$ as the fundamental parameter vector and assumed that the representation (5.187) is *quasiminimal* in the sense that there is no other Markovian representation with the same noise structure but with a state vector which is a linear transformation of the original state vector and has a smaller dimension. We shall follow their approach. As usual, we shall also assume that the model is stationary and furthermore invertible. It is also known that for stationary and invertible bilinear models, quasiminimality coincides with minimality discussed in Remark 4.11. Recall from Chapter 4 that

(1) $\rho(\mathbf{A} \otimes \mathbf{A} + \sigma^2 \mathbf{B} \otimes \mathbf{B}) < 1 \Rightarrow$ stationarity of model (5.187);

(2) together with stationarity $E[\ln \|\mathbf{A} - \mathbf{cH} - \mathbf{dH}X_t\|_\phi] < 0 \Rightarrow$ invertibility of model (5.187).

Here $\|.\|_\phi$ is the matrix norm induced by a vector norm ϕ such that for a matrix $\mathbf{K}$, $\|\mathbf{K}\|_\phi = \sup_{\phi(\mathbf{x}) \leq 1} \phi(\mathbf{Kx})$.

Note that for stationary (ergodic) $\{X_t\}$, (2) may be weakened to a condition involving the *largest Lyapunov exponent* (thus pointing to a possible connection with dynamical systems):

(2′) $\lim_{t \to \infty} (1/2t) \ln(\rho(\mathbf{K}_1 \ldots \mathbf{K}_t)^*(\mathbf{K}_1 \ldots \mathbf{K}_t)) < 0 \Rightarrow$ invertibility of model (5.187).

Here

$$\mathbf{K}_t = \mathbf{A} - \mathbf{cH} - \mathbf{dH}X_t \tag{5.189}$$

and the asterisk denotes the conjugate transpose. (Readers might like to use Exercise 25 of Chapter 4 to verify (2).)

If $\boldsymbol{\xi}_0$ is known, then the corresponding ε_t, denoted by $\varepsilon_t(\boldsymbol{\theta} \mid \boldsymbol{\xi}_0)$, is the solution of the recurrence equations

$$
\begin{aligned}
\varepsilon_t(\boldsymbol{\theta} \mid \boldsymbol{\xi}_0) &= X_t - \mathbf{H}\boldsymbol{\xi}_{t-1}(\boldsymbol{\xi}_0) \\
\boldsymbol{\xi}_t(\boldsymbol{\xi}_0) &= [\mathbf{A} + \mathbf{B}\varepsilon_t(\boldsymbol{\theta} \mid \boldsymbol{\xi}_0)]\boldsymbol{\xi}_{t-1}(\boldsymbol{\xi}_0) + c\varepsilon_t(\boldsymbol{\theta} \mid \boldsymbol{\xi}_0) + d\varepsilon_t(\boldsymbol{\theta} \mid \boldsymbol{\xi}_0) \quad t \geq 1
\end{aligned}
\tag{5.190}
$$

where typically $\boldsymbol{\xi}_t(\boldsymbol{\xi}_0)$ denotes the state vector at time t starting with $\boldsymbol{\xi}_0$ at time 0. In practice, $\boldsymbol{\xi}_0$ is rarely known and we may use an arbitrary value of it to calculate $\varepsilon_t(\boldsymbol{\theta} \mid \boldsymbol{\xi}_0)$, which may then be used as an estimate of ε_t.

5.5.4.2 The least-squares estimate of $\boldsymbol{\theta}$ Let $(X_1, \ldots, X_N)$ denote the observations. It is plausible to estimate $\boldsymbol{\theta}$ by minimizing

$$\sum_{t=1}^{N} \varepsilon_t^2(\bar{\boldsymbol{\theta}} \mid \boldsymbol{\xi}_0) \quad \text{w.r.t.} \quad \bar{\boldsymbol{\theta}} \in \Theta_N$$

(Θ_N to be defined), where $\varepsilon_t(\bar{\boldsymbol{\theta}} \mid \boldsymbol{\xi}_0)$ is the $\varepsilon_t(\boldsymbol{\theta} \mid \boldsymbol{\xi}_0)$ given by (5.190) with $\bar{\boldsymbol{\theta}}$ as the parameter vector. It is also intuitively clear that for this to make sense the effect of $\boldsymbol{\xi}_0$ on $\varepsilon_t(\bar{\boldsymbol{\theta}} \mid \boldsymbol{\xi}_0)$ should diminish as $t \to \infty$. More precisely, let there exist a stationary time series $\{\varepsilon_t(\bar{\boldsymbol{\theta}})\}$ s.t. $\varepsilon_t(\bar{\boldsymbol{\theta}} \mid \boldsymbol{\xi}_0) - \varepsilon_t(\bar{\boldsymbol{\theta}}) \to 0$ a.s. as $t \to \infty$. Note that $\varepsilon_t(\bar{\boldsymbol{\theta}})$ is then measurable w.r.t. the σ-algebra generated by X_s, $s \leq t$. In this case we say that the model (5.187) is *invertible at* $\bar{\boldsymbol{\theta}}$ *relative to the observation process* $\{X_t\}$. A sufficient condition for this is $\mathrm{E}_\theta(\ln \|\tilde{\mathbf{A}} - \tilde{\mathbf{c}}\tilde{\mathbf{H}} - \mathbf{d}\tilde{\mathbf{H}}X_t\|_\phi] < 0$, where $\tilde{\mathbf{A}}$, $\tilde{\mathbf{c}}$, $\tilde{\mathbf{d}}$, $\tilde{\mathbf{H}}$ are given by $\bar{\boldsymbol{\theta}}$. (A proof for this result may follow a similar argument as outlined in Exercise 25 of Chapter 4.) Although the condition as it stands cannot be verified, it suggests that a reasonable choice of Θ_n is

$$\Theta_{N,\delta} = \left\{ \bar{\boldsymbol{\theta}} \in \boldsymbol{\Theta}_0 : \prod_{t=1} \|\tilde{\mathbf{A}} - \tilde{\mathbf{c}}\tilde{\mathbf{H}} - \tilde{\mathbf{d}}\tilde{\mathbf{H}}X_t\|_\phi \leq (1-\delta)^N \right\} \tag{5.191}$$

where $\boldsymbol{\Theta}_0$ is a given compact set and δ is a small positive number. The set $\boldsymbol{\Theta}_0$ is chosen large enough to include $\boldsymbol{\theta}$, the true parameter, and the set of parameters satisfying the stationarity condition.

Let

$$Q_N(\bar{\boldsymbol{\theta}}) = \frac{1}{N}\sum_{t=1}^{N} \varepsilon_t^2(\bar{\boldsymbol{\theta}} \mid \boldsymbol{\xi}_0). \tag{5.192}$$

Let $\hat{\boldsymbol{\theta}}_N$ be the minimizer of $Q_N(\bar{\boldsymbol{\theta}})$ over the set $\Theta_{N,\delta}$. It is the least-squares estimate of $\boldsymbol{\theta}$.

5.5.4.3 Strong consistency of the least-squares estimates We start with a preliminary result. Let $k = 3p$.

¶ **Lemma 5.3:** Let $\{Q_N(\tilde{\theta})\}$ be a sequence of continuous measurable functions defined on a compact subset $\bar{\theta}$ of $\mathbf{R}^k$ which contains the true parameter θ. Let $\{\Theta_N\}$ be a sequence of random compact subsets of $\mathbf{R}^k$, s.t.

(1)   with probability 1, $\theta \in \Theta_N \subset \bar{\Theta}$ for N sufficiently large;

(2)   for any $\theta_0 \in \bar{\Theta}$, $\theta_0 \neq \theta$, there exists a neighbourhood $U(\theta_0)$ of θ_0 s.t.

$$\lim_{\substack{N \to \infty \\ \tilde{\theta} \in U(\theta_0)}} \inf \{Q_N(\tilde{\theta}) - Q_N(\theta)\} > 0 \quad \text{a.s.}$$

Then $\hat{\theta}_N$, the minimizer of Q_N on Θ_N, converges to θ a.s. as $N \to \infty$.

Proof. Let $U(\theta)$ be any neighbourhood of θ and for $\theta_0 \in \bar{\Theta} \backslash \dot{U}(\theta)$, let $U(\theta_0)$ be the neighbourhood of θ_0 given by (2).

Clearly

$$\bar{\Theta} \subseteq U(\theta) \cup \left\{ \bigcup_{\tilde{\theta} \in \bar{\Theta} \backslash U(\theta)} U(\tilde{\theta}) \right\}.$$

By the compactness of $\bar{\Theta}$, $\exists \theta_1, \ldots, \theta_m$, all in $\bar{\Theta}$, s.t. $\bar{\Theta}$ is covered by $U(\theta), U(\theta_1), \ldots, U(\theta_m)$. Let U be the union of the $U(\theta_i)$, $i = 1, \ldots, m$. By (2), we have the probability 1,

$$\inf_{\tilde{\theta} \in U} Q_N(\tilde{\theta}) - Q_N(\theta) = \inf_{i=1, \ldots, m} \left\{ \inf_{\tilde{\theta} \in U(\theta_i)} Q_N(\tilde{\theta}) - Q_N(\theta) \right\} > 0$$

for sufficiently large N. But if N is sufficiently large, $\Theta_N \backslash U(\theta) \subset U$. Therefore $\forall \tilde{\theta} \in \Theta_N \backslash U(\theta)$, $Q_N(\theta) < Q_N(\tilde{\theta})$. This implies that $\hat{\theta}_N \in U(\theta)$.   □ ¶¶

We can now *sketch* a proof of the following main result.

Theorem 5.9: Suppose that $\{X_t\}$ defined by eqn (5.187) with $\mathbf{B} = \mathbf{dH}$ is quasiminimal and ε_t has a continuous distribution. Then $\hat{\theta}_N \to \theta$ a.s. as $N \to \infty$.

¶ **Proof:** We only need to verify the conditions of Lemma 5.3. Condition (1) is obviously satisfied. To verify Condition (2), we note first that $Q_N(\theta) \to \sigma^2$ a.s. as $N \to \infty$ by the strong law of large numbers. It is technically quite delicate to prove that for $\theta_0 \in \bar{\Theta}$, $\theta_0 \neq \theta$, there exists a neighbourhood $U(\theta_0)$ of θ_0 s.t.

$$\liminf_{\substack{N \to \infty \\ \tilde{\theta} \in U(\theta_0)}} \inf Q_N(\tilde{\theta}) > \sigma^2 \quad \text{a.s.}$$

Once this is done, the theorem is proved. We omit the detail and refer readers to Pham Dinh Tuan and Lanh Tat Tran (1981).   □ ¶¶

Asymptotic normality of the parameter estimates has not been generally established to date. The difficulty may be illustrated by reference to the simple case

$$X_t = aX_{t-1} + \varepsilon_t + b\varepsilon_{t-1}X_{t-1}.$$

In this case, we may take

$$\varepsilon_t(\tilde{\boldsymbol{\theta}}) = X_t - \sum_{j=1}^{\infty} \left((-\tilde{b})^{j-1} \prod_{k=1}^{j} X_{t-k}(\tilde{a} + \tilde{b}X_{t-j}) \right).$$

Derivatives of $\varepsilon_t(\hat{\boldsymbol{\theta}})$ w.r.t. $\tilde{a}$, $\tilde{b}$ may not be square integrable because they are sums of $\prod_{k=1}^{j} X_{t-k}$, $j = 1, 2, \ldots$ and bilinear models are unlikely to enjoy the moment property. (See Exercise 13 of this chapter and Example 4.11.) Simulations suggest non-normality of the estimates for moderate sample size of between 100 to 600, and $\sigma^2 = 1$ (see e.g. Sessay 1982). For fixed sample size, Moeanaddin and Tong (1989b) have shown that the variability of b_{jk} tends to increase as $\sigma^2 \to 0$. We shall return to this in §7.2.11. See also Exercise 14.

By virtue of the fact that the ARCH models are special cases of the BL models, results in this subsection are also relevant to the former and the like.

5.5.5   A SIMPLE NON-LINEAR MOVING-AVERAGE MODEL

Let us consider a simple non-linear moving-average model

$$X_t = \varepsilon_t + \alpha\varepsilon_{t-1} + \beta\varepsilon_t\varepsilon_{t-1} \tag{5.193}$$

where $\{\varepsilon_t\} \sim \mathrm{IID}(0, \sigma^2)$. Given observations $X_0, X_1, \ldots, X_N$ we may proceed to obtain the maximum likelihood estimate of α, β, σ^2 as follows. Take $X_0 = \varepsilon_0$ and let $\varepsilon_0, \ldots, \varepsilon_N$ have a joint density $f_N(\varepsilon_0, \ldots, \varepsilon_N; \sigma^2)$ known up to σ^2. Using the recursion

$$\varepsilon_j = \frac{X_j - \alpha\varepsilon_{j-1}}{1 + \beta\varepsilon_{j-1}}, \qquad j = 1, \ldots, N \tag{5.194}$$

we may substitute the X_j, $j \leq N$, α, and β, for ε_j in $f_N(\varepsilon_0, \ldots, \varepsilon_N; \sigma^2) |\prod_{j=0}^{N-1} (1 + \beta\varepsilon_j)|^{-1}$ to obtain the likelihood $L_N(\alpha, \beta, \sigma^2; X_0, \ldots, X_N)$. It is clear that L_N is an extremely complicated function of $(\alpha, \beta, \sigma^2)$, and is certainly too difficult to handle analytically. It may, of course, be handled numerically just as in a linear moving-average case. The question of initialization is relevant for any numerical optimization of the likelihood function. For this and other reasons, it would be interesting to explore the method of moments in the case of non-linear MA models.

Suppose that $\alpha \neq 0$ and $\sigma^2 \neq 0$ and

$$E[(\varepsilon_j^2 - \sigma^2)(\varepsilon_k^2 - \sigma^2)] = 0, \qquad j \neq k.$$

It is easy to verify that

$$a = E[X_j^2] = (1 + \alpha^2)\sigma^2 + \beta^2\sigma^4, \qquad (5.195)$$

$$b = E[X_j X_{j-1}] = \alpha\sigma^2 \qquad (5.196)$$

$$c = E[X_j X_{j-1} X_{j-2}] = \alpha\beta\sigma^4. \qquad (5.197)$$

Solving (5.196) and (5.197), we get $\beta\sigma^2 = c/b$. Substituting this in (5.195), we get $a - (c/b)^2 = (1 + \alpha^2)\sigma^2$. Using (5.196), we have

$$\alpha^2 - (a/b - c^2/b^3)\alpha + 1 = 0. \qquad (5.198)$$

Equation (5.198) has two solutions which are the reciprocal of each other—cf. linear MA models. We may designate α as the one of

$$\tfrac{1}{2}(a/b - c^2/b^3) \pm [(a/b - c^2/b^3)^2 - 4]^{1/2}$$

which lies in $[-1, 1]$. Then we take $\sigma^2 = b/\alpha$, $\beta = c/(\alpha\sigma^2)$.

Let $\hat{a}_N$, $\hat{b}_N$, and $\hat{c}_N$ denote the sample moments, namely

$$\hat{a}_N = N^{-1} \sum_{j=1}^{n} X_j^2 \qquad \hat{b}_N = N^{-1} \sum_{j=2}^{N} X_j X_{j-1} \qquad \hat{c}_N = N^{-1} \sum_{j=3}^{N} X_j X_{j-1} X_{j-2}.$$

Then we take $\hat{\alpha}_N$ as our estimate of α which is the one of

$$\tfrac{1}{2}(\hat{a}_N/\hat{b}_N - \hat{c}_N^2/\hat{b}_N^3) \pm [(\hat{a}_N/\hat{b}_N - \hat{c}_N^2/\hat{b}_N^3)^2 - 4]^{1/2}$$

in $[-1, 1]$. Similarly we take $\hat{\sigma}_N^2 = \hat{b}_N/\hat{\alpha}_N$, $\hat{\beta}_N = \hat{c}_N/(\hat{\alpha}_N\hat{\sigma}_N^4)$. The method is abortive if the square root yields an imaginary value. Robinson (1977b) has studied the limiting behaviour of $\hat{\alpha}_N$, $\hat{\beta}_N$, $\hat{\sigma}_N^2$, and has shown that these estimates are strongly consistent and asymptotically Gaussian under appropriate conditions, which include stationarity and invertibility.

It might be interesting to extend the investigation to higher-order non-linear MA models, which remain largely unexplored.

5.5.6 RECURSIVE ESTIMATION

5.5.6.1 Engineering approach Up to now, our estimation methods have all been for a *fixed* sample. Recursive estimation is potentially very useful although not fully developed yet. We describe an early attempt here briefly, which deals with the case of one unknown parameter in an NLAR setting.

Consider the following general NLAR model with non-additive noise:

$$X_{t+1} = G_t + \theta F_t + \sigma_t \varepsilon_{t+1}, \qquad t = 0, 1, 2, \ldots \qquad (5.199)$$

where G_t, F_t, and σ_t are *given* non-linear, scalar real-valued functions measurable w.r.t. $\mathbb{B}_t$, the σ-algebra generated by X_s, $0 \le s \le t$, and $\{\varepsilon_t\}$ satisfies ($t = 0, 1, \ldots$)

$$E(\varepsilon_t \mid \mathbb{B}_{t-1}) = 0 \qquad (5.200)$$

$$E(\varepsilon_t^2 \mid \mathbb{B}_{t-1}) = 1. \qquad (5.201)$$

Note that *the 'noise variance'*, σ_t^2, *is assumed known*. This could be a serious limitation for practical applications. If $F_t \ne X_t$, all t, we asume that $\exists M > 0$ s.t. $\forall t$

$$E(F_t/\sigma_t)^2 \le M. \qquad (5.202)$$

The object is to estimate the scalar unknown θ recursively.

Aase (1983) has borrowed the engineering technique of 'model reference adaptive systems' and suggested the following algorithm:

$$\hat{\theta}_{t+1} = \hat{\theta}_t + F_t k_t (X_{t+1} - G_t - \hat{\theta}_t F_t)/(\sigma_t^2 + k_t F_t^2) \qquad (5.203)$$

$$k_{t+1} = k_t - (k_t F_t)^2/(\sigma_t^2 + k_t F_t^2). \qquad (5.204)$$

Here, k_t is the sequence of 'gains' (cf. the Kalman gain in §5.3.6) and from (5.204) we have

$$k_{t+1} = k_t/(1 + F_t^2 k_t/\sigma_t^2)$$

$$= 1 \Big/ \Big(k_0^{-1} + \sum_{s=0}^{t} (F_s/\sigma_s)^2 \Big) \qquad (5.205)$$

where k_0 is the initial gain assumed greater than 0.

From (5.203) and (5.204), we get

$$\hat{\theta}_{t+1}/k_{t+1} = (\hat{\theta}_t/k_t) + (F_t/\sigma_t^2)(X_{t+1} - G_t) \qquad (5.206)$$

from which we get

$$\hat{\theta}_{t+1} = \Big(\frac{\theta_0}{k_0} + \sum_{s=0}^{t} \frac{F_s}{\sigma_s^2} (X_{t+1} - G_s) \Big) \Big/ \Big[\frac{1}{k_0} + \sum_{s=0}^{t} \Big(\frac{F_s}{\sigma_s} \Big)^2 \Big] \qquad (5.207)$$

where θ_0 is an initial guess of θ.

Without assuming stationarity, we can still prove the strong consistency of $\hat{\theta}_t$ and asymptotic normality.

Theorem 5.10: Under assumptions (5.200)–(5.202), if

$$\liminf_{t \to \infty} \frac{1}{t} \sum_{s=1}^{t} (\sigma_s/F_s)^2 > 0 \quad \text{a.s.} \qquad (5.208)$$

then as $t \to \infty$

$$\hat{\theta}_t \to \theta \quad \text{a.s.}$$

¶ **Proof:** Rewrite (5.207) as

$$\hat{\theta}_{t+1} = \left(\frac{\theta_0}{k_0 t} + \frac{1}{t}\sum_{s=0}^{t}\frac{F_s}{\sigma_s^2}(X_{s+1} - G_s)\right) \bigg/ \left[\frac{1}{k_0 t} + \frac{1}{t}\sum_{s=0}^{t}\left(\frac{F_s}{\sigma_s}\right)^2\right]. \quad (5.209)$$

Now,

$$\frac{1}{t}\sum_{s=0}^{t}\left(\frac{F_s}{\sigma_s^2}\right)(X_{s+1} - G_s) = \theta\frac{1}{t}\sum_{s=0}^{t}\left(\frac{F_s}{\sigma_s}\right)^2 + \frac{1}{t}\sum_{s=0}^{t}\left(\frac{F_s}{\sigma_s}\right)\varepsilon_{s+1}.$$

Let $Y_{s+1} = (F_s/\sigma_s)\varepsilon_{s+1}$, $s = 0, 1, 2, \ldots.$ Clearly by (5.200), $\forall s$,

$$E[Y_{s+1} \mid \mathbb{B}_s] = 0.$$

Y_s is clearly measurable w.r.t. $\mathbb{B}_s$. By assumptions (5.201) and (5.202)

$$\sum_{s=1}^{t}\frac{1}{s^2}EY_{s+1}^2 \leq M\sum_{s=1}^{t}\frac{1}{s^2} < \infty, \quad \forall t.$$

Therefore $(1/t)\sum_{s=1}^{t}Y_{s+1} \to 0$ a.s. by a martingale convergence theorem. □ ¶¶

Let

$$V_t^2 = \sum_{s=1}^{t}(F_s/\sigma_s)^2 \qquad s_t^2 = EV_t^2.$$

Theorem 5.11: Let the following assumptions hold. As $t \to \infty$

(1) $V_t^2/s_t^2 \to 1$ in probability;

(2) $\forall\delta > 0$, $(1/s_t^2)\sum_{s=1}^{t}E[(F_s/\sigma_s)^2\varepsilon_{s+1}^2]I(|(F_s/\sigma_s)\varepsilon_{s+1}| \geq \delta s_t) \to 0$
     in probability;

(3) $V_t^2/t \to \sigma_1^2 > 0$.

Then $\sqrt{t}\,(\hat{\theta}_t - \theta) \rightsquigarrow \mathcal{N}(0, \sigma_1^{-1})$.

¶ **Proof:** Consider

$$\sqrt{t}\,(\hat{\theta}_{t+1} - \theta)$$

$$= \left(\frac{1}{\sqrt{t}}(\theta_0 - \theta)k_0^{-1} + \frac{1}{\sqrt{t}}\sum_{s=0}^{t}(F_s/\sigma_s)\varepsilon_{s+1}\right)\left(\frac{1}{k_0 t} + \frac{1}{t}\sum_{s=0}^{t}(F_s/\sigma_s)^2\right).$$

By (2) and a martingale limit theorem, as $t \to \infty$

$$s_t^{-2}\max_{s\leq t}(F_s/\sigma_s)^2 \to 0.$$

Also, by a martingale central limit theorem

$$\frac{1}{s_t}\sum_{s=0}^{t}(F_s/\sigma_s)\varepsilon_{s+1} \rightsquigarrow \mathcal{N}(0, 1).$$

But by (1) and (3), as $t \to \infty$

$$s_t / \sqrt{t} \to \sigma_1.$$

Therefore

$$\frac{1}{\sqrt{t}} \sum_{s=0}^{t} (F_s/\sigma_s)\varepsilon_{s+1} \rightsquigarrow \mathcal{N}(0, \sigma_1^2) \quad \text{as} \quad t \to \infty. \quad \square \, \P\P$$

See Exercise 10 for an application.

5.5.6.2 Estimation equation approach

It may perhaps be argued that the above approach is *ad hoc*. An alternative approach is now described briefly.

The starting point is the theory of estimating equations of Godambe (1960, 1985), which takes as its basis a sample of *finite* size, say $X_1, X_2, \ldots, X_N$, from a time series $\{X_t\}$. Let $\mathbf{F}$ be a class of distributions F on $\mathbf{R}^N$ and $\theta = \theta(F)$, $F \in \mathbf{F}$, be a real parameter. (The discussion can be generalized to a vector parameter $\boldsymbol{\theta}$.) Any real function g of $X_1, \ldots, X_N$ and the parameter θ, satisfying certain regularity conditions, is called a *regular unbiased estimating function* if

$$E_F[g\{X_1, \ldots, X_N; \theta(F)\}] = 0 \quad (F \in \mathbf{F}). \tag{5.210}$$

Among all regular unbiased estimating functions g, g^* is said to be *optimum* if

$$E_F[g^2\{X_1, \ldots, X_N; \theta(F)\}] \Big/ \left\{ E_F \left[\frac{\partial g(X_1, \ldots, X_N, \theta)}{\partial \theta} \right] \right\}^2 \tag{5.211}$$

is minimized for all $F \in \mathbf{F}$ at $g = g^*$. Here, the partial derivative is evaluated at $\theta = \theta(F)$. Let L be the class of estimating functions g of the form

$$g = \sum_{t=1}^{n} h_t a_{t-1} \tag{5.212}$$

where the function h_t is such that

$$E_{t-1,F}[h_t\{X_1, \ldots, X_t; \theta(F)\}] = 0, \quad (t = 1, \ldots, N, F \in \mathbf{F}). \tag{5.213}$$

Here, $E_{t-1,F}(.)$ denotes the expectation holding the first $t-1$ values, namely $X_1, \ldots, X_{t-1}$, fixed, h_t is a real function of $X_1, \ldots, X_t$ and θ. Henceforth, we suppress F in the expectation operator for convenience, that is $E_{t-1,F}(.) \equiv E_{t-1}(.)$, $E_{0,F(.)} \equiv E_F(.) \equiv E(.)$. Moreover, for $t = 1, \ldots, N$, a_{t-1} is a function of $X_1, \ldots, X_{t-1}$ and θ. An example of h_t is

$$h_t = X_t - E_{t-1}(X_t) \tag{5.214}$$

the (predictive) residual. Property (5.213) implies that $\forall F \in \mathbf{F}$,

$$E(h_i h_j) = 0 \quad (i \neq j). \tag{5.215}$$

We assume that h_t and a_t are differentiable w.r.t. θ for $t = 1, \ldots, N$.

Theorem 5.12 (Godambe 1985): In the class L of estimating functions g, the function g^* minimizing (5.211) is given by

$$g^* = \sum_{t=1}^{N} h_t a_{t-1}^* \qquad (5.216)$$

where

$$a_{t-1}^* = [E_{t-1}(\partial h_t / \partial \theta)] / E_{t-1}(h_t^2). \qquad (5.217)$$

Proof (Sketch): From (5.212), using (5.215) and (5.213) we have

$$E(g^2) = E\left(\sum_{t=1}^{N} (a_{t-1}^2) E_{t-1}(h_t^2)\right) = E(A^2) \quad \text{say} \qquad (5.218)$$

$$[E(\partial g / \partial \theta)]^2 = \left[E \sum_{t=1}^{N} \{a_{t-1} E_{t-1}(\partial h_t / \partial \theta) + (\partial a_{t-1} / \partial \theta) E_{t-1}(h_t)\}\right]^2$$

$$= \left[E \sum_{t=1}^{N} a_{t-1} E_{t-1}(\partial h_t / \partial \theta)\right]^2$$

$$= [EB]^2 \quad \text{say}.$$

Then (5.211) is given by

$$E(g^2) / [E(\partial g / \partial \theta)]^2 = E(A^2) / [EB]^2$$

$$\geq \frac{1}{E(B^2 / A^2)}$$

by the Cauchy–Schwarz inequality.

For $a_{t-1} = a_{t-1}^*$, we note that B^2 / A^2 is maximized and $E(B^2 / A^2) = [EB]^2 / E(A^2)$. This completes a sketch of the proof of the theorem. $\square$

Suppose that

$$h_t = X_t - \theta f_{t-1}$$

where f_{t-1} is measurable w.r.t. $\mathbb{B}_{t-1}$, the σ-algebra generated by $X_1, \ldots, X_{t-1}$. Then the optimal estimating function is

$$g^* = \sum_{t=1}^{N} a_{t-1}^* (X_t - \theta f_{t-1})$$

and the 'optimal' estimate based on the N observations is given from solving

$$\sum_{t=1}^{N} h_t a_{t-1}^* = 0$$

yielding

$$\hat{\theta}_N = \sum_{t=2}^{N} a_{t-1}^* X_t \bigg/ \sum_{t=2}^{N} a_{t-1}^* f_{t-1}.$$ (5.219)

($a_0^* \equiv 0$ by assumption.) Therefore

$$\hat{\theta}_t - \hat{\theta}_{t-1} = K_t \bigg(\sum_{s=2}^{t} a_{s-1}^* X_s - \hat{\theta}_{t-1} K_t^{-1} \bigg)$$

where

$$K_t^{-1} = \sum_{s=2}^{t} a_{s-1}^* f_{s-1}.$$

After a little more algebra, we arrive at the recursive algorithm ($t = 1, 2, \ldots$)

$$\hat{\theta}_t = \hat{\theta}_{t-1} + \frac{K_{t-1} a_{t-1}^*}{1 + f_{t-1} a_{t-1}^* K_{t-1}} [X_t - \hat{\theta}_{t-1} f_{t-1}].$$ (5.220)

5.5.7 MARKOVIAN MODELS WITH MISSING OBSERVATIONS

Let $\{X_1, X_2, \ldots, X_{j-1}, \tilde{X}_j, X_{j+1}, \ldots, X_N\}$ denote the observed time series, where the tilde indicates that X_j is missing. Let the model under consideration be Markovian, for example NLAR including SETAR, STAR, EXPAR, etc., and let θ denote the unknown parameters to be estimated. The EM algorithm (the expectation–maximization algorithm) expounded in Dempster *et al.* (1977) is well suited for this situation. It is best to describe the approach through an example. (See also Shumway 1988.)

Example 5.5 (NLAR(1)): Consider the model

$$X_t = \lambda(X_{t-1}; \theta) + \sigma \varepsilon_t, \quad t = 1, \ldots, N$$ (5.221)

with $\{\varepsilon_1, \varepsilon_2, \ldots, \varepsilon_N\}$ independently distributed as $\mathcal{N}(0, 1)$ and independent of X_0. We condition our estimation of $\Psi = (\theta, \sigma)$ on X_0. The two steps of the EM algorithm take the following specific forms in our case. Let $\Psi^{(i)}$ denote the ith iterate in the EM estimation of Ψ.

1. *E-step*: Obtain $E[X_j \mid \text{given data}; \Psi^{(i)}]$, $E[X_j^2 \mid \text{given data}; \Psi^{(i)}]$, $E[\lambda(X_j) \mid \text{given data}; \Psi^{(i)}]$, and $E[\lambda^2(X_j) \mid \text{given data}; \Psi^{(i)}]$. Let us denote them by $(X_j)^{(i)}$, $(X_j^2)^{(i)}$, $(\lambda(X_j))^{(i)}$, and $(\lambda^2(X_j))^{(i)}$ respectively.

2. *M-step*: Minimize w.r.t. Ψ the 'sum of squares'

$$\sum_{t=1}^{N} X_t^2 - 2 \sum_{t=1}^{N} X_t \lambda(X_{t-1}) + \sum_{t=1}^{N} \lambda^2(X_{t-1})$$

where we replace X_j, X_j^2, $\lambda(X_j)$, and $\lambda^2(X_j)$ by $(X_j)^{(i)}$, $(X_j^2)^{(i)}$, $(\lambda(X_j))^{(i)}$, and $(\lambda^2(X_j))^{(i)}$ respectively. This gives us $\Psi^{(i+1)}$, which may be used in the E-step of the next iteration. For brevity, we shall refer to this pair of four terms by the symbolism $g(X_j)$ and $(g(X_j))^{(i)}$.

Now, let $X_{\backslash j}$ denote the set $\{x_1, x_2, \dots, x_{j-1}, x_{j+1}, \dots, x_N\}$ where x_j is excluded. It is a simple exercise to verify that the conditional probability densities $p(.\,|\,.)$ satisfy

$$p(x_j \,|\, X_{\backslash j}) = p(x_j \,|\, x_{j-1})p(x_{j+1} \,|\, x_j)/K \tag{5.222}$$

where $K = p(x_{j+1} \,|\, x_{j-1})$, that is

$$K = \int_{-\infty}^{\infty} p(x_j \,|\, x_{j-1})p(x_{j+1} \,|\, x_j)\, dx_j. \tag{5.223}$$

Note that $p(x_j \,|\, x_{j-1}) = \phi(x_j - \lambda(x_{j-1}; \boldsymbol{\theta}))/\sigma)$, ϕ denoting the density of $\mathcal{N}(0, 1)$.

Thus, for g s.t. $E[|g(X_j)|] < \infty$, we have

$$(g(X_j))^{(i)} = E[g(X_j) \,|\, \text{given data}; \Psi^{(i)}]$$

$$= K^{-1} \int_{-\infty}^{\infty} g(x_j)\phi\left(\frac{x_j - \lambda(x_{j-1}; \theta^{(i)})}{\sigma^{(i)}}\right)\phi\left(\frac{x_{j+1} - \lambda(x_j; \theta^{(i)})}{\sigma^{(i)}}\right) dx_j \tag{5.224}$$

where

$$K = \int_{-\infty}^{\infty} \phi\left(\frac{x_j - \lambda(x_{j-1}; \theta^{(i)})}{\sigma^{(i)}}\right)\phi\left(\frac{x_{j+1} - \lambda(x_j; \theta^{(i)})}{\sigma^{(i)}}\right) dx_j. \tag{5.225}$$

Armed with $(g(X_j))^{(i)}$ from (5.224) and (5.225), the M-step follows the usual maximum likelihood procedure described earlier in this chapter. It remains to specify $(g(X_j))^{(0)}$. In the absence of any prior information, one possible choice is $g(\bar{X})$. For cyclical data, we may have to adopt other choices by reference to the within-cycle position of the missing data. $\square$

The method can be easily extended to the case with missing blocks of several observations each. We only need to note that if $X_{j-r+1}, \dots, X_{j+s-1}$ are missing, then for $j - r + 1 \leq t \leq j + s + 1$

$$E(g(X_t) \,|\, \text{given data}]$$

$$= \int_{-\infty}^{\infty} g(x_t)p(x_t \,|\, x_{j-r})p(x_{j+s} \,|\, x_t)\, dx_t \bigg/ \int_{-\infty}^{\infty} p(x_t \,|\, x_{j-r})p(x_{j+s} \,|\, x_t)\, dx_t. \tag{5.226}$$

Extension to NLAR(k), $k > 1$, is fairly straightforward by 'vectorizing' the observations so that a vector NLAR(1) results. Practical considerations of computation time may become critical in this case.

5.5.8   DETERMINING THE ORDER OF AN NLAR MODEL

Let $\{X_1, X_2, \ldots, X_N\}$ denote observations from a stationary NLAR(k) model

$$X_t = f(X_{t-1}, \ldots, X_{t-k}, \varepsilon_t) \tag{5.227}$$

where $\varepsilon_t \sim \text{IID}(0, \sigma^2)$. Suppose that X_s is missing. We may 'fill' the missing datum with the conditional expectation of X_s given $X_{s\pm i}$, $i = 1, \ldots, k$. In practice, this may be effected by its kernel estimate similar to that described in §5.2.4 of the present chapter. Specifically, we estimate $E[X_s \mid X_{s+i} = y_i, i = \pm 1, \ldots, \pm k]$ by $\hat{X}(y_i, i = \pm 1, \ldots, \pm k)$ or simply $\hat{X}$, where

$$\hat{X} = \hat{Q}/\hat{P}$$

$$\hat{Q} = \sum_{s=K}^{N-K} X_s \prod_{i=1}^{k} [\delta_N(y_i - X_{s+i})\delta_N(y_{-i} - X_{s-i})] \tag{5.228}$$

$$\hat{P} = \sum_{s=K}^{N-K} \prod_{i=1}^{k} [\delta_N(y_i - X_{s+i})\delta_N(y_{-i} - X_{s-i})]$$

and K is a pre-fixed integer such that $N \gg K \gg k$.

Suppose that k is unknown and we wish to determine it without assuming any specific functional form of f, that is without parametrizing f. One way to do so would be based on the *cross-validation* method. Accordingly, we delete X_j from the sample and obtain its 'fill-in' value as just described except that X_j is avoided in the computation for $\hat{Q}$ and $\hat{P}$. Let $\tilde{Q}_j$, $\tilde{P}_j$, and $\tilde{X}_j = \tilde{Q}_j/\tilde{P}_j$ denote respectively the results of $\hat{Q}$, $\hat{P}$, and $\hat{X}$ when X_j is treated as 'taboo'. We repeat this process for $j = K, K + 1, \ldots, N - K$ and let $CV(k)$ denote the sum of squares of the 'errors', that is

$$CV(k) = \sum_{j=K}^{N-K} (X_j - \tilde{X}_j)^2. \tag{5.229}$$

We repeat this calculation for $k = 1, 2, \ldots, K$. Then we may estimate k by $\bar{k}$ where

$$CV(\bar{k}) = \min_k CV(k).$$

We call $\bar{k}$ the cross-validation estimate of k.

Note that $\bar{k}$ depends on the smoothing parameter B_N defined in §5.2.4, which may also be determined by a cross-validation method. For example, we may write $CV(k)$ as $CV(k, B_N(k))$ so as to emphasize the dependence on B_N which may in turn depend on k. We may then minimize $CV(k, B_N(k))$ w.r.t. $B_N(k)$ for each k and then w.r.t. k. Note also that k is called the *embedding dimension* by the dynamicists. (See, e.g., Eckmann & Ruelle (1985), but also see Tong and Lim (1980, p. 267) for a related remark.) At an SERC International Non-linear Time Series Workshop at Edinburgh in 1989, D. Tjøstheim outlined a different approach, the so-called final prediction error. We can alternatively replace the 'fill-in' value of X_s by a kernel estimate of $E([X_s \mid X_{s-i} = y_i, i = 1, \ldots , k]$ using observations up to time $s - 1$ only.

5.5.9 CONTINUOUS TIME MODELS FOR DISCRETE TIME DATA

The discussion of section 5.3.7.1 has already shown how a continuous time (linear) autoregressive model may be fitted to discrete time data via the Kalman filter approach. The key idea lies in the explicit solution curve of the *linear* differential equation defining the autoregressive model. This leads to the fundamental equation (5.118). The same idea may be exploited for the case of piecewise linear differential equations, which also admit explicit solution curves by simply integrating regime by regime (c.f. section 2.3.) Thus, in principle, we can also fit continuous time SETAR models to discrete time data. In practice, we have to make some assumptions about the sample paths (or equivalently solution curves of the differential equations) because of the fact that the data are only observed at *discrete* time. To put it in another way, we have to make some assumptions about the 'sampling intervals'. Specifically, let us describe our assumptions for the case of two regimes, extension to more than two regimes being relatively obvious:

Assumption 1: The solution curve linking two consecutive observations which lie in the same regime will be assumed to lie wholly within that regime.

Assumption 2: The solution curve linking two consecutive observations which lie in two different regimes will be assumed to cross the threshold separating the two regimes once and once only.

It is intuitively clear that the assumptions above will be satisfied if the sampling intervals are sufficiently small.

For models more general than the continuous time SETAR models, solution curves are usually not available in an explicit form. In this case, Ozaki (1985a,b) has proposed an approach, the basic idea of which may be explained as follows. Consider the first order (deterministic) differential equation

$$\dot{X}(T) = f(X(t)), \tag{5.230}$$

where f is continuous almost everywhere. This model may be discretized:

$$X(t + \Delta t) - X(t) = \bar{f}(X(t))\Delta t, \tag{5.231}$$

where

$$\bar{f}(X(t)) = \begin{cases} (\Delta t J(t))^{-1}[\exp(\Delta t J(t)) - 1]f(X(t)) & \text{if } J(t) \neq 0 \\ f(X(t)) & \text{if } J(t) = 0 \end{cases} \tag{5.232}$$

and

$$J(t) = df/dX \text{ evaluated at } X(t). \tag{5.233}$$

This discretization gives us a discrete time model for the *equally spaced* data $\{X(t), X(t + \Delta t), X(t + 2\Delta t), \dots\}$. Note that $J(t)$ *is assumed to be slowly varying over the time interval* $[t, t + \Delta t)$. It is again intuitively clear that this assumption is satisfied if the sampling interval Δt is sufficiently small. Ozaki (op. cit.) has then gone on to suggest using

$$X(t + \Delta t) - X(t) = \bar{f}(X(t))\Delta t + \sqrt{\Delta t}\, \varepsilon_{t + \Delta t}, \tag{5.234}$$

where $\varepsilon_t \sim \mathcal{N}(0, 1)$ and are i.i.d., as a discretization of the stochastic differential equation

$$\dot{X}(t) = f(X(t)) + n(t), \tag{5.235}$$

where $\{n(t)\}$ is a 'continuous time Gaussian white noise with unit variance'. It has been claimed (op. cit.) that the Markov chain defined by equation (5.234) converges (presumably in an appropriate sense yet to be defined) to the diffusion process defined by equation (5.235).

The discussion of section 2.5 is relevant in suggesting a possible link between the continuous time SETAR approach and Ozaki's approach. Exercise 18 of Chapter 2 suggests caution with Ozaki's approach when instantaneous transformations of data are involved. An attractive feature of continuous time modelling of discrete data is that a *substantive* rather than a mere *empirical* model may be entertained. §§2.1–2.8 become more directly relevant.

5.6 Diagnostics

Diagnostic checks are an important integral part of all statistical modellings if the latter are to have any claim to being scientific endeavours. Borrowing from K. Popper (1972, p. 37): 'the criterion of the scientific status of a theory [≡a model in our case] is its falsifiability, or refutability, or testability'. The importance of diagnostics has been well established in linear time series modelling. We cannot overemphasize their importance in non-linear time series modelling. A logical consequence of this is that all diagnostic tools which have been found useful in linear time series modelling should be retained and used also in non-linear time series modelling.

We summarize below a number of diagnostic tools which we have found useful in our experience. Most of these are not standard practice in linear time series modelling. These tools will be applied in Chapter 7. Completeness is not intended in our listing; for brevity, we sometimes refer to a time series model simply as a model.

5.6.1   EXAMINATION OF THE RESIDUALS

The residuals should always be plotted. The plot would aid the exposure of any obvious aberation due to model inadequacy or simple numerical slips such as transposition in the recording, etc.

The residuals are often checked for approximate uncorrelatedness (i.e. white noise) and normality. The former needs no explanation and is standard practice in time series modelling. The latter may arise from the fact that the Gaussian assumption is often made on the white noise, which is probably motivated by the following considerations:

(1)   the likelihood function of the parameters may easily be derived under this Gaussian assumption;

(2)   uncorrelatedness plus normality imply independence, which facilitates the calculation of the conditional expectations involved in the least-squares multi-step prediction;

(3)   given non-Gaussian data we might prefer to model them by a non-linear model so as to gain some insight into the dynamical structure, in which case it would be reasonable to assume normality for the white noise.

Both formal and informal statistical methods may be used, and they are concerned with the test for approximate whiteness of the fitted residuals and the test for normality of the fitted residuals.

It seems to us that the the *simplicity* of the methods to be used has much to be commended. In this respect, informal methods are often indispensable.

5.6.1.1   White noise   Let $\{\hat{e}_t : t = 1, 2, \ldots, N\}$ denote the fitted residuals resulting from a fitted model to the time series data, $\{X_t : t = 1, \ldots, N\}$, sampled from a stationary time series. Let $\hat{\rho}_k$ denote the sample autocorrelation function of lag k, $k = 0, 1, \ldots$, of $\{\hat{e}_t\}$, given by

$$\hat{\rho}_k = \sum_{i=k+1}^{N} (\hat{e}_i - \bar{e})(\hat{e}_{i-k} - \bar{e}) \Big/ \sum_{i=1}^{N} (\hat{e}_i - \bar{e})^2$$

where

$$\bar{e} = N^{-1} \sum_{i=1}^{N} \hat{e}_i.$$

Most of the popular tests for whiteness are based on an examination of $\hat{\rho}_k$, $k = 1, 2, \ldots, L$ ($L \ll N$). A simple test may be constructed by plotting the $\hat{\rho}_k$ against k. Under the null hypothesis of white noise it is well known that $\sqrt{N}\hat{\rho}_k$, for $k = 1, 2, \ldots, L$, are asymptotically independent and Gaussian with zero mean and unit variance (see e.g. Priestley 1981, p. 491). Thus, we may expect that not less than 95% of the $\hat{\rho}_k$ should lie within the band $\pm 1.96/\sqrt{N}$ if the $\hat{e}_t$ are to be accepted as approximately white noise (see e.g. Jenkins and Watts 1968, p. 188). This simple method is particularly well suited to rapid checking as the plots can be conveniently produced by a computer line printer. Also, in practice, the first few $\hat{\rho}_k$ (e.g. $k = 1, 2, \ldots, 5$, say) should be watched much more closely than the later ones, unless seasonal effects are present. Sometimes a narrower band is suggested. More formal tests, such as the Ljung–Box test, based on the $\hat{\rho}_k$ have also been developed recently for the class of linear models. See for example Ljung and Box (1978).

However, to accept the $\hat{e}_t$ as approximately independent random variables (sometimes referred to as strict white noise) would require further scrutiny, such as an examination of higher-order moments, etc. We know of no practical methods of distinguishing strict white noise from white noise, and therefore content ourselves with concentrating on the second-order moments. We may also examine the squares of the residuals for whiteness. McLeod and Li (1983) have studied a Ljung–Box-type statistic based on the squared residuals, which we have discussed in §5.3.2 and §5.3.4.4.

Sometimes, it may be reasonable to normalize $\hat{e}_t$ by dividing it by the sample standard deviation of the residuals. We refer to these residuals as the *normalized residuals*.

5.6.1.2 Univariate normality Suppose that the $\hat{e}_t$ are accepted as approximately white noise. We may then proceed with the Gaussian investigation. A histogram usually contains a fair amount of information and provides a good graphical indicator. Sample coefficients of skewness and kurtosis are useful indicators. Normal probability plots are also standard practice. These informal methods may be complemented with a formal test for univariate normality. For example, we may employ a test for normality against asymmetric alternatives such as that developed by Lin and Mudholkar (1980). Specifically, we calculate

$$y_i = \left\{ \frac{1}{N} \left[\sum_{j \neq i}^{N} \hat{e}_j^2 - \frac{1}{N-1} \left(\sum_{j \neq i}^{N} \hat{e}_j \right)^2 \right] \right\}^{1/3} \qquad i = 1, 2, \ldots, N$$

and then

$$R = \sum_{i=1}^{N} (\hat{e}_i - \bar{e})(y_i - \bar{y}) \bigg/ \left[\sum_{i=1}^{N} (\hat{e}_i - \bar{e})^2 \sum_{i=1}^{N} (y_i - \bar{y})^2 \right]^{1/2}.$$

The Lin–Mudholkar (L–M) test statistic, $\frac{1}{2}(N/3)^{1/2} \ln[(1 + R)/(1 - R)]$, is asymptotically Gaussian with zero mean and unit variance, under the null hypothesis of Gaussian $\hat{e}_t$. This statistic is based on the characterization of a Gaussian distribution by the independence of the sample mean and sample variance.

5.6.1.3 Bivariate normality Again suppose that the $\hat{e}_t$ are accepted as approximately white noise. We may complement §5.6.1.2 with an investigation of bivariate normality. For example, we may treat $\{(\hat{e}_1, \hat{e}_2), (\hat{e}_3, \hat{e}_4), \ldots, (\hat{e}_{N-1}, \hat{e}_N)\}$ as our bivariate sample of $N/2$ observations. (We might have to discard one of the $\hat{e}_t$.) We note that other 'permutations' are clearly possible in constructing a bivariate sample from $\hat{e}_1, \hat{e}_2, \ldots, \hat{e}_N$. Generally, we may start with a bivariate histogram and the sample regressions of the first component $(\hat{e}_{2t-1})$ on the second $(\hat{e}_{2t})$, and the second on the first. We can complement these graphical methods with a formal test for bivariate normality such as that due to Cox and Small (1978). This test seems to be particularly relevant in the present context because it is based on an examination of the linearity of the above-mentioned regressions. Specifically, let $Q_{1,2}$ denote the standard Student-t statistic used to test the significance of the regression coefficient of $\hat{e}_{2t-1}$ on $\hat{e}_{2t}^2$ in a 'linear' model in which $\hat{e}_{2t-1}$ is regressed on $\hat{e}_{2t}$ and $\hat{e}_{2t}^2$. Let $Q_{2,1}$ be defined in a similar manner. Let r_{12} denote the sample correlation coefficient of $\hat{e}_{2t}$ and $\hat{e}_{2t-1}$. Then the Cox–Small (C–S) test statistic is defined by the quadratic form

$$P = [Q_{2,1}, Q_{1,2}] \begin{bmatrix} 1 & r_{12}(2 - 3r_{12}^2) \\ r_{12}(2 - 3r_{12}^2) & 1 \end{bmatrix}^{-1} \begin{bmatrix} Q_{2,1} \\ Q_{1,2} \end{bmatrix}$$

which has an asymptotic χ^2 distribution with two degress of freedom under the null hypothesis of bivariate Gaussian distribution for $(\hat{e}_{2t-1}, \hat{e}_{2t})$.

5.6.2 THE 'OBSERVED' DISTRIBUTION VERSUS THE 'FITTED' DISTRIBUTION

The fitted model should have joint distributions which resemble those of the data. Practical difficulties would usually prevent us from examining k-variate distributions for $k \geq 3$. Moreover, the mean, the auto-covariances, lag regression functions, the spectral density function, and the bispectral density function are important characteristics. Realizations from the fitted model are frequently quite useful in highlighting model inadequacy. These realizations may be in the form of a time plot or directed scatter diagrams.

5.6.3 SKELETON PLOTS

By stripping the fitted model of the innovations, the skeleton of the fitted model is obtained. A time plot and a directed scatter plot of the skeleton may be useful. Recall from §4.2.3 that the skeleton may be interpreted as the zeroth approximation corresponding to a (functional) expansion of the stochastic model. If the fitted model is linear, the skeleton plot reduces to the so-called *eventual forecasting function* of Box and Jenkins (1976). Previously (e.g. in Tong 1983a) we used the latter to mean the former. To avoid possible misunderstanding, the term of a skeleton plot is introduced here.

5.6.4 LIKELIHOOD PLOTS AND INFORMATION MATRIX

A likelihood plot could be very informative in data analysis. By fixing all but two of the parameters (say θ_{i_1} and θ_{i_2}) at the estimated values, we may trace a contour diagram of the (conditional) likelihood of θ_{i_1} and θ_{i_2}. Allowing $(\theta_{i_1}, \theta_{i_2})$ to vary over all possible pairs, we have a portfolio of likelihood surfaces. Unusually elongated likelihood surfaces tend to suggest problems. For example, the models may be ill-conditioned, over-parametrized, or even inappropriate, etc. Unusual likelihood surfaces then serve as a warning for further scrutiny of the fitted models.

Associated with a portfolio of two-dimensional likelihood plots of a fitted model, it is good practice to calculate the information matrix of the parameter estimates. Unusually large correlation between $\hat{\theta}_i$ and $\hat{\theta}_j$, say, tends to require further attention. However, it is not uncommon to have correlation coefficients in the 80% range as they clearly depend on the covariance structure of the time series. Consider, for example, an AR(2) model: $X_t - 0.10X_{t-1} - 0.89X_{t-2} = \varepsilon_t,$ $\varepsilon_t \sim$ IID.   The   correlation coefficient between the CLS estimates of autoregressive parameters is in the 90% range.

We may illustrate the type of difficulties by reference to the likelihood function based on 100 observations artifically generated by the following EXPAR model:

$$X_t = [b + (c + dX_{t-1}) \exp(-gX_{t-1}^2)]X_{t-1} + \varepsilon_t \qquad (5.227)$$

where $\varepsilon_t \sim \mathcal{N}(0, 1)$, $b = 0.6$, $c = -0.6$, $d = g = 1$.

The eigenvalues of the information matrix are 0.0098, 0.0603, 0.1125, and 1.5844.

The inverse of the information matrix

0.8988			
−1.8952	22.9870		
−0.7408	−17.7297	62.8325	
−0.3035	−15.0124	42.0293	41.8091

The likelihood surface of (g, d) shown in Fig 5.30 reveals the difficulty in the elongated shape of the contours. Shown in Table 5.9 is the theoretical information matrix of the four parameters based on numerical integration w.r.t. the stationary distribution of the model which may be obtained by numerical techniques. The eigenvalues range from 0.0098 to 1.5844 (ratio of maximum to minimum $\doteq$ 161.67) and the determinant is approximately 1.05×10^{-4}, which clearly highlights the near-singularity of the matrix. The ill-conditioning revealed here is closely connected with the relative variation of π_g as g varies over $[0, \infty]$, where π_g denotes the stationary distribution with parameter g. This aspect has been dealt with in §4.2.12 under the name of pre-ordering of stationary probability measures. Specifically, see Example 2.7.

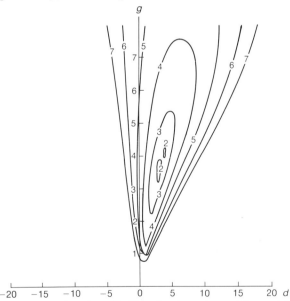

Fig. 5.30. Plot of negative log likelihood of an EXPAR model. 1 = 75.15, 2 = 75.21, 3 = 75.50, 4 = 76.50, 5 = 78.00, 6 = 80.00, 7 = 82.00

Table 5.9. (Model (5.227)) Information matrix

	b	c	d	g
b	1.5588			
c	0.1861	0.0802		
d	0.0568	0.0142	0.0561	
g	0.0210	0.0158	−0.0464	0.0764

5.6.5 REPARAMETRIZATION

With the benefit of hindsight, perhaps we should have anticipated problems in the last EXPAR example because of the 'exponential regression' nature of the EXPAR models. Analogy may be made with ordinary regression involving exponential-type functions (see e.g., Draper and Smith 1981, p. 489). The analogy then naturally suggests reparametrization as a way out of the difficulty. Specifically, we may replace $\exp(-gX_{t-1}^2)$ by $\exp[-g(X_{t-1}^2 - \mu_2')]$, c by $\tilde{c}\exp(-g\mu_2')$, and d by $\tilde{d} = d\exp(-g\mu_2')$ where

$$\mu_2' = \mathrm{E}X_{t-1}^2.$$

We shall refer to the above replacement by the term 'centring' and the reparametrized model as the 'centred model'. Typically μ_2' is estimated by the obvious second sample moment.

Comparing Fig. 5.31 for the centred version of model (5.227) with Fig. 5.30, we can see substantial improvement. The estimate of g is now much closer to the true value. ($\bar{X}^2 = 1.643$.)

The eigenvalues of the information matrix are 0.0227, 0.7601, 1.0456, and 2.5899.

The inverse of the information matrix

0.9217			
−0.4197	1.0798		
−0.1607	−0.8314	2.9510	
−0.3060	−3.2607	9.1112	41.8258

The visual improvement is confirmed by the calculations recorded in Table 5.10. Now the determinant has increased to 4.67×10^{-2} and the eigenvalues range from 0.0277 to 2.5899 (ratio $\doteqdot$ 114.09).

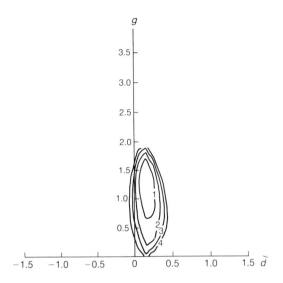

Fig. 5.31. Plot of negative log likelihood of a centred EXPAR model. $1 = 78.00$, $2 = 80.00$, $3 = 82.00$, $4 = 84.00$

5.6.6 INVERTIBILITY

It is well known that one way to obtain a unique identification of linear Gaussian moving-average models is by imposing the invertibility condition. It is also well known that the condition has a bearing on prediction. The major source of difficulties is the complexity of the likelihood function, which tends to have several local maxima. The situation with a more complicated case like a bilinear time series model is expected to be even more complex. We shall see this in Chapter 7.

It would therefore seem always prudent to check the invertibility of

Table 5.10. (Model (5.227) centred) Information matrix

	b	$\bar{c}$	$\bar{d}$	g
b	1.5281			
$\bar{c}$	0.8586	1.7614		
$\bar{d}$	0.2563	0.2987	1.0973	
g	0.0223	0.0750	−0.2139	0.0765

bilinear models fitted to real data, especially if prediction is part of the principal purpose of the exercise. We propose the following practical procedures for checking invertibility of non-linear time series models such as (5.187), because analytic conditions of invertibility such as Remark 4.14 are usually impractical except for the simplest situations. To describe the method, we consider the model

$$X_t = f(X_{t-j}, e_{t-j}, j = 1, \ldots, p) + e_t \qquad (5.228)$$

which has been fitted to data $X_1, \ldots, X_n$ conditional on $X_0 = X_{-1} = \ldots = X_{-p} = e_0 = e_{-1} = \ldots = e_{-p} = 0$. We can *extend* the sample by using the fitted model and a simulated random sample of $\varepsilon_{n+1}, \varepsilon_{n+2}, \ldots, \varepsilon_{n+m}$ (m say equal to 1000) from the fitted distribution of e_t. Replacing e_t by $\hat{\varepsilon}_t$ in (5.228) and setting $\hat{\varepsilon}_0 = \hat{\varepsilon}_{-1} = \ldots = \hat{\varepsilon}_{-p} = 0$, we may obtain $\hat{\varepsilon}_t$, $t = 1, 2, \ldots, n + m$, where by construction $\hat{\varepsilon}_j = e_j$ for $j = -p, \ldots, n$. Thus a practical check for invertibility is to calculate the sample mean of $(\varepsilon_t - \hat{\varepsilon}_t)^2$. Explosive tendency suggests non-invertibility. This technique is motivated by Exercise 25 of Chapter 4.

5.6.7   HAT MATRIX FOR OUTLIER DETECTION

In the conditional least-squares estimation of parameters of non-linear autoregressive models, a set of normal equations is usually obtained. By analogy with standard regression analysis, it would be useful to examine the hat matrix, which in many cases could be computed with little or almost no extra effort. It is a little surprising that this facility has not been routinely exploited in linear autoregressive modelling. To describe this diagnostic tool, we consider a linear AR(p) model The extension of the *mechanics* to more general NLAR models is then left to the readers as it is not difficult. However, the theory does not seem available for the latter case. The discussion will be informal.

We do not propose to give a formal definition of an outlier in time series. Here, by an outlier we simply mean an observation which exerts disproportionate influence on the model.

5.6.7.1   Linear autoregressive model   We consider the linear Gaussian autoregressive model of order $p(\mathrm{AR}(p))$:

$$X_t = \phi_1 X_{t-1} + \phi_2 X_{t-2} + \ldots + \phi_p X_{t-p} + \varepsilon_t \qquad (5.229)$$

where the ε_t are i.i.d. and $\varepsilon_t \sim \mathcal{N}(0, \sigma^2)$. Let

$$\mathbf{z}_t^T = (X_{t-1}, X_{t-2}, \ldots, X_{t-p}) \qquad \phi^T = (\phi_1, \phi_2, \ldots, \phi_p).$$

Then (5.229) can be rewritten as

$$X_t = \mathbf{z}_t^T \phi + \varepsilon_t. \qquad (5.230)$$

Suppose now we have n observations $X_1, X_2, \ldots, X_n$. Then we have the following n equations:

$$\underset{n \times 1}{\mathbf{X}} = \underset{n \times p}{\Gamma} \; \underset{p \times 1}{\phi} + \underset{n \times 1}{\boldsymbol{\varepsilon}}, \tag{5.231}$$

where $\mathbf{X} = (X_1, X_2, \ldots, X_n)^T$ is an $n \times 1$ observation vector, $\boldsymbol{\varepsilon} = (\varepsilon_1, \varepsilon_2, \ldots, \varepsilon_n)^T$ is an $n \times 1$ vector of random errors, and

$$\Gamma = \begin{bmatrix} X_0 & X_{-1} & \cdots & X_{-p+1} \\ X_1 & X_0 & \cdots & X_{-p+2} \\ \vdots & & \cdots & \vdots \\ X_{n-1} & X_{n-2} & \cdots & X_{n-p} \end{bmatrix} = \begin{bmatrix} \mathbf{z}_1^T \\ \mathbf{z}_2^T \\ \vdots \\ \mathbf{z}_n^T \end{bmatrix} \tag{5.232}$$

an $n \times p$ 'design matrix'. X_i, $i \leq 0$, are assumed fixed, say at zero. The usual root condition is assumed throughout so that $\{X_t\}$ is stationary.

We summarize first some well-known results as follows:

1. The least-squares (LS) estimate $\hat{\phi}$ of ϕ is given by

$$\hat{\phi} = (\Gamma^T \Gamma)^{-1} \Gamma^T \mathbf{X}. \tag{5.233}$$

2. Let $\hat{\mathbf{X}} = \Gamma\hat{\phi}$ be the fitted values. The least-squares fitted residuals (LSR), $\mathbf{r} = (r_1, r_2, \ldots, r_n)^T$, are defined by

$$\mathbf{r} = \mathbf{X} - \hat{\mathbf{X}}. \tag{5.234}$$

Note that $\hat{\mathbf{X}} = \Gamma\hat{\phi} = \Gamma(\Gamma^T \Gamma)^{-1} \Gamma^T \mathbf{X}$, that is

$$\hat{\mathbf{X}} = H\mathbf{X} \tag{5.235}$$

where $H = \Gamma(\Gamma^T \Gamma)^{-1} \Gamma^T$. Here, $H = [h_{ij}]$ is known as the *hat matrix* because 'it puts a hat on $\mathbf{X}$'. Since

$$(I - H)\Gamma\phi = \Gamma\phi - \Gamma(\Gamma^T \Gamma)^{-1} \Gamma^T \Gamma\phi = \mathbf{0}$$

we have from (5.234) and (5.235) that

$$\mathbf{r} = (I - H)\mathbf{X} \tag{5.236}$$
$$= (I - H)(\Gamma\phi + \boldsymbol{\varepsilon})$$
$$= (I - H)\boldsymbol{\varepsilon}. \tag{5.237}$$

In addition (5.236) and (5.237) can be rewritten in scalar forms, namely

$$r_t = (1 - h_{tt})X_t - \sum_{j \neq t} h_{tj}X_j \tag{5.236}$$

$$= (1 - h_{tt})\varepsilon_t - \sum_{j \neq t} h_{tj}\varepsilon_j. \tag{5.237}$$

3. The LS estimate of σ^2 is given by

$$\hat{\sigma}^2 = \mathbf{r}^T \mathbf{r}/n. \tag{5.238}$$

From now on, we denote the 'diagonal element(s) of the hat matrix' by DEH, and the tth DEH, h_{tt}, by h_t, that is

$$h_t = \mathbf{z}_t^T(\Gamma^T\Gamma)^{-1}\mathbf{z}_T.$$

4. By stationarity of $\{X_t\}$, it holds that as $n \to \infty$, $n^{-1}(\Gamma^T\Gamma) \to \Sigma$ in probability, where

$$\Sigma = \begin{bmatrix} \gamma_0 & \gamma_1 & \cdots & \gamma_{p-1} \\ \gamma_1 & \gamma_0 & \cdots & \gamma_{p-2} \\ \vdots & \vdots & \cdots & \vdots \\ \gamma_{p-1} & \gamma_{p-2} & \cdots & \gamma_0 \end{bmatrix} \quad \gamma_s = \mathrm{cov}(X_t, X_{t+s})$$

a Toeplitz matrix.

Now, conditional on H being fixed, it holds that

$$\mathrm{var}(\mathbf{r}) = (I - H)\,\mathrm{var}(\boldsymbol{\varepsilon}) = (I - H)\sigma^2. \tag{5.239}$$

In scalar form, eqn (5.239) becomes

$$\mathrm{var}(r_t) = (1 - h_t)\sigma^2 \tag{5.239a}$$
$$\mathrm{cov}(r_i r_j) = -h_{ij}\sigma^2. \tag{5.239b}$$

5.6.7.2 Interpretations
We summarize some well-known properties of H as follows:

1. H is idempotent, that is $H^2 = H$, $H^T = H$.
2. $\mathrm{Trace}(H) = \mathrm{rank}(H) = p = \mathrm{AR\ order}$. \hfill (5.240)
3. $H^2 = H \Rightarrow \forall t, j = 1, \ldots, \sum_j h_{t,j}^2 = h_t$. \hfill (5.241)
4. From (5.241), we have $h_t^2 + \sum_{j \neq t} h_{t,j}^2 = h_t$. Therefore $h_t \geq h_t^2$. \hfill (5.242)
    Therefore

$$0 \leq h_t \leq 1. \tag{5.243}$$

5. From (5.243) we have $\sum_{j \neq t} h_{ij}^2 \to 0$ as $h_t \to 1$.

    It follows that

$$h_{tj} \to 0\ \forall j \neq t \quad \text{as} \quad h_t \to 1. \tag{5.244}$$

1. Recall that the fitted values (sometimes also called the predictions) may be expressed as

$$\hat{\mathbf{X}} = \Gamma\hat{\phi} = \Gamma(\Gamma^T\Gamma)^{-1}\Gamma^T\mathbf{X} = H\mathbf{X}. \tag{5.245}$$

In scalar form, we may write

$$\hat{X}_t = h_t X_t + \sum_{j \neq t} h_{tj} X_j. \tag{5.246}$$

From (5.246) and (5), we know that if h_t is large (i.e. near 1), $\hat{X}_t$ will be dominated by the term $h_t X_t$. Therefore h_t may be interpreted as the amount of leverage or influence exerted on $\hat{X}_t$ by X_t. We note that the relationship between the fitted values and the estimate $\hat{\phi}$ is given by

$$\hat{\mathbf{X}} = \Gamma \hat{\phi} \quad \text{and} \quad \hat{\phi} = (\Gamma^T \Gamma)^{-1} \Gamma^T \hat{\mathbf{X}}.$$

Hence, knowing $\hat{\mathbf{X}}$ is equivalent to knowing $\hat{\phi}$. In our case, it is easier to interpret $\hat{\mathbf{X}}$ than $\hat{\phi}$. Therefore we refer more often to $\hat{\mathbf{X}}$.

2. Differentiating (5.246) w.r.t. X_t, we have

$$\frac{\partial \hat{X}_t}{\partial X_t} \doteq h_t \tag{5.247}$$

which shows that h_t measures approximately the *relative change* of the fitted value $\hat{X}_t$ when there is a small change in the observed value X_t.

3. Define $d_t = \mathbf{z}_t^T \Sigma^{-1} \mathbf{z}_t$, $t = 1, 2, \ldots, n$. Note also that for large n

$$n h_t = \mathbf{z}_t^T \left(\frac{\Gamma^T \Gamma}{n} \right)^{-1} \mathbf{z}_t \sim d_t. \tag{5.248}$$

Also, $n h_t$ has the interpretation as the Mahalanobis distance between $\mathbf{z}_t$ and the mean vector (zero vector in our case). Note that in conventional linear regression, the h_t do not have this explicit interpretation.

5.6.7.3 An approach to outlier detection in linear autoregressive models

We write the linear autoregressive process AR(p), $\{X_t\}$, in the following state space form:

$$\mathbf{z}_{t+1} = \underset{p \times 1}{\underset{p \times p}{B}} \underset{p \times 1}{\mathbf{z}_t} + \underset{p \times 1}{\bar{\varepsilon}} \qquad \underset{1 \times 1}{X_t} = (1, 0, \ldots, 0) \underset{p \times 1}{\mathbf{z}_{t+1}} \tag{5.249}$$

where $\bar{\varepsilon}_t = (\varepsilon_t, 0, \ldots, 0)^T$,

$$B = \begin{bmatrix} \phi_1 & \phi_2 & \cdots & \phi_{p-1} & \phi_p \\ 1 & 0 & \cdots & 0 & 0 \\ 0 & 1 & \cdots & 0 & 0 \\ \vdots & \vdots & \cdots & \vdots & \vdots \\ 0 & 0 & \cdots & 1 & 0 \end{bmatrix}.$$

Suppose now that we have a realization of size n, $X_1, X_2, \ldots, X_n$ say, from the AR(p) process. From the state space point of view, at time t, it is the relative position of $X_t, X_{t-1}, \ldots, X_{t-p+1}$ in the p-dimensional space that we are interested in, not just the X_t itself. Therefore, it is more reasonable to refer to the state vector $\mathbf{z}_{t+1} = (X_t, X_{t-1}, \ldots, X_{t-p+1})^T$, rather than just the first coordinate X_t of $\mathbf{z}_{t+1}$. Hence, for outlier detection in AR processes, we should look for outlying state vectors, that is 'remote' state vectors. Geometrically speaking, we look for remote points in the p-dimensional space spanned by the columns of Γ.

To measure the 'remoteness' of $\mathbf{z}_t$, we suggest using the *distance*, d_t, where

$$d_t = \mathbf{z}_t^T \Sigma^{-1} \mathbf{z}_t.$$

Now, under the hypothesis that the autoregressive process is Gaussian and there is no outlier, it holds that $\forall t = p + 1, \ldots, n$, d_t has a χ_p^2 distribution. Therefore, by (5.2.4.8) nh_t *lends itself as a useful measure for outlier detection within the linear Gaussian context*. The discussion in §5.6.7.2 suggests that it is practicable to use DEH to detect outlying state vectors. If h_t is sufficiently large, we may say $\mathbf{z}_t$ is an outlying state vector.

Recall that

$$\mathbf{z}_t = (X_{t-1}, X_{t-2}, \ldots, X_{t-p})^T, \quad t = 1, 2, \ldots, n$$
$$h_t = \mathbf{z}_t^T (\Gamma^T \Gamma)^{-1} \mathbf{z}_t.$$

Suppose that X_{t-1} is large; then its effect will enter into $\mathbf{z}_t$, $\mathbf{z}_{t+1}, \ldots, \mathbf{z}_{t+p-1}$ and $h_t, h_{t+1}, \ldots, h_{t+p-1}$ will be large. Therefore, if h_{t-1} is small (i.e. $X_{t-2}, X_{t-3}, \ldots, X_{t-p-1}$ are not outliers) and h_t is large, we may identify X_{t-1} as an outlier. We note that when some of the h_t are large, there are problems associated with using LSR for diagnostic checking and outlier detection. Now we see that when there are outliers, then some of the h_t will be large. In fact, a simple examination of the LSR is not a good tool for outlier detection. Suppose X_{t-1} is an outlier. Then $h_t, h_{t+1}, \ldots, h_{t+p-1}$ will be large and tend to reduce the residuals $r_t, r_{t+1}, \ldots, r_{t+p-1}$ by reference to (5.237). As a result, even if $X_t, X_{t+1}, \ldots, X_{t+p-1}$ are also outliers, $r_t, r_{t+1}, \ldots, r_{t+p-1}$ may not be sufficiently large and hence $X_t, X_{t+1}, \ldots, X_{t+p-1}$ may go unnoticed as outliers if only the LSR are examined.

We may conclude that for time series data adequately described by an autoregressive model, the presence of an outlier may lead to a situation in which outliers immediately following it may go unnoticed if we rely exclusively on LSR for outlier detection. However, in the context of time series, outliers can and do often occur in batches, for example when innovation outliers are present (see e.g. Fox 1972; Kleiner *et al.* 1979). Bruce and Martin (1989) have given an alternative approach and other references.

5.6.7.4 Examples

(A) Canadian lynx data

Tong (1977b) has fitted a Gaussian AR(11) model to the famous Canadian lynx data. The data set is listed in Appendix 3. Some background will be given in Chapter 7. The fitted model is given by

$$X_t = 1.13X_{t-1} - 0.51X_{t-2} + 0.23X_{t-3} - 0.29X_{t-4} + 0.14X_{t-5} - 0.14X_{t-6}$$
$$+ 0.08X_{t-7} - 0.04X_{t-8} + 0.13X_{t-9} + 0.19X_{t-10} - 0.31X_{t-11} + \varepsilon_t \quad (5.250)$$

where $X_t = \log_{10}$(number of lynx trapped in the year $(1820 + t)) - 2.9036$, for $t = 1, 2, \ldots, 114$, and $\{\varepsilon_t\}$ is a Gaussian white noise sequence with mean zero and variance equal to 0.0437. Fig. 5.32 reveals several potential outliers by reference of the h_t to the nominal x^2_{11} (10%) point divided by 100 (represented by the dashed horizontal line.) (The figure used by Tong in his discussion of Bruce and Martin (1989) was reproduced from an unpublished M.Phil thesis of M. C. Hau (1984). It now appears that that figure may contain some errors.) We return to this data set in Chapter 7.

(B) Lake Huron, USA

The next example is concerned with the level of Lake Huron for July for each year from 1875 to 1972 (Fig. 5.33) inclusively as listed in the recent book by Brockwell and Davis (1987, p. 499). Preliminary data analysis reveals that a first differencing or possibly a second differencing of the data is advisable so as to reduce the data to stationarity in the mean (cf Box and Jenkins, 1976). The hat matrix technique then suggests the patch of data points numbered approximately 55 to 63 and the last datum as outliers. On assuming that the listing is error free up to data point numbered say 65, then the suggested outlying patch corresponds to the period of the 1930s. It would then seem interesting to explore the

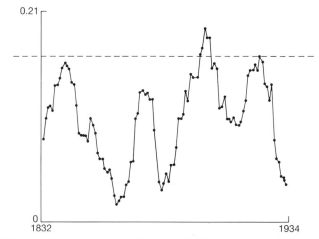

Fig. 5.32   A plot of h_t versus t for the AR(11) model fitted to the Canadian lynx data. (Produced by STAR package.)

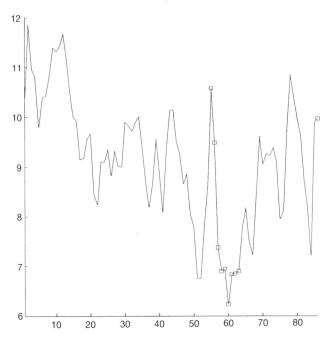

Fig. 5.33. Level of Lake Huron in feet (reduced by 570), 1875–1972: identified outliers are marked by □

connection between this and the famous dust-bowl period of the 1930s. As for the suggested outlying singleton, it seems that it may well be due to the omission of a column of 12 data taking place in the vicinity of the singleton. The book has inadvertently listed only 86 of the announced 98 data! (Professor P. J. Brockwell has since confirmed that the suspicion is valid.)

(C) Australian blow-fly data

The hat matrix check is useful even if the model is only piecewise linear, in which case the χ^2 asymptotics do not apply.

Tong (1983a, p. 273*) has reported a model fitted by one of his MSc students, Mr D. Nield, to the initial stretch of the bi-daily Australian blow-fly data collected by the Australian entomologist, A. J. Nicholson. Nield (1982) used an earlier version of a package for threshold autoregressive modelling which contained a small 'bug' (see the footnote on p. 187 of Tong 1983a). Using the revised version, we may modify

---

* Tong has misquoted Nield's fitting periods. They should be $20 \leq t \leq 145$ for the initial stretch and $218 \leq t \leq 299$ for the later stretch.

slightly Nield's threshold model for the period $20 \le t \le 145$ to

$$
X_t = \begin{cases}
\underset{(0.24)}{2.66} + \underset{(0.07)}{0.27X_{t-1}} + \varepsilon_t^{(1)} & \text{if } X_{t-8} \le 3.05 \\
& \hspace{2cm} [3.00, 3.09]^* \\
\underset{(0.09)}{0.45} + \underset{(0.11)}{1.52X_{t-1}} - \underset{(0.21)}{0.40X_{t-2}} - \underset{(0.13)}{0.27X_{t-3}} + \varepsilon_t^{(2)} & \text{if } X_{t-8} > 3.05 \\
& \hspace{2cm} [3.00, 3.09]
\end{cases}
$$

where var $\varepsilon_t^{(1)} = 0.024$, var $\varepsilon_t(2) = 0.010$ (pooled var $= 0.016$), and the standard errors are in parentheses. Here, X_t is measured on a $\log_{10}$ scale. The usual diagnostics on the residuals do not reveal any serious inadequacy. Specifically, only the sample autocorrelation (of the residuals) at lag 18 is just significant at the nominal 5% level. The sample partial autocorrelation behaves similarly. For the squared residuals, very marginally significant results are obtained at lag 2. The Ljung–Box statistic is 26.36 and the McLeod–Li statistic is 15.27; they are both not significant compared with χ_{20}^2 (5%). The normal probability plot does not reveal any obvious deviation from normality. (The Lin–Mudholkar statistic is -1.63 which is just non-significant at the nominal 5% point of $\mathcal{N}(0, 1)$.)

However, Fig. 5.34 shows the diagonal elements of the hat matrix associated with the piecewise linear autoregressive model. From these, it is clear that the 'influential pattern' remains cyclical with a period of about 20 units of time, which is about the same as that of the blow-fly population cycle. This suggests the need of at least a bivariate time series, incorporating the egg counts, for example. It is feasible that the interaction between the fly population and the egg population will give a better understanding of the cycle-generating mechanism.

Bibliographical notes

As many of the sources have been quoted in the text, we add only a few notes.

Section 5.2: The main reference is Tong (1983a), which is supplemented by Doukhan (1983), Moeanaddin (1989) and Robinson (1983).

Section 5.3: The idea of developing statistical tools using the squares of the residuals seems to originate with Granger and Andersen (1978). The example discussed in §5.3.4.5 represents only the tip of an iceberg as far as the recognition of non-linearity in the economics/econometrics literature is concerned (see e.g. Barnett *et al.* 1988; Hamilton 1989; Hinich & Patterson 1985). The kind of non-standard problems we encounter in

* In view of the non-Gaussian asymptotics for the threshold estimate, we give the interquartile range in the square brackets here.

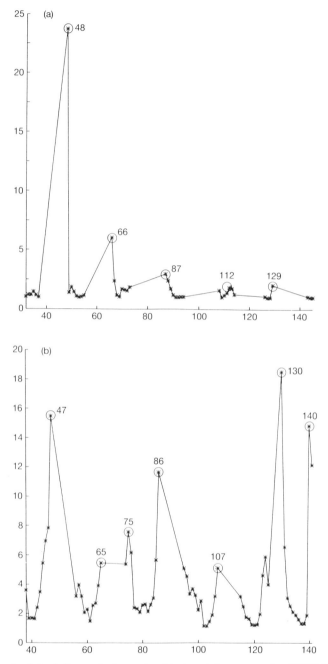

Fig. 5.34. A plot of diagonal elements of hat matrix versus t for SETAR $(2; 1, 3)$ fitted to the Australian blow-fly data $(20 \leq t \leq 145)$: (a) lower regime; (b) upper regime. The vertical axes have been inflated by the sample size.

§5.3.5 falls within the domain described in Davies (1977, 1987). The Gaussian process approach seems sophisticated but necessarily so and, as far as we are aware, it is new. It is based on ongoing collaborative research of the author with K. S. Chan. The table of percentage points in §5.3.5.2 is due to H. F. Ross. Partially observed data and irregularly spaced data require special handling. The results are new, to the best of our knowledge, and are based on Tong and Yeung (1988a,b) and Yeung (1989). Ordered autoregression is implicit in Tong and Lim (1980, §8; see also Lim 1981, pp. 46–7) and first used explicitly in Petruccelli and Davies (1986a) and later in Chan (1988c).

Section 5.4: This is an updated and widened version of §4.1 of Tong (1983a).

Section 5.5: Example 5.2 is based on Jones (1976). Example 5.4 is based on Chan and Tong (1986a). Section 5.5.3 is based on Chan (1988c), which has made significant progress beyond Tong and Lim (1980). Section 5.5.4 is based on Pham Dinh Tuan and Lanh Tat Tran (1981) and Guegan and Pham Dinh Tuan (1989). Section 5.5.5 is based on Robinson (1977b). Section 5.5.6 is based on Aase (1983) and Thavaneswaran and Abraham (1988). Sections 5.5.7 and 5.5.8 are probably new. Section 5.5.9 is based on collaborative work of the author with Yeung as reported in Yeung (1989) and on Ozaki (1985a,b). Robinson (1972) is also relevant.

Section 5.6: This is based on §4.4 of Tong (1983a). Hau and Tong (1984), and Chan *et al.* (1988). Künsch (1984) has also proposed the use of the Mahalanobis distance in outlier detection in linear autoregression and has given a rigorous account. Many of the diagnostic tools, for example normal probability plots, Lin–Mudholkar test, etc., were implemented with the computer listings of Tong (1983a).

Exercises and complements

(1)   Prove that if $\{X_t\}$ admits a linear representation of the form (5.2), then for all $k \geq 2$ and for all $\omega_1, \ldots, \omega_k$, $(-\pi \leq \omega_i \leq \pi)$, the ratios $|h_k(\omega_1, \ldots, \omega_k)|^2 \{h(\omega_1), \ldots, h(\omega_k)h(\omega_1 + \ldots + \omega_k)\}^{-1}$ are constant.

(Brillinger 1965)

(2)   Let $\{X_t\}$ denote a stationary Gaussian time series. Verify that
$$\rho_\tau(X_t^2) = \{\rho_\tau(X_t)\}^2, \quad \text{all } \tau$$
where $\rho_\tau(Z_t) = \text{corr}(Z_{t+\tau}, Z_t)$.

(3)   Referring to §5.3.4, let $Z_{0t} = (-1, X_{t-1}, \ldots, X_{t-p})^T$. Verify that
$$\text{LM(BL)} = \hat{\sigma}^{-2} \left(\sum_{t=1}^N Z_{1t}\hat{\varepsilon}_t \right)^T (M_{11} - M_{10}M_{00}^{-1}M_{01})^{-1} \left(\sum_{t=1}^N Z_{1t}\hat{\varepsilon}_t \right)$$

where

$$M_{i0} = M_{0i}^T = \sum_{t=1}^{N} Z_{it}Z_{0t}^T, \quad i = 0, 1$$

$$M_{11} = \sum_{t=1}^{N} Z_{1t}Z_{1t}^T$$

$$Z_{1t} = (\hat{\varepsilon}_{t-1}X_{t-1}, \hat{\varepsilon}_{t-1}X_{t-2}, \ldots, \hat{\varepsilon}_{t-m}X_{t-k})^T.$$

(Luukkonen et al. 1988a)

(4) Let Z_{0t} be as in Exercise 3 but with -1 replaced by 1. Let $Z_{1t} = (I_{t-d}, I_{t-d}X_{t-1}, \ldots, I_{t-d}X_{t-q})^T$. Verify that for each fixed r,

$$\text{LM(TAR}, r) = \hat{\sigma}^{-2}\left(\sum_{t=1}^{N} Z_{1t}\hat{\varepsilon}_t\right)^T (M_{11} - M_{10}M_{00}^{-1}M_{01})^{-1}\left(\sum_{t=1}^{N} Z_{1t}Z_{0t}\right)$$

where

$$M_{i0} = M_{0i}^T = \sum_{t=1}^{N} Z_{it}Z_{0t}^T, \quad i = 0, 1$$

$$M_{11} = \sum_{t=1}^{N} Z_{1t}Z_{1t}^T.$$

(Chan and Tong 1988a)

(5) For the $u_i(\theta)$ defined in §5.5.1, evaluate it when X^N is a random sample. Verify that $I_N(\theta)$ is then the Fisher information.

(6) Generalize the analysis of Example 5.2 to the case where ε_t has the density $\mathcal{N}(0, \sigma^2)$, σ^2 unknown. Let $\hat{\theta}$ and $\hat{\sigma}^2$ denote the maximum likelihood estimate of θ and σ^2 respectively. Verify that

$$\text{var } \hat{\theta} \approx \sigma^2 \Big/ N\text{E}\left(\frac{\partial}{\partial\theta} \lambda(X_1; \theta)\right)^2$$

$$\text{var } \hat{\sigma}^2 \approx 2\sigma^4/N$$

and

$$\text{cov}(\hat{\theta}, \hat{\sigma}^2) \approx 0.$$

(Jones 1976)

(7) Consider an EXPAR model of order 1;

$$X_t - [\alpha + \beta \exp(-\gamma X_{t-1}^2)]X_{t-1} = \varepsilon_t, \ |\alpha| < 1.$$

$\varepsilon_t \sim \text{IID}(0, \sigma^2)$ has a density with infinite support and $\text{E}\varepsilon_t^6 < \infty$. Find the conditional least squares estimates of $(\alpha, \beta, \gamma, \sigma^2)$ and verify that they are strongly consistent and asymptotically normal.

(Tjøstheim 1986b)

(8) Consider the RCA model of order k:

$$X_t = \sum_{i=1}^{k} \{\beta_i + B_i(t)\}X_{t-i} + \varepsilon_t$$

as defined in §3.7. Suppose that second moments of $\{B_i(t)\}$, $i = 1, \ldots, k$, and $\{\varepsilon_t\}$ exist. Using the conditional least squares, prove that there exists a strongly consistent sequence of estimates $\hat{\boldsymbol{\beta}}_N$ for $(\beta_1, \ldots, \beta_k)$ and that $\hat{\boldsymbol{\beta}}_N$ is asymptotically normal if $EX_t^4 < \infty$. Moreover, if in addition ε_t cannot take on only two values almost surely, then there exist strongly consistent sequences of estimates for $\mathbf{C}$ and σ^2. These estimates are asymptotically normal if in addition $EX_t^8 < \infty$.

(Nicholls and Quinn 1982; Tjøstheim 1986b)

(9) Consider a NEAR(2) model

$$X_t = \varepsilon_t + \begin{cases} \beta_1 X_{t-1} & \text{with probability } \alpha_1 \\ \beta_2 X_{t-2} & \text{with probability } \alpha_2 \\ 0 & \text{with probability } 1 - \alpha_1 - \alpha_2 \end{cases}$$

where $\varepsilon_t \sim$ IID with the distribution

$$\varepsilon_t = \begin{cases} E_t & \text{with probability } 1 - p_2 - p_3 \\ b_2 E_t & \text{with probability } p_2 \\ b_3 E_t & \text{with probability } p_3 \end{cases} \qquad (*)$$

E_t being IID with density e^{-x} $(0 \le x < \infty)$. Suppose that $\alpha_1 \beta_1 + \alpha_2 \beta_2 < 1$, $0 \le \alpha_1$, $\alpha_2 \le 1$ and $0 \le \beta_1$, $\beta_2 \le 1$, so that $\{X_t\}$ are stationary. Suppose that X_t has the marginal density e^{-x} $(0 \le x < \infty)$. Determine b_2, b_3, p_2, and p_3 in terms of α_1, α_2, β_1, and β_2.

Verify that the NEAR(2) model may be written as a second-order RCA

$$X_t = B_1(t)X_{t-1} + B_2(t)X_{t-2} + \varepsilon_t$$

where the joint distribution of $(B_1(t), B_2(t))$ is given

$$P(B_1(t) = \beta_1, B_2(t) = \beta_2) = 0$$
$$P(B_1(t) = \beta_1, B_2(t) = 0) = \alpha_1$$
$$P(B_1(t) = 0, B_2(t) = \beta_2) = \alpha_2$$
$$P(B_1(t) = 0, B_2(t) = 0) = 1 - \alpha_1 - \alpha_2.$$

and ε_t has the distribution specified by $(*)$. Let $a_i = E(B_i(t))$, $\sigma_{ii} = \text{var}(B_i(t))$, $i = 1, 2$ and $\sigma_{12} = \text{cov}(B_1(t), B_2(t))$. Verify that for

$$i = 1, 2$$

$$a_i = \alpha_i \beta_i \qquad \sigma_{ii} = \beta_i^2 \alpha_i (1 - \alpha_i) \qquad \sigma_{12} = -a_1 a_2.$$

Given $X_1, \ldots, X_N$, let $\hat{a}_1$ and $\hat{a}_2$ denote respectively the conditional least-squares estimates of a_1 and a_2 obtained by minimizing w.r.t. a_1 and a_2

$$\sum \{(x_t - 1) - E[(X_t - 1) \mid \mathbb{B}_{t-1}]\}^2$$

$\mathbb{B}_{t-1}$ being the σ-algebra generated by X_s, $s \le t - 1$. Verify that $\hat{a}_1$ and $\hat{a}_2$ are given by ($i = 1, 2$)

$$\sum_{t=3}^{N} (X_{t-1})(X_{t-i} - 1) = \sum_{j=1}^{2} \hat{a}_j \sum_{t=3}^{N} (X_{t-j} - 1)(X_{t-i} - 1).$$

By considering the process $\{U_t^2\}$, where

$$U_t = X_t - E(X_t \mid \mathbb{B}_{t-1})$$

verify that the conditional least-squares estimates $\hat{\sigma}_{11}$, $\hat{\sigma}_{22}$ of σ_{11}, σ_{22} are given by ($i = 1, 2$)

$$\sum_{t=3}^{N} \hat{H}_t (X_{t-i}^2 - 2) = \sum_{j=1}^{2} \hat{\sigma}_{jj} \sum_{t=3}^{N} (X_{t-j}^2 - 2)(X_{t-i}^2 - 2)$$

where

$$\hat{H}_t = \left[X_t - \sum_{i=1}^{2} \hat{a}_i X_{t-i} - (1 - \hat{a}_1 - \hat{a}_2) \right]^2$$
$$+ 2\hat{a}_1 \hat{a}_2 X_{t-1} X_{t-2} + 1 - (\hat{a}_1 - \hat{a}_2)^2.$$

Prove that $\hat{\alpha}_i = \hat{a}_i^2 / (\hat{\sigma}_{ii} + \hat{a}_i^2)$ and $\hat{\beta}_i = (\hat{\sigma}_{ii} + \hat{a}_i^2) / \hat{a}_i$ ($i = 1, 2$) are strongly consistent for α_i and β_i respectively and asymptotically Gaussian.

(Karlsen and Tjøstheim 1988)

(10) Consider a stochastic logistic model

$$X_{t+1} = \theta X_t (1 - X_t) I(X_t \in [0, 1]) + \sigma \varepsilon_{t+1}$$

where $\sigma > 0$, $\theta \in [0, 4]$, and ε_t satisfies assumptions (5.200) and (5.201). Let σ be known. Implement Aase's algorithm to obtain the recursive scheme

$$\hat{\theta}_{t+1} = \frac{\sigma^2 \theta_0 k_0^{-1} + \sum_{s=0}^{t} X_s (1 - X_s) I(X_s \in [0, 1]) X_{s+1}}{\sigma^2 k_0^{-1} + \sum_{s=0}^{t} X_s^2 (1 - X_s)^2 I(X_s \in [0, 1])}, \qquad t \ge 0$$

θ_0 being the initial guess of θ. What happens to $\hat{\theta}_{t+1}$ if $\sigma = 0$?

(Aase 1983)

(11) Consider a simple RCA model

$$X_t = \beta + B(t)X_{t-1} + \varepsilon_t$$

as defined in §3.7. Using the estimation equation approach of Godambe, derive the estimate based on $X_1, \ldots, X_N$

$$\hat{\beta}_N = \sum_{t=2}^{N} a_{t-1}^* X_t \Big/ \sum_{t=2}^{N} a_{t-1}^* X_{t-1}$$

where $a_{t-1}^* = -X_{t-1}/(\sigma_\varepsilon^2 + X_{t-1}^2 \sigma_B^2)$, $\sigma_\varepsilon^2 = \operatorname{var} \varepsilon_t$, $\sigma_B^2 = \operatorname{var} B(t)$.

Compare the above $\hat{\beta}_N$ with that obtained by the conditional least-squares method.

(Thavaneswaran and Abraham 1988)

(12) Consider a *non-ergodic* SETAR model

$$X_t = \alpha I(X_{t-1} \leq 0)X_{t-1} + \alpha^{-1}I(X_{t-1} > 0)X_{t-1} + \varepsilon_t^{'}$$

where $\varepsilon_t \sim \text{IID}(0, \sigma^2)$, $\sigma^2 \neq 0$. Let $\hat{\alpha}$ denote the (conditional) least-squares estimate of α given the observations $X_1, X_2, \ldots, X_n$ on minimizing

$$Q_n(\alpha) = \sum_{t=2}^{n} [X_t - \mathrm{E}(X_t \mid X_{t-1})]^2$$

w.r.t. α. Let α_0 denote the true value of α and $S_n = X_2^2 + \ldots + X_n^2$. Verify that for all $\delta > 0$

$$\lim_{n \to \infty} \inf_{\alpha: |\alpha - \alpha_0| \geq \delta} [Q_n(\alpha) - Q_n(\alpha_0)]/S_n > 0 \quad \text{a.s.}$$

Hence deduce that $\hat{\alpha}$ is strongly consistent.

(Pham Dinh Tuan *et al.* 1989)

(13) Consider the bilinear model ($|\theta| < 1$)

$$X_t = \varepsilon_t + \theta \varepsilon_t X_{t-1}$$

where $\varepsilon_t \sim \mathcal{N}(0, 1)$. Show that $I_N(\theta)$, the Fisher information, is not defined because

$$\mathrm{E}[(X_0/(1 + \theta X_0))^2]$$

is not finite. Here the expectation is w.r.t. the stationary distribution of (X_t). Repeat the exercise with a simple ARCH model.

(14) Consider the bilinear model, assumed stationary

$$X_t = aX_{t-1} + \varepsilon_t + b\varepsilon_{t-1}X_{t-1}$$

where $\varepsilon_t \sim \text{IID}(0, \sigma^2)$. Verify that

$$b = \frac{(1-a)\mathrm{E}X_t}{\sigma^2}$$

where EX_t is assumed to exist. What implications does this result have on bilinear modelling?

(15) Consider the non-linear moving-average model

$$X_t = \alpha \varepsilon_{t-1}^2 + \varepsilon_t$$

where $\varepsilon_t \sim \mathcal{N}(0, \sigma^2)$. Let σ^2 be known and let $X_1, X_2, \ldots, X_n$ be given. Verify that the estimate

$$\hat{\alpha} = \sum_{t=1}^{n} X_t / (n\sigma^2)$$

obtained by the method of moments is unbiased and consistent. Verify also that var $\hat{\alpha} \to \infty$ as $\sigma^2 \to 0$.

(Moenaddin and Tong 1989*b*)

6
Non-linear least-squares prediction based on non-linear models

知者不言言者不知 *He who knows does not predict.*
He who predicts does not know.

Ch. LVI Lao Tzu

6.1 Introduction

Let $\{X_t : t = 0, \pm 1, \ldots\}$ denote a stationary and invertible time series. We assume that X_t has at least finite variance. As in §4.7, we let $\mathbb{B}_t$ denote the σ-algebra generated by X_s, $s \leq t$ and H_t the Hilbert space of square integrable random variables measurable w.r.t. $\mathbb{B}_t$. Let $Z \in H_m$. It is well known that the least-squares predictor, $\hat{Z}$, of Z in terms of the 'present' and the 'past', $\{X_s : s \leq 0\}$, is uniquely given by the conditional expectation, namely

$$\hat{Z} = \mathrm{E}[Z \mid \mathbb{B}_0] \tag{6.1}$$

which is the unique projection of Z on H_0. As usual, it has been understood here and in §4.7 that we take for H_t the inner product defined by the covariance w.r.t. the stationary distribution. In practice, the evaluation of the conditional expectation is non-trivial if only a model for the time series has been given. We shall study specific cases in this chapter. Another important aspect of prediction is the 'precision' problem. We may, for example, use $\{\mathrm{var}[Z \mid \mathbb{B}_0]\}^{1/2}$ as a possible measure of variability/precision of $\hat{Z}$. If feasible, it is always useful to have available the 'predictive distribution', that is the conditional distribution of Z given $\mathbb{B}_0$.

Sometimes we denote $\mathrm{E}[X_m \mid \mathbb{B}_0]$ by $\hat{X}_0(m)$ and call it the m-step least-squares predictor of X_m given $\mathbb{B}_0$. We denote the $\mathrm{var}(X_m - \hat{X}_0(m))$ conditional on $\mathbb{B}_0$ by $\hat{\sigma}_0^2(m)$, or simply $\hat{\sigma}^2(m)$ if there is no danger of confusion.

The assumptions and notations introduced in this section will be adopted in the rest of this chapter without further mention.

6.2 Non-linear autoregressive models

6.2.1 RECURSIVE FORMULAE

Without loss of generality, we restrict our discussion to the first-order case:

$$X_t = h(X_{t-1}) + \varepsilon_t, \qquad t = 0, \pm 1, \pm 2, \dots \qquad (6.2)$$

where $\{\varepsilon_t\}$ is a sequence of i.i.d. random variables with $E\varepsilon_t = 0$ and var $\varepsilon_t = \sigma^2$, $0 < \sigma^2 < \infty$ all t. Since we have here a Markov chain over $\mathbf{R}$, we may recall the Chapman–Kolmogorov relation

$$f(x_{t+m} \mid x_t) = \int_{-\infty}^{\infty} f(x_{t+m} \mid x_{t+1}) f(x_{t+1} \mid x_t) \, dx_{t+1} \qquad (6.3)$$

where $f(x_s \mid x_t)$ denotes the conditional probability density function of X_s given $X_t = x_t$ (assumed to exist). Suppose that model (6.2) is (strictly) stationary. Let g denote the probability density function of ε_t. Let k denote a well-behaved (i.e. Baire) function of X_t and suppose $E |k(X_t)| < \infty$. Let $K_m(X_t)$ denote the conditional expectation $E(k(X_{t+m}) \mid X_t)$. Equation (6.3) gives immediately

$$K_m(x_t) = \int_{-\infty}^{\infty} K_{m-1}(x_{t+1}) f(x_{t+1} \mid x_t) \, dx_{t+1} \qquad (6.4)$$

that is

$$K_m(x) = \int_{-\infty}^{\infty} K_{m-1}(y) g(y - h(x)) \, dy. \qquad (6.5)$$

Equation (6.5) gives, in particular, recursive formulae for conditional expectations and conditional variances. Except for special cases of h (e.g. the linear case), the integral equation in (6.5) does not usually admit analytic solution and numerical integration is commonly the only solution. We may employ readily the numerical integration methods described in §4.2.4 for this purpose. These methods extend to higher-order cases quite straightforwardly by converting each of the latter to a vector first-order case.

An alternative method which is especially useful for higher-order autoregressive models is the Monte Carlo method. Here, a sufficiently long record of data is simulated in accordance with the model (i.e. eqn (6.2) or its higher-order generalization) and the sample estimate of $K_m(x)$ is taken as an approximation of $K_m(x)$. Detailed comparison is given by Moeanaddin (1989). Suffice it to say that both methods give reasonable approximations. With the facility afforded by the recursive formulae, *it is not true that non-linear m-step prediction is impossible to compute,* at least as far as NLAR models are concerned.

It may be noted that by allowing m to tend to infinity, the solution (if it exists) for K_∞ in eqn (6.5) will provide information about the effect of the remote past upon prediction of the future.

It is clear that $K_\infty(x) \equiv$ constant is one solution of (6.5) for the case $m = \infty$. In fact, this is the only solution within our context, which can be shown by appealing to results in the martingale theory (see Exercise 1). Thus, in our case, the remote past plays no material role in prediction.

6.2.2 NON-MONOTONICITY OF CONDITIONAL VARIANCE

In linear least-squares prediction theory of stationary time series, it is well known that $\hat{\sigma}(1) \leq \hat{\sigma}(2) \leq \ldots$. To investigate the influence of the *skeleton* on the multi-step prediction of (6.2), we conduct two experiments.

On using the recursive formulae (6.5) and the technique described in §4.2.4.3, Table 6.1 gives the results of the two experiments. In Experiment I, $x_0 = 4.0435$ and

$$h(x) = \begin{cases} 1.5 - 0.9x & \text{if } x \leq 0 \\ -0.4 - 0.6x & \text{if } x > 0 \end{cases} \tag{6.6}$$

and in Experiment II, $x_0 = 5.0$ and

$$h(x) = \begin{cases} 1.5 - 0.7x & \text{if } x \leq 0 \\ 1.0 + 0.8x & \text{if } x > 0. \end{cases} \tag{6.7}$$

In each experiment, $\varepsilon_t \sim \mathcal{N}(0, \sigma^2)$.

Several comments are in order:

1. Let $h^m(x)$ denote $h(h(\ldots (h(x))\ldots))$, the m-fold application of h. With increasing signal-to-noise ratio, the difference between $\hat{X}_0(m)$ and $h^m(x_0)$ increases.

2. For model (6.7), which admits only a limit point (i.e. $h^m(x) \to 5.0$ as $m \to \infty$, $\forall x$), $\hat{\sigma}(m)$ is a monotonic increasing function of m for all the three choices of σ. The limit is clearly var X_t.

3. In contrast, for model (6.6), which admits a limit cycle of period 2 at $C = \{-2.8261, 4.0435\}$ (i.e. $H^m(x) \to C$ as $m \to \infty$, $\forall x$), we observe that for $\sigma = 0.4$ and 1.0, $\hat{\sigma}(1) < \hat{\sigma}(3) < \hat{\sigma}(5) < \ldots < $ var X_t and $\hat{\sigma}(2) < \hat{\sigma}(4) < \hat{\sigma}(6) < \ldots < $ var X_t. However, $\hat{\sigma}(2m) \not< \hat{\sigma}(2m + 1)$, $m = 1, 2, \ldots$. It is clear that it would be interesting and important to establish the precise role of limit cycles in m-step prediction. We leave this challenging problem to future research.

Table 6.1. Conditional means and conditional variance of two threshold autoregressive models

	$\sigma = 0.4$		$\sigma = 1.0$		$\sigma = 2.0$	
m	$\hat{X}_0(m)$	$\hat{\sigma}(m)$	$\hat{X}_0(m)$	$\hat{\sigma}(m)$	$\hat{X}_0(m)$	$\hat{\sigma}(m)$
Experiment I						
1	-2.8261	0.4000	-2.8261	1.0000	-2.8261	2.0000
2	4.0435	0.5381	4.0392	1.3571	3.9151	2.8762
3	-2.8261	0.5141	-2.8177	1.3076	-2.5339	2.9890
4	4.0435	0.6116	4.0092	1.6107	3.5602	3.6110
5	-2.8261	0.5428	-2.7736	1.4859	-2.1061	3.5869
6	4.0435	0.6314	3.9524	1.7772	3.1537	4.0278
7	-2.8261	0.5509	-2.7073	1.6497	-1.6943	3.9603
8	4.0435	0.6371	3.8805	1.9228	2.7753	4.2814
9	-2.8261	0.5533	-2.6309	1.8038	-1.3321	4.2007
10	4.0435	0.6387	3.8022	2.0557	2.4444	4.4415
11	-2.8261	0.5540	-2.5508	1.9454	-1.0225	4.3601
12	4.0435	0.6392	3.7217	2.1769	-2.1615	4.5453
13	-2.8261	0.5542	-2.4701	2.0741	-0.7604	4.4685
14	4.0435	0.6393	3.6414	2.2871	1.9217	4.6137
15	-2.8261	0.5542	-2.3902	2.1905	-0.5394	4.5438
Experiment II						
1	5.0000	0.4000	5.0000	1.0000	5.0000	2.0000
2	5.0000	0.5123	5.0000	1.2806	5.0091	2.5477
3	5.0000	0.5727	5.0000	1.4315	5.0524	2.7939
4	5.0000	0.6082	5.0003	1.5198	5.0159	2.9150
5	5.0000	0.6299	5.0007	1.5731	5.1551	2.9802
6	5.0000	0.6433	5.0012	1.6058	5.1966	3.0177
7	5.0000	0.6518	5.0018	1.6260	5.2300	3.0401
8	5.0000	0.6572	5.0024	1.6387	5.2565	3.0542
9	5.0000	0.6606	5.0029	1.6466	5.2772	3.0633
10	5.0000	0.6628	5.0033	1.6515	5.2934	3.0693
11	5.0000	0.6642	5.0037	1.6546	5.3058	3.0734
12	5.0000	0.6651	5.0040	1.6566	5.3154	3.0763
13	5.0000	0.6657	5.0042	1.6578	5.3228	3.0784
14	5.0000	0.6660	5.0044	1.6586	5.3285	3.0799
15	5.0000	0.6663	5.0046	1.6591	5.3329	3.0810

Note: $\hat{\sigma}(m) = (\mathrm{var}(X_m \mid x_0))^{1/2}$.

4. We can give a heuristic explanation of points (2) and (3). If h has a limit cycle of period r say, that is

$$h^m(x) \to \{c_1, c_2, \ldots, c_r\} \quad \text{as} \quad m \to \infty$$

where $h : c_i \to c_{i+1}$, $i = 1, 2, \ldots, r-1$, $h : c_r \to c_1$, then the stationary marginal density is of the form

$$\{g_1(x - c_1) + g_2(x - c_2) + \ldots + g_r(x - c_r)\}/r$$

where g_i is a density function with var σ_i^2, tending to a δ function as the noise variance tends to zero. Therefore, unless the σ_i are all equal (which is the exception rather than the rule—see Exercise 2), *monotonicity of $\hat{\sigma}(m)$ in m will not be obtained*.

5. Pemberton (1989) has reinforced the so far implicit observation of the dependence of prediction performance on x_0.

6.2.3 'PREDICTIVE' DISTRIBUTIONS

Least-squares prediction can sometimes produce misleading results. We demonstrate this point now.

Example 6.1: Consider a simple first-order EXPAR model

$$X_t = -0.9X_{t-1} - 0.95X_{t-1} \exp(-X_{t-1}^2) + \varepsilon_t \tag{6.8}$$

where $\{\varepsilon_t\}$ is a sequence of i.i.d. random variables with the distribution $\mathcal{N}(0, 0.36)$. Note that the skeleton has a limit cycle $(-1.500\,43, +1.500\,43)$. Let the present observation be zero. It is self-evident from the conditional densities of X_m given $X_0 = 0$ shown in Fig. 6.1 that the m-step least squares predictions (all equal to zero) are increasingly misleading with increasing m.

The numerical method described in §4.2.4.3 has been used here.

In any practical situation, we recommend the examination of the 'predictive' (i.e. the conditional) distributions whenever possible. For high-order models, the possibility may be somewhat hampered by computational time at present.

6.2.4 BIAS CORRECTION

Sometimes the data (X) may be instantaneously transformed to (Y) via a smooth 1–1 map, say f.

Let g denote the smooth inverse map. Suppose that a model is fitted to the transformed series (Y) and we wish to forecast the original series (X). Let $\mathbb{B}_t^{(X)}$ denote the σ-algebra generated by $\{X_s, s \le t\}$. $\mathbb{B}_t^{(Y)}$ may be

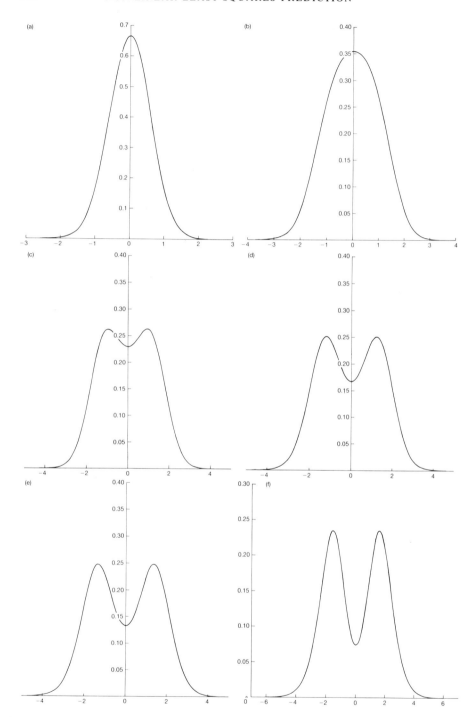

Fig. 6.1. Conditional density of X_1 given $X_0 = 0$; (b) conditional density of X_2 given $X_0 = 0$; (c) conditional density of X_3 given $X_0 = 0$; (d) conditional density of X_4 given $X_0 = 0$; (e) conditional density of X_5 given $X_0 = 0$; (f) marginal density of X_0.

defined in a similar way. Now

$$
\begin{aligned}
E[X_{t+m} \mid \mathbb{B}_t^{(X)}] &= E[g(Y_{t+m}) \mid \mathbb{B}_t^{(Y)}] \\
&\doteq g(\hat{Y}_t(m)) + E[(Y_{t+m} - \hat{Y}_t(m))g'(\hat{Y}_t(m)) \mid \mathbb{B}_t^{(Y)}] \\
&\quad + \tfrac{1}{2}E[(Y_{t+m} - \hat{Y}_t(m))^2 g''(\hat{Y}_t(m)) \mid \mathbb{B}_t^{(Y)}] \\
&= g(\hat{Y}_t(m)) + \tfrac{1}{2}g''(\hat{Y}_t(m)) \, \mathrm{var}[Y_{t+m} \mid \mathbb{B}_t^{(Y)}]. \qquad (6.9)
\end{aligned}
$$

In other words, we only need to adjust the naive forecast $g(\hat{Y}_t(m))$ by the correction term specified above. Note that the conditional variance of Y is involved in the correction term. A similar argument yields

$$
\mathrm{var}[X_{t+m} \mid \mathbb{B}_t^{(X)}] \doteq [g'(\hat{Y}_t(m))]^2 \, \mathrm{var}[Y_{t+m} \mid \mathbb{B}_t^{(Y)}]. \qquad (6.10)
$$

The correction formulae (6.9) and (6.10) are not restricted to the non-linear autoregressive models and may be of use in other cases too.

6.3 Non-linear moving-average models

The prediction problem of non-linear moving-average models does not seem to have attracted much attention in the literature. The problem is quite difficult because first we have to tackle the non-trivial question of invertibility. As in the case of the bilinear models in Chapter 4, it is often difficult to verify sufficient conditions even if they are available in the literature. Secondly, we have seen in Chapter 1, for the case of *linear* moving-average models with non-Gaussian white noise, that the evaluation of just $E[X_{t+1} \mid X_t]$ is already quite tedious. We can envisage that the evaluation of $E[X_{t+m} \mid \mathbb{B}_t]$, $m > 1$, $\mathbb{B}_t$ being the σ-algebra generated by X_s, $s \leq t$, will be much more horrendous. We do not pursue this area further but refer the interested readers to Shepp *et al.* (1980).

6.4 Bilinear models

The evaluation of the relevant conditional expectations (assume to exist) are quite straightforward. We only need to observe the following simple facts concerning $\varepsilon_t X_s$. (We follow the notation of Chapter 3 and let $\mathbb{B}_t$ denote the σ-algebra generated by X_s, $s \leq t$.)

1. *For $t > s$*:

$$
E[\varepsilon_t X_s \mid \mathbb{B}_0] = 0 \quad \text{for} \quad t > 0
$$

because ε_t and X_s are independent.

$$
E[\varepsilon_t X_s \mid \mathbb{B}_0] = \varepsilon_t X_s \quad \text{for} \quad t \leq 0
$$

by invertibility (which is assumed).

2. *For $t = s$*:

$$E[\varepsilon_t X_t \mid \mathbb{B}_0] = \text{var } \varepsilon_t \ (= \sigma^2 \text{ say}) \quad \text{for} \quad t > 0$$

because $X_t = \varepsilon_t + f(\varepsilon_{t-1}, \varepsilon_{t-2}, \ldots)$ by stationarity.

$$E[\varepsilon_t X_t \mid \mathbb{B}_0] = \varepsilon_t X_t \quad \text{for} \quad t \leq 0$$

by invertibility (which is assumed).

3. *For $t < s$*: We use the bilinear model to express X_s in terms of $X_{s-1}, X_{s-2}, \ldots$ and $\varepsilon_t, \varepsilon_{t-1}, \ldots$. We may repeat this process until the subscripts of the X terms are $\leq t$ and then appeal to (1) and (2), the independence of the ε terms, and the marginal distribution of ε_0. We may also recall the elementary fact that for Borel functions g and h,

$$E[(g(\varepsilon_0, \varepsilon_{-1}, \ldots, \varepsilon_{-k})h(\varepsilon_1, \varepsilon_2, \ldots, \varepsilon_l) \mid \mathbb{B}_0]$$
$$= g(\varepsilon_0, \varepsilon_{-1}, \ldots, \varepsilon_{-k})E[h(\varepsilon_1, \varepsilon_2, \ldots, \varepsilon_l) \mid \mathbb{B}_0].$$

Example 6.2: Consider the bilinear model

$$X_t = aX_{t-1} + b\varepsilon_{t-2}X_{t-1} + \varepsilon_t \tag{6.11}$$

where the model is assumed stationary and invertible and $\varepsilon_t \sim \text{IID}(0, \sigma^2)$. Now, we may obtain the following recursive formulae:

$$E[X_1 \mid \mathbb{B}_0] = aX_0 + b\varepsilon_{-1}X_0 \tag{6.12}$$
$$E[X_2 \mid \mathbb{B}_0] = aE[X_1 \mid \mathbb{B}_0] + b\varepsilon_0 E[X_1 \mid \mathbb{B}_0] \text{ using 3 above} \tag{6.13}$$
$$E[X_3 \mid \mathbb{B}_0] = aE[X_2 \mid \mathbb{B}_0] + bE[\varepsilon_1 X_2 \mid \mathbb{B}_0] \tag{6.14}$$

where using (6.11) we have

$$E[\varepsilon_1 X_2 \mid \mathbb{B}_0] = E[\varepsilon_1(aX_1 + b\varepsilon_0 X_1 + \varepsilon_2) \mid \mathbb{B}_0]$$
$$= a\sigma^2 + b\varepsilon_0\sigma^2, \text{ using 2 above} \tag{6.15}$$
$$E[X_4 \mid \mathbb{B}_0] = aE[X_3 \mid \mathbb{B}_0] + bE[\varepsilon_2 X_3 \mid \mathbb{B}_0]$$

where $E[X_3 \mid \mathbb{B}_0]$ is given by (6.14) and, using (6.11), we have

$$E[\varepsilon_2 X_3 \mid \mathbb{B}_0] = E[\varepsilon_2(aX_2 + b\varepsilon_1 X_2 + \varepsilon_3) \mid \mathbb{B}_0]$$
$$= a\sigma^2 + bE[\varepsilon_2\varepsilon_1(aX_1 + b\varepsilon_0 X_1 + \varepsilon_2) \mid \mathbb{B}_0], \text{ using 2 above}$$
$$= a\sigma^2, \text{ using 1 and 3 above.} \tag{6.16}$$

Higher-step predictions may be obtained similarly. $\square$

We re-emphasize that *the assumption of invertibility is crucial for the prediction of bilinear models*. This may pose a practical difficulty in using bilinear models for prediction because, as mentioned previously, there is no simple way of verifying invertibility of bilinear models. We return to this point in Chapter 7.

6.5 Random coefficient autoregressive models

The least-squares prediction of these models can be easily dealt with because the 'autoregressive' coefficients $\beta_i + B_i(t)$ are independent of the driving white noise $\{\varepsilon_t\}$. This independence immediately shows that $E[X_t \mid \mathbb{B}_0]$ is linear in X_s, $s \leq 0$, that is the least-squares predictors of RCA models are *linear* predictors.

6.6 Non-Gaussian state space model approach

Consider the state space model

$$x_n = Fx_{n-1} + Gv_n \qquad y_n = Hx_n + w_n \qquad (6.17)$$

where F, G, and H are linear transformations $\mathbf{R} \to \mathbf{R}$, and v_n and w_n are independent sequences of i.i.d. random variables with probability density function $q(v)$ and $r(w)$, respectively. They need not be Gaussian. The variables x and y are usually called the *state* and the *observation* respectively. The initial state x_0 is distributed on $\mathbf{R}$ with density $p(x_0)$. Let $p(x_n \mid Y_m)$ denote typically the conditional density of the state x_n given the observations $(y_1, \ldots, y_m) = Y_m$. Kitagawa (1987) has developed a method for obtaining recursively the *one-step-ahead prediction*, $p(x_n \mid Y_{n-1})$, the *filtering*, $p(x_n \mid Y_n)$, and the *smoothing*, $p(x_n \mid Y_N)$, where Y_N denotes the entire observation sequence. His method is based on the following fundamental equations, which generalize the well-known Kalman filter and fixed-interval smoothing and in which all integrals are over $(-\infty, \infty)$:

$$p(x_n \mid Y_{n-1}) = \int p(x_n, x_{n-1} \mid Y_{n-1}) \, \mathrm{d}x_{n-1}$$

$$= \int p(x_n \mid x_{n-1}) p(x_{n-1} \mid Y_{n-1}) \, \mathrm{d}x_{n-1} \qquad (6.18)$$

where we have used $p(x_n \mid x_{n-1}) = p(x_n \mid x_{n-1}, Y_{n-1})$;

$$\begin{aligned}
p(x_n \mid Y_n) &= p(x_n \mid y_n, Y_{n-1}) \\
&= p(x_n, y_n \mid Y_{n-1}) / p(y_n \mid Y_{n-1}) \\
&= p(y_n \mid x_n) p(x_n \mid Y_{n-1}) / p(y_n \mid Y_{n-1}) \qquad (6.19)
\end{aligned}$$

where $p(y_n \mid Y_{n-1})$ is obtained by $\int p(y_n \mid x_n) p(x_n \mid Y_{n-1}) \, \mathrm{d}x_n$ and we have used $p(y_n \mid x_n) = p(y_n \mid x_n, Y_{n-1})$; and

$$p(x_n \mid Y_N) = \int p(x_n, x_{n+1}) \mid Y_N) \, \mathrm{d}x_{n+1}$$

$$= p(x_n \mid Y_n) \int p(x_{n+1} \mid Y_N) p(x_{n+1} \mid x_n) / p(x_{n+1} \mid Y_n) \, \mathrm{d}x_{n+1}. \qquad (6.20)$$

(Verify these equations as an exercise.)

To implement the above algorithms, Kitagawa (1987) proposed a numerical technique based on approximating each density by a piecewise linear (i.e. first-order spline) function. Each density is specified by the number of segments, location of nodes (cf threshold), and the value at each node. The density is assumed to be negligible outside the two outermost nodes. Kitagawa (1987) has also suggested that the technique can be extended to the more general case where $F: \mathbf{R}^k \to \mathbf{R}^k$, $G: \mathbf{R}^l \to \mathbf{R}^k$, and $H: \mathbf{R}^k \to \mathbf{R}$ and even to the non-linear cases

$$x_n \sim q(. \,|\, x_{n-1}) \qquad y_n \sim r(. \,|\, x_n) \tag{6.21}$$

where q and r are conditional distributions of x_n given x_{n-1} and of y_n given x_n respectively. The initial state x_0 is distributed as $p(x_0 \,|\, Y_0)$.

6.7 Concluding remarks

An alternative method of obtaining non-linear least-squares prediction is to obtain the conditional expectations directly from the data without stipulating any model. For example, we may employ the 'non-parametric' techniques described in §5.2.4 subject to any necessary extension to include higher-dimensional lagged regressions. Priestley (1980) has suggested that the algorithms proposed for the SDM may be used for this purpose too. Another recent development is the use of noise-free chaotic models for short-to medium-term prediction. (See e.g. Farmer and Sidorowich 1988.)

Bibliographical Notes

Section 6.2.1 summarizes Al-Qassem and Lane (1987), Moeanaddin (1989), Pemberton (1987), and Tong and Moeanaddin (1988). Sections 6.2.2 and 6.2.4 are based on Tong and Moeanaddin (1988) and a private communication from Dr R. Gerrard (1987). Section 6.4 streamlines the discussion of Subba Rao and Gabr (1984). Section 6.6 is based on Kitagawa (1987).

Exercises and complements

(1) Consider the situation leading to eqn (6.5). Suppose that there exists a probability density ψ and a Baire function ϕ on $\mathbf{R}$ s.t.

$$\int |K_m(x) - \phi(x)| \, \psi(x) \, dx \to 0 \quad \text{as} \quad m \to \infty.$$

Show that $\{\phi(X_t)\}$ is a martingale and uniformly integrable. Hence deduce that

$$E_\psi |\phi(X_{t+1}) - \phi(X_t)| \to 0 \quad \text{as} \quad t \to \infty$$

and that $\phi(x) \equiv$ constant for almost all x w.r.t. ψ.

(Private communication from R. Gerrard (1987))

(2) In the set-up of §6.2.2(4) suppose that $\sigma^2 \ll \min_{i,j} |c_i - c_j|^2$ and $a_s = h'(c_s)$, let $\sigma_s^2 = \text{var}(X_s)$ conditional on X_s being near c_s. Verify that

$$\sigma_{s+1}^2 \approx \sigma^2 + a_s^2\sigma_s^2.$$

Suppose that $A = \prod_{i=1}^r a_i^2 < 1$ and that $\sigma_{r+1}^2 = \sigma_1^2$. Verify that

$$\sigma_s^2 = (1 - A)^{-1}\sigma^2\{1 + a_{s-1}^2 + a_{s-1}^2 a_{s-2}^2 + \ldots + a_{s-1}^2 a_{s-2}^2 \ldots a_1^2$$
$$+ a_{s-1}^2 a_{a-2}^2 \ldots a_1^2 a_r^2 + \ldots + a_{s-1}^2 a_{s-2}^2 \ldots a_1^2 a_r^2 a_{r-1}^2 \ldots a_{s+1}^2\}.$$

(Private communication from R. Gerrard (1987))

(3) Consider the Markovian bilinear model

$$X_t = \varepsilon_t + \alpha\varepsilon_{t-1}X_{t-2}, \quad t = 0, \pm 1, \ldots$$

where $\varepsilon_t \sim \text{IID}(0, \sigma^2)$ and $\alpha^2\sigma^2 < \frac{1}{2}$. Verify that $\hat{\sigma}(m)$, $m = 1, 2, \ldots$, need not be a monotonic non-decreasing sequence.

(Tong and Moeanaddin 1988)

(4) Consider a *zero-delay* SETAR model

$$X_t = \varepsilon_t + aX_{t-1}I(X_t \leq r) + bX_{t-1}I(X_t > r)$$

where $\varepsilon_t \sim \text{IID}(0, \sigma^2)$. Verify that if $E|X_t| < \infty$, all t, then $E[X_t \mid X_{t-1} = x] = aX_{t-1}P[X_t \leq r \mid X_{t-1} = x] + bX_{t-1}P[X_t > r \mid X_{t-1} = x]$. Compare this with 'multi-process' approach of Harrison and Stevens (1976).

(5) Consider a SETAR $(k; p, p, \ldots, p)$ model

$$X_t = \sum_{j=1}^p [L^{(j)}(1, X_{t-1}, \ldots, X_{t-p}) + \sigma^{(j)}\varepsilon_t]I_{(r_{j-1}, r_j]}(X_{t-d})$$

where I is the indicator function, $\mathbf{R} = \bigcup_{j=1}^p (r_{j-1}, r_j]$, $r_0 = -\infty$, $r_p = \infty$, $\varepsilon_t \sim \text{IID}(0, 1)$ and independent of X_s $(s < t)$, and $\sigma_{(j)} > 0$ all j:

$$L_{(j)}(1, X_{t-1}, \ldots, X_{t-p}) = a_0^{(j)} + \sum_{i=1}^p a_i^{(j)}X_{t-i}.$$

We assume that $p \geq d$. At time t, let the observed values of X_s be x_s for $s \leq t$. These then determine $I_{(r_{j-1}, r_j]}(x_s)$ completely for $s \leq t$. For $m = 1, 2, \ldots, d$, let $x_{t+m-d} \in (r_{j_m-1}, r_{j_m}]$, so that

$$X_{t+m} = L^{(j_m)}(1, X_{t+m-1}, \ldots, X_{t+m-p}) + \sigma^{(j_m)}\varepsilon_{t+m}$$

where by convention X_s is replaced by x_s for $s \leq t$. Let $\mathbb{B}_t$ denote the σ-algebra generated by X_s, $s \leq t$. Let $\hat{X}_t(m) = E[X_{t+m} \mid \mathbb{B}_t]$. Prove that for $m = 1, 2, \ldots, d$,

$$\hat{X}_t(m) = L^{(j_m)}(1, \hat{X}_t(m-1), \ldots, \hat{X}_t(m-p)).$$

(Tong 1983a)

(6) Under the set-up of Exercise (5), verify that for $m = 1, 2, \ldots, d$

$$\mathrm{var}(X_{t+m} \mid \mathbb{B}_t) = \sum_{i=1}^{m} (\alpha_m^{(i)} \sigma^{(j_i)})^2$$

where

$$\alpha_1^{(1)} = 1 \text{ and, for } m \geq 2, \qquad \alpha_m^{(m)} = 1$$
$$\alpha_m^{(m-1)} = \alpha_{m-1}^{(m-1)} a_1^{(j_m)}$$
$$\alpha_m^{(m-2)} = \alpha_{m-1}^{(m-2)} a_1^{(j_m)} + \alpha_{m-2}^{(m-2)} a_2^{(j_m)}$$
$$\vdots$$
$$\alpha_m^{(1)} = \alpha_{m-1}^{(1)} a_1^{(j_m)} + \alpha_{m-2}^{(1)} a_2^{(j_m)} + \ldots + \alpha_1^{(1)} a_{m-1}^{(j_m)}.$$

(Private communication from R. Moeanaddin (1989) and

J. Pemberton (1989)

7
Case studies

知 止 不 殆 *Know when to stop*
And you will meet with no danger.

Ch. XLIV Lao Tzu

7.1 Introduction

Although systematic studies of non-linear time series modelling are fairly recent activities, non-linearity has been recognized for quite a considerable time. In the past, a popular approach was first to pass the data through a simple non-linear filter (e.g. a *limiter*; cf. the hard censoring device of §3.3.2) and then the filtered data could be modelled by a linear model. This is somewhat similar in spirit to the pre-whitening approach advocated by Tukey in the 1950s in spectral analysis (see e.g. Priestley 1981, p. 556). An early example of successful application of this prefiltering approach to non-linear time series modelling was in control engineering (see e.g. Otomo *et al.* 1972).

More recently, we have been witnessing almost exponential growth in the applications of non-linear time series models, ranging from solar science to earth sciences, from bioscience to economics and finance, etc. It can safely be predicted that this growth will continue for a considerable time to come.

In Table 7.1 below is a list of some recent real applications. No pretence to completeness is intended. Naturally, some of these applications are more successful than others. In all cases, the experiences reported are very valuable.

It is clear from the table that the classic Canadian lynx data and the ongoing Wolf's sunspot numbers have attracted the most attention among non-linear time series analysts. It is perhaps no exaggeration to say that they have attained the status of 'benchmark data sets', which every non-linear time series analyst must 'dissect' at least once in his career.

7.2 The Canadian lynx data (1821–1934)

We start with some background history.

Table 7.1. A list of examples of real applications

Data set	Subject classification	Model type	Key reference
Canadian lynx	Ecology/ population	Threshold	Tong and Lim (1980) Ozaki (1981) Tong (1983a) Pemberton (1985) Wang et al. (1984)
		EXPAR	Haggan and Ozaki (1982) Ozaki (1982) Pemberton (1985)
		Bilinear	Subba Rao and Gabr (1984)
		SDM	Haggan et al. (1984)
		RCA	Nicholls and Quinn (1982)
Wolf's sunspot numbers	Solar physics	Threshold	Tong and Lim (1980) Tong (1983a) Pemberton (1985)
		Bilinear	Granger and Andersen (1978) Subba Rao and Gabr (1984)
		EXPAR	Haggan and Ozaki (1981) Pemberton (1985)
		SDM	Cartwright (1985) Haggan et al. (1984)
Nicholson's blow-fly data	Entomology/ population dynamics	Threshold	Tong (1983a) Tsay (1988) Chan et al. (1988)
Unemployment figures in West Germany	Economics	Bilinear	Subba Rao and Gabr (1984)
IBM daily common stock closing prices	Finance	Bilinear	Granger and Andersen (1978)
		Threshold	Hamilton (1989)
		SDM	Cartwright (1985)
		Threshold	Tyssedal and Tjøstheim (1988)
		Threshold	Chapter 5 of this book
BIH annual report for 1979	Earth rotation/ geodynamics	Threshold	Zheng and Chen (1982)
67 real data sets	Finance, etc.	Threshold	Petruccelli and Davies (1986b)

Table 7.1. continued

Data set	Subject classification	Model type	Key reference
OECD Data	Economics	Bilinear/ EXPAR	Chapter 5 of this book
Hang Seng index	Finance	Threshold	Chapter 5 of this book
Respiration data	Medical	Threshold	Chapter 5 of this book
Lupus erythematosis	Medical	Threshold	Chapter 5 of this book
Hong Kong beach data	Pollution	Threshold	Chapter 5 of this book
Neuron firing data	Neural science	Threshold	Brillinger and Segundo (1979)
Human pupillary system	Bioscience	Non-linear moving average	Hung et al.(1979)
Earth's magnetic reversal data	Geophysics	Bilinear	Subba Rao (1988)
SO$_2$ data	Pollution	Threshold	Mélard and Roy (1988)
Various real data sets in China	Earthquake prediction/ railway passenger flow rate/ meteorology, etc.	Threshold	Abstracts of 1st Natl Conf. on Time Series Analysis, 1984, Beijing, China
Canadian mink and Muskrat data	Population dynamics	Threshold	Tong (1983a)
Kanna rainfall river flow data	Hydrology	Threshold	Tong and Lim (1980)
		Polynomial	Ozaki (1985b)
Icelandic river flow data	Hydrology	Threshold	Tong et al. (1985)
Spanish economic data	Economics	Bilinear	Maravall (1983)
Market portfolio	Finance	Threshold	Wecker (1981)
Industrial prices	Finance	Threshold	Wecker (1981)
Wind velocity	Geophysics	NEAR	Lawrance and Lewis (1985)
Urinary introgen excretion	Medical	RCA	Robinson (1978)
Exchange rate	Finance	ARCH	Engle and Bollerslev (1986)
Cement production	Automatic control	Threshold	Otomo et al. (1972)
Earthquake magnitude data in China	Geophysics	Threshold	Li and Liu (1985)

7.2.1 A BRIEF HISTORICAL BACKGROUND

The classic Canadian lynx data set consists of the annual record of the numbers of the Canadian lynx trapped in the Mackenzie River district of North-west Canada for the period 1821–1934 inclusively, as listed by Elton and Nicholson in 1942. From the information given in their paper, it is clear that there was a time lag between the year in which a lynx was trapped and the year in which its fur was sold at auction in London by the Hudson Bay Company, whose record forms the basis of the data. The time lag was not constant but depended on the month in which the animal was trapped and the date of the shipment, etc. To complicate matters further, several other factors should be borne in mind too.

1. There was apparently a change in the sale arrangements in about 1915.

2. The catchment area of the animal did not remain constant throughout the period 1821–1934.

3. The post-1915 data seem to be 'cleaner' than the pre-1915 data.

4. The Elton–Nicholson data set seemed to be based on three different sources: the London archives of the Hudson Bay Company (1821–91 and 1897–1913), The Company's Fur Trade Department in Winnipeg (1915–34), Mr Charles French, then Fur Trade Commissioner of the Company in Canada (1892–6 and 1914).

It is clear that we are dealing with a fairly noisy set of field data. A scientific value of the data set seems to lie in its apparent population cycles, the underlying assumption being that the trapping records are proportionate estimates of the total population. As Williamson (1972) has commented, the clearly cyclical variation is unusual, but not confined to the lynx. He has mentioned other examples (Williamson 1972, p.7) such as the clear cycle in the numbers of ptarmigan and in the larch bud moth. The large number of research papers written on the Canadian lynx data set probably justifies the many grants received by Elton and others for putting the data in a form reasonably fit for scientific examination!

A plot of the data on a log scale was given in Fig. 1.4 of this book.

7.2.2 PRELIMINARY STUDY

The first time series model built for the above data set was probably that by Moran (1953). Specifically, we follow Moran and let X_t denote $\log_{10}$(number recorded as trapped in year $1820 + t$) ($t = 1, 2, \ldots, 114$).

Moran argued in favour of the log transformation. We may summarize his reasons as follows.

1. It is observed that the cycle is very asymmetrical with a sharp and large peak and a relatively smooth and small trough. The log transform will, *to the eye at least* (quoting him verbatim), give a series which appears to vary symmetrically about the mean.

2. As the population of lynx is not exactly proportional to the number caught, a better representation would perhaps be obtained by incorporating an additional 'error of observation' in the model, thereby resulting in a more complicated model. The log transformation will substantially reduce the effect of ignoring this error of observation.

If what he had in mind in (1) was time reversibility, then clearly it was not strictly valid because, as we have seen in §4.4, no instantaneous transformation can render a time-irreversible time series time reversible. On the other hand, the second point seems plausible. Indeed, the use of the log transformation in modelling the lynx data has been widespread among biologists and statisicans, and we shall follow suit as our primary interest is not so much the absolute population fluctuation but the relative (percentage) population fluctuation (cf. Williamson 1972, p. 4).

Moran's model was an AR(2) model:

$$X_t - 1.05 + 1.41X_{t-1} - 0.77X_{t-2} + \varepsilon_t \qquad (7.1)$$

where $\varepsilon_t \sim \text{IID}(0, 0.045\,91)$. The fit was later judged to be inadequate by Bartlett (1954), Hannan (1960) (who also gave the standard errors of the 'slope parameters' at 0.26), Campbell and Walker (1977), and Tong (1977*b*), etc. It should also be mentioned that Moran (1953, p. 171) conducted a very interesting and ingenious analysis of the fitted residuals. He drew attention to what he called a 'curious feature' in that half of the residuals correspond to values of X_t greater than the mean and the other half to values of X_t smaller than the mean. However, the sum of squares of the former is equal to 1.781 whilst that of the latter is equal to 4.007, giving a ratio of 2.250, which would be judged significant at the 1% level if the two sets could be regarded as random samples from the same normal population. It would therefore seem plausible that he had a premonition of the limitation of linearity.

Of course, the data plot as shown in Fig. 1.4, together with the associated reverse data plot as shown in Fig. 5.1 and the nonparametric regression of X_t on X_{t-3} shown in Fig. 1.6, should alert us against the uncritical acceptance of linearity.

In the next subsection we shall run through some of the initial data analysis as described in §5.2.

7.2.3   EXPLORATORY DATA ANALYSIS

1.   From the time plot of the data (Fig. 1.4) and Table 7.2 we can see that the ascent periods tend to exceed the descent periods by approximately 50%

2.   The marginal histogram of the data shows obvious bimodality with the anti-mode at approximately 3 (Fig. 7.1), which is close to the turning point of Fig. 1.6.

A bootstrap test (Tong 1988) based on Silverman's method (1981) for multimodality rejects unimodality at the nominal 5% significance level (see Table 7.3). Briefly, the method is based on the fact that the number of modes is a decreasing function of the window width, h, of a *Gaussian* kernel used to smooth the raw density function consisting of spikes of height n^{-1} at each of the sample points, $x_1, \ldots, x_n$. We start with a very large h so that the window estimate, $\hat{f}_h$, of the density is unimodal. Let h_{crit} be such that for all $h \geq h_{crit}$, $\hat{f}_h$ is unimodal, while for all $h < h_{crit}$, $\hat{f}_h$ will be multimodal. Therefore, we may use h_{crit} as a test statistic for bimodality. Large values of h_{crit} tend to reject unimodality. A similar argument may be developed for testing for bimodality, trimodality, etc.

It is plausible that the modes and the anti-mode might correspond to stable equilibria and unstable equilibrium respectively of an underlying dynamical system, rather than static mixture densities.

The bivariate histograms (Fig. 7.2) show interesting 'crater-like' structure. Readers might find it helpful to join the vertical diagonals on the base planes in the figures marked (ii).

3.   The directed scatter diagrams (Fig. 7.3) exhibit a systematic change of orientation from Figs. 7.3(a) to 7.3(f), with the earlier figures being more clearly indicative of an underlying periodic skeleton (sketched by the numbers $2, 3, 4, \ldots, 10$.) The void in the centre of (a)

Table 7.2. Ascent and descent periods of log lynx data

Ascent	7	6	6	5	5	6	6	6	6(5–8)		6	≥5
Descent	4	4	4	4	3	4	4	3		4(6–3)	4	

Table 7.3. *P* values of bootstrap test for multimodality

No. of modes	1	2	3	4
P values	0.03	0.45	0.72	0.67

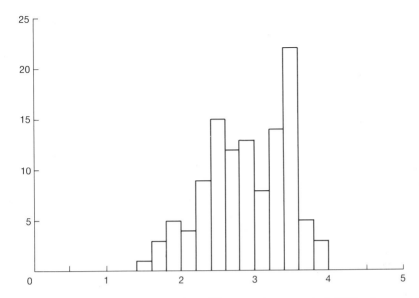

Fig. 7.1. Histogram of log lynx data. The sample mean is 2.9036, the sample variance is 0.3090, the sample coefficient of skewness is −0.36, and the sample kurtosis is 2.27

and (b) reinforces the observation of non-normality of the data. In population biology, the undirected scatter diagrams (and their variants) have been in use for quite a considerable time and are called the *Moran diagrams* or the *reproductive curves* (see e.g. Williamson 1972).

4. The non-parametric lag regression estimates $\hat{m}_j(x)$, $j = -1, \ldots, -10$ (Fig. 7.4), show a gradual shift from a linear function through a single hump curve back to a linear function, with the single hump at approximately 3 (i.e. near the sample mean of 2.90). The single hump is first visible when $j = -2$ and most transparent when $j = -3$. If a SETAR model is entertained, these observations tentatively suggest *two* regimes with a tentative estimate of the threshold parameter at 3 and the delay parameter at 2 or 3.

Non-parametric lag regression estimates $\hat{m}_j(x)$, $j = 1, 2, \ldots, 10$, are also included in Fig. 7.4. Generally speaking, $\hat{m}_{-j}(x)$ and $\hat{m}_{+j}(x)$ look quite different, again suggesting time irreversibility.

Non-parametric estimates of $\text{var}(X_t \mid X_{t-j})$, $j = 1, 2, \ldots, 10$, are given in Fig. 7.5. They show essentially a one-hump curve with the turning point at approximately 3.

5. Table 7.4 merely reflects that the data are cyclical but suggests that the damping is quite weak. This can be best seen by the sharp peak at the

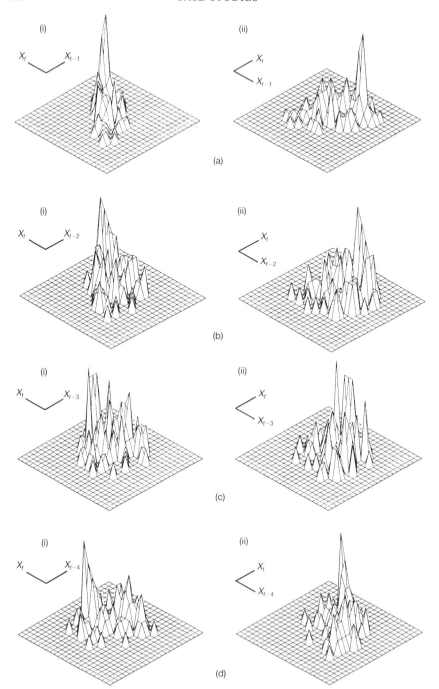

Fig. 7.2. Bivariate histograms of log lynx data (1821–1934)

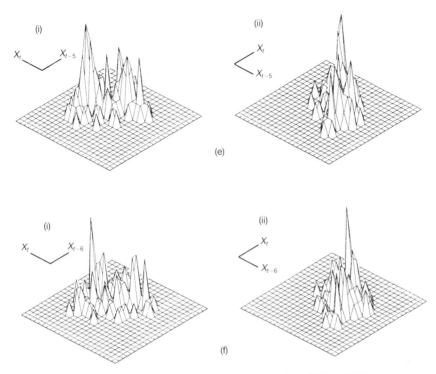

Fig. 7.2. Bivariate histograms of log lynx data (1821–1934)

approximate frequency of 1 cycle/9.5 years in the spectral density estimate of Fig. 7.6. Of particular note are the peaks at higher harmonics to the above fundamental peak. Formal tests confirm the existence of at least the peak at the approximate frequency of 2 cycles/9.5 years besides the fundamental.

As we have seen in Chapter 2, the existence of higher harmonics is also indicative of non-linearity.

A bispectral density function estimate, $\hat{f}(\omega_1, \omega_2)$, of the log lynx data was shown in Figs. 5.8 and 5.9. The argument, that is $\tan^{-1} |[\mathrm{Re}\,\hat{f}(\omega_1, \omega_2)/\mathrm{Im}\,\hat{f}(\omega_1, \omega_2)]$, of the estimated bispectral density function is clearly not identically zero, again indicating time irreversibility. The modulus of the estimated bispectral density has a dominant peak at $(0.20\pi, 0.20\pi)$ and a smaller one at $(0.40\pi; 0.40\pi)$, which compare well with the peak positions of the estimated spectral density function at approximately 0.20π and 0.40π. These positions are probably quite significant. Note that the variable ω of a spectral density function, $f(\omega)$, is a physical frequency measured in cycles/unit time or equivalently in radians/unit time. However, the variables (ω_1, ω_2) of a bispectral

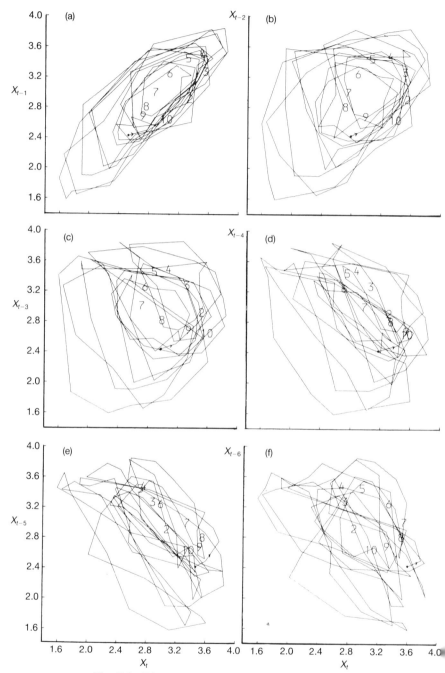

Fig. 7.3. Directed scatter diagrams of log lynx data

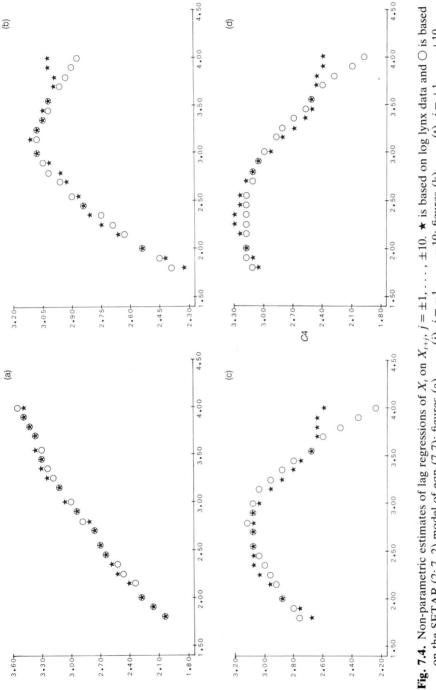

Fig. 7.4. Non-parametric estimates of lag regressions of X_t on X_{t+j}, $j = \pm1, \ldots, \pm10$. ★ is based on log lynx data and ○ is based on the SETAR (2; 7, 2) model of eqn (7.7): figures (a), ..., (i). $j = -1, \ldots, -10$; figures (k), ..., (t), $j = +1, \ldots, +10$

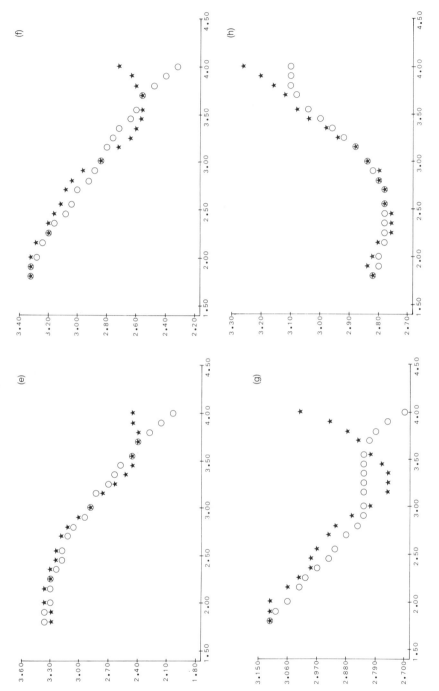

Fig. 7.4. continued

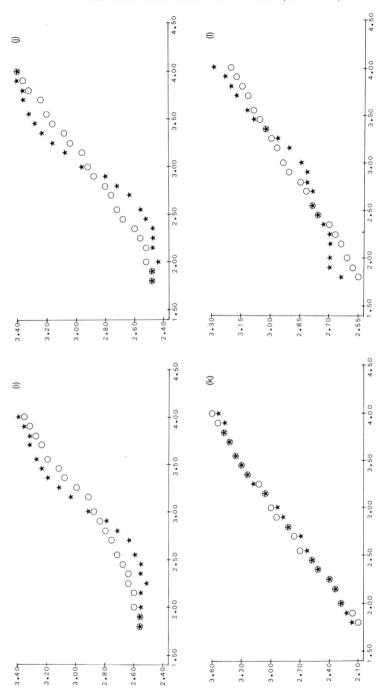

Fig. 7.4. continued

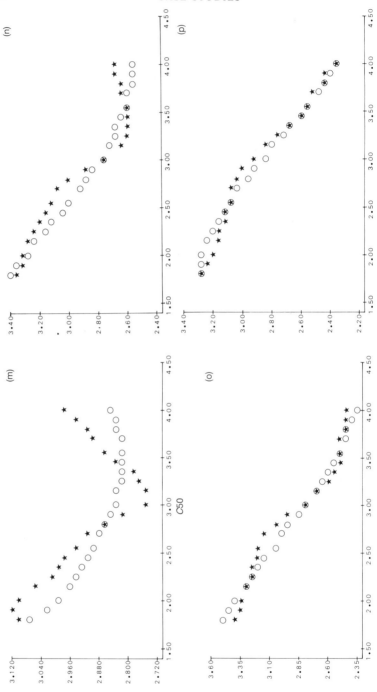

Fig. 7.4. continued

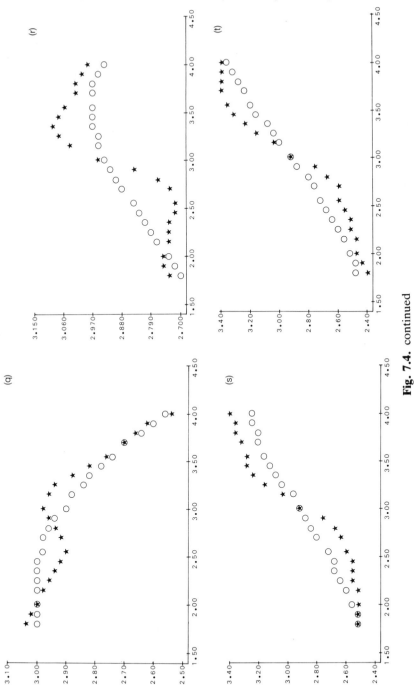

Fig. 7.4. continued

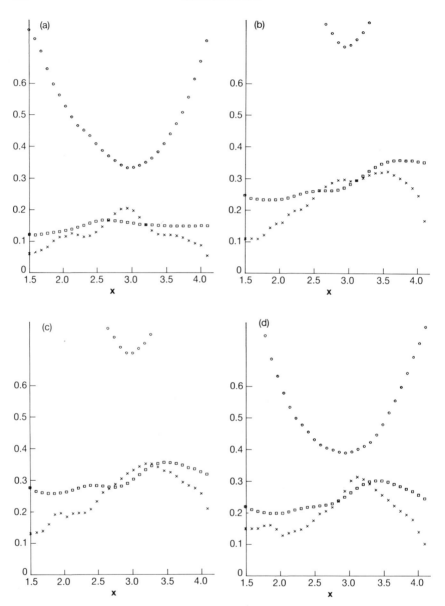

Fig. 7.5. Non-parametric estimates of var$(X_t \mid X_{t-j})$, $j = 1, 2, \ldots, 10$. $\times$ is based on log lynx data, $\square$ is based on the SETAR $(2; 7, 2)$ model of eqn (7.7), and $\odot$ is based on the Gabr and Subba Rao's BL model of §7.2.11. In (g), no $\odot$ are shown because of their being out of field

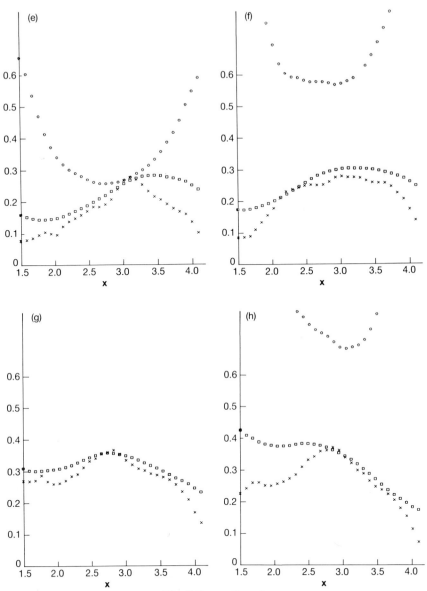

Fig. 7.5. continued

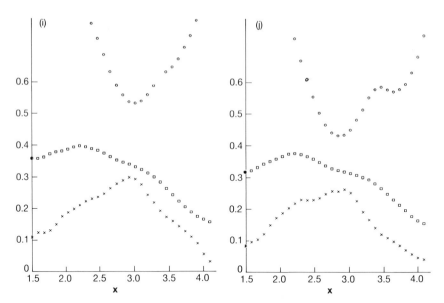

Fig. 7.5. continued

Table 7.4. Sample autocorrelation for log lynx data

j	$\hat{\rho}_j$	j	$\hat{\rho}_j$	j	$\hat{\rho}_j$
1	0.785 13	10	0.605 51	19	0.455 00
2	0.340 24	11	0.382 95	20	0.446 50
3	−0.132 29	12	−0.012 29	21	0.217 60
4	−0.493 89	13	−0.384 80	22	−0.115 51
5	−0.620 55	14	−0.607 34	23	−0.399 55
6	−0.487 96	15	−0.610 20	24	−0.507 49
7	−0.157 81	16	−0.406 91	25	−0.414 62
8	0.234 85	17	−0.072 72	26	0.163 18
9	9.537 21	18	0.253 18	27	0.150 91

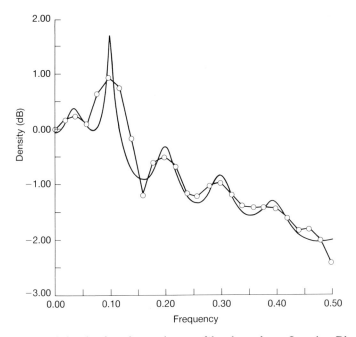

Fig. 7.6. Spectral density function estimate of log lynx data: ⊙, using Blackman Tukey window; ——, using an AR (11) model

density function $f(\omega_1, \omega_2)$ do not have any physical interpretation, as previously mentioned in §4.2.9.

Note that $|\hat{\rho}_j|$ attains its first local minimum at $j = 3$. This feature is closely related with the visible hump at $j = -3$ mentioned in 4 above. See also §1.4.2(4).

7.2.4 FORMAL TESTS FOR LINEARITY

Using a nominal 5% significance level, the following tests have rejected linearity for the log lynx data:

(1) CUSUM test described in §5.3.5.3 (with AR(9) and delay parameter = 2 or 3);

(2) Tsay's F-test described in §5.3.5.3 (with AR(9) and delay parameter = 1 or 2 or 3);

(3) Likelihood ratio test described in §5.3.5.2 (with AR(2) and delay parameter = 1; the nominal 5% point is 15.6).

The test based on bispectral functions (see §5.3.1) and Keenan's test have also been applied; they have not rejected linearity at the nominal 5% significance level.

As the three tests which lead to a rejection of linearity above are all designed to test departure from linearity in the direction of threshold autoregression, it would seem reasonable to entertain a SETAR model for the data. We shall therefore start with a SETAR model and then follow with other models. Before doing so, it would be appropriate to look at the biological perspective.

7.2.5. BIOLOGICAL PERSPECTIVE

There are numerous mathematical population models describing the time evolution of the population cycles. One simple model due to Oster and Ipaktchi (1978) is the delayed differential equation model (cf. Hutchinson's model of eqn (2.83)):

$$\frac{dN(t)}{dt} = l(\alpha)b(N(t - \alpha))N(t - \alpha) - \mu N(t) \tag{7.2}$$

where $N(t)$ is the number of adults at time t, α is the delayed regulation time due to, for example, (i) time taken for the young to develop into adults and (ii)·discrete breeding seasons, $l(\alpha)$ is the fraction of new-borns surviving to adulthood, $b(.)$ is the age-averaged birth rate, and μ is the age-averaged death rate, assumed constant.

7.2.5.1 The birth curve In many biological populations, the crucial birth rate is a function of the population size, due to, for example, competition for the resources of the habitat, the limitation of food, an underlying predator–prey ecosystem, etc. A commonly used or rather *hypothesized birth curve,* that is, $b(N)N$ *versus* N, is the one-humped curve shown in Fig. 7.7, where N_c denotes the *critical population size,*

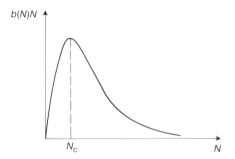

Fig. 7.7. An idealized birth curve

that is the *threshold*, above which the birth curve decreases and below which the birth curve increases. The hypothesized birth curve is a 'feedback control mechanism' reminiscent of the 'feedback control mechanism' in the triode valve described in §2.3.

It is clear that the lag regressions must be related to a discrete-time analogue of the birth curve and are therefore important statistics.

If we accept the hypothesis of the existence of a one-humped birth curve in the regulation of the lynx population, then it would not be unreasonable to entertain a SETAR model on biological grounds alone.

7.2.5.2 The time delay According to *The Canadian Encyclopaedia* (1985), a Canadian lynx (*Lynx canadensis*) is fully grown in the autumn of its second year and births of kittens (1–4 per litter) take place about 63 days after breeding in March–April. It would therefore seem reasonable to try $\alpha = 2$ or 3.

7.2.6 A PRIMITIVE SETAR MODEL: A PRECURSOR

A simple way of improving Moran's AR(2) model is to incorporate the biological features described in §7.2.5. Specifically, we may consider a SETAR $(2; 2, 2)$ model with delay parameter equal to 2, and threshold value approximately equal to $3\frac{1}{4}$ in view of the positioning of the turning point of the lag regression esimate $\hat{m}_{-2}(x)$ in Fig. 7.4(b). In fact, the model (4.158) was the result of fitting such a primitive SETAR $(2; 2, 2)$ model to the log lynx data where the non-structural (i.e. autoregressive) parameters have been estimated straightforwardly with the least-squares method. Comparing the lag regressions of the fitted model (Fig. 4.12) with those of the data (Fig. 7.4), we can see that the fit is already quite good in this respect. Later, the SETAR $(2; k_1, k_2)$ model, with $k_1, k_2 \geq 2$, may be used as fine tuning.

Let us rewrite the skeleton of the fitted SETAR $(2; 2, 2)$ model:

$$X_t - X_{t-1} = \begin{cases} 0.62 + 0.25X_{t-1} - 0.43X_{t-2} & \text{if } X_{t-2} \leq 3.25 \\ -(1.24X_{t-2} - 2.25) + 0.52X_{t-1} & \text{if } X_{t-2} > 3.25. \end{cases} \quad (7.3)$$

We note in Fig. 7.1 that the dynamic range of X is approximately 1.5 to 4.0. In the upper regime (i.e. if $X_{t-2} > 3.25$), $X_t - X_{t-1}$ tends to be negative (hence a population decrease). In the lower regime (i.e. if $X_{t-2} \leq 3.25$), $X_t - X_{t-1}$ tends to be marginally positive (hence a slow population growth). In fact, there is an 'energy balance' between population expansion and the population contraction, which gives rise to a stable limit cycle of period 9 years (with ascent period 6 years and descent period 3 years) in good agreement with the observed asymmetric cycles.

We would argue that the discontinuity of model (7.3) is unimportant because it is not an essential feature of the threshoild models and can easily be removed if desired by replacing the SETAR model with a STAR model (*cf.* Chan and Tong 1986*a*). Further, the threshold estimate in model (7.3) lies in the vicinity of the antimode (which happens to be near the mean too) of the histogram (Fig. 7.1). This implies that there is insufficient information anyway in the data to model more precisely the functional form of the dynamics over the state space near the sample mean.

We note that the essence of the skeleton (7.3) may be expressed in the following form:

$$X_t - X_{t-1} = \begin{cases} \alpha & \text{if } X_{t-2} \le r \\ \beta - \gamma X_{t-2} & \text{if } X_{t-2} > r \end{cases} \tag{7.4}$$

where $\alpha > 0$. $r > 0$, $\beta > 0$, $\gamma > 0$, and $\beta - \gamma r < 0$. We leave the analysis of eqn (7.4) to the readers as an exercise. (It is good fun to try the recursion (7.4) on a personal computer and watch the stable limit cycles over a wide range of values of α, β, γ, and r!)

In conclusion, by incorporating the basic biological features described in §7.2.5, we have obtained with very little effort a *primitive* SETAR $(2; 2, 2)$ model which not only is amenable to interpretation in terms of population dynamics but also gives a reasonable statistical fit. We should emphasize that our primary concern is an understanding of the lynx cycles and the above SETAR $(2; 2, 2)$ model should be only so used. Readers who are interested in a comparative study of '*predictions*'* of the' log lynx data may refer to Section 7 of Chapter Three of Tong (1983*a*) and compare these results with predictions obtained by other models, such as AR, BL, EXPAR, RCA, etc. They will see that SETAR models perform quite well. However, such predictions can only be of very limited scientific value in our opinion. We shall discuss the issue of genuine prediction in §7.3.

7.2.7   FINE TUNING

As prediction is not one of our primary objectives, we shall use the complete set of 114 data covering 1821–1934. The class of models under

* We use the quotes '*predictions*' because we really know the 'answers'. The possibility of *genuine predictions* does not present itself since the Canadian lynx record terminates in 1934. Here, by *genuine predictions* we mean predictions of data which are genuinely unavailable to the forecaster at the time when he makes his predictions. We are grateful to Sir David Cox for suggesting the term.

consideration is

$$X_t = \begin{cases} a_0 + \sum_{j=1}^{k_1} a_j X_{t-j} + \varepsilon_t^{(1)} & \text{if } X_{t-d} \le r \\ b_0 + \sum_{j=1}^{k_2} b_j X_{t-j} + \varepsilon_t^{(2)} & \text{if } X_{t-d} > r. \end{cases} \tag{7.5}$$

Table 7.5 details the results of a 'least-squares' search over a grid of points with coordinates $(d, r, k_1, k_2, a_0, \ldots, a_{k_1}, b_0, \ldots, b_{k_2})$. For each fixed d and each fixed r, the search over k_1 and k_2 is equivalent to the order determination of AR models and could be automated by using, for example, the minimum AIC method which also gives the associated estimates of the a_i and the b_i. Specifically, let $X_{(1)} \le X_{(2)} \le \ldots \le X_{(N)}$, $N = 114$, denote the order statistics of the log lynx data. Let d and r be fixed. Let J ($\ll N$) be a fixed positive integer greater than or equal to $\max(k_1, k_2)$; in the construction of Table 7.5, J is chosen to be 10. Let $\boldsymbol{\theta}_1 = (k_1, a_0, \ldots, a_{k_1})$, $\boldsymbol{\theta}_2 = (k_2, b_0, \ldots, b_{k_2})$ and

$$L_{1N}(\boldsymbol{\theta}_1) = \sum_{X_{(j)-d} \le r} \left[X_{(j)} - a_0 - \sum_{i=1}^{k_1} a_i X_{(j)-i} \right]^2$$

$$L_{2N}(\boldsymbol{\theta}_2) = \sum_{X_{(j)-d} > r} \left[X_{(j)} - b_0 - \sum_{i=1}^{k_2} b_i X_{(j)-i} \right]^2 \tag{7.6}$$

where care is taken to ensure that only those j will be included in the summations for which $X_{(j)} \in \{X_{J+1}, \ldots, X_N\}$, the *effective data set* of *effective sample size* $N - J$. For each $k_1 \in \{0, 1, \ldots, J\}$, $L_{1N}(\boldsymbol{\theta}_1(k_1))$ is minimized w.r.t. $a_0, \ldots, a_{k_1}$ to give their least-squares estimates $\hat{a}_0(k_1), \ldots, \hat{a}_{k_1}(k_1)$. Let $L_{1N}(\hat{\boldsymbol{\theta}}_1(k_1))$ denote the minimized sum of squares, where $\hat{\boldsymbol{\theta}}_1(k_1) = (k_1, \hat{a}_0(k_1), \ldots, \hat{a}_{k_1}(k_1))$. Calculate $\text{AIC}_1(k_1) = n_1 \ln\{L_{1N}(\hat{\boldsymbol{\theta}}_1(k))/2\} + 2(k_1 + 1)$, where n_1 denotes the number of the j in the summation for $L_{1N}(\theta_1)$. Minimizing $\text{AIC}_1(k_1)$ w.r.t. k_1 gives us the minimum AIC estimate, $\hat{k}_1$, of k_1 together with the associated least-squares estimates $\hat{\boldsymbol{\theta}}_1(\hat{k}_1)$. We repeat a similar procedure with $L_{2N}(\boldsymbol{\theta}_2)$ to get $\hat{k}_2$ and $\hat{\boldsymbol{\theta}}_2(\hat{k}_2)$. Write NAIC for $\{\text{AIC}_1(\hat{k}_1) + \text{AIC}_2(\hat{k}_2)\}/(\text{effective sample size})$ which is entered into Table 7.5 under NAIC for each choice of d and r. As far as the search for r is concerned, we may use each of $X_{(1)}, X_{(2)}, \ldots, X_{(N)}$ as a candidate. To save time, we may sometimes decide to use only a subset S say, of these order statistics first and then follow with a finer search in the vicinity of a small number of (say one or two) elements of S. Readers may use their ingenuity to devise their own scheme of search.

We note from (7.6) that conditional on r, d, and k_1, approximate standard errors for the estimates of $a_0, a_1, \ldots, a_{k_1}$ may be obtained from

Table 7.5. Least-squares search

d	r	n_1	n_2	$\hat{k}_1+1$	$\hat{k}_2+1$	NAIC	Pooled noise variance	Skeleton	Remark
1	2.4378	23	81	3	10	-3.0563	0.0360	Limit cycle	It has a very long period; see Fig. 7.8
	2.6074	36	68	3	10	-3.0203	0.0376	Limit cycle	5↑4↓5↑4↓5↑5↓ (see note)
	2.7769	46	58	3	10	-2.9595	0.0415	Possibly chaotic	See Fig. 7.9
	2.9464	56	48	3	10	-2.9311	0.0425	Limit cycle	4↑2↓
	3.1160	61	43	3	10	-2.8959	0.0432	Limit point	
	3.2855	72	32	5	3	-2.8400	0.0493	Limit point	
	3.4550	86	18	11	3	-2.8592	0.0435	Limit point	
2	2.4378	23	81	11	10	-3.1240	0.0331	Limit point	It has a very long period; see Fig. 7.10
	2.6074	36	68	5	3	-3.0515	0.0424	Limit cycle	
	2.7769	46	58	5	3	-3.0911	0.0389	Possibly chaotic	See Fig. 7.11
	2.9464	56	48	5	3	-3.1190	0.0383	Possibly chaotic	See Fig. 7.12
	3.1160	61	43	8	3	-3.1492	0.0360	Limit cycle	6↑3↓
	3.2855	72	32	11	3	-3.1596	0.0336	Limit cycle	6↑3↓6↑4↓5↑4↓6↑3↓
	3.4550	85	19	11	10	-3.1227	0.0294	Limit point	
3	2.4378	23	81	2	11	-3.0581	0.0374	Limit point	5↑4↓6↑5↓5↑4↓
	2.6074	36	68	5	10	-3.0835	0.0367	Limit cycle	4↑5↓5↑5↓5↑4↓6↓
	2.7769	46	58	6	10	-3.1954	0.0334	Limit cycle	5↑4↓
	2.9464	56	48	6	10	-3.3438	0.0284	Limit cycle	6↑4↓5↑4↓
	3.1160	61	43	11	3	-3.1083	0.0378	Limit cycle	
	3.2855	71	33	9	3	-3.1290	0.0370	Limit point	

	3.4550	84	20	11	10	-3.1217	0.0289	Limit point	
4	2.4378	23	81	3	11	-3.0561	0.0377	Limit point	
	2.6074	36	68	9	6	-2.9493	0.0406	Limit point	
	2.7769	46	58	9	6	-2.9652	0.0309	Limit point	
	2.9464	56	48	11	3	-3.0416	0.0408	Limit cycle	$6\!\uparrow\!4\!\downarrow$
	3.1160	60	44	9	3	-3.0496	0.0417	Limit point	
	3.2855	70	34	11	4	-3.1226	0.0349	Limit point	
	3.4550	83	21	9	7	-3.1091	0.0326	Limit point	
5	2.4378	23	81	10	8	-2.9017	0.0400	Unstable	
	2.6074	36	68	9	6	-2.9227	0.0421	Unstable	
	2.7769	46	58	9	3	-2.0610	0.0440	Possibly chaotic	See Fig. 7.13; double loop
	2.9464	55	49	9	3	-2.9751	0.0430	Possibly chaotic	See Fig. 7.14; double loop
	3.1160	59	45	9	3	-2.8735	0.0460	Limit point	
	3.2855	69	35	9	6	-2.9424	0.0300	Limit point	
	3.4550	83	21	11	3	-2.9166	0.0416	Limit point	
6	2.4378	23	81	7	6	-2.9675	0.0424	Unstable	
	2.6074	36	68	3	5	-2.8634	0.0483	Limit point	
	2.7769	45	59	3	5	-2.8514	0.0487	Limit point	
	2.9464	54	59	3	5	-2.8661	0.0480	Limit point	
	3.1160	58	46	3	8	-2.8768	0.0447	Limit point	
	3.2855	69	35	10	11	-2.8983	0.0363	Limit point	
	3.4550	83	21	5	3	-3.0990	0.0407	Limit point	

Note: The symbolism $a\!\uparrow\!b\!\downarrow\!c\!\uparrow\!d\!\downarrow$ means a limit cycle with ascent period a, then descent period b, then ascent period c, then descent period d, making a complete cycle in $a + b + c + d$ units of time.

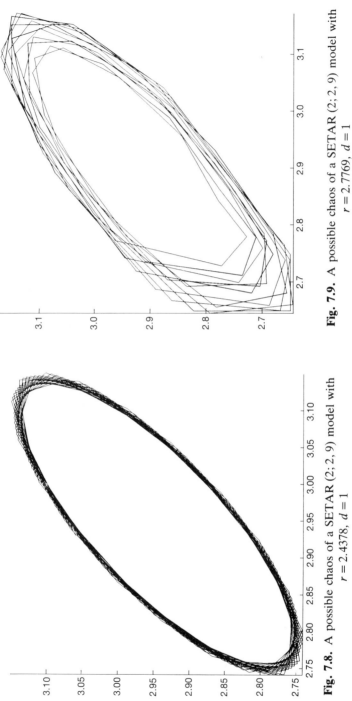

Fig. 7.9. A possible chaos of a SETAR $(2; 2, 9)$ model with $r = 2.7769$, $d = 1$

Fig. 7.8. A possible chaos of a SETAR $(2; 2, 9)$ model with $r = 2.4378$, $d = 1$

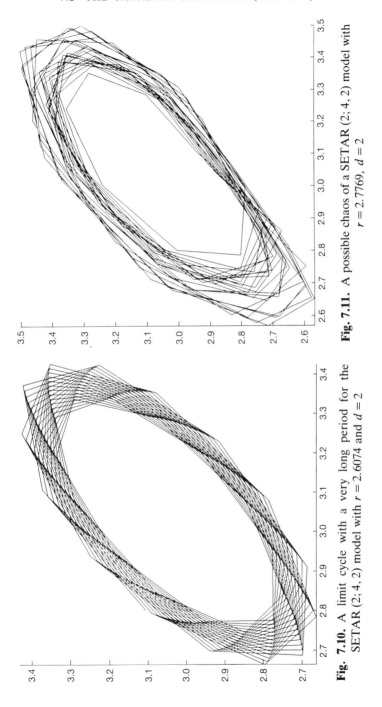

Fig. 7.11. A possible chaos of a SETAR $(2; 4, 2)$ model with $r = 2.7769$, $d = 2$

Fig. 7.10. A limit cycle with a very long period for the SETAR $(2; 4, 2)$ model with $r = 2.6074$ and $d = 2$

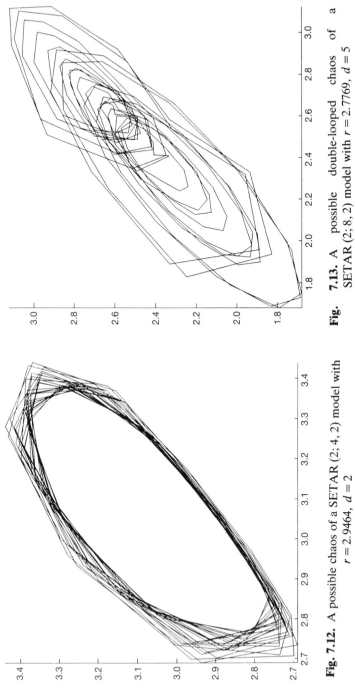

Fig. **7.13.** A possible double-looped chaos of a SETAR $(2; 8, 2)$ model with $r = 2.7769$, $d = 5$

Fig. 7.12. A possible chaos of a SETAR $(2; 4, 2)$ model with $r = 2.9464$, $d = 2$

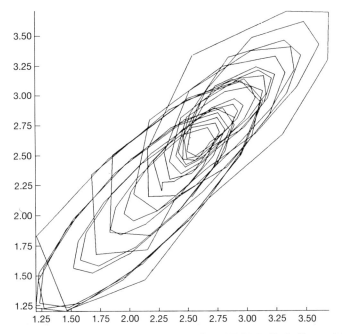

Fig. 7.14. A possible double-looped chaos of a SETAR $(2; 8, 2)$ model with $r = 2.9464$, $d = 5$

standard regression theory w.r.t. the model

$$X_{(j)} = a_0 + \sum_{i=1}^{k_1} a_i X_{(j)-i} + \varepsilon_{(j)}^{(1)}, \qquad j \text{ s.t. } X_{(j)-d} \le r.$$

Approximate standard errors for the estimates of $b_0, b_1, \ldots, b_{k_2}$ may be obtained in a similar way. This practice may be justified by Theorem 5.7 and Theorem 5.8.

Table 7.5 lists the normalized AIC values (NAIC) at coordinates $(d, r, \hat{k}_1, \hat{k}_2)$, where d is over $\{1, 2, \ldots, 6\}$ and $r \in \{r_1, \ldots, r_7\}$ with

$$r_i = \bar{X} - \left(1 - \frac{ci - 1}{7}\right)\hat{\sigma}_X$$

where $\bar{X}$ is the sample mean, $\hat{\sigma}_X^2$ is the sample variance, and c is an arbitrary positive real constant ($c = 2.13$ in the table).

Computer programs are available for *fast* execution, which produces the above table, as well as a majority of the diagnostics described in Chapter 5. Several research workers in different parts of the world have also written their own programs which all seem to run very smoothly and fast. In other words, *computation has never been a real problem for a small number of regimes.* Even for SETAR $(m; k_1, k_2, \ldots, k_m)$ with m large, the computation problem is solvable with care and ingenuity. (See for example Casdagli (1987), Tsay's method, and our method based on the profile likelihood in §7.2.9 below.)

In using Table 7.5, we recall the cautionary remarks on the use of AIC in §5.4.3. Accordingly, we discard all models with $\max(\hat{k}_1 + 1, \hat{k}_2 + 1) \geq 9$, noting that the maximum AR order has been pre-fixed at 10 and that eight is dangerously close to this pre-fixed maximum allowable order. This discarding results in a drastic reduction in the number of potential models. For example, it eliminates all those with $d = 5$. Next, we discard those models whose skeletons are either unstable or whose AIC are too large. At this stage, we are left with only five models, which are listed in Table 7.6. (We have included AIC and BIC this time.)

It is interesting to note that four of the models share the same delay parameter, namely 2. These four models also suggest a bifurcation as r decreases from 3.1160 in that the limit cycle leads to the chaotic regime around $r = 3$, with d fixed at 2. In fact, bifurcation phenomena can be observed in Table 7.5 (i) with d fixed and r varying and, to a lesser extent, (ii) with r fixed and d varying. The regularity of the route to (from) chaos is quite intriguing and merits further research.

The 'final' choice (if there is such a need) seems to be between models III and IV, that is between a model with a possibly chaotic skeleton and a model with a limit cycle skeleton. AIC prefers the latter whilst BIC prefers the former. Readers are invited to make their own choices if they want to (cf Schaffer 1984; Brown 1989; and Exercise 12).

We now turn to diagnostics of these models. However, space will only allow us to present the details for model IV, namely the following SETAR $(2; 7, 2)$ model with approximate standard errors in

Table 7.6. Survivors after initial screening

Serial no.	d	r	$\hat{k}_1 + 1$	$\hat{k}_2 + 1$	AIC	BIC	Skeleton
I	2	2.6074	5	3	-317.4	-296.2	Limit cycle (with a very long period)
II	2	2.7769	5	3	-321.5	-300.3	Possibly chaotic
III	2	2.9464	5	3	-324.4	-303.2	Possibly chaotic
IV	2	3.1160	8	3	-327.5	-298.4	Limit cycle (6↑3↓)
V	6	3.4550	5	3	-322.3	-301.1	Limit point

parentheses):

$$X_t = \begin{cases} \begin{array}{l} 0.546 + 1.032X_{t-1} - 0.173X_{t-2} + 0.171X_{t-3} - 0.431X_{t-4} \\ \;\;(0.275) \quad\;\; (0.094) \qquad\; (0.156) \qquad\;\; (0.149) \qquad\;\; (0.153) \end{array} \\[2mm] \begin{array}{l} \quad + 0.332X_{t-5} - 0.284X_{t-6} + 0.210X_{t-7} + \varepsilon_t^{(1)} \quad \text{if } X_{t-2} \leq \;\; 3.116 \\ \qquad (0.170) \qquad\; (0.167) \qquad\; (0.101) \qquad\qquad\qquad\qquad\qquad [2.926, 3.123]^* \end{array} \\[2mm] \begin{array}{l} 2.632 + 1.492X_{t-1} - 1.324X_{t-2} + \varepsilon_t^{(2)} \qquad\qquad\;\; \text{if } X_{t-2} > 3.116 \\ (0.655) \quad\;\; (0.102) \qquad\;\; (0.195) \end{array} \end{cases}$$

$$(7.7)$$

where var $\varepsilon_t^{(1)} = 0.0259$, var $\varepsilon_t^{(2)} = 0.0505$ (pooled var $= 0.0358$).

Note that the SETAR $(2; 7, 2)$ model given by eqn (7.7) preserves the basic dynamics of the primitive SETAR $(2; 2, 2)$ model given by eqn (7.3). The 'padding' (note the alternating signs of the AR parameters too) by the higher-order autoregressive terms (i.e. X_{t-j}, $j \geq 3$) is merely to improve the statistical fit. It should be noted that the model (7.7) may be further fine-tuned by searching $\hat{r}$ in the neighbourhood of 3.116. Such facilities exist in the package STAR.

Let us subject the SETAR $(2; 7, 2)$ model to the diagnostics described in Chapter 5.

7.2.8 DIAGNOSTICS

7.2.8.1 Examination of the fitted residuals For homogeneity, the fitted residuals are normalized to give unit variance by dividing by the appropriate var $\varepsilon_t^{(i)}$. Figures 7.15–7.20 together do not show any significant deviation from a Gaussian white noise sequence for the residuals. However, the two largest normalized residuals (at 1842 and 1917) in modulus (circled in Fig. 7.15) seem to merit further scrutiny. They clearly account for the slightly thicker 'negative' tail indicated by the normal probability plot in Fig. 7.19, and the negative though small coefficient of skewness (-0.037) and coefficient of kurtosis (-0.237). Sample autocorrelations (ACF) and partial autocorrelations (PACF) for the normalized residuals are given in Table 7.7 and in Fig. 7.16. All but the ACF at lag 18 lie well within the two σ-lines. It is interesting to note that the ACF at lag 18 for fitted residuals of many other published models for the log lynx data (some SETAR and some non-SETAR) also tends to be significant. This is probably associated with the periodicity of the data. Sample ACF and PACF for the squared normalized residuals are given in Table 7.8 and in Fig. 7.20. All but the ACF at lag 6 and the PACF at lag 6 lie well

---

* The square brackets give a bootstrap interquartile range based on 1000 replications of sample size 114. Recall that $\hat{r}$ does not have an asymptotic normal distribution.

Table 7.7. Sample autocorrelation function (ACF) and sample partial autocorrelation function (PACF) for normalized residuals from the SETAR model $(2; 7, 2)$ of eqn (7.7). (Nominal critical value $= 1.96/\sqrt{104} = 0.19$.)

Lag	ACF	Lag	PACF
1	−0.010	1	−0.010
2	0.033	2	0.033
3	0.026	3	0.026
4	0.034	4	0.034
5	0.114	5	0.114
6	0.104	6	0.106
7	0.010	7	0.006
8	−0.129	8	−0.145
9	0.070	9	0.052
10	0.032	10	0.024
11	0.097	11	0.080
12	−0.124	12	−0.138
13	−0.114	13	−0.109
14	−0.074	14	−0.066
15	0.158	15	0.168
16	−0.102	16	−0.131
17	−0.014	17	0.004
18	−0.194	18	−0.171
19	−0.007	19	0.078
20	0.018	20	−0.035

within the two σ-lines. Therefore, no obvious lack of fit is detected but the possibility of two or three 'outliers' should not be ruled out.

The Ljung–Box statistic (20.11), the Mudholkar statistic (0.176), and the McLeod–Li statistic (17.82) are non-significant w.r.t. χ_{20}^2 (5%), 5% point of $\mathcal{N}(0, 1)$, and $\chi_{20}^2(5\%)$ respectively.

7.2.8.2 The fitted characteristics versus the observed The first four moments about the origin of the fitted model based on the Monte Carlo method (using 10 000 artificial data) match those of the data reasonably well (see Table 7.9). Henceforth, we rely on the Monte Carlo method to obtain population characteristics for this and other models.

Figure 7.21 shows a partial realization of the SETAR $(2; 7, 2)$ model, which depicts obvious cyclicity with slow ascension and fast descension and an approximate 9 year period.

Table 7.8. Sample autocorrelation function (ACF) and sample partial autocorrelation function (PACF) of squared normalized residuals from the SETAR $(2; 7, 2)$ model of eqn (7.7). (Nominal critical value $= 0.19$.)

Lag	ACF	Lag	PACF
1	0.029	1	0.029
2	0.030	2	0.030
3	−0.065	3	−0.067
4	−0.054	4	−0.052
5	−0.165	5	−0.159
6	0.223	6	0.237
7	0.066	7	0.056
8	0.014	8	−0.030
9	0.106	9	0.120
10	0.115	10	0.122
11	−0.118	11	−0.064
12	−0.077	12	−0.114
13	−0.039	13	−0.032
14	−0.122	14	−0.085
15	−0.036	15	−0.072
16	−0.035	16	−0.152
17	0.028	17	0.029
18	−0.022	18	0.005
19	−0.011	19	−0.071
20	−0.002	20	0.046

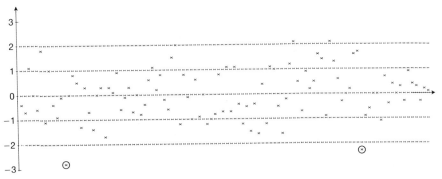

Fig. 7.15. A plot of the normalized residuals from the SETAR $(2; 7, 2)$ model of eqn (7.7)

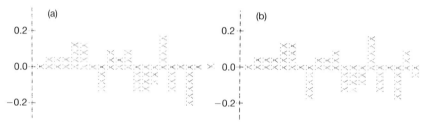

Fig. 7.16. (a) Autocorrelations of normalized fitted residuals from the SETAR $(2; 7, 2)$ model of eqn (7.7); (b) Partial autocorrelations of the same fitted residuals

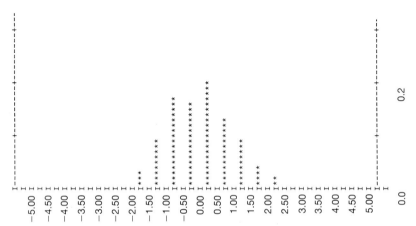

Fig. 7.17. Bar chart of normalized residuals from the SETAR $(2; 7, 2)$ model of eqn (7.7). Coefficient of skewness, -0.037, coefficient of kurtosis, -0.237

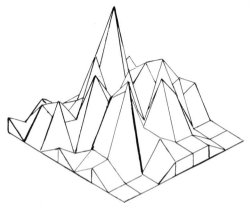

Fig. 7.18. Sample joint distribution of normalized fitted residuals $(\hat{e}_{2t-1}, \hat{e}_{2t})$ from the SETAR $(2; 7, 2)$ model of eqn (7.7)

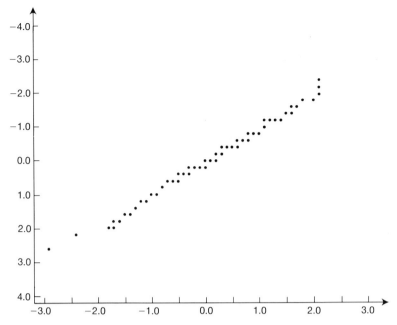

Fig. 7.19. Normal probability plot of normalized fitted residuals from the SETAR $(2; 7, 2)$ model of eqn (7.7). The two largest values in modulus are circled

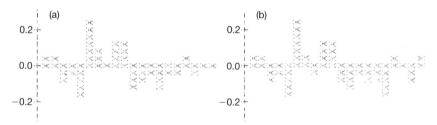

Fig. 7.20. (a) Autocorrelations of squared normalized residuals from the SETAR $(2; 7, 2)$ model of eqn (7.7); (b) Partial autocorrelations of the same fitted residuals

Table 7.9

	1st moment	2nd moment	3rd moment	4th moment
Data (1821–1934)	2.90	8.74	27.11	86.21
SETAR $(2; 7, 2)$	2.89	8.70	27.16	87.15

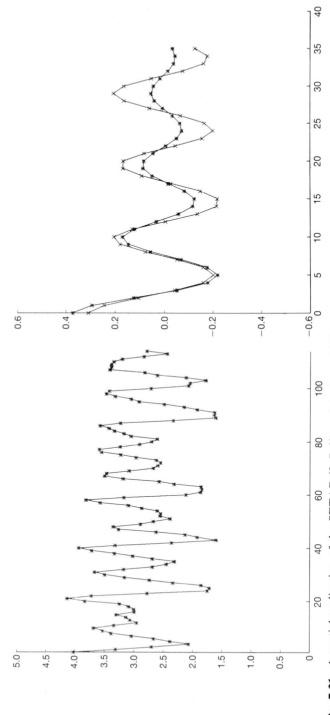

Fig. 7.22. Autocovariance function plot

Fig. 7.21. A partial realization of the SETAR (2; 7, 2) model of eqn (7.7)

Figures 7.22 and 7.23 suggest that the fitted model gives a dominant signal at the same frequency as the data. The first harmonic and the subharmonic are moderately discernible for the fitted model.

The modulus of the bispectral density function of the model (Fig. 7.24) exhibits a dominant peak at the same position as that of the data (Fig. 5.8). However, instead of a minor peak at $(0.40\pi, 0.40\pi)$ only a shoulder is discernible. This might be due to the choice of the smoothing parameter or some inadequacy of the model. The agreement between the argument of the bispectral density function of the model (Fig. 7.25) and that of the data (Fig. 5.9) seems quite good.

Bimodality of the univariate density of X_t is observed in the fitted model. (See exercise 14.) However, the general non-Gaussian shape of the bivariate distributions seems to be adequately captured by those of the fitted model (Fig. 7.26). The lag regressions $E[X_t \mid X_{t\pm j}]$ and the plots of $\text{var}[X_t \mid X_{t-j}]$, $j = 1, 2, \ldots, 10$, for the fitted model and the data have previously been given in Figs 7.4 and 7.5. The agreement seems quite good for $E[X_t \mid X_{t-j}]$, good for $E[X_t \mid X_{t+j}]$, but only reasonable for $\text{var}[X_t \mid X_{t-j}]$. Improvement might be possible by further tuning and/or appropriate handling of the influential data points, whose existence was alluded to earlier.

7.2.8.3 Skeleton plot

The limit cycle shown in Fig. 7.27 is apparently quite stable in that, with the many initial values we have tried, the same limit cycle is obtained. Figure 7.27 shows two typical instances.

The time plot of the limit cycle has period 9 with ascent period 6 and descent period 3 in consonance with the strong periodic movement of the data plot.

Rather intriguingly, the skeleton of eqn (7.7) exhibits the *synchronization* property almost identical to that exhibited by eqn (2.138) and shown in Fig. 2.30. We are not aware of any sound biological interpretation of this phenomenon.

7.2.8.4 Likelihood plots and correlation matrix of parameter estimates

For a multiparameter situation like ours, a convenient way to study the likelihood function (or equivalently the $-2 \ln$ likelihood function) is by producing a collection of likelihood plots, in each of which all but a different pair of the parameters are kept at their optimum values. Figure 7.28 shows a fairly representative plot. (Details are available in Moeanaddin (1989)).

Table 7.9 gives the correlation matrix of the $(\hat{a}_i, \hat{b}_i)$. We have not included $\hat{r}$ as it is known that $\hat{r}$ is $1/N$ consistent, N being the sample size,

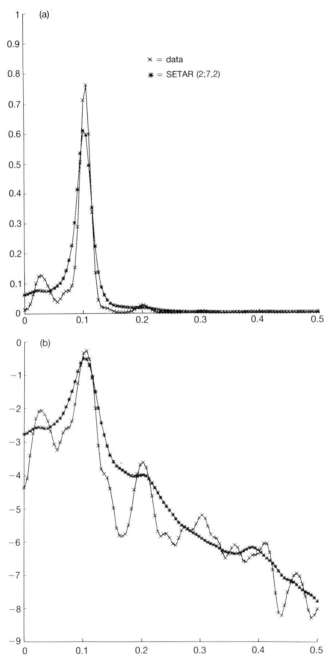

Fig. 7.23. Spectral density function plot on ordinary scale (a) and log scale (b).
(The Parzen window is used)

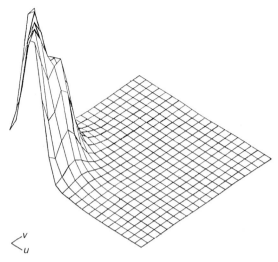

Fig. 7.24. Modulus of the bispectral density function of the SETAR $(2; 7, 2)$ model of eqn (7.7)

$\omega_2 \backslash \omega_1$	0.00	0.05	0.10	0.15	0.20	0.25	0.30	0.35	0.40	0.45	0.50	0.55	0.60	0.65
1.00	0.00													
0.95	−0.00	−0.39	−0.60											
0.90	0.00	−0.43	−0.73	−1.08	−1.61									
0.85	−0.00	−0.53	−0.88	−1.22	−1.69	−2.32	−3.05							
0.80	−0.00	−0.72	−1.18	−1.51	−1.90	−2.42	−3.07	2.63	2.20					
0.75	−0.00	−0.98	−1.56	−1.85	−2.13	−2.54	−3.09	2.62	2.18	1.80	1.31			
0.70	−0.00	−1.20	−1.84	−2.18	−2.35	−2.64	−3.10	2.62	2.14	1.75	1.31	0.78	0.49	
0.65	−0.00	−1.42	−2.30	−2.52	−2.58	−2.76	−3.11	2.64	2.11	1.70	1.33	0.91	0.58	0.42
0.60	−3.14	2.28	2.75	−2.03	−2.86	−2.92	3.12	2.69	2.14	1.68	1.35	1.10	0.81	
0.55	−3.14	2.05	1.82	2.15	2.86	3.09	2.99	2.69	2.23	1.71	1.36	1.22		
0.50	−3.14	2.10	1.69	1.64	1.83	2.48	2.68	2.58	2.31	1.88	1.49			
0.45	−3.14	2.16	1.67	1.51	1.56	1.84	2.22	2.36	2.32	2.15				
0.40	−3.14	2.01	1.58	1.40	1.38	1.51	1.81	2.11	2.26					
0.35	−3.14	1.80	1.43	1.27	1.20	1.25	1.47	1.81						
0.30	−3.14	2.40	1.46	1.25	1.15	1.10	1.19							
0.25	−3.14	2.50	1.72	1.36	1.21	1.12								
0.20	−3.14	2.77	2.17	1.60	1.33									
0.15	3.14	2.88	2.55	2.07										
0.10	3.14	2.94	2.77											
0.05	3.14	3.02												
0.00	0.00													

Fig. 7.25. Argument of the bispectral density function of the SETAR $(2; 7, 2)$ model of eqn (7.7)

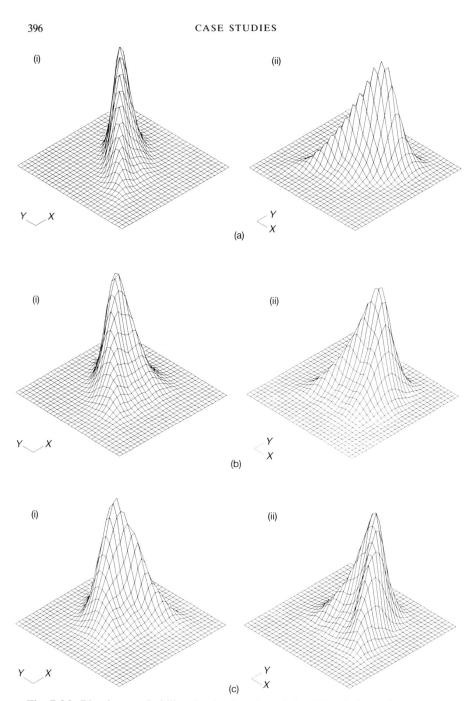

Fig. 7.26. Bivariate probability density function of the SETAR $(2; 7, 2)$ model of eqn (7.7)

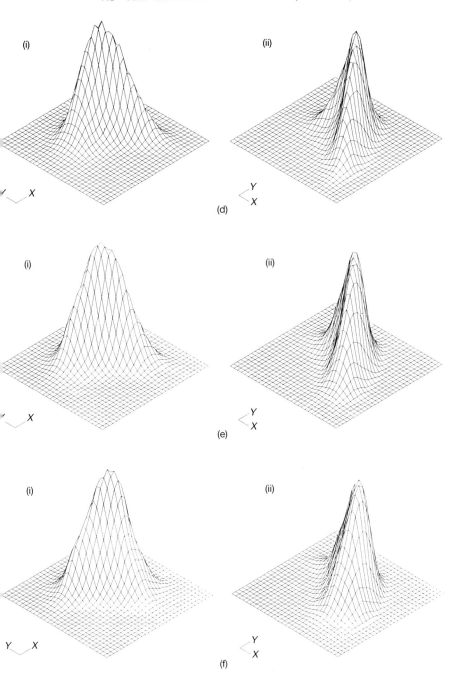

Fig. 7.26. continued

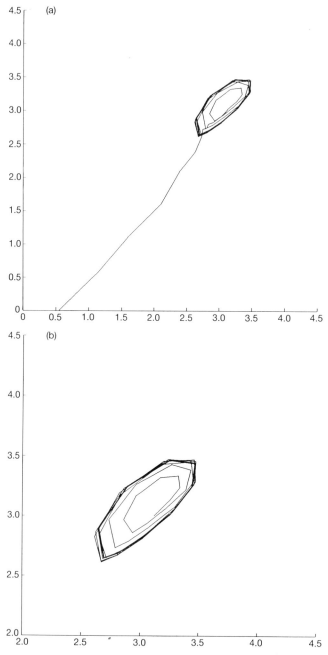

Fig. 7.27. Skeleton plots of the SETAR $(2; 7, 2)$ model of eqn (7.7) with two different initial points

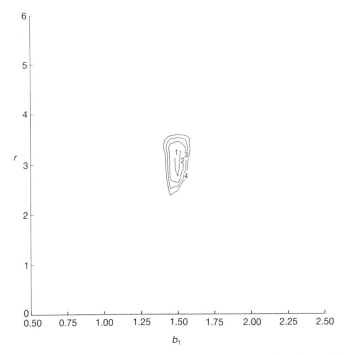

Fig. 7.28. A plot of (conditional) sum of squared errors as a function of (r, b_1) of the SETAR $(2; 7, 2)$ model of eqn (7.7), where r is the threshold parameter and b_1 is the coefficient of X_{t-1} in the upper regime. Other parameters are fixed at their respective conditional least-squares estimates. Key: $1 = 4.50$, $2 = 5.50$, $3 = 6.50$, $4 = 7.50$

and is asymptotically *independent* of the $\hat{a}_i$ and the $\hat{b}_i$ (see §5.5.3). However, as yet the tabulation of the limiting distribution of $N(\hat{r} - r_0)$ is not available. (Here r_0 denotes the true value.) We have, therefore, used the bootstrap method (based on 1000 replications of 114 observations each) to obtain the approximate interquartile range of $\hat{r}$ in eqn (7.7) for the SETAR $(2; 7, 2)$ model. (Recall that $\hat{r}$ does not have asymptotic normality.) We have not included $\hat{d}$ either because, being an integer-valued parameter, its conditional least-squares estimate will attain the true value in *finite* sample, by the strong consistency result of §5.5.3 of Chapter Five. Thus, Table 7.9 and the standard errors of the $\hat{a}_i$ and the $\hat{b}_i$ are constructed as if r and d were known.

Correlation Matrix for the $\hat{a}_j$:

$$
\begin{array}{l}
\hat{a}_0 \\
\hat{a}_1 \\
\hat{a}_2 \\
\hat{a}_3 \\
\hat{a}_4 \\
\hat{a}_5 \\
\hat{a}_6 \\
\hat{a}_7
\end{array}
\left[
\begin{array}{cccccccc}
1.0000 \\
-0.3366 & 1.0000 \\
-0.0498 & -0.7930 & 1.0000 \\
-0.0800 & 0.4417 & -0.7388 & 1.0000 \\
-0.0210 & -0.1311 & 0.3308 & -0.7623 & 1.0000 \\
-0.1425 & 0.1122 & -0.1460 & 0.4161 & -0.7726 & 1.0000 \\
0.1277 & 0.0277 & 0.0648 & -0.2304 & 0.4306 & -0.8248 & 1.0000 \\
-0.3964 & -0.0879 & 0.0076 & 0.1547 & -0.1766 & 0.5083 & -0.8331 & 1.0000
\end{array}
\right]
$$

Correlation matrix for the $\hat{b}_j$:

$$
\begin{array}{l}
\hat{b}_0 \\
\hat{b}_1 \\
\hat{b}_2
\end{array}
\left[
\begin{array}{ccc}
1.0000 \\
-0.2090 & 1.0000 \\
-0.8701 & -0.2977 & 1.0000
\end{array}
\right].
$$

We may note that a few pairs of parameter estimates have correlation coefficients in the 80% range. It may be recalled that correlation coefficients for parameter estimates in the 80% range are not uncommon in time series analysis. (See the discussion in §5.6.) For example, Moran's AR(2) model for the log lynx data is a case in point. Clearly, these correlation coefficients depend on the covariance structure of the time series. The strongly cyclical nature of the lynx data could lead to high correlations among parmeter estimates.

7.2.8.5 Hat matrix From Fig. 7.29, it is clear that the data vectors

$$\{(X_{1892}, \ldots, X_{1886})^T, (X_{1893}, \ldots, X_{1887})^T, \ldots, (X_{1901}, \ldots, X_{1895})^T\}$$

form the most influential ·batch. (These entries are circled in the figure.) It is interesting to note that over a similar period, 1892–6, the 'private' data of Mr Charles French, then Fur Trade Commissioner of the Hudson Bay Company in Canada, have been incorporated in the final list of Elton and Nicholson's data set, which we have used. It might be possible that this irregular source of data has imparted some irregularity into the data, which has been detected by the hat matrix diagnostic (Table 7.10). On the other hand, the hat matrix analysis only lends modest support to the suggestion in §7.2.8.1 that X_{1842} and X_{1917} might merit further scrutiny.

7.2.8.6. Comparison with the precursor As we have said previously, the SETAR $(2; 7, 2)$ model of eqn (7.7) is a refinement of the SETAR $(2; 2, 2)$ model of eqn (7.3). It is therefore of interest to compare the fitted residuals of these two models. Let $\{\varepsilon_{Ht}\}$ and $\{\varepsilon_{Lt}\}$ denote the normalized residuals of the SETAR $(2; 7, 2)$ model and the SETAR $(2; 2, 2)$ model respectively. The correlation coefficient of $(\varepsilon_{Ht}, \varepsilon_{Lt}) = 0.90$. Clearly the two models have a lot in common.

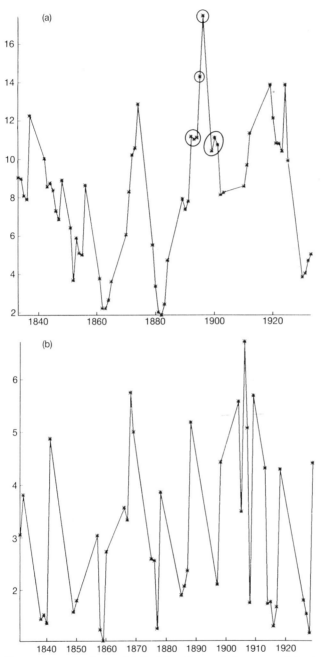

Fig. 7.29. Plots of sample size multiplied by diagonal elements of the hat matrix for the SETAR $(2; 7, 2)$ model for the log lynx data: (a) for the lower regime and (b) for the upper regime

Table 7.10. Diagonal elements of the hat matrix × sample size for the SETAR $(2; 7, 2)$ model of eqn (7.7)

Lower regime		Upper regime	
Year	Diagonal element ×61	Year	Diagonal element ×43
1833	9.0413	1831	3.0545
1834	8.9697	1832	3.8155
1835	8.0861	1838	1.4425
1836	7.9055	1839	1.5251
1837	12.2712	1840	1.3700
1842	10.0303	1841	4.8841
1843	8.5739	1849	1.5801
1844	8.7452	1850	1.7960
1845	8.3708	1857	3.0381
1846	7.3017	1858	1.2415
1847	6.8558	1859	1.0239
1848	8.8941	1860	2.7280
1851	6.4151	1866	3.5712
1852	3.6982	1867	3.3319
1853	5.8710	1868	5.7501
1854	5.0908	1869	5.0069
1855	5.0026	1875	2.5925
1856	8.6284	1876	2.5603
1861	3.7779	1877	1.2621
1862	2.2326	1878	3.8616
1863	2.2257	1885	1.8961
1864	2.6633	1886	2.0705
1865	3.6224	1887	2.3678
1870	6.0493	1888	5.1860
1871	8.2892	1897	2.1025
1872	10.2093	1898	4.4292
1873	10.5733	1904	5.5767
1874	12.8517	1905	3.4978
1879	5.5171	1906	6.7159
1880	3.3871	1907	5.0764
1881	2.0195	1908	1.7535
1882	1.8787	1909	5.6896
1883	2.4349	1913	4.3171
1884	4.7160	1914	1.7355
1889	7.9190	1915	1.7659
1890	7.3695	1916	1.3022

Table 7.10 continned

Lower regime		Upper regime	
Year	Diagonal element ×61	Year	Diagonal element ×43
1891	7.7872	1917	1.6695
1892	11.1602	1918	4.2954
1893	11.0301	1926	1.7995
1894	11.1072	1927	1.5389
1895	14.2920	1928	1.1774
1896	17.4525	1929	4.4136
1899	10.4148	1934	3.1923
1900	11.1100		
1901	10.7409		
1902	8.1391		
1903	8.2489	$[\chi^2_3(5\%)$	$= 7.81]$
1910	8.5765		
1911	9.6897		
1912	11.3188		
1919	13.8792		
1920	12.1260		
1921	10.8141		
1922	10.7991		
1923	10.3956		
1924	13.8709		
1925	9.9113		
1930	3.8675		
1931	4.0631		
1932	4.6954		
1933	5.0403		
$[\chi^2_8(5\%)$	$= 15.51]$		

Note: The χ^2 significance points are given only as a very rough guide. They are approximately valid in the linear autoregressive case but may not be so in the SETAR case.

7.2.9 OTHER TOOLS FOR TENTATIVE IDENTIFICATION OF THRESHOLDS AND DELAYS

In §7.2.3, we suggested the use of non-parametric lag regression estimates to provide a tentative identification of thresholds and delay parameters. Another possibility is to include estimates of var$[X_t \mid X_{t-j}]$, $j = 1, 2, \ldots, 10$ say. Figure 7.5 suggests that $\hat{d} = 2$ and $\hat{r} \approx 3$ is reasonable. Other suggestions have been made. For example, Haggan *et al.* (1984) *have suggested the plotting of* $\hat{a}_1(\xi_{t-1})$ and $\hat{a}_2(\xi_{t-1})$ against components of ξ_{t-1}, where $\hat{a}_j(\xi_{t-1})$ is an estimate of the $a_j(\xi_{t-1})$ coefficient in a 'state'-dependent model defined in eqn (3.63), and ξ_t is the carrier variable. The estimate they have used is based on some non-parametric function-fitting technique which smoothes an initial estimate obtained by a Kalman filter. They have chosen $\xi_{t-1} = X_{t-1}$ in the above equation for the log lynx data and have plotted $\hat{a}_1(X_{t-1})$ and $\hat{a}_2(X_{t-1})$ in Figures 15 and 16 of their paper. (These figures have been reproduced in Figs. 5.16 and 5.17 of Priestley (1988, pp. 128–9). He has used the notation $\hat{\phi}_1(X_{t-1})$ and $\hat{\phi}_2(X_{t-1})$ where we have used $\hat{a}_1(X_{t-1})$ and $\hat{a}_2(X_{t-1})$ respectively.) They have drawn particular attention to the sharp 'dip' in the neighbourhood of $X_{t-1} = 2.2$ in both graphs, although they have then gone on to dismiss the value 2.2 as any plausible 'threshold'. Interestingly, if the value 2.2 were entertained as a candidate for threshold, it would be in the neighbourhood of an 'unsubstantiated' anti-mode (by reference to the bootstrap test for multimodality in Table 7.3, which suggests that there is only one anti-mode and the obvious one seems to be in the neighbourhood of the value 3) of the histogram in Fig. 7.1. Besides, there are only 13 observations below 2.2, which would form a rather small sample for any meaningful modelling. Haggan *et al.* then conclude that their technique has not detected any thresholds. However, the above authors have also mentioned one rather worrying feature concerning $\hat{a}_1(X_{t-1})$ and $\hat{a}_2(X_{t-1})$. To describe their observation, we propose tracing their figure for $\hat{a}_1(X_{t-1})$ on a transparency, rotating the transparency about the horizontal axis by 180°, and then placing it on their figure for $\hat{a}_2(X_{t-1})$. Readers should be able to observe an almost exact matching. Priestley (1988) has also given simulations results which suggest that the Haggan *et al.* technique, in its present form, is not ready as a practical proposition for threshold estimation.

A more successful suggestion has been described by Tsay (1989), which also relies heavily on the use of graphics. The first group of plots used are similar to the traditional on-line residual plots in quality control. Specifically they are:

1.   The scatter plots of the predictive residuals described in §5.3.5.3 against X_{t-d}. Here we watch for any systematic deviation from randomness.

The second group of plots are:

2.   The scatter plots of the t-ratios of recursive estimates of AR coefficients (i.e. the estimates of **b** of eqn (5.108)). Here we watch for any systematic change in the t-ratios.

The essential ingredient is the ordered autoregression as described in §5.3.5.3. The change points in (1) and (2) are then used as tentative thresholds. These may give more than one threshold. The delay parameter, d, is tentatively identified before the thresholds by treating Tsay's F-statistic described in §5.3.5.3 as a function of d and choosing the maximizer as a tentative estimate of d. (The order of the AR model is assumed given here, which may be previously selected by using one of the order determination procedures.) Using the above graphics, Tsay (1988) has tentatively identified $\hat{d} = 2$ and two thresholds, $\hat{r}_1 = 2.373$ and $\hat{r}_2 = 3.154$, for the log lynx data, and has fitted the following SETAR $(3; 1, 7, 2)$ model:

$$X_t = \begin{cases} 0.083 + 1.096X_{t-1} + \varepsilon_t^{(1)} & \text{if } X_{t-2} \leq 2.373 \\[2mm] 0.63 + 0.96X_{t-1} - 0.11X_{t-2} + 0.23X_{t-3} - 0.61X_{t-4} \\ \quad + 0.48X_{t-5} - 0.39X_{t-6} + 0.28X_{t-7} + \varepsilon_t^{(2)} & \text{if } 2.373 < X_{t-2} \leq 3.154 \\[2mm] 2.323 + 1.530X_{t-1} - 1.266X_{t-2} + \varepsilon_t^{(3)} & \text{if } 3.154 < X_{t-2} \end{cases}$$

$$(7.8)$$

where var $\varepsilon_t^{(1)} = 0.015$, var $\varepsilon_t^{(2)} = 0.025$, var $\varepsilon_t^{(3)} = 0.053$.

It is obvious that $\hat{d}$ of Tsay's model is identical to the $\hat{d}$ in the model given by eqn (7.7). Tsay has noted that there is only one observation (3.142) between his $\hat{r}_2$ and the threshold value 3.116 of eqn (7.7). He has also remarked on the closeness between $\hat{r}_1$ and the value 2.2 mentioned but dismissed in Haggan et al. (1984). Interestingly Tsay's model lends support to the 'limit cycle hypothesis' rather than the 'chaotic hypothesis' as it has a limit cycle with period 9 $(6\uparrow3\downarrow)$ similar to that shown in Fig. 7.27 for eqn (7.7).

Yet another practical tool for tentative identification of the thresholds may be based on the profile log likelihood of r, with the autoregressive orders appropriately fixed. Obvious local maxima of the profile log likelihood of r may be entertained as preliminary estimates of the thresholds. These may give more than one threshold. By scanning a portfolio of the profile log likelihoods of r with d varying over $\{1, 2, \ldots, 10\}$ say, we may also gain some insight into a preliminary estimate of d. (See Exercise 10.)

In conclusion, tools for tentative identification of the structural parameters (namely d and r) form an important part of the armoury of any non-linear time series analyst. With these tools, rough estimates of the structural parameters can be obtained economically, on the basis of which some fine tuning may be performed if desired.

7.2.10   EXPAR MODELS

We shall follow the notation of eqns (3.27) and (3.28). The method of estimation is conditional least squares, or equivalently conditional maximum likelihood if it is assumed that $\varepsilon_t \sim \mathcal{N}(0, \sigma^2)$.

Haggan and Ozaki (1981) have fitted an EXPAR model of order 11 to the *mean-deleted* log lynx data. We may reproduce their model as follows (using the circumflex to denote the conditional least-squares estimator):

i	1	2	3	4	5	6	7	8	9	10	11
$\hat{\alpha}_i$	1.09	−0.28	0.27	−0.45	0.41	−0.36	0.22	−0.10	0.22	−0.07	−0.38
$\hat{\beta}_i$	0.01	−0.49	−0.06	0.30	−0.54	0.61	−0.53	0.30	−0.18	0.18	0.16

$\hat{\delta} = 3.89$, $\hat{\sigma}^2 = \text{var } \hat{\varepsilon}_t = 0.0321$. The motivation of this model is as described in Example 2.13. Haggan and Ozaki have claimed that

(1)   the roots of the equation

$$z^{11} - \sum_{i=1}^{11} \hat{\alpha}_i z^{11-i} = 0$$

are all inside the unit circle; and

(2)   one pair of the roots of the equation

$$z^{11} - \sum_{i=1}^{11} (\hat{\alpha}_i + \hat{\beta}_i) z^{11-i} = 0$$

lies out side the unit circle.

Their final conclusion is that the skeleton of the fitted EXPAR(11) model has a limit cycle of period 397 consisting of 42 sub-cycles.

It would appear that there are several difficulties with the Haggan–Ozaki model which may be listed as follows:

1.   With the estimates of the α and the β as given by Haggan and Ozaki and reproduced exactly above, their first claim is questionable as one pair of the roots appears to be *outside* the unit circle at 1.03 exp($\pm$0.213i). We can only assume that their first claim was based on parameter estimates before they were rounded to two decimal places as given in their paper. A similar comment may be made on their second claim.

2.   It is clearly difficult to interpret the parameters without their standard errors, which unfortunately have not been given by these authors. However, it would seem reasonable to assume that the standard errors are such that it would not be sensible to quote the estimates to more than two or three decimal places. Experience has

also suggested that there can be difficulties with the estimation of δ, the crucial *structural parameter*, which we have discussed in §5.6.4.

3. We have discussed in Chapter 2 (especially §2.12 and §2.13) the difficulties with stretching the physical arguments too far without a solid mathematical back-up. Questions can therefore be raised on the validity of their conclusion. In fact, in view of (1) and (2) above, are we sure that their claimed 'limit cycle' is real and is not due to the skeleton having a pair of roots on the unit circle instead?

4. By Theorem 4.6, the Haggan–Ozaki model gives symmetric joint distributions and is therefore not ideally suited for the log lynx data which do not have symmetric joint distributions.

5. It is not easy to justify a model with 23 parameters for 114 observations.

Later, Ozaki (1982) attempted to improve the Haggan–Ozaki model and suggested the following EXPAR model to the mean-deleted log lynx data:

$$X_t = [0.138 + (0.316 + 0.982X_{t-1})e^{-\hat{\delta}X_{t-1}^2}]X_{t-1}$$
$$- [0.437 + (0.659 + 1.260X_{t-1})e^{-\hat{\delta}_{t-1}^2}]X_{t-2} + \varepsilon_t \qquad (7.9)$$

where $\varepsilon_t - \mathcal{N}(0, \hat{\sigma}^2)$, $\hat{\delta} = 3.89$, $\hat{\sigma}^2 = 4.327 \times 10^{-2}$. However, as has been pointed out by Lim (1987), this model gives a rather peculiar fit. We have been unable to reproduce the estimates using conditional least squares and suspect that there has been a misprint or a computing error. *Keeping $\hat{\delta}$ at 3.89, our least-squares estimation of the other parameters results in replacing 0.138 by 1.167*. We shall refer to the replacement model as the *modified Ozaki model*. Over the dynamic range of the data, the modified Ozaki model is 'closer' to Moran's AR(2) model (eqn (7.1)) than the unmodified version. This tends to support further our suspicion of an error. We should add that the unmodified Ozaki model may be further improved by a complete refitting without fixing $\hat{\delta}$ *a priori*. In other words we have introduced only the minimum necessary modification.

The modified Ozaki model is certainly a substantial improvement over the earlier Haggan–Ozaki model in terms of interpretation, parsimony, and statistical goodness of fit. (Readers are encouraged to do the comparison for themselves.) In fact, the skeletons of the modified Ozaki model and the SETAR (2; 2, 2) model are not too dissimilar (Fig. 7.30). Over the dynamic range of the data the regression surfaces $E[X_t \mid X_{t-1}, X_{t-2}]$ of the SETAR (2; 2, 2) model and the modified Ozaki model are only mildly different (see Fig. 7.31). They may be compared with that of the polynomial AR model suggested by Cox (1977) (see

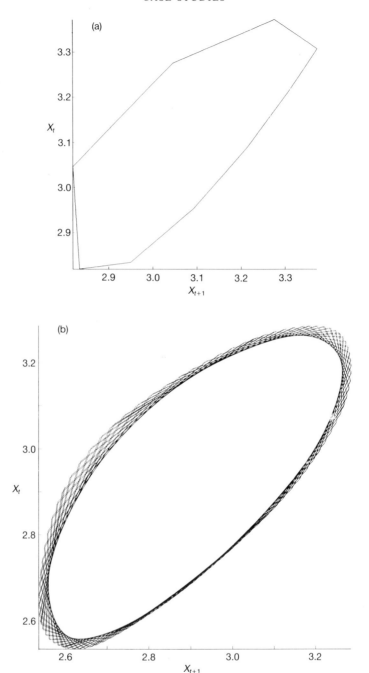

Fig. 7.30. (a) Limit cycle of the skeleton of the SETAR $(2; 2, 2)$ model for log lynx data. (b) Limit cycle of skeleton of modified Ozaki model for log lynx data

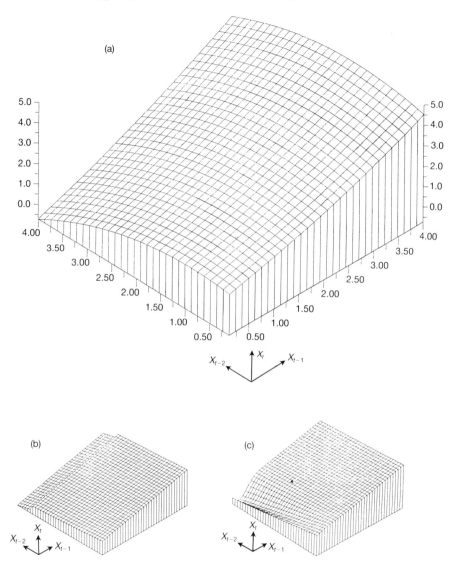

Fig. 7.31. Regression surface $E[X_t \mid X_{t-1}, X_{t-2}]$: (a) Cox's model; (b) SETAR $(2; 2, 2)$ model; (c) modified Ozaki model

Table 7.11. Modified Ozaki model for mean-deleted log lynx data

| | Information matrix $\times \hat{\sigma}^2$ | | | | | | |
	$\hat{\alpha}_1$	$\hat{\gamma}_0^{(1)}$	$\hat{\gamma}_1^{(1)}$	$\hat{\alpha}_2$	$\hat{\gamma}_0^{(2)}$	$\hat{\gamma}_1^{(2)}$	$\hat{\delta}$
$\hat{\alpha}_1$	7.6136						
$\hat{\gamma}_0^{(1)}$	1.2113	0.5055					
$\hat{\gamma}_1^{(1)}$	−0.0238	−0.0161	0.0880				
$\hat{\alpha}_2$	5.9868	0.9862	−0.0067	7.6136			
$\hat{\gamma}_0^{(2)}$	0.9862	0.4218	−0.1200	2.2380	1.4088		
$\hat{\gamma}_1^{(2)}$	−0.0067	−0.0120	0.0714	−0.0257	−0.246	0.1209	
$\hat{\delta}$	0.0818	0.0205	0.0007	0.1575	0.0554	0.0132	0.0102

Tong 1983a, p. 183):

$$X_t = 0.3452X_{t-1} + 1.0994X_{t-2} + 0.1204X_{t-1}^2$$
$$+ 0.1162X_{t-1}X_{t-2} - 0.3838X_{t-2}^2 + \varepsilon_t \qquad (7.10)$$

$\varepsilon_t \sim \text{IID}(0, 0.0469)$.

However, the modified Ozaki model is not without its problems. We list some of them below.

1′. From the inverse of the matrix in Table 7.11, we may deduce the approximate standard errors of the parameter estimates: $\hat{\alpha}_1(0.216)$, $\hat{\gamma}_0^{(1)}(0.486)$, $\gamma_1^{(1)}(1.152)$, $\hat{\alpha}_2(0.268)$, $\hat{\gamma}_0^{(2)}(0.360)$, $\hat{\gamma}_1^{(2)}(1.146)$, $\hat{\delta}(3.679)$. The small approximate t-ratios cast doubt on the significance of the non-linear parameter estimates, namely $\hat{\gamma}_j^{(i)}$ ($i = 1, 2$; $j = 0, 1$) and $\hat{\delta}$. Furthermore, we note that the matrix in Table 7.11 is *nearly singular* with a determinant approximately equal to 4.2×10^{-5}! (Recall that this is the matrix which has to be inverted to produce the standard errors.) The table is obtained with the aid of the numerical method in §4.2.4.3.

Figure 7.32 highlights the type of problem which will be encountered in numerical optimization.

As we have discussed in § 5.6.4.6, we should always watch out for this type of difficulty when fitting EXPAR models.

2′. Unlike the Haggan–Ozaki model, Ozaki's model (7.9), modified or not, does not have zero expectation for X_t (assuming stationarity and existence of mean). Therefore, it violates the least-squares principle to estimate the unknown parameters by minimizing $\Sigma \varepsilon_t^2$ *when the data are mean-deleted*—Ozaki (1982) seems to have violated the said principle in so far as we can judge from reading his paper. Fortunately for the present example, the effect does not seem very serious and we shall therefore ignore it here. In practice, we recommend either (i) minimizing $\Sigma \varepsilon_t^2$

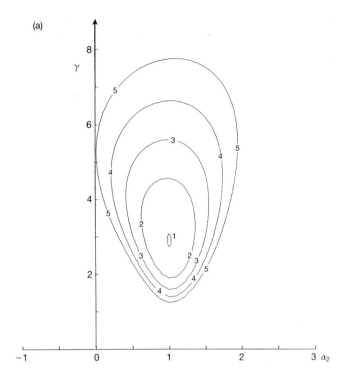

(a)

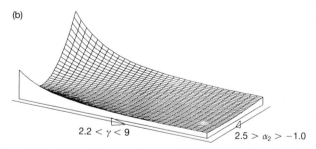

(b)

2.2 < γ < 9

2.5 > α₂ > −1.0

Fig. 7.32. Plot of (conditional) sum of squared errors as a function of (α_2, γ) of the modified Ozaki model fitted to mean-deleted log lynx data. Other parameters are fixed at their respective conditional least-squares estimates $(1 = 4.80, 2 = 4.90, 3 = 5.00, 4 = 5.10, 5 = 5.20)$

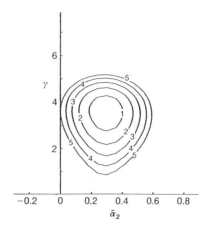

Fig. 7.33. Plot of (conditional) sum of squared errors as a function of $(\tilde{\alpha}_2, \gamma)$ of the modified Ozaki model fitted to mean-deleted log lynx data. Other parameters are fixed at their respective conditional least-squares estimates ($1 = 4.90$, $2 = 5.00$, $3 = 5.10$, $4 = 5.20$, $6 = 5.30$)

without mean-deleting the data or (ii) mean-deleting the data but adding a constant term to the model before minimizing $\Sigma \varepsilon_t^2$.

3′. As suggested in §5.6.4, we may consider a reparametrization by centring, that is by typically replacing $\gamma_0^{(1)}$ by $\bar{\gamma}_0^{(1)} = \gamma_0^{(1)} \exp(-\delta\mu_2')$, where $\mu_2' = EX_t^2$ and $\hat{\mu}_2' = 0.30908$.

Substantial improvement seems to be gained by the centring device as can be seen by comparing Fig. 7.33 with Fig. 7.32(a) and Table 7.12 with Table 7.11. The determinant has increased dramatically from 4.2×10^{-5} to approximately 2.33!

4′. Keeping the autoregressive order at 2, a profile negative log likelihood of δ (Fig. 7.34) w.r.t. the modified Ozaki (without centring)

Table 7.12. Centred EXPAR model for mean deleted log lynx data

Information matrix $\times \hat{\sigma}^2$

8.0011						
4.6131	7.2820					
−0.1157	−0.2301	1.2814				
6.3353	3.7912	−0.0501	8.0024			
3.7912	6.1543	−0.1917	8.6580	20.7964		
−0.0501	−0.1917	1.0474	−0.1340	−0.4225	1.8025	
0.0849	0.0786	0.0025	0.1628	0.2153	0.0518	0.0106

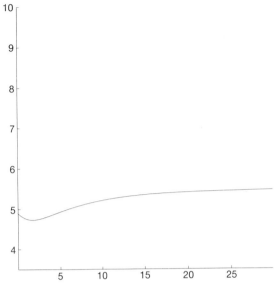

Fig. 7.34. Profile negative log likelihood of δ w.r.t. the modified Ozaki model. This is the partially minimized negative log likelihood in which the negative log likelihood is minimized for each fixed δ

has global minimum at 1.77, which is substantially different from the estimate adopted by Ozaki at 3.89. However, note the small range of values assumed by the profile negative log likelihood as δ varies over $[0, 30]$. This flatness is, of course, consistent with comment 1' above.

5'.   A more systematic reparametrization and re-estimation of the parameters might be necessary.

7.2.11   BILINEAR MODELS

We shall follow the notation of eqn (3.40) and the convention of the circumflex of §7.2.10. Gabr and Suba Rao (1981) have fitted a subset BL model to the log lynx data (1821–1920) keeping the next 14 observations for prediction experiments. Assuming $\varepsilon_t \sim \mathcal{N}(0, \sigma_\varepsilon^2)$, they have used the maximum likelihood estimation coupled with AIC for model selection.* Specifically, they have given the following parameter estimates, which we duplicate here without modification,† although it can be

---

* In view of the fact that AIC presupposes the existence of the Fisher information (cf W of eqn (5.150)), it is not clear to the author how AIC could be justified for selecting BL models (cf §5.5.4.3 and Exercise 13).
† It appears that Subba Rao and Gabr (1984, p. 204) and Gabr and Subba Rao (1981) differ in the values of $\hat{a}_1$ and $\hat{\alpha}$. Our checking suggests that the 1981 version should be adopted, as we have.

argued that excessive decimal places have been used (all unlisted coefficients are zero):

$$\hat{a}_1 = -0.772\,27 \qquad \hat{a}_2 = 0.091\,572 \qquad \hat{a}_3 = -0.083\,073$$

$$\hat{a}_4 = 0.261\,493 \qquad \hat{a}_9 = -0.225\,585 \qquad \hat{a}_{12} = 0.245\,841$$

$$\hat{\alpha} = 1.486\,292$$

$$\hat{b}_{3,9} = -0.7893 \qquad \hat{b}_{9,9} = 0.4798 \qquad \hat{b}_{6,2} = 0.3902 \qquad (7.11)$$

$$\hat{b}_{1,1} = 0.1326 \qquad \hat{b}_{2,7} = 0.079\,44 \qquad \hat{b}_{4,2} = -0.3212$$

$$\hat{\sigma}_\varepsilon^2 = 0.0223 \qquad \text{NAIC} = -3.508.$$

A few comments are in order.

1.   As far as we are aware, the Gabr–Subba Rao model is primarily motivated by prediction. It is therefore vital to check that the fitted BL model is invertible. Before doing this, an examination of the negative log likelihood function of the above model (see Fig. 7.35) suggests that there may well be problems ahead.

On using the device described in §5.6.6 for checking invertibility, it seems that Fig. 7.36 casts doubt on the invertibility of the Gabr–Subba Rao's BL model.

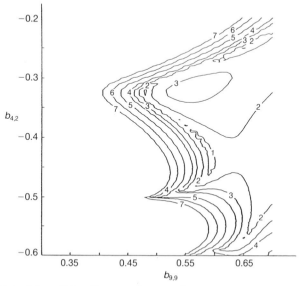

Fig. 7.35. Plot of (conditional) sum of squared errors as a function of $(b_{4,2}, b_{9,9})$ of a bilinear model fitted to log lynx data. Other parameters are fixed at their respective maximum likelihood estimates. $(1 = 5.0,\ 2 = 20.0,\ 3 = 80.0,\ 4 = 200.0,\ 5 = 700.0,\ 6 = 2000.0,\ 7 = 5000.0)$

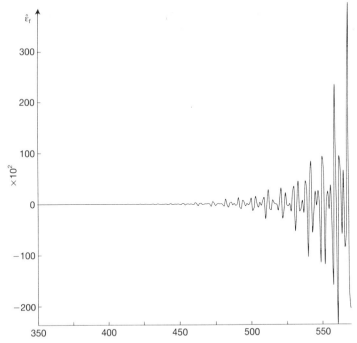

Fig. 7.36. Plot of $\hat{\varepsilon}_t$ versus t of bilinear model fitted to log lynx data. The first 114 points are just the original fitted residuals. Explosion is triggered off at around $t = 500$. Our computer (DEX VAX 8800 plus 8200) overflows at $t = 1308$, where $\hat{\varepsilon}_t$ exceeds 10^{38} in double precision

2. Lim (1987) has reported other worrying features about the above BL model. First, she has obtained the first four moments of the model using a Monte Carlo method based on 10 000 points, having observed that the dynamic range of the artificial data is unusually wide at $(-120, 120)$ with about 20% of the data (i.e. ·about 2000 points) outside the range $(0, 6)$. We note that BL models tend to have sudden large excursions (cf Fig. 1.3 and Example 4.11). By comparison, the dynamic range of the log lynx data is only $(1.5, 4.0)$ approximately. It is therefore not surprising to see the unusually large moment estimates of the model (Table 7.13), suggesting that the model may well be lacking in the moment property. Lim's results are entered in Table 7.13 under BL(Lim). We have also included our own results based on the average of four independent 10 000 point simulations. A related point is the absence of 'standard errors' of the parameter estimates, which makes a proper assessment of the significance of the $\hat{b}_{ij}$ difficult (see §5.5.4.3 and Exercise 13). A pragmatic remedy is to use the observed Fisher information or bootstrapped interquartiles. (See Exercise 1).

3. Lim (1987) has also reported rather disappointing covariance

Table 7.13. First four moments about the origin

	Mean	2nd moment	3rd moment	4th moment	Approximate dynamic range
Data (1821–1920)	2.88	8.62	26.68	84.77	$(1.5, 4.0)$
BL (Lim)	2.91	168.00	1607.00	5968.00	$(-120, 120)$
BL (four replications)	2.90	18.33	106.42	4653.19	$(-20, 25)$

structure (i.e. the autocovariance function and its Fourier transform) of the fitted BL model. This is not surprising in view of 2.

4. Lag regression functions of the fitted BL model are nearly linear over the dynamic range of the log lynx data (Fig. 7.37 is typical). $\mathrm{Var}(X_t \mid X_{t-j})$, $j = 1, 2, \ldots, 10$, of the fitted model seem to deviate substantially from the observed (Fig. 7.5).

The message of the above findings suggests that it is not always wise to overemphasize the importance of the size of $\hat{\sigma}_\varepsilon^2$ (the noise variance) or the NAIC values (even if their use is justified) in model building. We would argue that, in a loose sense, there is an inherent upper bound on the 'signal-to-noise ratio' in any *finite* statistical data set. In this connection, Lim's study (1987) seems to suggest that if a BL model is really desired for some reason, then an earlier BL model briefly mentioned by Subba Rao in his discussion of Tong and Lim (1980, p. 279) would be a better

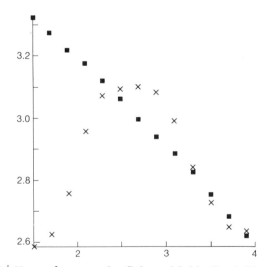

Fig. 7.37. $E[X_t \mid X_{t-3} = x]$ versus x for Gabr and Subba Rao's BL model: ×, from real data; ■, from 10 000 artificial data generated by the BL model

candidate, despite its larger $\hat{\sigma}_\varepsilon^2$ (at 0.033) and larger NAIC (at -3.222)—
see Exercise 1. The basic point is that $\text{var}(\hat{b}_{ij})$ tends to increase as $\sigma_\varepsilon^2 \to 0$,
for fixed sample size (Exercise 13 and Moeanaddin and Tong 1989b). An
explanation for this phenomenon is that all BL models become linear at
$\sigma_\varepsilon^2 = 0$ and then there will be no information for the 'bilinear' parameters,
b_{ij}. In this sense, the 'white tail wags the bilinear dog'!* The same remark
applies to the ARCH model and the like.

7.2.12 A RANDOM COEFFICIENT AUTOREGRESSIVE MODEL

We shall adopt the notation of §3.7.

The primary motivation of fitting an RCA model to the log lynx data
also seems to be a prediction. Nicholls and Quinn (1982) have fitted the
following RCA to the log lynx data (1821–1920) using apparently the
maximum likelihood method. (We say 'apparently' because the precise
method of estimation used for these 100 observations does not seem clear
in their book. However, it seems clear that it is either the maximum
likelihood method or the conditional least-squares method which has
been used.)

$$X_t = (1.4132 + B_1(t))X_{t-1} + (-0.7942 + B_2(t))X_{t+2} + \varepsilon_t \quad (7.12)$$

where $X_t = \log_{10}(\text{number of lynx in year } (1820 + t)) - 2.8802$, $\sigma^2 = 0.0391$, and

$$E\{[B_1(t)B_2(t)]'[B_1(t)B_2(t)]\} = \begin{bmatrix} 0.0701 & -0.0406 \\ -0.0406 & 0.0492 \end{bmatrix}.$$

Clearly, the basic form of (7.12) is that of an AR(2) and the
coefficients are very close to Moran's AR(2) model given by eqn (7.1).
By the independence among $\{B_i(t)\}$, $i = 1, 2$, and $\{\varepsilon_t\}$, the least-squares
predictor for the above RCA model is linear. Thus, the least-squares
one-step-ahead predictor, $\hat{X}_t(1)$ for X_{t+1} given X_s, $s \le t$, is given by

$$\hat{X}_t(1) = 1.4132X_t - 0.7942X_{t-1}. \quad (7.13)$$

Nicholls and Quinn (1982) have also considered predictors other than
the least-squares predictor and have obtained interesting results.

7.2.13 CLUSTERS OF FITTED MODELS

Tong and Dabas (1989) have applied techniques in multivariate analysis,
namely the principal coordinate analysis and the dendrograms, to 12
models reported in the literature, including (A) Moran's AR(2), (B)

---

* Sir David Cox has suggested in a private communication that one way out is to replace b_{ij}
by $b_{ij}/\sigma_\varepsilon$.

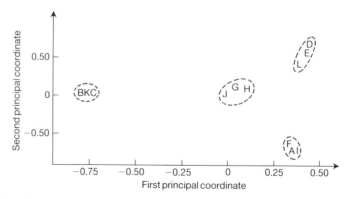

Fig. 7.38. Principal coordinates plot of 12 models fitted to lynx data, based on a 12×12 matrix of sample correlation coefficients of fitted residuals. They account for about 60% of the random variation

Tong's AR(11), (C) Tong's subset AR(11), (D) Gabr and Subba Rao's AR(12), (E) Gabr and Subba Rao's subset AR(12), (F) Tong's SETAR$(2; 2, 2)$, (G) Tong's SETAR$(2; 5, 2)$, (H) Tong's SETAR$(2; 7, 2)$, (I) Ozaki's EXPAR(2), (J) Ozaki's EXPAR (9), (K) Subba Rao's 9 parameter subset BL, and (L) Gabr and Subba Rao's 13 parameter subset BL. Most of the non-linear models are listed in various parts of this book. The references of the models are Moran (1953), Tong (1977*b*), Gabr and Subba Rao (1981), Tong (1983*a*), Ozaki (1982), and Subba Rao (1980). Tong and Dabas (1989) have suggested that there may be four discernible clusters: $\{A, F, I\}\{B, C, K\}\{D, E, L\}\{G, H, J\}$ see Fig. 7.38. The implications of this clustering may be listed as follows:

1. If modelling is confined to an autoregressive model of order not higher than 2, then the end products share a high degree of affinity, be they non-linear or not.

2. On the other hand, non-linear autoregressive models of order higher than 2 tend to break this affinity.

3. Bilinear models generally exhibit substantial affinity with the linear autoregressive models.

From the point of view of perturbation of linear models, it seems that different classes of non-linear models exert different strengths of perturbation. Thus, some models may be *strongly non-linear* whilst others are *weakly non-linear*. It is still an open question as to how to quantify the strengths of perturbation.

7.3. Sunspot numbers and genuine predictions

7.3.1 INTRODUCTION

It is generally accepted that the earliest recorded date of a sunspot event was 10 May 28 BC during the reign of Emperor Liu Ao (Cheng Di) of the Western Han Dynasty in China. (See for example Needham (1959, p. 435). It seems that he has given a different rendering of the Emperor's name. We have followed the modern Chinese phonetic practice.) It is quite possible that earlier dates could be found from the Chinese dynastic historical records. As we have mentioned in §2.8, it was in the year 1843 that the sunspot *cycle* was apparently first noted by the German pharmaceutical chemist and amateur astronomer, Samuel Heinrich Schwabe (1789–1875), after 17 years of painstaking daily observations. Since the dawn of time series analyis early this century, the Zurich series of sunspot relative numbers has been analyzed in almost every respectable textbook on time series analysis. Izenman (1983) has traced the history of these numbers and has attributed full credit for the origin and subsequent development of the Zurich series to Johann Rudolf Wolf (1816–93). For convenience we shall refer to the record given in Appendix 3 and in Fig. 7.39 as the annual means of Wolf's sunspot numbers, or simply the sunspot numbers.

The *solar cycle,* that is the roughly 11 year period with which sunspots occur, remains a mystery to date because the most fundamental questions about the nature of the solar cycle remain unanswered. Consequently, the only feasible method to predict future sunspot numbers seems to be the so-called 'black-box' technique. (This was the 'black virtue' alluded to in the opening quotation of Chapter 3!) That is to say, we build a time series model for the sunspot numbers not so much to gain any deep insight into their nature but rather as a pragmatic tool with which we may obtain, say, least-squares predictions. Since the series is unlikely to

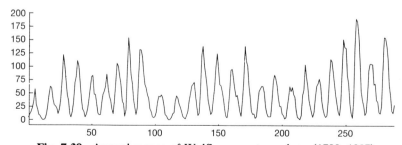

Fig. 7.39. Annual means of Wolf's sunspot numbers (1700–1987)

end in the near future barring human folly, we are presented with the challenge of genuine predictions! We shall address ourselves to this aspect of the exercise. We shall omit the modelling details in order to save space. Readers who are interested in these and other aspects might wish to consult Tong (1983a) and the references therein. Moreover, we recall the definition of the technical term *genuine prediction* in §7.2.6. We argue that non-genuine prediction has very limited value in scientific reporting because it is open to abuse. The following *extreme* example serves to amplify the point. Let $\{x_1, x_2, \ldots, x_n, x_{n+1}, \ldots, x_{n+m}\}$ be available. A cheater can always fit an AR(m) model say to $\{x_{n+1}, \ldots, x_{n+m}\}$ which has *zero* residual sum of squares. He can then report this AR(m) model as the model fitted to $\{x_1, \ldots, x_n\}$ and claim its remarkable prediction performance over the 'post-fitting period' $\{x_{n+1}, \ldots, x_{n+m}\}$! It is surprising how often people are hoodwinked by this kind of trickery or its more cunning variations, in which, for instance, the parameters are fine-tuned over the fitting period $\{x_1, \ldots, x_n\}$ so as to optimize the model's non-genuine forecast performance over the 'post-fitting' period.

7.3.2   AN EXAMPLE OF GENUINE PREDICTION

To the sunspot numbers of the period 1700–1979, after an instantaneous square-root transformation, Ghaddar and Tong fitted a threshold auto-regressive (SETAR) model in 1980, on the basis of which they derived genuine multi-step least-squares predictions for the period 1980–7 and their results were in print in 1981. Their fitted model was (with coefficients rounded to two decimal places):

$$Y_t = \begin{cases} 1.92 + 0.84Y_{t-1} + 0.07Y_{t-2} - 0.32Y_{t-3} + 0.15Y_{t-4} - 0.20Y_{t-5} \\ \quad - 0.00Y_{t-6} + 0.19Y_{t-7} - 0.27Y_{t-8} + 0.21Y_{t-9} + 0.01Y_{t-10} \\ \quad + 0.09Y_{t-11} + \varepsilon_t^{(1)} \qquad\qquad\qquad\quad \text{if } Y_{t-8} \le 11.93 \\ 4.27 + 1.44Y_{t-1} - 0.84Y_{t-2} + 0.06Y_{t-3} + \varepsilon_t^{(2)} \quad \text{if } Y_{t-8} > 11.93 \end{cases} \tag{7.14}$$

where $Y_t = 2\{[1 + (\text{sunspot number in year } (1699 + t))]^{1/2} - 1\}$, var $\varepsilon_t^{(1)} = 1.946$, var $\varepsilon_t^{(2)} = 6.302$, and pooled var $= 3.734$. Their genuine multi-step least-squares predictions (Ghaddar and Tong 1981, p. 247) are reproduced as follows:

Year	Prediction	Observation*	Error
1980	160.1	154.7	−5.4
1981	141.8	140.5	−1.3
1982	96.4	115.9	19.5
1983	61.8	66.6	4.8
1984	31.1	45.9	14.8
1985	18.1	17.9	−0.2
1986	18.9	13.4	−5.5
1987	29.9	29.2	−0.7

The base year is 1979.

* These observations have been kindly supplied to the author by the Sunspot Index Data Centre, Brussels, Belgium.

The mean squared error of prediction over the years 1980–7 is 85.50.

An addendum circulated privately with Tong (1983a, *see the explanation in the footnoe on p.* 187 *there*) noted some *minor* corrections of the autoregressive parameter estimates, which modified model (7.14) to the following:

$$Y_t = \begin{cases} 1.89 + 0.86Y_{t-1} + 0.08Y_{t-2} - 0.32Y_{t-3} + 0.16Y_{t-4} - 0.21Y_{t-5} \\ \quad - 0.00Y_{t-6} + 0.19Y_{t-7} - 0.28Y_{t-8} + 0.20Y_{t-9} + 0.10Y_{t-10} + \varepsilon_t^{(1)} \\ \qquad\qquad\qquad\qquad \text{if } Y_{t-8} \leq 11.93 \\ 4.53 + 1.41Y_{t-1} - 0.78Y_{t-2} + \varepsilon_t^{(2)} \quad \text{if } Y_{t-8} > 11.93 \end{cases}$$

$$(7.15)$$

where var $\varepsilon_t^{(1)} = 1.946$, var $\varepsilon_t^{(2)} = 6.302$, and pooled var $= 3.734$. The mean squared error of prediction over the years 1980–7 based on model (7.15) with(out) bias correction is 50.3(55.8). The predicted values together with $\hat{\sigma}^2(m)$, var$(X_{t+m} \mid X_t, X_{t-1}, \dots)$, are given in Fig. 7.40.

As a *benchmark* for comparison, we may fit a linear AR(p) model to the raw data following Yule (1927), Box and Jenkins (1976), Granger and Andersen (1978), and others. To avoid potential subjective tinkering, we agree to adopt the minimum AIC estimate of p. Figure 7.41 shows the prediction performance based on the AR(9) model selected by Akaike's information criterion.

Some comments are now in order.

1. Over the period 1980–7, it would appear that the genuine non-linear prediction based on either (7.14) or (7.15) has generally out-performed the linear prediction by a noticeable margin in respect

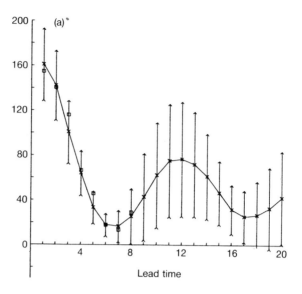

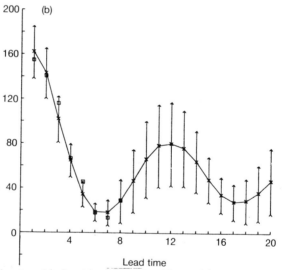

Fig. 7.40. Estimates $\hat{\sigma}(m)$ with (b) and without (a) bias corrections of the non-linear model of (7.15) fitted to Wolf's annual sunspot numbers 1700–1979. (The point forecast for the year $(1979 + m)$ is denoted by the $\times$ at the centre of the vertical line corresponding to abscissa m, the length of which represents twice $\hat{\sigma}(m)$. For 1980–7, the true Wolf's annual sunspot numbers are denoted by $\square$. Mean square error of prediction (without bias correction) = 55.8, mean squared error of prediction (with bias correction) = 50.3

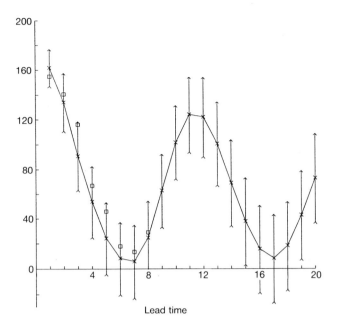

Fig. 7.41. Estimates $\hat{\sigma}(m)$ of the linear autoregressive model of order 9 fitted by using Akaike's information criterion to the Wolf's annual sunspot numbers 1700–1979, X_t. (The   model   is $X_t = 6.9627 + 1.2064X_{t-1} - 0.4507X_{t-2} - 0.1747X_{t-3} + 0.1974X_{t-4} - 0.1366X_{t-5} + 0.0268X_{t-6} + 0.0128X_{t-7} - 0.0312X_{t-8} + 0.2123X_{t-9} + e_t$, where var $e_t = 221.2366$. Point forecasts are denoted by the $\times$ at centres of vertical lines, the lengths of which represent twice $\hat{\sigma}(m)$. For 1980–7, the true Wolf's annual sunspot numbers are denoted by $\square$. Mean squared error of prediction = 190.7

of root mean squares of $|\hat{X}_t(m) - X_{t+m}|$, where $\hat{X}_t(m) = E[X_{t+m} | X_t, X_{t-1}, \dots]$. However, associated with the non-linear predictions of peak values are greater conditional variances.

2. Note that the vertical lines at the troughs in Fig. 7.41 have the tendency of extending below zero into the negative regime, sometimes quite substantially. A square-root transform will avoid this problem. It may also be remarked that the 'coefficients of variation', $\hat{\sigma}(m)/\hat{X}_t(m)$, fluctuate quite violently over m in the linear case but much less so in the non-linear case. The ranges are $0.09 \sim 4.92$ and $0.19 \sim 1.01$ respectively (cf approximately 0.8 for the coefficient of variation of the data).

3. The non-linear predictions for 1988–93 seem to be much vaguer than their linear counterparts. However, both approaches appear to

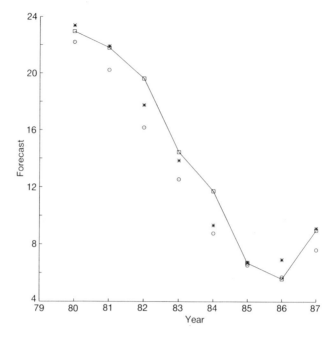

Fig. 7.42. Comparison of point forecasts for 1980–7. □, square-root-transformed value of observed sunspot number; *, point forecast based on SETAR model of eqn (7.14); ⊙, point forecast based on an AR (9) model fitted by the minimum AIC method (maximum lag set at 12) to the square-root-transformed sunspot numbers of 1700–1979. The fitted model is $Y_t = 1.6019 + 1.2212Y_{t-1} - 0.4896Y_{t-2} - 0.1579Y_{t-3} + 0.2746Y_{t-4} - 0.2489Y_{t-5} + 0.0257Y_{t-6} + 0.1593Y_{t-7} - 0.2222Y_{t-8} + 0.2980Y_{t-9} + \varepsilon_t, \; \varepsilon_t \sim \mathrm{IID}(0, 4.0560)$. Mean squared error of prediction for the linear model $= 3.65$, mean squared error of prediction for the SETAR model $= 1.44$

predict that 1988–93 will correspond to an 'upward' swing of a sunspot cycle.

4. To study the effect of the square-root transformation, we repeat the comparison with an AR(9) model selected by Akaike's information criterion to the square-root data $\{Y_t\}$. It is clear from Fig. 7.42 that comment (1) remains valid.

5. In the above comparison, it should be emphasized that in the linear case the predictions are not genuine predictions as they are obtained in 1989. Also, in all our estimation of parameters, we have used the same numerical algorithm for both the linear AR and SETAR models, namely the conditional least-squares approach with the Householder transformation.

7.3.3 COMBINATION PREDICTION

Despite the encouraging performance demonstrated in the last subsection of the non-linear least-squares prediction based on a threshold model, as far as medium to long-range prediction is concerned our limited experience suggests that a linear multi-step least-squares prediction often provides a *robust* benchmark especially in dealing with a fairly complex situation. Now it is well known that Wolfs sunspot numbers represent one such complex situation (see e.g. Tong 1983*a*, p. 230). For example, the rise from 38.0 in 1955 to 141.7 in 1956 is unusually steep. Tong and Lim (1980, p. 261) fitted a threshold model to the annual Wolf's sunspot numbers of 1700–1920, using the databank available at the University of Manchester Institute of Science & Technology, UK, at the time which contained the data only for the period 1700–1955 (cf. the listings of data set in Subba Rao and Gabr (1984), who used the same data source available at UMIST). We have listed in Table 7.14 a comparison of the prediction performance of the Tong–Lim threshold model (labelled SETAR) and that of a linear autoregressive model fitted by Subba Rao and Gabr (1984, p. 196) using Akaike's information criterion (labelled Full AR(9)). The fitting period and the prediction period for both models are identical. These are 1700–1920 and 1956–79 respectively. The prediction period of 1956–79 represents roughly two sunspot cycles and is so chosen as to retain some realism in the comparison since these data were unknown to Tong and Lim at the time of their fitting their SETAR model. Another motivation is to investigate the 'robustness' of various predictors to 'unusual shocks' similar to that of 1956. The period 1980–7 is reserved for further experimentation, bearing in mind the results of the last section over the same period. The specific forms of the two models are as follows;

1. The SETAR (2; 3, 11) model fitted to the sunspot numbers (1700–1920) by Tong and Lim (1980), incorporating the minor corrections to the autoregressive parameters as mentioned in §7.3.2, was:

$$X_t = \begin{cases} 11.97 + 1.71X_{t-1} - 1.26X_{t-2} + 0.43X_{t-3} + \varepsilon_t^{(1)} & \text{if } X_{t-3} \leq 36.6 \\ 7.84 + 0.73X_{t-1} - 0.04X_{t-2} - 0.20X_{t-3} + 0.16X_{t-4} \\ \quad - 0.22X_{t-5} + 0.02X_{t-6} + 0.15X_{t-7} - 0.24X_{t-8} \\ \quad + 0.31X_{t-9} - 0.37X_{t-10} + 0.38X_{t-11} + \varepsilon_t^{(2)} & \text{if } X_{t-3} > 36.6 \end{cases}$$

$$(7.16)$$

where var $\varepsilon_t^{(1)} = 254.64$, var $\varepsilon_t^{(2)} = 66.80$, and pooled var $= 153.7$. (Note: The uncorrected version is also available in Tong (1983*a*, p. 241).)

Table 7.14. Mean squared errors of multi-step least-squares predictions of sunspot numbers (1956–79)

Condition variances	Full AR (9) Below the mean	Above the mean	Overall	SETAR Below the mean	Above the mean	Oveall	Combination forecast
(Noise)			(199.270)			(153.710)	
$\hat{\sigma}^2(1)$	319.314	649.528	525.698	101.848	693.617	422.389	422.269
$\hat{\sigma}^2(2)$	524.930	1386.058	1049.095	135.520	1579.983	951.956	873.047
$\hat{\sigma}^2(3)$	472.676	1314.480	970.106	131.457	1516.083	886.707	766.840
$\hat{\sigma}^2(4)$	420.746	991.899	747.119	107.278	1549.852	862.912	560.380
$\hat{\sigma}^2(5)$	408.146	790.305	618.333	290.332	1287.316	738.974	460.611
$\hat{\sigma}^2(6)$	362.916	778.666	603.613	87.201	1619.232	812.900	443.408
$\hat{\sigma}^2(7)$	340.204	881.548	640.951	112.816	1553.409	833.112	490.115
$\hat{\sigma}^2(8)$	278.068	820.207	565.083	41.246	1701.446	822.516	407.398
$\hat{\sigma}^2(9)$	303.954	865.245	619.680	49.513	1477.544	852.780	462.638
$\hat{\sigma}^2(10)$	349.445	867.454	660.250	23.627	1469.052	890.882	488.420
$\hat{\sigma}^2(11)$	433.262	873.236	684.675	213.992	1412.040	984.166	580.982
$\hat{\sigma}^2(12)$	709.895	870.906	808.979	626.640	1652.273	1178.904	620.539

2. Subba and Gabr's AR(9) model was (with coefficients rounded to two decimal places):

$$\bar{X}_t = 1.22\bar{X}_{t-1} - 0.47\bar{X}_{t-2} - 0.14\bar{X}_{t-3} + 0.17\bar{X}_{t-4} - 0.15\bar{X}_{t-5}$$
$$+ 0.05\bar{X}_{t-6} - 0.05\bar{X}_{t-7} + 0.07\bar{X}_{t-8} + 0.11\bar{X}_{t-9} + \varepsilon_t \qquad (7.17)$$

where ε_t are i.i.d. $\mathcal{N}(0, 199.27)$ random variables, and $\bar{X}$ is X mean-deleted.

It is clear from Table 7.14 that whilst the non-linear prediction (column 7) has outperformed the linear prediction (column 4) over the short range, the reverse is true over the longer range. Closer investigation reveals that whilst the non-linear prediction does a better job than the linear prediction over the 'troughs', (compare column 5 with column 2), the reverse is true over the 'peaks' (compare column 6 with column 3). This therefore suggests that it might be beneficial to combine the two predictions so as to exploit their complementary performances. The final column of Table 7.14 gives the results when the non-linear prediction (NL) and the linear prediction (L) are combined in the following manner. (Let M stand for the historical mean over the fitting period 1700–1920.)

If both NL and $L \le M$, then adopt NL.

If both NL and $L > M$, then adopt L.

If $NL \le M$ and $L > M$, then adopt $\frac{1}{2}(NL + L)$.

If $NL > M$ and $L \le M$, then adopt $\frac{1}{2}(NL + L)$.

Our combination rule implies a probability distribution of combination weights of predictions which is 'self-excited' by the predictions themselves (cf. Granger and Newbold 1977). Our approach seems to be closer to an empirical Bayes approach in spirit. Accordingly, we should emphasize the pragmatic (empirical) nature of our results in this respect at present. Further exploration is interesting.

Finally, we return to the multi-step least-squares predictions of Tong and Lim's threshold model (7.16) and Subba Rao and Gabr's linear AR model (7.17) for the period 1980–7. The point predictions are shown in Table 7.15. It seems that the adverse effect of the 1956 shock on the threshold prediction performance has subsided. With a mean-squared error (MSE) of 253.9, the non-linear least-squares prediction now performs nearly as well as the linear least-squares prediction (MSE at 222.4). Nevertheless the combination prediction as prescribed earlier still gives an improvement over the non-linear prediction with a lower MSE at 237.9 (Table 7.15).

It could be suggested that we should adjust our predictions/models in the light of the rather unusual datum of 1956. For example, the

Table 7.15. Predictions of sunspot numbers (1980–7) with 1979 as the base year using pre-1956 shock models

Year	Observation	Linear prediction	Prediction error	SETAR prediction	Prediction Error	Combination prediction	Prediction error
1980	154.7	162.8	8.1	174.7	20.0	162.8	8.1
1981	140.5	133.5	−7.0	147.5	7.0	133.5	−7.0
1982	115.9	91.5	−24.4	92.4	−23.5	91.5	−24.4
1983	66.6	53.3	−13.3	62.9	−3.7	53.3	−13.3
1984	45.9	23.1	−22.8	24.1	−21.8	24.1	−21.8
1985	17.9	4.6	−13.3	12.6	−5.3	12.6	−5.3
1986	13.4	2.0	−11.4	0.2	−13.2	0.2	−13.2
1987	29.2	21.1	8.1	10.8	18.4	10.8	18.4
MSE			222.4		253.9		237.9

parameters of the models could be more robustly fitted by modifying the least-squares method. However, is the adjustment really relevant or justified prior to 1956? It would nevertheless seem worthwhile to explore the possibilities of combination of predictions in the manner in which we have experimented as a means of reducing the adverse effect of unusual *future* shocks on prediction.

7.4 Incorporating covariates: the first few words on non-linear multiple time series modelling

Up to now we have been dealing with the modelling of a *single* time series only. Incorporating covariates into our modelling requires multiple time series analysis. Although much of the probabilistic and statistical theory can be carried over relatively straightforwardly into the latter analysis, practical experience of non-linear multiple time series modelling remains scanty. This is not surprising in view of the relative infancy of *linear multiple time series modelling*.

What we propose to do in this section is to highlight some of the potential of as well as some of the problems in non-linear multiple time series modelling. It is inevitable at this stage that the examples that we are going to give in this section can only be considered very preliminary modelling indeed; they represent, at best, only some of the first words on the fascinating and challenging subject of *non-linear multiple time series modelling*. The whole field is awaiting development!

7.4.1 PRELIMINARY MODELLING OF A HYDROLOGICAL–METEOROLOGICAL SYSTEM

Hydrology has a long history and is of immense importance to many countries. It may be interesting to note that some of the earliest civil servants were hydrologists in the ancient China of approximately 100 BC. Their sole duty was to supervise waterworks and compile records about the rivers! It seems a pity that their functions have changed so much since then.

The observable river flow, at a point in a river and at a particular instant of time may be thought of as the observable output of a system, the input of which is the past effective precipitation. The dynamics and memory length of the system are dictated by the geography, geology, and topography of the river region. Commonly mentioned factors are catchment retention, losses through evaporation, transpiration from plants, infiltration into the ground, underground sources, catchment storage, and melting snow. Deterministic models describing the relationship between river flow and meteorological variables must, therefore, inevitably be elaborate and require extensive measurements. The possibility of constructing simpler stochastic models, based on a few meteorological variables, may therefore be worth exploring. Such models can be useful for simulation and prediction and may provide some quantitative information about the relationship between the river flow and some of the more important meteorological variables. A substantial literature is available on the stochastic modelling of the river flow alone without incorporating any meteorological variables. An excellent review in this respect is given by Lawrance and Kottegoda (1977). An extension of the transfer function–noise model approach of Box and Jenkins (1976) to analyze the relationship between river flow and three input series was described by Snorrason *et al.* (1984).

The statistical analysis of time series data is greatly facilitated if the mean and covariances do not change with time. However, this is not a realistic assumption in hydrology. Seasonal variations and non-linear relationships between meteorological variables and the river imply that river flow is neither Gaussian nor stationary. Seasonal variations in second-order properties of river-flow data were described by Gudmundsson (1975), and Kavvas and Delleur (1984). Gudmundsson (1970) examined seasonal variations in the relationship between river flow and meteorological variables.

For many rivers, the associated precipitation may alternate between rainfall and snowfall. In addition, there may be glaciers on the drainage area. In such cases, the meteorological variable of temperature plays a naturally important role. The *threshold* at the freezing point has a readily identified hydrological–meteorological meaning here and it seems reasonable to expect that it will explain some of the non-linearity (see Fig. 1.7).

The simplest non-trivial model for the system may take the form

$$X_t = f(Y_t, Y_{t-1}, \dots) + \text{error} \tag{7.18}$$

where X_t denotes the river flow in $\text{m}^3\,\text{s}^{-1}$ measured at some observation point of the river on day t, Y_t denotes the precipitation in the drainage area of the river, measured in mm/day on day t, f is non-linear. The error is typically stochastic, non-white, and non-Gaussian because

(1) it represents the accumulated effect of neglected hydrological variables, such as groundwater level, temperature, wind velocity, etc.; and

(2) more importantly, the assumed form of f is often inadequate. In conventional hydrology, f is usually assumed linear and the method of 'unit hydrograph' is used, which is just the impulse response

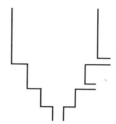

Fig. 7.43. Sugawara's tank model

function of a linear system. Figure 1.7 has demonstrated that this assumption of linearity is hardly realistic. Some hydrologists have proposed conceptual models which are non-linear. For example, Sugawara (1961) has, in fact, presented his ideas in a most graphic way by introducing a structure shown in Fig. 7.43 which is to represent the piecewise linear functions shown in Fig. 7.44 (see Sugawara 1961, p. 85). The change points indicated by the broken lines in Fig. 7.44 are caused by the changing widths of the structure in Fig. 7.43. For convenience, let us call the structure *Sugawara's tank model*. The content of the tank represents the amount of stored water. The outlets represent run-off/infiltration.

Sugawara's tank model suggests the possibility of a threshold model of the TARSO type for river flow data sets. It is pertinent to point out that the hydrological–meteorological system can be accepted as an open-loop system because of the absence of feedback from the river-flow on meteorological variables such as temperature and precipitation, etc., except over the very long term.

Models to be considered below are of the general form

$$X_t = L^{(J_t)}(1; X_{t-1}, X_{t-2}, \ldots ; Y_t, Y_{t-1}, \ldots ; Z_t, Z_{t-1}, \ldots) \qquad (7.19)$$

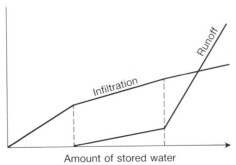

Amount of stored water

Fig. 7.44. Some functional relationship

where the indicator variable J_t is to be defined. Its range is restricted to $\{1, 2\}$, although this is clearly not essential. To simplify the notation, the convention typified by the following example, with fictitious numbers, will be adopted:

$$X_t = \begin{cases} L^{(1)}(0.5 \| 1.1 \| 2.7, 1.1 \| 4.3, 2.8) \\ L^{(2)}(2.3 \| 0.1, 0.2 \| 1.7 \| 0.1, 2.1) \end{cases} \tag{7.20}$$

means that

$$X_t = \begin{cases} 0.5 + 1.1X_{t-1} + 2.7Y_t + 1.1Y_{t-1} + 4.3Z_t + 2.8Z_{t-1} + \varepsilon_t^{(1)} & \text{if } J_t = 1 \\ 2.3 + 0.1X_{t-1} + 0.2X_{t-2} + 1.7Y_t + 0.1Z_t + 2.1Z_{t-1} + \varepsilon_t^{(2)} & \text{if } J_t = 2. \end{cases}$$
$$\tag{7.21}$$

In what follows it is understood that an identification procedure similar to that employed in modelling the Canadian lynx data has been applied.

7.4.2 HYDROLOGICAL AND METEOROLOGICAL CONDITIONS OF VATNSDALSÁ AND JÖKULSÁ EYSTRI, ICELAND

In order to examine empirically the possiblilities of threshold models in dealing with the non-linear effects associated with the melting of snow and ice we obtained observations of two rivers in north-west Iceland, Vatnsdalsá and Jökulsá Eystri. Geographical and meteorological conditions are, in many aspects, rather similar on the drainage areas of both rivers. The bedrock consists mainly of basalts of low permeability. These are partly covered by sediments. There are no woods and vegetation is negligible. No direct observations of evaporation are available, but it might be of the order of 20% with a substantial seasonal variation. A detailed description of the hydrological conditions in this area was given by Richter and Schunke (1981).

The main characteristic of Vatnsdalsá is direct run-off. There are, however, some highly permeable post-glacial lavas on the southern part of the drainage area which contribute a component of groundwater that is not sensitive to short-term variations in the weather. The drainage area is $450 \, \text{km}^2$. The presence of the glacier has the effect that temperatures above zero at its altitude, 1000–1800 m, always produce meltwater, whereas from July and into the autumn there is negligible snow on other parts of the drainage areas.

The meteorological station at Hveravellir lies between the two drainage areas on a level with their southern borders at an altitude of 641 m. The average temperature is about $-1°\text{C}$ and the amplitude of the annual variation 6–7°C. The temperature measurements should provide a fairly good indicator of temperatures on the drainage areas, but it must be kept in mind that, as a result of different altitudes and different distances from the sea, the temperature (at any time) will differ within each area. A difference in altitude of 100 m may correspond to a difference in temperature of 0.5–1.0°C. The diurnal variation implies that on a day when the average temperature is at the freezing point the actual temperature is somewhat higher for a couple of hours.

The precipitation is less well represented by the observations at Hveravellir. It is difficult to measure accurately, especially when the wind is high as is common in these areas. Precipitation is subject to much more local variation than temperature, so that no single station will provide an accurate indicator of precipitation within a large area.

7.4.3 PRELIMINARY TARSO MODELLING OF THE VATNSDALSÁ RIVER (1972–4)

The data consist of the daily flow of the River Vatnsdalsá (X_t) in $m^3 s^{-1}$, the daily precipitation (Y_t) in mm, and the mean daily temperature (Z_t) in °C at the meteorological station at Hveravellir. The data span the period of 1972, 1973, and 1974. The precipitation record is actually several hours late as the recorded value is the accumulated rain at 9 a.m. from the same time the day before. (We have adjusted for this in our modelling by a forward translation by one day.) Some of the data are illustrated in Fig. 7.45.

Before examining threshold models, it is informative to look at ordinary linear models with precipitation and temperature as inputs and the river flow as output. For the data in 1972 alone, the model is

$$X_t = 9.40 - 0.07Y_t + 0.17Z_t + 0.11Z_{t-1} + \varepsilon_t \tag{7.22}$$

where var $\varepsilon_t = 215.64$ and NAIC $= 3.09$. The inadequacy of these models is indicated by the negative coefficient of precipitation and magnitude of var ε_t which is larger than the squared average value of X_t. An explanation of this lies in the model's inability to cope with the obviously highly non-linear relationship between the river flow and the meteorological variables; an increase in temperature from -15 to $-5°C$ can have very different effects from an increase from 0 to 10°C.

Within the linear framework, the fit is greatly improved by including past values of X:

$$X_t = 0.73 + 1.12X_{t-1} - 0.23X_{t-2} + 0.12X_{t-3} - 0.09X_{t-4} + 0.01Y_t + 0.07Y_{t-1}$$

$$- 0.06Y_{t-2} + 0.02Y_{t-3} + 0.09Z_t - 0.03Z_{t-1} - 0.04Z_{t-2} + \varepsilon_t \tag{7.23}$$

where var $\varepsilon_t = 2.85$ and NAIC $= 1.11$. A great deal of water that is

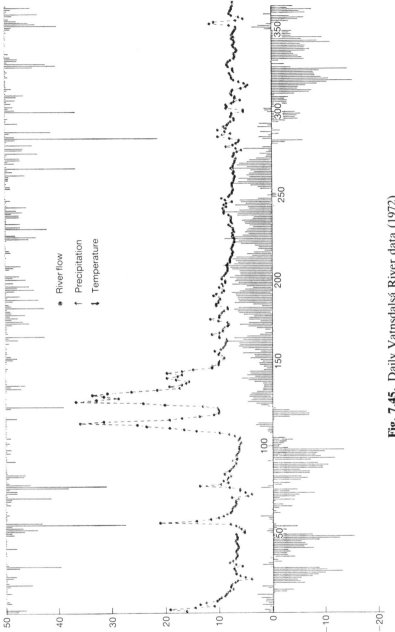

Fig. 7.45. Daily Vatnsdalsá River data (1972)

released on the drainage area by rain or melting snow reaches the point of observation on the same day, but part of it arrives later because of long distances, low slopes, and delays through the groundwater system. Past and present flow is therefore a useful indicator of tomorrow's flow. In fact, the magnitudes of the parameters show that the role of the meteorological variables in (7.23) is limited to modifying the dynamics described by the autoregressive part rather than providing a description of the actual relationship between X and (Y, Z).

The non-linear effects of Z on X, described earlier, suggest that the 'autoregressive' dynamics may well be 'state' dependent; for example (i) it may depend on whether there has been a prolonged period of frost or a prolonged period of warm weather, and (ii) it may depend on the unobserved state of the groundwater.

Now, there are three obvious methods of selecting J_t:

(1)
$$J_t = \begin{cases} 1 & \text{if } X_{t-1} \leq r_x \\ 2 & \text{if } X_{t-1} \geq r_x \end{cases} \tag{7.24a}$$

(2)
$$J_t = \begin{cases} 1 & \text{if } Y_{t-1} \leq r_y \\ 2 & \text{if } Y_{t-1} > r_y \end{cases} \tag{7.24b}$$

(3)
$$J_t = \begin{cases} 1 & \text{if } Z_t \leq r_z \\ 2 & \text{if } Z_t > r_z. \end{cases} \tag{7.24c}$$

Note that Y_{t-1} consists of a 15 hour accumulation of rain on day $(t-1)$ and a 9 hour accumulation of rain on day t. Thus, it is not realistic to use Y_t for J_t.

Experimentations suggest that method (2) is the least efficient and that X_{t-1} is a parsimonious choice for J_t (see Table 7.16). A hydrological explanation of this is that X_{t-1} gives an indication of whether and how much water is being released on the drainage area.

We now use method (1) and the pooled data from 1972, 1973, and 1974. The pooling is essential because the spring floods which account for a large proportion of the variation only last for a few days. The following

Table 7.16. Choice of indicator variables (for 1972 data set)

Method	Threshold estimate	Minimum normalized AIC
(1)	$\hat{r}_x = 12$	0.20
(2)	$\hat{r}_y = 9$	0.62
(3)	$\hat{r}_z = 0$	0.52

threshold model is identified:

$$
X_t = \begin{cases}
L^{(1)}(\underset{(0.13)}{0.13} \,\|\, \underset{(0.05)}{1.31}, \underset{(0.06)}{-0.56}, \underset{(0.04)}{0.22} \,\|\, \underset{(0.01)}{0.02}, \underset{(0.01)}{0.08}, \underset{(0.01)}{-0.02} \,\|\, \underset{(0.01)}{0.03}, \underset{(0.01)}{0.03}) \\[2pt]
\quad \text{with var } \varepsilon_t^{(1)} = 1.03 \\[4pt]
L^{(2)}(\underset{(1.46)}{7.17} \,\|\, \underset{(0.08)}{1.03}, \underset{(0.12)}{-0.28}, \underset{(0.12)}{-0.03}, \underset{(0.12)}{0.13}, \underset{(0.12)}{-0.10}, \underset{(0.12)}{-0.09}, \underset{(0.11)}{0.16}, \underset{(0.11)}{-0.16}, \underset{(0.11)}{0.18}, \underset{(0.07)}{-0.19}\| \\[2pt]
\quad \underset{(0.18)}{0.34}, \underset{(0.10)}{-0.16}, \underset{(0.06)}{-0.03}, \underset{(0.05)}{-0.06}, \underset{(0.05)}{-0.07}, \underset{(0.12)}{-0.40}, \underset{(0.06)}{0.17}, \underset{(0.05)}{0.11}, \underset{(0.05)}{0.09}, \underset{(0.05)}{-0.17}\| \\[2pt]
\quad \underset{(0.24)}{0.44}, \underset{(0.40)}{1.09}, \underset{(0.47)}{-2.18}, \underset{(0.40)}{0.40}, \underset{(0.42)}{-0.66}, \underset{(0.39)}{0.46}, \underset{(0.41)}{0.23}, \underset{(0.39)}{0.79}, \underset{(0.27)}{0.20}) \\[2pt]
\quad \text{with var } \varepsilon_t^{(2)} = 12.54 \text{ (pooled var = 2.13)}
\end{cases}
$$

$$
\tag{7.25}
$$

$\hat{r}_X = 13$, and $\text{NAIC} = 0.3441$. Estimated standard deviations are presented in parentheses below the respective parameters. These estimates are based on the assumption of independent (Gaussian) residuals. The actual residual distribution is somewhat skewed and leptokurtic so that the parameter estimates are less accurate than suggested by these values. There is also evidence of positive autocorrelation among the residuals. (We will return to this point in §7.4.5.) A piecewise linear transfer function–noise model may be worthy of exploration. The same comment applies to the next preliminary study in §7.4.4.

The equation for the previous day's flow below $13 \text{ m}^3 \text{ s}^{-1}$ applies to 982 days out of 1085. The coefficients of the meteorological variables are on the whole negligible, so that either their effect is small or the model is inadequate to describe it. In the equation for the previous day's flow above the threshold, which applies to only 103 days, meteorological variables have a substantial influence. The coefficient of this flow is 1.03 and the sum of the coefficients of past flows is 0.65. As a result of the large autoregressive effects, the coefficients of the meteorological variables, say, Y_{t-j}, Z_{t-j}, cannot be interpreted directly as a measure of the effects of these variables j days ago on the present flow. Nor is it appropriate to eliminate the past values of the flow and describe the flow as a function of past values of the meteorological variables alone; the model thus obtained differs substantially from what is obtained by a direct estimation of this form. The past flow contains information which cannot be expressed by the meteorological variables within the present model.

In interpreting the above model, it is useful to keep in mind the fact that the equation for the previous day's flow above $13 \text{ m}^3 \text{ s}^{-1}$ will not be applicable unless that day's temperature is about or above freezing point, since otherwise that flow will be below the threshold value. In this connection, therefore, it is interesting to re-analyse the data using a temperature threshold. The following model is identified:

$$X_t = \begin{cases} L^{(1)}(1.79 \parallel 0.76, -0.05) & \text{with var } \varepsilon_t^{(1)} = 0.69 \\ L^{(2)}(0.87 \parallel 1.30, -0.71, 0.34) & \text{with var } \varepsilon_t^{(2)} = 7.18 \quad (7.26) \\ (\text{pooled var} = 4.50) \end{cases}$$

$\hat{r}_Z = -1$, and NAIC = 1.01. We have essentially two different autoregressive models, one for frost and the other for thaw. In the lower temperature range, the model mainly describes a convergence towards a constant flow of about $6 \, \text{m}^3 \, \text{s}^{-1}$ reached in a few days after frost sets in. This agrees well with the fact that stable flows in this range are often observed for days or weeks. There is a great difference in residual variation between the two models. A few large floods, caused by the melting of a large proportion of the snow on the drainage area, are responsible for much of the variation in the model above the threshold temperature. This applies also to $L^{(2)}$ in eqn (7.25); the peaks of the floods are preceded and followed by days of large flows. The temperature is below $-1°C$ for 448 days. Thus, in spite of its relatively inferior NAIC value, model (7.26) may be used to complement model (7.25).

7.4.4 PRELIMINARY TARSO MODELLING OF THE JÖKULSÁ EYSTRI RIVER (1972–4)

Some of the data are illustrated in Fig. 7.46. Note the much bigger dynamic range of the data.

An important hydrological feature of the River Jökulsá Eystri is that there is a glacier on the drainage area. This effects a substantial difference in the response of the two rivers to changes in temperature. In Vatnsdalsá, high temperature only enhances the flow when there is snow to melt, whereas the glacier at Jökulsá is still there after all the winter has vanished. It turns out that for 1972 the minimum normalized AIC using method (1) (i.e. with X_{t-1} as the indicator) is 1.91 and that using using method (3) (i.e. with Z_t as the indicator) is 1.99. For the other two years the results are quite similar with the minor difference that, for 1973, the result based on method (1) has a slightly bigger minimum normalized AIC that that based on method (3). Method (2) gives a consistently larger value. We may draw the conclusion that for Jökulsá Z_t is just as good an indicator of hydrological conditions as X_{t-1}.

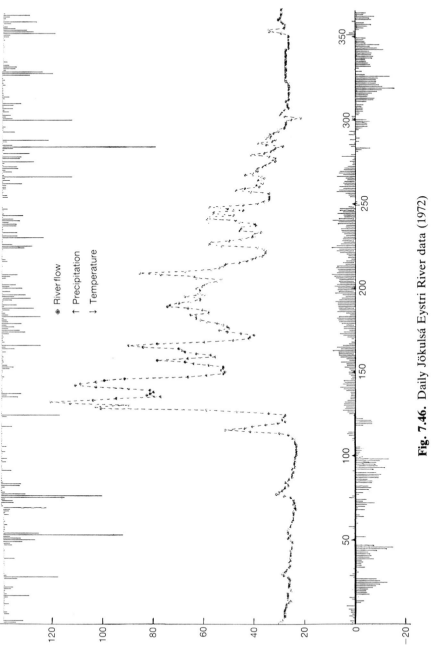

Fig. 7.46. Daily Jökulsá Eystri River data (1972)

The following threshold model has been fitted to the Jökulsá data of 1972–4:

$$X_t = \begin{cases} L^{(1)}(\underset{(0.48)}{6.15} \,\|\, \underset{(0.04)}{0.69}, \underset{(0.05)}{0.04}, \underset{(0.03)}{0.03}, \underset{(0.02)}{-0.05}, \underset{(0.02)}{-0.01}, \underset{(0.01)}{0.06} \,\|\, \underset{(0.01)}{-0.02}, \underset{(0.02)}{-0.01}, \underset{(0.01)}{-0.03}, \underset{(0.02)}{0.03}, \\ \qquad \underset{(0.01)}{-0.01}, \underset{(0.01)}{0.01}, \,\|\, \underset{(0.01)}{0.05}, \underset{(0.02)}{0.00}, \underset{(0.02)}{-0.01}, \underset{(0.02)}{-0.04}) \\ \quad \text{with var } \varepsilon_t^{(1)} = 0.67 \\[4pt] L^{(2)}(\underset{(0.87)}{1.15} \,\|\, \underset{(0.04)}{1.17}, \underset{(0.06)}{-0.47}, \underset{(0.06)}{0.31}, \underset{(0.06)}{-0.20}, \underset{(0.06)}{0.14}, \underset{(0.06)}{-0.11}, \underset{(0.06)}{0.01}, \underset{(0.03)}{0.05} \,\| \\ \qquad \underset{(0.04)}{0.01}, \underset{(0.04)}{0.37}, \underset{(0.05)}{-0.21}, \underset{(0.04)}{-0.05}, \underset{(0.05)}{0.04}, \underset{(0.05)}{-0.00}, \underset{(0.05)}{0.06}, \underset{(0.04)}{0.11} \,\| \\ \qquad \underset{(0.16)}{0.72}, \underset{(0.19)}{0.57}, \underset{(0.17)}{-0.11}, \underset{(0.18)}{-0.21}, \underset{(0.19)}{0.03}, \underset{(0.19)}{-0.12}, \underset{(0.19)}{-0.03}, \underset{(0.14)}{-0.21} \,\| \\ \quad \text{with var } \varepsilon_t^{(2)} = 48.96 \text{ (pooled var} = 31.77) \end{cases} \quad (7.27)$$

$\hat{r}_Z = -2°C$. A non-parametric estimate of $E[X_t \mid Z_t]$ suggests that the latter is piecewise linear consisting of a horizontal line cutting the vertical axis at 26 m³ s⁻¹ and a line of positive slope, the knot being at $Z_t = -2°C$. Thus, the estimate $\hat{r}_Z = -2°C$ seems reasonable (see Fig. 7.47).

In days of frost the model describes a gradual decrease, very similar to that for Vatnsdalsá, with negligible contribution from the meteorological variables. According to the model, the flow approaches 26 m³ s⁻¹ in

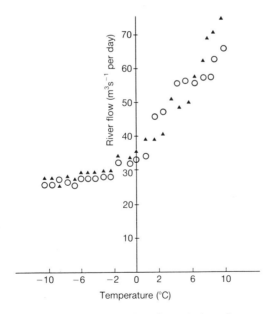

Fig. 7.47. Non-parametric regression function of river flow on temperature for Jökulsá Eystri data; ○, from real data; ▲, from fitted threshold model

prolonged periods of frost, which is in reasonable agreement with the observations.

In $L^{(2)}$, the sum of the coefficients of past flows is 0.90 and the previous day's flow has the coefficient 1.17. Coefficients of the meteorological coefficients are not negligible. Considering the numerical values of the coefficients of the meteorological variables and the fact that the flow is usually greater than $30 \, \text{m}^3 \, \text{s}^{-1}$ with a standard deviation of $7 \, \text{m}^3 \, \text{s}^{-1}$ it is, however, clear that the role of these variables is to modify the dynamics described by the autoregressive part rather than to provide a description of the actual relationship between X and (Y, Z). The coefficient of Y_t is practically zero, which implies that the effect of the present day's precipitation of the present day's flow is adequately accounted for by multiplying the previous day's flow by 1.17. The previous day's precipitation is, on the other hand, under-represented by $1.17X_{t-1} - 0.47X_{t-2}$ and this is compensated by the term $0.37Y_{t-1}$, which is probably also related to the fact that it takes the water about half a day to travel from the glacier to the point of observation. The coefficients of the present and the previous day's temperature are positive, but those of days $t - 2, t - 3, \ldots, t - 7$ are mainly negative. To some extent this does take into account the effects of snow melting. A present temperature of 8°C, say in March–April, when there is snow to be melted, will usually be preceded by days of lower temperatures than a day of 8°C in August.

The model obtained with the previous day's flow as the threshold parameter is very similar to model (7.27) when the flow is larger than $30 \, \text{m}^3 \, \text{s}^{-1}$ and the temperatures higher than -2°C. When the previous day's flow is less than $30 \, \text{m}^3 \, \text{s}^{-1}$, the former model gives 'the present flow is practically the same as the previous day's'.

7.4.5   DISCUSSION

To a certain extent the results support the view that threshold models may be suitable for analysing these kinds of data. These models are more realistic than linear models and the temperature thresholds identified by the AIC are in accordance with the main characteristics of the rivers. Further details are available in the unpublished thesis of Thanoon (1984).

Apart from long-term changes in the geography the flow is completely determined by the weather,; there is no *feedback* detectable on the level of accuracy attainable by actual observations. We might initially think that the estimated models hardly accord with this, for the autoregressive coefficients contribute much more to the description of the variations of the rivers than the meteorological variables. It is not surprising, however, that past observations of river flow contain a great deal of information about its present level. The weather affects the river with 'distributed lags'. Thus some of the run-off after a burst of rain reaches the point of observation within a few hours as direct run-off along steep slopes over a short distance, whereas the rain from other parts of the area, falling at the same time, may have to pass through layers of soil or travel longer distances over lower slopes. Observations of the river itself thus may be expected to contain information about its future.

If the models provide a satisfactory description of the relationship between the respective variables (included), elimination of the auto-regressive part should lead to expressions

$$X_t = L^{(J_t)}(1; Y_t, Y_{t-1}, \ldots; Z_t, Z_{t-1}, \ldots) + \eta^{(J_t)} \qquad (7.28)$$

where the coefficients of the meteorological variables provide realistic estimates of the actual time lags.

The residual term $\eta_t^{(J_t)}$ is a moving average of $\varepsilon_t^{(J_t)}$. The new residuals would possess high positive autocorrelations. This is, however, not unrealistic. The river responds differently to the weather depending upon the temperature, and the threshold models take account of this. However, the river also responds differently to a given sequence of meteorological variables depending upon the state of the drainage area. Here the amount of snow is most important, but groundwater and frost in the ground can also have large effects (Rist 1983). The thresholds cannot fully cope with both the non-linear character of the relationship in given hydrological conditions and the effect of the weather for altering the hydrological conditions. They are better suited to deal with the first, but the residual errors associated with variations in the state of the drainage area are obviously positively correlated.

Some of the models with large and apparently well determined autogressive parts do not lead to sensible expressions when rewritten in the form of (7.28). Past values of the rivers, therefore contain useful information which cannot be expressed by the meteorological variables within the present models.

The distribution of rainfall and meltwater production, which may be regarded as the inputs to the hydrological system, are very skewed. Therefore, residuals will not be Gaussian unless a model presents a fairly accurate description of the actual relationships. Presumably realistic and accurate hydrological models can be produced with non-Gaussian residuals. Provided the residuals are approximately uncorrelated, the non-Gaussian property does not seem to have much effect on the large sample standard errors of the parameter estimates. However, available finite sample results are too scanty.

The threshold models described in this section can only be considered preliminary and partially successful from the point of view of reducing the data to 'Gaussian white noise'. There are various possibilities of improving upon the modelling. Among these is the introduction of more meteorological variables, such as wind and radiation or precipitation from more than one station. Direct observations of the state of the hydrological system, however, might be more to the point. With such information appropriate modelling would obviously differ a great deal from the models presented in this section. However, sharp changes in relationships acccording to temperature and presence of snow would still be present. Thresholds in some form could, therefore, also be convenient for dealing with the non-linearity in more elaborate models.

Bibliographical notes

Section 7.2.1–7.2.8 represent update and corrections of Tong (1983a). Section 7.2.9 is based on Haggan et al. (1984) and Tsay (1989). Section 7.2.10 amalgamates Haggan and Ozaki (1981), Ozaki (1982), Lim (1987), and Chan et al. (1988). Together with Exercises 2 and 8, §7.2.10 gives a comprehensive listing of EXPAR models fitted to the lynx and sunspot data, which have been reported to date. Section 7.2.11, together with Exercises 1, 3, and 7 does the same for BL models. Section 7.2.1.2 is based on Nicholls and Quinn (1982).

Section 7:3 is based on Tong (1983a) and Tong and Moeanaddin (1988).

Section 7.4 is based on Tong et al. (1985).

Exercises and complements

(1)   Subba Rao (1980) has fitted the following BL model to the log lynx data (1821–1920):

$$X_t - 0.8845X_{t-1} + 0.1699X_{t-2} + 0.1271X_{t-4} - 0.5514X_{t-10} + 0.5280X_{t-11}$$
$$\underset{[-1.065,-0.869]}{} \quad \underset{[0.166,0.347]}{} \quad \underset{[0.060,0.159]}{} \quad \underset{[-0.530,-0.332]}{} \quad \underset{[0.344,0.517]}{}$$

$$= \underset{[0.977,1.293]}{1.117} - \underset{[-0.198,-0.092]}{0.1653X_{t-8}\varepsilon_{t-10}} - \underset{[-0.148,-0.068]}{0.0970X_{t-5}\varepsilon_{t-8}} + \underset{[-0.032,0.089]}{0.0922X_{t-1}\varepsilon_{t-1}} + \varepsilon_t,$$

where var $\varepsilon_t = 0.0329$, NAIC $= -3.222$. Perform diagnostics on this model. Do you agree with our suggestion in §7.2.11 that this model is preferred to the BL model of §7.2.11 fitted later by Gabr and Subba Rao in 1981, although the latter has a smaller var ε_t and smaller NAIC? The entries in square brackets are bootstrap interquartiles by sampling with replacements from the fitted residuals; 500 replications have been used. Try the same. Run an invertibility check. Would you agree that, unlike

Gabr and Subba Rao's BL model, there is no evidence to suggest that Subba Rao's BL model is non-invertible?

(Partially due to Lim (1987))

(2) M. C. Wong (see Tong and Lim 1980) has fitted the following EXPAR model to the *mean-deleted* sunspot numbers (1700–1945):

i	1	2	3	4	5	6	7
$\hat{\alpha}_i$	0.789	−0.170	−0.053	0.166	−0.034	−0.078	0.113
$\hat{\beta}_i$	0.802	−0.402	−0.252	−0.120	−0.182	0.273	

$\hat{\delta} = 0.001\,168$. (No value was given for var ε_t.) Fit an appropriate AR(p) model to the same data set. (We suggest that you might try $p = 10$.) Compare the prediction performance of the two models over (1946–55) and over (1956–86).

(Tong and Lim 1980)

(3) Gabr and Subba Rao (1981) have fitted the following BL to the sunspot numbers (1700–1920):

$$X_t - 1.5012X_{t-1} + 0.7670X_{t-2} - 0.115X_{t-9} - 6.8860$$
$$= -0.014\,58X_{t-2}\varepsilon_{t-1} + 0.006\,312X_{t-8}\varepsilon_{t-1}$$
$$- 0.007\,152X_{t-1}\varepsilon_{t-3} + 0.006\,047X_{t-4}\varepsilon_{t-3}$$
$$+ 0.003\,619X_{t-1}\varepsilon_{t-6} + 0.004\,334X_{t-2}\varepsilon_{t-4}$$
$$+ 0.001\,782X_{t-3}\varepsilon_{t-2} + \varepsilon_t$$

where var $\varepsilon_t = 124.33$. They have calculated the least-squares predictions over (1921–55) and given the following table:

j	1	2	3	4	5
$\hat{\sigma}^2(j)$	123.77	337.54	569.79	659.05	718.87

Verify the above figures and repeat the exercise over the period (1956–79). Do you agree that the corresponding figures over the period (1956–79) are worrying? Using 1979 as the base year, obtain genuine predictions with the above model for 1980–6. Do you agree that they compare poorly with those given in Table 7.15? Have you investigated the invertibility of the model by this stage?

(Chan *et al.* 1988)

(4) The outlier detection technique of Künsch (1984) is based on a linear autoregression. It has picked out the following outliers in the

log lynx data (1821–1934) w.r.t. a fitted AR model:

1832 (too low)

1868 (too low)

1887, 1888 (too low)

1897, 1989 (too low)

1916 (too high).

What non-linearity effects have these outliers revealed?
(Private communication from H. Künsch (1987))

(5) Verify the following table, in which the jth row gives the average of squares of errors of genuine j-step least-squares predictions of sunspot numbers over the period (1956–79), the first column is based on the AR(9) model of eqn (7.17), and the second column is based on Gabr and Subba Rao's BL model described in Exercise 3.

Linear Gaussian	Bilinear
525.7	21 122.9
1049.1	146 517.2
970.1	592 805.7
747.1	174 075.5
618.3	126 232.6
603.6	152 870.9
640.9	174 587.7
565.1	140 566.5
619.7	89 642.9
660.2	59 455.7
684.7	71 424.9
809.0	151 970.9

(Chan *et al.* 1988)

(6) Fit an AR(p) model, where p is obtained by the AIC, to the square-root-transformed sunspot numbers, that is to $2\{[1 + \text{sunspot number in year } (1699 + t)]^{1/2} - 1\}$, $t = 1, \ldots, 280$. Using 1979 as the bas year, obtain predictions for the years $1980, \ldots, 1986$ and compare these with those obtained (i) by model (7.14), (ii) by model (7.15), and (iii) by the AR(9) model given in Fig. 7.41.

(7) Subba Rao (1981) has fitted the following BL model to the sunspot numbers (1700–1945): $\hat{a}_1 = -1.93$, $\hat{a}_2 = 1.46$, $\hat{a}_3 = -0.27$, $\alpha =$

10.9132, and

$$100 \times (\hat{b}_{ij}) = \begin{bmatrix} -0.55 & 0.32 & -0.18 & 0.08 \\ -0.57 & -0.56 & -0.82 & 0.58 \\ -0.17 & 0.71 & 0.11 & -0.08 \end{bmatrix} \qquad \hat{\sigma}_\varepsilon^2 = 143.86.$$

Is this model stationary? Is it invertible? Assume that the model is stationary and invertible. Obtain the least-squares predictions of this model for (1946–55) and then for (1956–86).

Repeat the exercise with the following subset BL model also fitted by Subba Rao (1981) to the same data set:

$$X_t - 1.209X_{t-1} + 0.502X_{t-2} - 0.173X_{t-9}$$
$$= 5.891 - 0.0098X_{t-2}\varepsilon_{t-1} + 0.0103X_{t-8}\varepsilon_{t-8} - 0.0048X_{t-8}\varepsilon_{t-3}$$
$$+ 0.0016X_{t-3}\varepsilon_{t-2} + 0.0014X_{t-4}\varepsilon_{t-7} + \varepsilon_t, \qquad \hat{\sigma}_\varepsilon^2 = 141.18.$$

(Tong and Lim 1980)

(8) Ozaki (1982) has fitted the following EXPAR model (II) to the mean-deleted log lynx data:

$$X_t = -0.481X_{t-1} - 0.247X_{t-2} + 0.318X_{t-3} + 0.230X_{t-4} + 0.352X_{t-5}$$
$$+ 0.096X_{t-6} - 0.085X_{t-7} - 0.289X_{t-8} - 0.181X_{t-9} + Y_t$$

where

$$Y_t = [1.514 + (0.480 - 3.332Y_{t-1} - 0.610Y_{t-1}^2 + 8.906Y_{t-1}^3)e^{-\hat{\gamma}Y_{t-1}^2}]Y_{t-1}$$
$$+ [-0.902 + (-0.228 + 0.923Y_{t-1} + 0.193Y_{t-1}^2$$
$$- 4.216Y_{t-1}^3)e^{-\hat{\gamma}Y_{t-1}^2}]Y_{t-2} + \varepsilon_t$$

$\varepsilon_t \sim \text{IID}(0, 0.031\,53)$, $\hat{\gamma} = 3.89$. Lim (1987) has obtained simulation results which suggest that lag regressions of this model do not fit the observed lag regressions well. Try a 10 000 point simulation. Using a triangular window with a suitable smoothing parameter, verify (or refute) Lim's results. Perform other diagnostics on the model. Extend the same diagnostics to model (7.4). Would you agree that between the two EXPAR models, namely model (II) and model (7.9), the latter gives a better fit to the mean-deleted log lynx data?

(Partially based on Lim (1987))

(9) Consider an EXPAR(1) model

$$X_t = (\phi_1 + \phi_2 e^{-\psi X_{t-1}^2})X_{t-1} + \varepsilon_t$$

$\varepsilon_t \sim \text{IID}\mathcal{N}(0, \sigma^2)$. Given n observations, let $l(\psi, \phi_1, \phi_2)$ denote the log likelihood. Let $i_{\psi\phi_2}$ denote typically the information per observation, that is

$$i_{\psi\phi_i} = \frac{1}{n} E\left(-\frac{\partial^2 l}{\partial\psi\,\partial\phi_i}\right), \qquad i = 1, 2.$$

If $i_{\psi\phi_i}$ is zero, ψ and ϕ_i are said to be *orthogonal* (Cox and Reid 1987). Are they orthogonal? Suppose that we reparametrize (ψ, ϕ_1, ϕ_2) to $(\psi, \lambda_1, \lambda_2)$. Investigate the functions

$$\phi_1 = \phi_1(\psi, \lambda_1, \lambda_2) \qquad \phi_2 = \phi_2(\psi, \lambda_1, \lambda_2)$$

which satisfy the following partial differential equations to achieve local orthogonality (Cox and Reid 1987)

$$\sum_{r=1}^{2} i_{\phi_r\phi_s}\frac{\partial\phi_r}{\partial\psi} = -i_{\psi\phi_s}, \qquad s = 1, 2.$$

(10) Obtain the profile sum-of-squares plots of r for SETAR $(2; p, p)$, $p = 7, 8, 9$ say, with delay $= 1, 2, \ldots, d$ say for the log blow-fly data $(20 \leq t \leq 145)$. Use these to obtain a *rough* identification of the SETAR model for the blow-fly data. Compare your conclusion with the model given in Example C in §5.6.7.4.

(11) Repeat Exercise 10 with the log lynx data. Try $d = 1, 2, \ldots, 20$ and let the autoregressive orders be determined by the AIC method (setting 10 as the maximum order). Would you agree that $d = 12$ is quite reasonable? How would you use this to justify $\hat{d} = 2$ or 3 as a rough estimate?

(12) Model III of Table 7.6 reads

$$X_t = \begin{cases} 0.932 + 1.032X_{t-1} - 0.117X_{t-2} - 0.010X_{t-3} - 0.174X_{t-4} + \varepsilon_t^{(1)} \\ \quad \text{if } X_{t-2} \leq 2.9464 \\ 2.185 + 1.484X_{t-1} - 1.184X_{t-2} + \varepsilon_t^{(2)} \\ \quad \text{if } X_{t-2} > 2.9464 \end{cases}$$

where var $\varepsilon_t^{(1)} = 0.0298$, var $\varepsilon_t^{(2)} = 0.0486$ (pooled var $= 0.0389$). Determine the largest Lyapunov exponent of the skeleton. Is it possible to obtain the same for the clothed model and compare the result with that of the data?

(13) Consider the bilinear model

$$X_t = \beta X_{t-1}\varepsilon_{t-1} + \varepsilon_t$$

where $\beta^2\sigma^2 < \frac{1}{2}$ and $\varepsilon_t \sim \mathcal{N}(0, \sigma^2)$. Let $\hat{\beta}$ denote the maximum likelihood estimate of β, given $X_1, X_2, \ldots, X_n$. (You may set $\varepsilon_0 = 0$ and $X_0 = \beta\sigma^2$.) Investigate the effect of reducing σ^2 on the sampling distribution of $\hat{\beta}$. It has been reported that the distribution of $\hat{\beta}$ becomes more diffused as σ^2 decreases. Verify this. Compare this result with Exercise 15 of Chapter 5. Generalize your result to the case

$$X_t = \sum_{j=1}^{k} \beta_j X_{t-j} \varepsilon_{t-j} + \varepsilon_t, \qquad k > 1.$$

(Moeanaddin and Tong 1989*b*)

(14) Run the Forecasting Menu on the STAR3 package which is a companion to this book, and verify that there is evidence of bimodality in the predictive histograms (i.e. the empirical conditional probability distributions, of X_{114+m} given X_s, $s \le 114$, for $m \ge 250$) of the SETAR model (7.7) for the Canadian lynx data.

Appendix 1
Deterministic stability, stochastic stability, and ergodicity

K. S. Chan, Statistics Department
University of Chicago, USA

A1.1 Introduction

We consider the asymptotic behaviour of Markov chains defined by vectorial difference equations in the framework of stability theory. As is well known, many time series models such as ARMA models, threshold autoregressive models, exponential autoregressive models, and some bilinear models can be cast in the form of stochastic difference equations. In the following, we outline the problems informally, leaving the rigorous definition of many notions to later sections. The first kind of problems can be formulated as follows. The transition probability of a Markov chain induces an operator on the metric space of probability measures. (The definition of the operator will be given in §A1.2.) This operator defines a semi-dynamical system. The dynamics need not be continuous, or (Lagrange) stable pointwise. If it is, the theory of stability of a semi-dynamical system on a metric space is applicable and may yield valuable information on the asymptotic behaviour of the semi-dynamical system, which, in turn, may yield useful information on the asymptotic behaviour of the Markov chain. Viewed from this perspective, for example, the Markov chain is ergodic if there exists a globally attracting equilibrium (stationary) probability measure, that is it attracts every probability measure. For the validity of the statement, we first note that the stationary probability measure must be unique because it is globally attracting. Then the above statement follows readily from the proof of Theorem 1.2 in Billingsley (1961). The existence of a finite invariant, invariantly connected, and globally attracting set of probability measures corresponds to the case of a positive recurrent Markov chain with cyclically moving subsets. However, we will not pursue these matters further here.

Our goal is rather modest and we only try to present some fundamentals relevant to the above. In §A1.2, we first discuss a simple criterion for the continuity of the dynamical system. A sufficient condition, in terms of stochastic Lyapunov functions, for the Lagrange stability of the operator follows. Then we state a theorem on the asymptotic nature of some Markov chains and a local version of it. These results may be useful in determining the convergence properties of some algorithms.

In time series analysis, we are generally interested in ergodic models. This is partly because of the theoretical importance of stationarity. However, it seems that geometric ergodic models are more important since the rate of approaching stationarity ought to be fast for the stationarity assumption to be relevant. Many time series models consist of two components, a fast varying component and a slowly varying component. The slowly varying component is invariably in the form of a regular deterministic motion while the fast varying component is some 'noisy' stochastic motion. In §A1.4, we consider a class of stochastic difference equations which makes precise the above idea. We show that, under suitable regularity conditions, the global exponential asymptotic stability of the slowly varying component ensures that the model is geometric ergodic. A partial converse of this result then follows under suitable regularity conditions; the global exponential asymptotic instability of the slowly varying component implies that the process tends to infinity with positive probability. These results make use of recent Markov chain techniques. Section A1.3 contains a brief summary of some relevant Markov chain theories.

A1.2 Stability of the dynamical system

Consider the following stochastic difference equation

$$\mathbf{X}_{t+1} = f(\mathbf{X}_t, \boldsymbol{\varepsilon}_{t+1}), \qquad t \in \mathbf{Z}_+ \qquad (A.1)$$

where $\mathbf{X}_t$ and $\boldsymbol{\varepsilon}_t$ are m- and k-dimensional vectors in Euclidean spaces. Furthermore the $\boldsymbol{\varepsilon}_t$'s are i.i.d. and $\boldsymbol{\varepsilon}_t$ is independent of $\mathbf{X}_s$, $s < t$. Equation (A1.1) is a higher-dimensional generalization of (4.14). Then $\{\mathbf{X}_t\}$ is a Markov chain with $\mathbf{R}^m$ as its state space. In the following, let $\mathbf{x}$ denote an arbitrary vector in $\mathbf{R}^m$ and A a Borel set of $\mathbf{R}^m$. Let $P(.\,,.)$ be the transition probability of $\{\mathbf{X}_t\}$ so that $P(\mathbf{x}, A) = P(\mathbf{X}_1 \in A \mid \mathbf{X}_0 = \mathbf{x})$. Let μ_0 be the initial distribution, that is $P(\mathbf{X}_0 \in A) = \mu_0(A)$. To denote the dependence on the initial distribution, all expectations are denoted by $E_{\mu_0}(.)$ and probabilities by $P_{\mu_0}(.)$. In the case of $\mu_0 = \delta_x$, the probability measure concentrated at $\mathbf{x}$, we shall write $E_x(.)$ instead of $E_{\delta_x(.)}$.

Let $\mathscr{L}$ be the space of probability measures on $\mathbf{R}^m$. The transition probability $P(.\,,.)$ induces an operator $U : \mathscr{L} \to \mathscr{L}$ defined by

$$(U\mu)(A) = \int P(\mathbf{x}, A)\mu(d\mathbf{x}), \qquad \text{for any } \mu \in \mathscr{L}. \qquad (A.2)$$

Thus, if μ is the distribution of $\mathbf{X}_0$, $U\mu$ is the distribution of $\mathbf{X}_1$.

It is well known that $\mathscr{L}$ equipped with the weak topology is a complete separable metric space. See, for example, Theorems 6.2 and 6.5 of Parthasarathy (1967, p. 43 and p. 46 respectively). Let ρ denote a metric on $\mathscr{L}$, which generates the weak topology, that is μ_n, $\mu \in \mathscr{L}$, and $\rho(\mu_n, \mu) \to 0$ iff $\int g(\mathbf{x})\mu_n(d\mathbf{x}) \to \int g(\mathbf{x})\mu(d\mathbf{x})$ for all bounded continuous functions $g: \mathbf{R}^m \to \mathbf{R}$. Henceforth, $\mathscr{L}$ is always equipped with the metric ρ.

Let (S, d) be a metric space and $T: S \to S$ be an operator. Consider the difference equation in S given by

$$\mathbf{X}_{t+1} = T(\mathbf{X}_t), \qquad t \in \mathbf{Z}_+. \tag{A1.3}$$

Many of the stability notions such as positive limit sets, invariant sets, invariant connectedness, and Lyapunov functions defined in §2.12 have straightforward generalization in this setting. Some notions such as Lagrange stability need more care in generalization. In the case of $S = \mathbf{R}^m$ with the Euclidean metric, bounded and closed sets are compact. The compactness is essential for Theorem 2.7 to hold. So, in the context of a metric space, the following definition of Lagrange stability is adopted. $\forall s \in S$, let $T^t(s) = T(T^{t-1}(s))$, $t = 1, 2, \ldots$; $T^0(s) = s$.

Definition: T is *Lagrange stable* if $\{T^t(s), t = 0, 1, 2, \ldots\}$ is relatively compact, $\forall s \in S$. (Recall that *relative compactness* of a set means that every open cover of the closure of the set has a finite open sub-cover.)

In general, concepts that require boundedness in §2.12 have to be strengthened to require relative compactness. Then Theorems 2.7, 2.9, and 2.10 can be readily generalized. See also La Salle (1977) for an excellent survey of the stability theory of dynamical systems.

Since we are interested in the metric space $(\mathscr{L}, \rho)$ and the operator U, we now formulate conditions for U to be Lagrange stable and continuous. The following well-known characterization of relatively compact sets in $(\mathscr{L}, \rho)$ will be useful.

Theorem A1.1: Let Γ be a subset of $\mathscr{L}$, $\bar{\Gamma}$, the closure of Γ, is compact iff $\forall \varepsilon > 0$, there exists a compact set $K_\varepsilon \subseteq \mathbf{R}^m$ such that

$$\mu(K_\varepsilon) \geq 1 - \varepsilon, \qquad \forall \mu \in \Gamma. \tag{A1.4}$$

For a proof of the above theorem, see, for example, Theorem 6.7 in Parthasarathy (1967, p. 47). A subset $\Gamma \subseteq \mathscr{L}$ satisfying (A1.4) is also said to be uniformly tight. It is known that a singleton subset of $\mathscr{L}$ satisfies (A1.4) (see e.g. Theorem 3.2 in Parthasarathy (1967, p. 29)). Following Kishner (1971, p. 201), we formulate the following Lyapunov function criterion for the Lagrange stability of U.

Theorem A1.2: Let U be as defined in (A1.2). Suppose there exists a continuous, non-negative function $V: \mathbf{R}^m \to \mathbf{R}$ such that

(1) $\dot{V}(\mathbf{x}) = E_{\mathbf{x}}(V(\mathbf{X}_1)) - V(\mathbf{x}) \le 0, \quad \mathbf{x} \in \mathbf{R}^m$ (A1.5a)

(2) $V(\mathbf{x}) \to \infty$ as $\|\mathbf{x}\| \to \infty, \quad \mathbf{x} \in \mathbf{R}^m.$ (A1.5b)

Then U is Lagrange stable, that is $\forall \mu \in \mathcal{L}$, $\{U^t\mu, t = 0, 1, 2, \ldots\}$ is a relatively compact subset of $\mathcal{L}$. In the above, $\|.\|$ denotes the Euclidean norm, U^0 is the identity map, and $U^t = UU^{t-1}$, $t \ge 1$.

Let $E = \{\mathbf{x}: \dot{V}(\mathbf{x}) = 0\}$. Assume that for each sequence $\{\mathbf{x}_n\}$ for which $\dot{V}(\mathbf{x}_n) \to 0$, it holds that $\mathbf{x}_n \to E$. Then for any initial distribution $\mu \in \mathcal{L}$, $\mathbf{X}_n \to E$ with P_μ probability 1. (Equivalently, the support of the probability measure $U^t\mu$ tends to E, that is the distance between the support of $U^t\mu$ and E tends to zero as $t \to \infty$. Here, the *support* of a $\mu \in \mathcal{L}$ is the complement of the largest μ-null open set in $\mathbf{R}^m$.)

Before we prove the above theorem, it is interesting to note that the assumption stated for E will hold if, for example, $\dot{V}$ is continuous and $\dot{V}(\mathbf{x}) \to \infty$ as $\|\mathbf{x}\| \to \infty$.

Proof. Let $\mu \in \mathcal{L}$. For the first part of the theorem, it suffices to show that (A1.4) holds with $\Gamma = \{U^t\mu, t = 0, 1, 2, \ldots\}$. Let $1 > \varepsilon > 0$ be given. Since μ satisfies (A1.4), there exists a compact set K_1 such that

$$\mu(K_1) > 1 - \varepsilon/2. \qquad (A1.6)$$

Let λ be chosen such that

$$\max_{\mathbf{x} \in K_1} V(\mathbf{x}) \le \lambda\varepsilon/2. \qquad (A1.7)$$

Now, for the initial distribution $\mu_0 = \delta_x$, it follows from (A1.5a) that $\{V(\mathbf{X}_t)\}$ forms a supermartingale. It follows from a supermartingale inequality (see e.g. Theorem 3.2 in Doob (1953, p. 313)) that

$$P\left(\sup_{0 \le t < \infty} V(\mathbf{X}_t) > \lambda \mid \mathbf{X}_0 = \mathbf{x} \right) \le V(\mathbf{x})/\lambda. \qquad (A1.8)$$

Thus, in view of (A1.6)–(A1.8),

$$P_\mu\left(\sup_{0 \le t < \infty} V(\mathbf{X}_t) > \lambda \mid \mathbf{X}_0 \in K_1 \right) \le \varepsilon/2. \qquad (A1.9)$$

By (A1.5b), $K_2 = \{\mathbf{x}: V(\mathbf{X}) \le \lambda\}$ is a compact set. Inequalities (A1.6) and (A1.9) combined imply that $(U^t\mu)(K_2) \ge 1 - \varepsilon$, $t = 0, 1, 2, \ldots$.

We now prove the second part of the theorem. Conditional on $\mathbf{X}_0 = \mathbf{x}$, it follows from a supermartingale convergence theorem (c.f. Theorem 5.14 in Breiman (1968)) that $V(\mathbf{X}_t)$ converges almost surely to some random variable and hence $\dot{V}(\mathbf{X}_t)$ tends to zero. Let $\mu \in L$ be the initial distribution. Since **x** is arbitrary, $\dot{V}(\mathbf{X}_t) \to 0$ with P_μ probability 1. It now follows readily from the assumption of E made in the second part of the theorem that $\mathbf{X}_n \to E$ with P_μ probability 1. $\square$

The Markov chain $\{\mathbf{X}_t\}$ defined by (A1.1) is said to be *weakly continuous* if for all bounded continuous functions $g: \mathbf{R}^m \to \mathbf{R}$, $\int P(\mathbf{x}, d\mathbf{y})g(\mathbf{y})$ is continuous in **x**. A simple sufficient condition for $\{\mathbf{X}_t\}$ satisfying (A1.1) to be weakly continuous is that f is continuous.

Lemma A1.1: If $\{\mathbf{X}_t\}$ satisfying (A1.1) is weakly continuous, then $U: \mathcal{L} \to \mathcal{L}$ is continuous.

Proof. Let $\rho(\mu_n, \mu) \to 0$, that is for any bounded continuous function $g: \mathbf{R}^m \to \mathbf{R}$,

$$\int g(\mathbf{y})\mu_n(d\mathbf{y}) \to \int g(\mathbf{y})\mu(d\mathbf{y}).$$

Now

$$\int g(\mathbf{y})(U\mu_n)(d\mathbf{y}) = \int g(\mathbf{y}) \int P(\mathbf{x}, d\mathbf{y})\mu_n(d\mathbf{x})$$

$$= \int \left(\int g(\mathbf{y})P(\mathbf{x}, d\mathbf{y}) \right) \mu_n(d\mathbf{x})$$

but $\int g(\mathbf{y})P(\mathbf{x}, d\mathbf{y})$ is a bounded continuous function in **x**; so

$$\int g(\mathbf{y})(U\mu_n)(d\mathbf{y}) \to \int \left(\int g(\mathbf{y})P(\mathbf{x}, d\mathbf{y}) \right) \mu(d\mathbf{x}) = \int g(\mathbf{y})(U\mu)(d\mathbf{y}).$$

Hence $\rho(U\mu_n, U\mu) \to 0$ and thus U is continuous. $\square$

We now state one of the main results. It follows from Theorem A1.2, Lemma A1.3, and the obvious generalization of Theorem 2.7 to the case where the state space is a metric space.

Theorem A1.3: Suppose the Markov chain $\{\mathbf{X}_t\}$ satisfying (A1.1) is weakly continuous and the conditions of Theorem A1.2 are satisfied. Then, for each $\mu \in \mathcal{L}$, the positive limit set $\omega(\mu)$ (i.e. the set of limit points of the sequence $(U^t\mu)_{t\geq 0}$) is non-empty, compact, invariant, invariantly connected, and the smallest closed set that $U^t\mu$ approaches as $t \to \infty$. Furthermore, $\bigcup_{\nu \in \omega(\mu)} \text{supp}(\nu) \subseteq E$, where $\text{supp}(\nu)$, is the support of ν.

Remark: $\bigcup_{\nu \in \omega(\mu)} \text{supp}(\nu)$ is called the *support* of $\omega(\mu)$. It is clear that among the invariant sets of $\mathcal{L}$ whose supports are subsets of E, there is a largest one. Let us call the support of the latter the *largest invariant support* in E. Then the conclusion of the above theorem implies that $\mathbf{X}_t$ tends to the largest invariant support in E with P_μ probability 1. In many applications, the largest invariant support in E is a singleton. $\square$

Sometimes, a global Lyapunov function satisfying conditions (A1.5) may not exist. Suppose, instead there exists a continuous function V such that condition (A1.5a) holds only for $\mathbf{x}$ in Q_λ for some $\lambda > 0$ and $Q_\lambda = \{\mathbf{x} : V(\mathbf{x}) < \lambda\}$ is a bounded set. A gradually stopped process $\{\tilde{\mathbf{X}}_t\}$ is now defined so that the conditions (A1.5a) and (A1.5b) for $\tilde{\mathbf{X}}_t$ are met. Let $0 < \lambda_1 < \lambda$ and $\lambda - \lambda_1 = d$. Define

$$\tilde{\mathbf{X}}_0 = \mathbf{X}_0 \tag{A1.10a}$$

and the transition probability $\bar{P}(.\,,.)$ of $\{\tilde{\mathbf{X}}_t\}$ by

$$\bar{P}(\mathbf{x}, A) = \begin{cases} \delta_{\mathbf{x}} & \text{with probability } 1 - \tau(\mathbf{x}) \\ P(\mathbf{x}, A) & \text{with probability } \tau(\mathbf{x}) \end{cases} \tag{A1.10b}$$

where

$$\tau(\mathbf{x}) = \begin{cases} 1 & \text{if } V(\mathbf{x}) < \lambda_1 \\ (\lambda - V(\mathbf{x}))/d & \text{if } \lambda_1 \le V(\mathbf{X}) < \lambda \\ 0 & \text{otherwise.} \end{cases} \tag{A1.10c}$$

Clearly $\{\tilde{\mathbf{X}}_t\}$ is weakly continuous if $\{\mathbf{X}_t\}$ is. Also, conditions (A1.5) are satisfied for $\{\tilde{\mathbf{X}}_t\}$. Note that, since Q_λ is bounded. $V(.)$ can always be modified to satisfy condition (A1.5b). Suppose the initial distribution $\mu_0 = \delta_{\mathbf{x}}$ with $\mathbf{x} \in Q_{\lambda_1}$. Then $V(\tilde{\mathbf{X}}_t)$ is a supermartingale. Following the proof of Theorem A1.2, we have

$$P_{\mathbf{x}}\left(\sup_{0 \le t < \infty} V(\tilde{\mathbf{X}}_t) > \lambda_1\right) \le V(\mathbf{X})/\lambda_1. \tag{A1.11}$$

Thus, with probability not less than $1 - V(\mathbf{x})/\lambda$, $\tilde{\mathbf{X}}_t$ always stays inside Q_{λ_1} and hence so does $\mathbf{X}_t$. Thus, we have the following local version of Theorem A1.3. The proof is an easy modification of the arguments leading to Theorem A1.3 and hence omitted. The theorem may be compared with Theorem 2.9.

Theorem A1.4: Let $\mathbf{X}_t$ be given by eqn (A1.1). Suppose there exists a continuous function $V : \mathbf{R}^m \to \mathbf{R}$ such that

$$E_{\mathbf{y}}(V(\mathbf{X}_1)) - V(\mathbf{y}) \le 0, \qquad \mathbf{y} \in Q_\lambda \tag{A1.12}$$

and $Q_\lambda = \{\mathbf{y} : V(\mathbf{y}) < \lambda\}$ is a bounded set. Suppose that $\dot{V}$ is continuous. Let $\tilde{\mathbf{X}}_t$ be defined as in (A1.10). Let the initial distribution $\mu_0 = \delta_{\mathbf{x}}$ and $\mathbf{x} \in Q_{\lambda_1}$. Then with probability greater than $1 - V(\mathbf{x})/\lambda_1$, $\tilde{\mathbf{X}}_t$ stays inside Q_{λ_1} for ever and tends to $E_\lambda = \{\mathbf{y} : \dot{V}(\mathbf{y}) = 0\} \cap \bar{Q}_{\lambda_1}$. Moreover, the probability measures of $\tilde{\mathbf{X}}_t$ tend to the largest invariant support of $E_{\lambda_1} \cup Q'_{\lambda_1}$ with probability 1. Note that the invariance is with respect to the U induced by $\bar{P}(.\,,.)$ of $\{\tilde{X}_t\}$.

Remark: Kushner (1971) mentions a generalization of his Theorem 3 (p. 204) to the case of continuous state space in discrete time. He introduced the stopped process corresponding to our $\tilde{\mathbf{X}}_t$ with $\lambda_1 = \lambda$, and stated an analogue of the above theorem for this type of abruptly stopped process. His approach has some difficulty in that $\{\hat{\mathbf{X}}_t\}$ need not be weakly continuous even if $\{\mathbf{X}_t\}$ is. Thus, it is still open whether the generalization of his Theorem 3 is true or not. □

A1.3 Some relevant Markov chain theories

In this section, we summarize some relevant Markov chain techniques that are needed in §A1.4. The results are stated for a general Markov chain living on an Euclidean space. Hence, there is some slight overlap with §A1.2. For a lucid account of Markov chain theory and the proofs of many results stated here, see Nummelin (1984).

Let $\{\mathbf{X}_t\}$ be a Markov chain with state space $(\mathbf{R}^m, \mathbb{B})$, $\mathbb{B}$ being the collection of Borel sets. The nth step transition probability of $\{\mathbf{X}_t\}$ is denoted by $P^n(\mathbf{x}, A)$, that is

$$P^n(\mathbf{x}, A) = P(\mathbf{X}_n \in A \mid \mathbf{X}_0 = \mathbf{x}), \qquad \mathbf{x} \in \mathbf{R}^m, \qquad A \in \mathbb{B}. \quad (A1.13)$$

For simplicity, $P^1(\mathbf{x}, A)$ is simply written as $P(\mathbf{x}, A)$. Let ϕ be a non-trivial (i.e. $\phi(\mathbf{R}^m) > 0$) σ-finite measure on $(\mathbf{R}^m, \mathbb{B})$, $\{\mathbf{X}_t\}$ is ϕ-*irreducible* if, $\forall \mathbf{x} \in \mathbf{R}^m$, $\forall A \in \mathbb{B}$ with $\phi(A) > 0$.

$$\sum_{n=1}^{\infty} P^n(\mathbf{x}, A) > 0. \quad (A1.14)$$

If $\{\mathbf{X}_t\}$ is ϕ-irreducible for some ϕ, it is simply called *irreducible*. An irreducible Markov chain $\{\mathbf{X}_t\}$ admits a *maximal irreducibility measure M* which satisfies

(1) $\{\mathbf{X}_t\}$ is M-irreducible;   (A1.15a)

(2) if $\{\mathbf{X}_t\}$ is μ-irreducible, μ is absolutely continuous w.r.t. M;

(A1.15b)

(3) $M(A) = 0 \Rightarrow M\left(\left\{\mathbf{x}: \sum_{n=0}^{\infty} P^n(\mathbf{x}, A) > 0\right\}\right) = 0.$ (A1.15c)

Henceforth in this section, we assume that $\{\mathbf{X}_t\}$ is ϕ-irreducible and M always stands for the corresponding maximal irreducibility measures. By (A1.15b), ϕ-non-null set is always M-non-null. For simplicity, in this section, null and non-null sets are relative to the measure M unless stated otherwise.

Definition: A non-null set $C \in \mathbb{B}$ is *small if there exists a positive integer k, a constant $b > 0$, and a probability measure $v(.)$* such that

$$P^k(\mathbf{x}, A) \geq bv(A), \qquad \mathbf{x} \in C, \qquad A \in \mathbb{B}. \quad (A1.16)$$

It can be shown that there exists a small set. Let C be a small set. Define

$$I(C) = \{k \geq 1 : (A1.16) \text{ holds for some } b \text{ and } v\}. \qquad (A1.17)$$

Let $d(C)$ be the greatest common divisor of $I(C)$. It can be shown that $d(C)$ is the same for all small sets. So, we shall write d instead of $d(C)$. Then the state space, $\mathbf{R}^m$, can almost be partitioned into a disjoint d-cycle of non-null Borel sets, that is $\exists (E_0, E_1, \ldots, E_{d-1})$ such that

(1) $M(\mathbf{R}^m \setminus \cup E_i) = 0;$ \hfill (A1.18a)

(2) the E_i are disjoint non-null Borel sets; \hfill (A1.18b)

(3) $\forall i, \forall \mathbf{x} \in E_i,\ P(\mathbf{x}, E_j) = 0$ for all $j \neq i + 1 \pmod{d}$. \hfill (A1.18c)

Furthermore, for any cycle $(\bar{E}_0, \bar{E}_1, \ldots, \bar{E}_{d'-1})$ satisfying (A1.18), d/d' is a positive integer and any $\bar{E}_i$ is, up to a null set, a union of d/d' sets from $(E_0, E_1, \ldots, E_{d-1})$.

If $d = 1$, the Markov chain is called *aperiodic* otherwise it is called *periodic with period d*. By considering $\{X_{nd}\}$, we have d irreducible aperiodic Markov chains with state spaces E_i. Thus theoretically, we can focus on studying aperiodic Markov chains. Sometimes, we need to check if a Markov chain is aperiodic.

Proposition A1.1: A necessary and sufficient condition for $\{\mathbf{X}_t\}$ to be aperiodic is that there exists a small set C and a positive integer n such that

$$P^n(\mathbf{x}, C) > 0 \quad \text{and} \quad P^{n+1}(\mathbf{x}, C) < 0 \qquad \mathbf{x} \in C. \qquad (A1.19)$$

Proof. We first prove the sufficiency part of the proposition. Without loss of generality, it can be assumed that $\exists \gamma > 0$ such that

$$P^n(\mathbf{x}, C) > \gamma \quad \text{and} \quad P^{n+1}(\mathbf{x}, C) > \gamma, \qquad \mathbf{x} \in C. \qquad (A1.20)$$

This is because $C = \bigcup_{j=1}^{\infty} C_j$ where $C_j = \{\mathbf{x} \in C : P^n(\mathbf{x}, C) > 1/j$ and $P^{n+1}(\mathbf{x}, C) > 1/j\}$. Since C is non-null, some C_j, say C_h, is non-null and clearly (A1.16) holds for C_h. We can now relabel C_h as C. From (A1.16),

$$P^k(\mathbf{x}, A) \geq b v(A), \qquad \mathbf{x} \in C, \qquad A \in \mathbb{B}.$$

In view of (A1.20), for all $\mathbf{x} \in C$

$$P^{n+k}(\mathbf{x}, C) = \int P^n(\mathbf{x}, d\mathbf{y}) P^k(\mathbf{y}, A)$$

$$\geq \int_C P^n(\mathbf{x}, d\mathbf{y}) P^k(\mathbf{y}, A)$$

$$\geq \gamma b v(A).$$

Similarly, we have

$$P^{n+1+k}(\mathbf{x}, C) \geq \gamma b v(A), \qquad \mathbf{x} \in C.$$

So both $n + k$ and $n + k + 1 \in I(C)$ and therefore $d = 1$. The necessity part follows readily from Proposition A1.1 and Theorem 3.1 in Orey (1971). $\square$

It is known that every ϕ-non-null set contains a small set. Therefore, Proposition A1.1 can be generalized as follows.

Proposition A1.2: A necessary and sufficient condition for $\{X_t\}$ to be aperiodic is that there exists an $A \in \mathbb{B}$ with $\phi(A) > 0$ and $\forall B \in \mathbb{B}$, $B \subseteq A$ with $\phi(B) > 0$, there exists a positive integer n such that

$$P^n(\mathbf{x}, B) > 0 \quad \text{and} \quad P^{n+1}(\mathbf{x}, B) > 0, \quad \mathbf{x} \in B. \tag{A1.21}$$

A small set is the counterpart of a single state in the case of an irreducible Markov chain with countable state space. Therefore, it is pertinent to know when a set is small. We now present two criteria.

Proposition A1.3: A non-null Borel set C is small if there exists an $A \in \mathbb{B}$ with $\phi(A) > 0$ such that for all ϕ-non-null Borel subsets, B, of A, there exists a positive integer L such that

$$\inf_{\mathbf{x} \in C} \sum_{n=0}^{L} P^n(\mathbf{x}, B) > 0. \tag{A1.22}$$

Proposition A1.4: Suppose $\{X_t\}$ is weakly continuous, that is for all bounded continuous functions $g : \mathbf{R}^m \to \mathbf{R}$, $\int g(\mathbf{y})P(\mathbf{x}, d\mathbf{y})$ is a continuous function in $\mathbf{x}$. Then all ϕ-non-null relatively compact sets are small.

For the proofs of Propositions A1.3 and A1.4, see Proposition 2.11 in Nummelin (1984) and Feigin and Tweedie (1985) respectively.

Definition: $\{X_t\}$ is *geometrically ergodic if* there exists a probability measure π on $(\mathbf{R}, \mathbb{B})$, a positive constant $\rho < 1$, and a π-integrable non-negative measurable function h such that

$$\|P^n(x, .) - \pi(.)\|_\tau \leq \rho^n h(x), \qquad x \in \mathbf{R} \tag{A1.23}$$

where $\|.\|_\tau$ denotes the total variation norm.

It is readily seen that $\pi(.)$ in (A1.23) satisfies the so-called *invariant equation*

$$\pi(A) = \int P(\mathbf{x}, A)\pi(d\mathbf{x}), \qquad A \in \mathbb{B}. \tag{A1.24}$$

Hence, π is called the *invariant measure*. Suppose $\{X_t\}$ is geometrically ergodic. Then (A1.23) implies that $\{X_t\}$ is asymptotically stationary exponentially fast. Furthermore, if the initial distribution $\{X_t\}$ is π, that is the distribution of $\mathbf{X}_0$ is π, $\{X_t\}$ is strictly stationary.

It is desirable to have practical criteria guaranteeing a Markov chain to be geometrically ergodic. One of the earliest such criteria is Doeblin's condition D as in Doob (1953):

(D): There is a finite non-negative measure ϕ on $(\mathbf{R}^m, \mathbb{B})$ with $\phi(\mathbf{R}^m) > 0$, an integer $k \geq 1$, and a positive ε, such that

$$P^k(\mathbf{x}, A) \leq 1 - \varepsilon \quad \text{if} \quad \phi(A) \leq \varepsilon. \tag{A1.25}$$

It is shown in Doob (1953) that if $\{\mathbf{X}_t\}$ is aperiodic and irreducible and condition (D) holds, then $\{\mathbf{X}_t\}$ is geometric ergodic with h in (A1.23) being a bounded function. Tweedie (1975) pointed out that Doeblin's condition (D) works because it insists that, with positive probability, from anywhere in the state space, the chain moves in a *fixed* number of steps to the 'centre' of the state space. A natural generalization is to allow the number of steps for the chain to move back to the 'centre' to be dependent on the initial position of the chain. To be precise, we have the following so-called *drift criterion* for *geometric ergodicity*.

Theorem A1.5: Let $\{\mathbf{X}_t\}$ be aperiodic and irreducible. Suppose that there exists a small set C, a non-negative measurable function g, and constants $r > 1$, $\gamma > 0$, and $B > 0$ such that

$$E(rg(\mathbf{X}_{t+1}) \mid \mathbf{X}_t = \mathbf{x}) < g(\mathbf{x}) - \gamma, \qquad \mathbf{x} \notin C \tag{A1.26a}$$

and

$$E(g(\mathbf{X}_{t+1}) \mid \mathbf{X}_t = \mathbf{x}) < B, \qquad \mathbf{x} \in C. \tag{A1.26b}$$

Then $\{\mathbf{X}_t\}$ is geometrically ergodic.

Remarks: Here, $g(\mathbf{x})$ can be interpreted as a generalized energy function. Thus, (A1.26a) says that, if the Markov chain starts outside C, it would, on average, dissipate energy in the next step. Condition (A1.26b) says that if the chain starts inside C, the average gain in energy in the next step is uniformly bounded. C is a sort of 'centre' of the state space.

A1.4 Ergodicity of stochastic difference equations

We now discuss an approach to the geometric ergodicity of a class of stochastic difference equations. Let $\{\mathbf{X}_t\}$ be a Markov chain, with state space $(\mathbf{R}^m, \mathbb{B})$, which satisfies the stochastic difference equation

$$\mathbf{X}_t = f(\mathbf{X}_{t-1}, \varepsilon_t), \qquad t \geq 1 \tag{A1.27}$$

where $\varepsilon_t \sim \text{IID}$, scalar valued, and independent of $\mathbf{X}_s$, $s < t$. Furthermore, it is assumed that

$$f(\mathbf{X}_{t-1}, \varepsilon_t) = T(\mathbf{X}_{t-1}) + S(\mathbf{X}_{t-1}, \varepsilon_t). \tag{A1.28}$$

Associated with eqn (A1.27) is the following deterministic difference equation:

$$\mathbf{x}_t = T(\mathbf{x}_{t-1}). \qquad (A1.29)$$

In many time series models, the observed time series is a functional of $\mathbf{X}_t$, and eqn (A1.27) is known as the state space equation. We shall formulate some results relating the stability of (A1.29) and the asymptotic behaviour of the Markov chain defined by (A1.27). The Markov chain techniques discussed in the previous section will be our principal tools.

The following set of conditions will be useful later:

(A1) $\mathbf{0} \in \mathbf{R}^m$ is an equilibrium state for eqn (A1.29), that is $\mathbf{0} = T(\mathbf{0})$, and is *exponentially asymptotically stable in the large*, that is $\exists K$, $c > 0$ s.t. $\forall t \geq 0$, and starting with $\mathbf{x}_0 \in \mathbf{R}^m$, $\|\mathbf{x}_t\| \leq Ke^{-ct}\|\mathbf{x}_0\|$.

(A2) $\forall \mathbf{x} \in \mathbf{R}^m$ and for all neighbourhoods W of $\mathbf{0} \in \mathbf{R}^m$ there is a non-null conditional probability of $S(\mathbf{X}_{t-1}, \varepsilon_t)$ being in W given that $\mathbf{X}_{t-1} = \mathbf{x}$.

(A3) The distribution of ε_t has an absolutely continuous component (w.r.t. Lebesgue measure) with positive probability density function over some open interval $(-\delta, \delta)$.

(A4) $\{U, JU, \ldots, J^{m-1}U\}$ is a linearly independent set where J is the partial derivative of f w.r.t. $\mathbf{X}$ at $(\mathbf{0}, 0)$ and U is the partial derivative of f w.r.t. ε at $(\mathbf{0}, 0)$.

(A5) T is Lipschitz continuous over $\mathbf{R}^m$, that is $\exists M > 0$, s.t. $\forall \mathbf{x}, \mathbf{y} \in \mathbf{R}^m$, $\|T(\mathbf{x}) - T(\mathbf{y})\| \leq M\|\mathbf{x} - \mathbf{y}\|$.

(A6) For some $\tau > 0$, $\mathrm{E}[\|S(\mathbf{X}_{t-1}, \varepsilon_t)\|$ given $\mathbf{X}_{t-1} = \mathbf{x}] \leq \tau$, $\forall \mathbf{x} \in \mathbf{R}^m$.

(A7) $\mathbf{0} \in \mathbf{R}^m$ is an equilibrium state for eqn (A1.29) and is *exponentially asymptotically unstable in the large*, that is $\exists K > 0$, $c > 0$ s.t. $\forall t \geq 0$, and starting with $\mathbf{x}_0 \in \mathbf{R}^m$, $\|\mathbf{x}_t\| \geq Ke^{ct}\|\mathbf{x}_0\|$.

(A8) $S(\mathbf{0}, \varepsilon_t)$ is not identically equal to $\mathbf{0}$ a.s.

Theorem A1.6: Assume that f is continuous everywhere and continuously differentiable in a neighbourhood of the origin. Suppose that conditions (A1)–(A6) hold. Then $\{\mathbf{X}_t\}$ defined by eqn (A1.27) is geometrically ergodic.

We shall give the proof in several steps, which would also provide some other interesting results. First, we prove a converse theorem on the existence of a Lyapunov function.

Theorem A1.7: If conditions (A1) and (A5) hold, then there exists a function g such that, for some constants K_1, L, β, and $0 < \alpha < 1$, $\forall \mathbf{x}$,

$\mathbf{y} \in \mathbf{R}^m$

(1) $\quad \|\mathbf{x}\| \leq g(\mathbf{x}) \leq K_1 \|\mathbf{x}\|;$ $\qquad\qquad$ (A1.30a)

(2) $\quad |g(\mathbf{x}) - g(\mathbf{y})| \leq L \|\mathbf{x} - \mathbf{y}\|;$ $\qquad\qquad$ (A1.30b)

(3) $\quad g(T(\mathbf{x})) \leq \alpha g(\mathbf{x}).$ $\qquad\qquad$ (A1.30c)

Proof. Let q be a positive constant less than 1 and c be as defined in (A1). Define

$$g(\mathbf{z}) = \sup_{t \geq 0} (\|\mathbf{x}(t; \mathbf{z})\| \, e^{qct}), \qquad \mathbf{z} \in \mathbf{R}^m \qquad (A1.31)$$

where $\mathbf{x}(t; \mathbf{z})$ denotes the solution of (A1.29) with the initial condition $\mathbf{x}_0 = \mathbf{z}$.

From condition (A1).

$$e^{qct} \|\mathbf{x}(t; \mathbf{z})\| \leq K e^{(q-1)ct} \|\mathbf{z}\| \qquad (A1.32)$$

and the right-hand side is not greater than $\|\mathbf{z}\|$ for all $t \geq \log(K)/(1 - q)c$. Thus, the supremum on the right-hand side of (A1.31) is only over a finite number of terms. Under (A5), T is Lipschitz continuous and since

$$| \|\mathbf{x}(t; \mathbf{x})\| - \|\mathbf{x}(t; \mathbf{y})\| | \leq \|\mathbf{x}(t; \mathbf{x}) - \mathbf{x}(t; \mathbf{y})\| \qquad (A1.33)$$

for fixed t, $e^{qct} \|\mathbf{x}(t, \mathbf{z})\|$ is Lipschitz continuous in $\mathbf{z}$. So (A1.30a) holds trivially. Also (A1.30b) holds as the maximum of a finite number of Lipschitz continuous functions is Lipschitz continuous.

Now,

$$g(T(\mathbf{x})) = \sup_{t \geq 0} \|\mathbf{x}(t; T(\mathbf{x}))\| \, e^{qct}$$

$$= e^{-qc} \sup_{t \geq 0} \|\mathbf{x}(t + 1; \mathbf{x})\| \, e^{qc(t+1)}$$

$$\leq e^{-qc} g(\mathbf{x}). \qquad (A1.34)$$

Hence, (A1.30c) holds with $\alpha = e^{-qc} < 1$.

Proposition A1.5: Suppose that F is continuously differentiable in a neighbourhood around $\mathbf{0}$ and conditions (A3) and (A4) hold. Then there exists an open sphere, say W, centred at $\mathbf{0}$ such that, conditional on $\mathbf{X}_0 = \mathbf{x} \in W$, $\mathbf{X}_m$ has an absolutely continuous component whose p.d.f. is positive over W.

Proof. Let $m = 1$. Consider the map $V: \mathbf{R}^2 \to \mathbf{R}^2$ which takes (x, ε) to $(x, f(x, \varepsilon))$. Then V is continuously differentiable around a neighbourhood of $(0, 0)$. The Jacobian at $(0, 0)$ is

$$\begin{bmatrix} 1 & 0 \\ J & U \end{bmatrix} \qquad (A1.35)$$

where $J = \partial f / \partial x|_{(0,0)}$ and $U = \partial f / \partial \varepsilon|_{(0,0)}$. It follows from (A4) that the above Jacobian is invertible. Hence, $\exists W_1, W_2$ neighbourhoods of $(0,0)$ such that V is a diffeomorphism from W_1 onto W_2. Without loss of generality, W_1 may be assumed to lie inside $(-\delta, \delta) \times (-\delta, \delta)$ where δ is defined in (A3). Then $\exists \theta > 0$ such that if $C = (-\theta, \theta) \times (-\theta, \theta)$, $C \subseteq W_1 \cap W_2$. Thus, conditional on $X_0 = x \in (-\theta, \theta)$, $X_1 = f(x, \varepsilon_1)$ possesses an absolutely continuous component (w.r.t. the Lebesgue measure) whose p.d.f. is positive over $(-\theta, \theta)$.

The proof for $m > 1$ is similar and hence omitted. $\square$

Proposition A1.6: Assume that f is continuous everywhere and continuously differentiable in a neighbourhood of the origin. Suppose conditions (A1)–(A5) hold. Then $\{X_t\}$ is ϕ-irreducible and aperiodic, where ϕ is the Lebesgue measure restricted on W and W is as defined in Proposition A1.5.

Proof. Let W contain the sphere $S_\delta = \{x \in \mathbf{R}^m : \|x\| \leq \delta\}$ for some $\delta > 0$. Let $x \in \mathbf{R}^m$ and $X_0 = x$. Let k be an integer and γ a positive constant to be determined later. By (A2), the event

$$W_{\gamma,k} = \{\|S(X_{t-1}, \varepsilon_t)\| < \gamma, t = 1, 2, \ldots, k\} \qquad (A1.36)$$

is easily seen to have positive probability. Let g be the Lyapunov function as in Proposition A1.7. Equations and inequalities between random variables are in the sense of probability 1. On the event $W_{\gamma,k}$, $\forall 1 \leq i \leq k$,

$$\begin{aligned} g(X_i) &= g(T(X_{i-1}) + S(X_{t-1}, \varepsilon_t)) \\ &\leq g(T(X_{i-1})) + L\gamma \\ &\leq \alpha g(X_{i-1}) + L\gamma \end{aligned} \qquad (A1.37)$$

by (A1.30b) and (A1.30c) respectively. Then, on $W_{\gamma,k}$,

$$g(X_k) \leq (L\gamma/(1-\alpha)) + \alpha^k g(x). \qquad (A1.38)$$

By choosing γ sufficiently small and k sufficiently large, the right-hand side of (A1.38) is smaller than δ. In view of (A1.30), it must be that, on $W_{\gamma,k}$, $\|X_k\| < \delta$ and hence $X_k \in S_\delta \subseteq W$. Combined with Proposition A1.5, this means that, for all $A \subseteq W$ with $\phi(A) > 0$,

$$P(X_{k+n} \in A \mid X_0 = x) > 0. \qquad (A1.39)$$

Thus $\{X_t\}$ is ϕ-irreducible with ϕ being the Lebesgue measure restricted on W.

It follows from (A2) and the continuity of f that

$$P(X_{k+m+1} \subseteq S_\delta \mid X_0 = x) > 0. \qquad (A1.40)$$

Since f is continuous, $\{X_t\}$ is weakly continuous. Hence, S_δ is small by Proposition A1.4. Proposition A1.1 then implies that $\{X_t\}$ is aperiodic. $\square$

Proof of Theorem A1.6: It suffices to verify that the conditions of Theorem A1.5 hold. Let g be as in Theorem A1.7 and $\{\mathbf{X}_t\}$ the Markov chain satisfying (A1.27):

$$
\begin{aligned}
E(g(\mathbf{X}_{t+1}) \mid \mathbf{X}_t = \mathbf{x}) &= E(g(T(\mathbf{X}_t)) + S(\mathbf{X}_t, \varepsilon_{t+1})) \mid \mathbf{X}_t = \mathbf{x}) \\
&\le E(g(T(\mathbf{X}_t)) \mid \mathbf{X}_t = \mathbf{x}) + LE(\|S(\mathbf{X}_t, \varepsilon_{t+1})\| \mid \mathbf{X}_t = \mathbf{x}) \\
&\le \alpha g(\mathbf{x}) + L\tau.
\end{aligned}
\tag{A1.41}
$$

The last inequality follows from condition (A6). Thus, conditions (A1.26a) and (A1.26b) hold if $r < 1/\alpha$ and $C = \{\mathbf{x} \in \mathbf{R}^m, \|\mathbf{x}\| < \rho\}$ with ρ sufficiently large. Clearly, C is ϕ-non-null and compact, so it is small as $\{\mathbf{X}_t\}$ is weakly continuous. □

The following is a partial converse to the above theorem.

Theorem A1.8: Consider the Markov chain $\{\mathbf{X}_t\}$ defined by eqn (A1.27). Suppose that conditions (A2), (A5)–(A8) hold. Then, for any initial distribution, $\|X_t\| \to \infty$ with positive probability.

Before proving the theorem, we first state a converse theorem on the existence of a Lyapunov function under condition (A7).

Theorem A1.9: Suppose that conditions (A5) and (A7) hold. Then there exists a function g such that, for some constants K_1, L, β, $\alpha > 1$, and $\forall \mathbf{x}$, $\mathbf{y} \in \mathbf{R}^m$,

(1) $\|\mathbf{x}\| \le g(\mathbf{x}) \le K_1 \|\mathbf{x}\|$; (A1.42a)

(2) $|g(\mathbf{x}) - g(\mathbf{y})| \le L \|\mathbf{x} - \mathbf{y}\|$; (A1.42b)

(3) $g(T(\mathbf{x})) \ge \alpha g(\mathbf{x})$. (A1.42c)

Proof. Let $0 < q < 1$ be a constant and c be as in (A7). Define

$$
g(\mathbf{z}) = \inf_{t \ge 0} \|\mathbf{x}(t; \mathbf{z})\| \, e^{-qct}
\tag{A1.43}
$$

where $\mathbf{x}(t; \mathbf{z})$ defines the solution to (A1.29) with $\mathbf{x}_0 = \mathbf{z}$. The rest of the proof is similar to that of Theorem A1.7 and hence omitted. □

Proof of Theorem A1.8: The notation in the above theorem will be adopted. Let $\mathbf{x}_0 \ne \mathbf{0}$ and $\mathbf{X}_0 = \mathbf{x}_0$. Let $\beta = (\alpha + 1)/2$ and $d = (\alpha - 1)g(\mathbf{x}_0)/(2L)$. Now provided that $g(\mathbf{X}_t) \ge \beta^t g(\mathbf{x}_0)$ and $\|\delta(\mathbf{X}_t, \varepsilon_{t+1})\| \le d\beta^t$,

$$
\begin{aligned}
g(\mathbf{X}_{t+1}) &= g(T(\mathbf{X}_t) + S(\mathbf{X}_t, \varepsilon_{t+1}) \\
&\ge \alpha g(\mathbf{X}_t) - L \|S(\mathbf{X}_t, \varepsilon_{t+1})\| \\
&\ge \beta g(\mathbf{X}_t) + (\alpha - 1)g(\mathbf{X}_t)/2 - Ld\beta^t \\
&\ge \beta^{t+1} g(\mathbf{x}_0).
\end{aligned}
\tag{A1.44}
$$

By the Markov inequality and (A6), for every $\mathbf{x} \in \mathbf{R}^m$,

$$
P(\|S(\mathbf{X}_t, \varepsilon_{t+1})\| \ge d\beta^t \mid \mathbf{X}_0 = \mathbf{x}) \le \tau/(d\beta^t).
\tag{A1.45}
$$

Also, by condition (A2), the left-hand side of (A1.45) is always less than 1. Hence, there exists a positive constant $\theta(\mathbf{x}_0)$ such that

$$P(g(\mathbf{X}_t) \geq d\beta^t g(\mathbf{x}_0), t \geq 1 \mid \mathbf{X}_0 = \mathbf{x}_0)$$

$$\geq \theta \prod_{n=N}^{\infty} [1 - \tau/(d\beta^n)]$$

$$> 0 \qquad\qquad\qquad\qquad\qquad (A1.46)$$

where N is the smallest positive integer such that $\tau/(d\beta^N) < 1$. Hence, there is a positive probability that $\|\mathbf{X}_t\|$ tends to ∞ as $t \to \infty$. If $\mathbf{x}_0 = \mathbf{0}$, by (A8), there is still a positive probability that $\|\mathbf{X}_t\|$ tends to ∞ as $t \to \infty$. $\quad\square$

Remarks:

1. The above results in this section are due to Chan (1986), which develop further the link between stationarity and ergodicity of some stochastic difference equations studied in Chan and Tong (1985).

2. Both conditions (A1) and (A7) refer to the equilibrium point $\mathbf{0}$ w.r.t eqn (A1.29). Indeed, if (A1.29) admits an equilibrium point other than $\mathbf{0}$, then by suitable transformation it can be arranged that the equilibrium point is $\mathbf{0}$.

3. In the decomposition (A1.28), $T(\mathbf{X}_t)$ can be identified as the slowly varying component while $S(\mathbf{X}_t, \varepsilon_{t+1})$ is the fast varying component. Thus Theorem A1.6 suggests that, under suitable regularity conditions, an exponentially stable slowly varying component ensures that the process is geometric ergodic.

4. The requirement of conditions (A2)–(A4) in Theorem A1.6 can be dropped if $\{\mathbf{X}_t\}$ is irreducible and aperiodic. If, furthermore, ϕ-non null compact sets are small, the smoothness condition on f can be dropped.

In view of the last point, we now state another useful condition for geometric ergodicity.

Theorem A1.10: Suppose that $\{\mathbf{X}_t\}$ defined by eqn (A.127) is ϕ-irreducible, aperiodic, and that ϕ-non null compact sets are small. If conditions (A1), (A5), and (A6) hold, then $\{\mathbf{X}_t\}$ is geometric ergodic.

We now present a simple yet useful set of sufficient conditions for the first part of the above theorem to hold. Specifically, assume $\{X_t\}$ satisfies the following difference equation:

$$X_t = h(X_{t-1}, X_{t-2}, \ldots, X_{t-m}) + \varepsilon_t \qquad\qquad (A1.47)$$

where $h : \mathbf{R}^m \to \mathbf{R}$, ε_t is as before, and $X_t \in \mathbf{R}$.

Define $\mathbf{X}_t = (X_t, X_{t-1}, \ldots, X_{t-m+1})'$. Then

$$\mathbf{X}_t = T(\mathbf{X}_{t-1}) + \varepsilon_t \mathbf{u} \tag{A1.48}$$

where $\mathbf{u} = (1, 0, \ldots, 0)'$ and $T(\mathbf{X}_{t-1}) = (h(X_{t-1}, \ldots, X_{t-m}),$ $X_{t-1}, \ldots, X_{t-m+1})'$.

Note that, for $m = 1$, $\mathbf{X}_t$ is simply X_t. $\{\mathbf{X}_t\}$ has the advantage of being Markov. We consider the geometric ergodicity of $\{\mathbf{X}_t\}$.

Proposition A1.7 (Chang and Tong 1985): Suppose the following conditions hold: (i) ε_t has an absolutely continuous component with a p.d.f., say $g(.)$, which is continuous and positive everywhere; (ii) $h(.)$ is bounded over bounded sets. Then $\{\mathbf{X}_t\}$ satisfying (A1.48) is aperiodic and ϕ-irreducible with ϕ being the Lebesgue measure. Furthermore, ϕ-non-null compact sets are small sets.

Proof. Let $m = 2$ and suppose that ε_t has a p.d.f., $g(.)$ which is positive and continuous everywhere. Let $\mathbf{z} = (z_1, z_2)'$ and $\mathbf{y} = (y_1, y_2)'$ be two arbitrary vectors in $\mathbf{R}^2$. Let A denote a Borel set in $\mathbf{R}^2$ and with positive Lebesgue measure. It is then straightforward to show that

$$P^2(\mathbf{z}, A) = \iint_A g(y_2 - h(z_1, z_2))g(y_1 - h(y_2, z_1)) \, dy_1 \, dy_2. \tag{A1.49}$$

Since $g(.)$ is positive everywhere, $P^2(\mathbf{z}, A) > 0$, $\forall \mathbf{z}$, and hence $P^3(\mathbf{z}, A) > 0$, $\forall \mathbf{z}$. This shows that $\{\mathbf{X}_t\}$ is aperiodic and ϕ-irreducible with ϕ being the Lebesgue measure. Suppose A is furthermore compact. Let B be a Borel subset of A and have positive Lebesgue measure. Since h is bounded over bounded sets and g is continuous and positive everywhere,

$$\inf_{\mathbf{y},\mathbf{z}\in A} g(y_2 - h(z_1, z_2))g(y_1 - h(y_2, z_1)) > 0. \tag{A1.50}$$

So, $\inf_{\mathbf{z}\in A} P^2(\mathbf{z}, B) < 0$. Hence, it follows from Proposition A1.3 that A is a small set. The proof is easily adapted to the case $m \neq 2$ and general ε_t satisfying condition (i). □

Example A1.1 (SETAR $(2; m, m)$):

$$X_t = \begin{cases} \phi_{10} + \phi_{11}X_{t-1} + \phi_{12}X_{t-2} + \ldots + \phi_{1m}X_{t-m} + \varepsilon_t & \text{if } X_{t-d} \leq r \\ \phi_{20} + \phi_{21}X_{t-1} + \phi_{22}X_{t-2} + \ldots + \phi_{2m}X_{t-m} + \varepsilon_t & \text{otherwise} \end{cases}$$

$$\tag{A1.51}$$

where $1 \leq d \leq p$; ε_t is IID, $\mathrm{E}(|\varepsilon_t|) < \infty$, and ε_1 admits a positive and continuous p.d.f. Now $\{X_t\}$ can be decomposed in the form of (A1.47), with h being piecewise linear. Hence, the conditions of Proposition A1.7 are satisfied. Therefore $\{\mathbf{X}_t\}$ defined by (A1.48) is aperiodic and irreducible. Also, compact sets with positive Lebesgue measure are non-null.

We now consider another decomposition of $\{X_t\}$ in the form of (A1.28) and such that conditions (A1)–(A8) can be checked more easily. Let $T : \mathbf{R}^m \to \mathbf{R}^m$ be defined by

$$T(Y) = \begin{cases} \mathbf{\Phi}_1 Y & \text{if } Y_d \le R \\ \mathbf{\Phi}_2 Y & \text{if } Y_d > r \end{cases} \tag{A1.52a}$$

where $\mathbf{Y} = (Y_1, Y_2, \dots, Y_m)'$,

$$\mathbf{\Phi}_i = \begin{bmatrix} \phi_{i1} & \phi_{i2} & \cdots & & \phi_{im} \\ 1 & 0 & \cdots & & 0 \\ 0 & 1 & \cdots & & 0 \\ \vdots & \vdots & & \vdots & \vdots \\ 0 & 0 & \cdots & 1 & 0 \end{bmatrix}. \tag{A1.52}$$

Then

$$\mathbf{X}_t = T(\mathbf{X}_{t-1}) + S(\mathbf{X}_{t-1}, \varepsilon_t) \tag{A1.53}$$

with $S(\mathbf{X}_{t-1}, \varepsilon_t)$ defined as $\mathbf{X}_t - T(\mathbf{X}_{t-1})$. Note that, in general, only in the case $m = 1$ does condition (A5) hold. So, let $m = 1$. Now, condition (A1) holds iff

(C1): $\phi_{11} < 1$ $\phi_{21} < 1$ and $\phi_{11}\phi_{21} < 1$.

Thus, it follows from Theorem A1.10 that $\{X_t\}$ is geometric ergodic under condition (C1). On the other hand, condition (A7) holds if

(C2): $\phi_1 > 1$ or $\phi_2 > 1$ or $\phi_1 \phi_2 > 1$.

Therefore, it follows from Theorem A1.8 that under (C2) $\{X_t\}$ is transient.

To handle the above example for the case $m > 1$, we need the following theorem from Chan and Tong (1988).

Theorem A1.11: Let $\{X_t\}$ satisfy (A1.48). Let T be continuous and homogeneous (i.e. $T(c\mathbf{X}) = cT(\mathbf{X}), \forall c > 0, \mathbf{X} \in \mathbf{R}^m$). Let the origin be an asymptotically stable equilibrium point of eqn (A1.29). Then $\{X_t\}$ is geometric ergodic.   □

Example A1.2 (SETAR $(2; m, m)$ revisited): Let $m > 1$. T is continuous if and only if $\phi_{1j} = \phi_{2j}, \forall j \ne d$. Suppose that T is continuous. Consider the following condition:

(C3): $\max_i \left(\sum_{j=1}^m |\phi_{ij}| \right) < 1.$ \tag{A1.54}

Under condtion (C3), 0 is an asymptotically equilibrium point for eqn (A1.29) (for a proof, see Lemma 3.1 of Chan and Tong (1985)). It now follows from Theorem A1.11 that under condition (C3) and the conditions on the noise as stated in Example A1.1, $\{\mathbf{X}_t\}$ is geometric ergodic and hence there is a stationary solution to eqn (A1.51). In fact, even for discontinuous T, the above conditions are sufficient for the geometric ergodicity of $\{\mathbf{X}_t\}$. For a proof see Chan and Tong (1985). In general, (C3) can be replaced by the more general condition of total stability of the origin, which is, however, not easy to verify. For the special case of $m = 2$, using geometric arguments, some specific results can be obtained. See Chan (1986). □

Example A1.3: Consider the following separable NLAR(m) model

$$X_t = \alpha_1 f_1(X_{t-1}; \boldsymbol{\theta}_1) + \alpha_2 f_2(X_{t-2}; \boldsymbol{\theta}_2) + \ldots + \alpha_m f_m(X_{t-m}; \boldsymbol{\theta}_m) + \varepsilon_t.$$
(A1.55)

It is assumed that

(1) $\forall \boldsymbol{\theta}_i, f_i(.\,; \boldsymbol{\theta}_i)$ is a fixed function bounded over bounded subsets of $\mathbf{R}$; (A1.56a)

(2) ε_t is as in Example A1.1; (A1.56b)

(3) $\forall i, \exists \phi_i(\alpha_i, \boldsymbol{\theta}_i)$ s.t. $\alpha_i f_i(x; \boldsymbol{\theta}_i) - \phi_i x$ is a bounded function. (A1.56c)

Then Proposition A1.7 implies that $\{\mathbf{X}_t\}$ defined by (A1.48) is irreducible, aperiodic, and compact sets with positive Lebesgue measure are small. We now employ a different decomposition than (A1.48) so that Theorems A1.8 and A1.10 are applicable. Specifically, consider

$$\mathbf{X}_t = \boldsymbol{\Phi}\mathbf{X}_{t-1} + S(\mathbf{X}_{t-1}, \varepsilon_t)$$
(A1.57)

where

$$\boldsymbol{\Phi} = \begin{bmatrix} \phi_1 & \phi_2 & \cdots & \cdot & \phi_m \\ 1 & 0 & \cdots & \cdot & 0 \\ 0 & 1 & \cdots & \cdot & 0 \\ \vdots & \vdots & \vdots & \vdots & \vdots \\ 0 & 0 & \cdots & 1 & 0 \end{bmatrix}$$
(A1.58)

and by definition

$$S(\mathbf{X}_{t-1}, \varepsilon_t) = \mathbf{X}_t - \boldsymbol{\Phi}\mathbf{X}_{t-1}.$$
(A1.59)

The associated deterministic difference equation is

$$\mathbf{x}_t = \boldsymbol{\Phi}\mathbf{x}_{t-1}.$$
(A1.60)

It is well known (see e.g. La Salle 1977) that the origin is exponentially asymptotically stable in the large w.r.t. (A1.60) if all the roots of the characteristic equation

$$x^m - \phi_1 x^{m-1} - \phi_2 x^{m-2} - \ldots - \phi_m = 0$$
(A1.61)

lie inside the unit circle. If some roots lie outside the unit circle, the origin becomes exponentially asymptotically unstable in the large w.r.t. (A1.60). Therefore it follows from Theorem A1.10 that $\{\mathbf{X}_t\}$ is geometric ergodic if all the roots lie inside the unit circle. Also, Theorem A1.8 implies that $\{\mathbf{X}_t\}$ is transient if some roots of eqn (A1.61) lie outside the unit circle.

The separable NLAR(m) model includes many commonly used models. For example, if $f_i(x; \boldsymbol{\theta}_i) = x$, $\forall i$, then $\{X_t\}$ satisfying (A1.55) becomes the usual AR(m) model. Next, if $f_i(x; \boldsymbol{\theta}_i) = [1 + \theta_{i1} \exp(-\theta_{i2} x^2)]x$ and $\boldsymbol{\theta}_i = (\theta_{i1}, \theta_{i2})'$, then $\{X_t\}$ satisfying (A1.55) becomes a modified EXPAR(m) model. The case with $\theta_{i2} = \gamma$, $\forall i$, is considered in Chan and Tong (1985).

So far in this section we have assumed that ε_t is scalar valued. For a multivariate version of (A1.47), we need to consider vector-valued noise. It is easy to see that most of the results in this section could be generalized to the case of vectorial noise.

Appendix 2
Martingale limit theory

We introduce the terminology and state without proof a few standard results. Standard references are Hall and Heyde (1980) and Pollard (1984).

Let (Ω, F, P) be a probability space with Ω denoting a set, F a σ-algebra of subsets of Ω, and P a probability measure defined on F. Let I be an index set which is a subset of the set of integers. Let $\{F_n : n \in I\}$ denote an increasing sequence of σ-algebras of F sets. The sequence $\{X_n : n \in I\}$ of random variables on Ω is said to be a *martingale* w.r.t. $\{F_n : n \in I\}$ if (i) X_n is measurable w.r.t. F_n, (ii) $E|X_n| < \infty$, and (iii) $E[X_n \mid F_m] = X_m$ a.s. for all $m < n$, m, $n \in I$. We sometimes say that $\{X_n, F_n : n \in I\}$ is a martingale. If in (i)–(iii), (iii) is replaced by the inequality $E[X_n \mid F_m] \geq X_m$ a.s. $(E[X_n \mid F_m] \leq X_m$ a.s.$)$, then $\{X_n, F_n : n \in I\}$ is called a *submartingale* (*supermartingale*).

Theorem A2.1 (The martingale convergence theorem): Let $\{X_n, F_n : n \geq 1\}$ be an L^1-bounded submartingale. Then there exists a random variable X s.t. $\lim_{n \to \infty} X_n = X$ a.s. and $E|X| \leq \liminf_{n \to \infty} E|X_n| < \infty$. If the submartingale is uniformly integrable, then X_n converges to X in L^1, and if $\{X_n, F_n\}$ is an L^2-bounded martingale, then X_n converges to X in L^2.

Theorem A2.2 (A weak law of large numbers for martingales): Let $\{X_n = \sum_{i=1}^{n} Z_i, F_n : n \geq 1\}$ be a martingale and $\{b_n\}$ a sequence of positive constants with b_n increasing to ∞ as $n \to \infty$. Then, writing $Z_{ni} = Z_i I(|X_i| \leq b_n)$, $1 \leq i \leq n$, I being the indicator function, we have that $b_n^{-1} X_n \to 0$ in probability as $n \to \infty$ if

$(1) \quad \sum_{i=1}^{n} P(|Z_i| > b_b) \to 0$

$(2) \quad b_n^{-1} \sum_{i=1}^{n} E[Z_{ni} \mid F_{i-1}] \to 0$

$(3) \quad b_n^{-2} \sum_{i=1}^{n} \{EZ_{ni}^2 - E[E[Z_{ni} \mid f_{i-1}]]^2\} \to 0.$

Let $\{X_n : n \geq 1\}$ be a sequence of square integrable random variables on a probability space (Ω, F, P), and let $\{F_n : -\infty < n < \infty\}$ be an

increasing sequence of sub-σ-algebras of F. Then $\{X_n, F_n\}$ is called a *mixingale (difference) sequence* if, for sequences of non-negative constants c_n and d_m, where $d_m \to 0$ as $m \to \infty$, we have for all $n \geq 1$ and $m \geq 0$
(i) $\|E[X_n \mid F_{n-m}]\|_2 \leq d_m c_n$, and (ii) $\|X_n - E[X_n \mid F_{n+m}]\|_2 \leq d_{m+1} c_n$,
where for a random variable Y, $\|Y\|_2^2 = E[|Y|^2]$.

Theorem A2.3 (A strong law of large numbers for mixingales): If $\{X_n, F_n\}$ is a mixingale and $\{b_n\}$ is a sequence of positive constants increasing to ∞ s.t.

$$\sum_{n=1}^{\infty} b_n^{-2} c_n^2 < \infty \quad \text{and} \quad d_n = o(n^{-1/2}(\ln n)^{-2}) \quad \text{as} \quad n \to \infty,$$

then

$$b_n^{-1} \sum_{i=1}^{n} X_i \to 0 \quad \text{a.s.}$$

Theorem A2.4 (A central limit theorem for martingales): Let $\{X_n, F_n\}$ denote a zero-mean martingale whose increments have finite variance. Let

$$X_n = \sum_{i=1}^{n} Z_i \qquad V_n^2 = \sum_{i=1}^{n} E[Z_i^2 \mid F_{i-1}] \quad \text{and} \quad \sigma_n^2 = EV_n^2 = EX_n^2.$$

If $\sigma_n^{-2} V_n^2 \to 1$ in probability and

$$\sigma_n^{-2} \sum_{i=1}^{n} E[Z_i^2 I(|Z_i| \geq \varepsilon \sigma_n)] \to 0$$

and $n \to \infty$, $\forall \varepsilon > 0$, then

$$\lim_{n \to \infty} P(\sigma_n^{-1} X_n \leq x) = (2\pi)^{-1/2} \int_{-\infty}^{x} e^{-u^2/2} \, du.$$

Appendix 3
Data

Lynx data (1821–1934)

1–11	12–22	23–33	34–44	45–55	56–66	67–77	78–88	88–99	100–110	111–114
269	98	68	731	3311	1426	389	105	382	108	1000
321	184	213	1638	6721	756	73	153	808	229	1590
585	279	546	2725	4254	299	39	387	1388	399	2657
871	409	1033	2871	687	201	49	758	2713	1132	3396
1475	2285	2129	2119	255	229	59	1307	3800	2432	
2821	2685	2536	684	473	469	188	3465	3091	3574	
3928	3409	957	299	358	736	377	6991	2985	2935	
5943	1824	361	236	784	2042	1292	6313	3790	1537	
4950	409	377	245	1594	2811	4031	3794	674	529	
2577	151	225	552	1676	4431	3495	1836	81	485	
523	45	360	1623	2251	2511	587	345	80	662	

Annual sunspot numbers (1700–1988)*

1–28	29–56	57–84	85–112	113–140	141–168	169–196	197–224	225–252	253–280	281–288
5.0	103.0	10.2	10.2	5.0	64.6	37.6	41.8	16.7	31.5	154.7
11.0	73.0	32.4	24.1	12.2	36.7	74.0	26.2	44.3	13.9	140.5
16.0	47.0	47.6	82.9	13.9	24.2	139.0	26.7	63.9	4.4	115.9
23.0	35.0	54.0	132.0	35.4	10.7	111.2	12.1	69.0	38.0	66.6
36.0	11.0	62.9	130.9	45.8	15.0	101.6	9.5	77.8	141.7	45.9
58.0	5.0	85.9	118.1	41.1	40.1	66.2	2.7	64.9	190.2	17.9
29.0	16.0	61.2	89.9	30.1	61.5	44.7	5.0	35.7	184.8	13.4
20.0	34.0	45.1	66.6	23.9	98.5	17.0	24.4	21.2	159.0	29.2
10.0	70.0	36.4	60.0	15.6	124.7	11.3	42.0	11.1	112.3	100.2
8.0	81.0	20.9	46.9	6.6	96.3	12.4	63.5	5.7	53.9	
3.0	111.0	11.4	41.0	4.0	66.6	3.4	53.8	8.7	37.5	
0.0	101.0	37.8	21.3	1.8	64.5	6.0	62.0	36.1	27.9	
0.0	73.0	69.8	16.0	8.5	54.1	32.3	48.5	79.7	10.2	
2.0	40.0	106.1	6.4	16.6	39.0	54.3	43.9	114.4	15.1	
11.0	20.0	100.8	4.1	36.3	20.6	59.7	18.6	109.6	47.0	
27.0	16.0	81.6	6.8	49.6	6.7	63.7	5.7	88.8	93.8	
47.0	5.0	66.5	14.5	64.2	4.3	63.5	3.6	67.8	105.9	
63.0	11.0	34.8	34.0	67.0	22.7	52.2	1.4	47.5	105.5	
60.0	22.0	30.6	45.0	70.9	54.8	25.4	9.6	30.6	104.5	
39.0	40.0	7.0	43.1	47.8	93.8	13.1	47.4	16.3	66.6	
28.0	60.0	19.8	47.5	27.5	95.8	6.8	57.1	9.6	68.9	
26.0	80.9	92.5	42.2	8.5	77.2	6.3	103.9	33.2	38.0	
22.0	83.4	154.4	28.1	13.2	59.1	7.1	80.6	92.6	34.5	
11.0	47.7	125.9	10.1	56.9	44.0	35.6	63.6	151.6	15.5	
21.0	47.8	84.8	8.1	121.5	47.0	73.0	37.6	136.3	12.6	
40.0	30.7	68.1	2.5	138.3	30.5	85.1	26.1	134.7	27.5	
78.0	12.2	38.5	0.0	103.2	16.3	78.0	14.2	83.9	92.5	
122.0	9.6	22.8	1.4	85.7	7.3	64.0	5.8	69.4	155.4	

* The 1983–1988 data are by courtesy of the Sunspot Index Data Centre, Observatoire Royal de Belgique, Avenue Circulaire 3, 1180 Bruxelles.

Blow-fly data

1–36	37–72	73–108	109–144	145–180	181–216	217–252	253–288	289–324	325–361
948	2656	7939	4473	3935	2342	1465	4436	2652	4547
942	1967	4868	5221	3479	3328	1676	4369	2330	4823
911	1295	3952	6592	3415	3599	3075	3394	3123	4970
858	915	2712	6400	3861	4081	3815	3869	3955	4940
801	551	1734	4752	3571	7643	4639	2922	4494	5793
676	313	1224	3521	3113	7919	4424	1843	4780	7836
504	167	703	2719	2319	6098	2784	2837	5753	4457
397	95	508	1931	1630	6896	5860	4690	5555	6901
248	93	366	1500	1297	5634	5781	5119	5712	8191
146	60	279	1082	861	5134	4897	5839	4786	6766
1801	68	243	849	761	4188	3920	5389	4066	5165
6235	5259	343	774	659	3469	3835	4993	2891	2919
5974	6673	761	864	701	2442	3618	4446	3270	3415
8921	5441	1025	1308	762	1931	3050	4851	4404	3431
6610	3987	1221	1624	1188	1790	3772	4243	4398	3162
5973	2952	1600	2224	1778	1722	3517	4620	4112	2525
5673	3648	2267	2423	2428	1488	3350	4849	4401	2290
3875	4222	3290	2959	3806	1416	3018	3664	5779	1955
2361	3889	3471	3547	4519	1369	2625	3016	6597	1936
1352	2295	3637	7237	5646	1666	2412	2881	8091	2384
1226	1509	3703	5218	4851	2627	2221	3821	11282	4666
912	928	4876	5311	5374	3840	2619	4300	12446	7219
521	739	5364	4273	4713	4044	3203	4168	13712	8306
363	566	4890	3270	7367	4929	2706	5446	11017	8027
229	383	3029	2281	7236	5111	2717	5477	14683	7010
142	274	1950	1549	5245	3152	2175	8579	7258	8149
82	192	1225	1091	3636	4462	1628	7533	6195	8949
542	226	1076	796	2417	4082	2388	6884	5962	6105
939	519	905	610	1258	3026	3677	4127	4213	5324
2431	1224	772	445	766	1589	3156	5546	2775	5766
3687	2236	628	894	479	2075	4272	6313	1781	6214
4543	3818	473	1454	402	1829	3771	6650	936	7007
4535	6208	539	2262	248	1386	4955	6304	898	8154
5441	5996	825	2363	254	1149	5584	4842	1160	9049
4412	5789	1702	3847	604	968	3891	4352	3158	6883
3022	6652	2868	3876	1346	1170	3501	3215	3386	8103
									6803

Vatnsdalsà

(1972)

1610	1920	1450	1100	1360	1250	1050	1010	968	902	880	858	814	750	792	792
771	710	670	398	516	610	690	690	710	730	730	571	690	814	750	710
690	670	670	690	690	670	650	650	670	690	710	670	670	670	690	534
534	590	630	690	792	2100	1420	1160	1010	924	858	814	792	771	771	750
710	690	690	690	650	771	465	398	516	610	610	814	1360	968	836	924
858	836	792	902	902	815	792	750	730	690	690	750	670	670	690	670
650	630	630	630	630	610	590	650	630	610	710	814	990	1420	1650	1920
2350	2520	3590	3150	1920	1690	1360	1100	1010	990	1010	1030	1300	2010	2410	3670
3290	2870	3150	3370	3080	2630	2150	1730	1920	1690	1610	1560	1800	1970	1770	1690
1970	1690	1480	1130	1130	1010	1010	990	924	902	946	1010	990	1080	968	924
902	880	880	858	858	990	990	1130	990	924	924	902	836	814	836	1010
1160	990	990	968	946	902	836	836	1050	1050	1010	1010	968	990	1100	1050
946	902	924	990	924	946	880	880	946	946	902	880	858	836	836	836
858	836	792	792	792	771	750	750	730	750	771	750	730	730	710	710
710	750	730	750	710	730	730	771	814	750	771	771	771	771	814	902
902	902	924	858	902	858	750	880	946	814	792	750	750	730	730	750
750	750	730	710	710	690	710	730	710	730	771	730	730	710	690	690
670	730	710	710	650	571	670	858	730	670	630	610	792	1010	924	771
880	1010	858	902	836	814	771	710	710	771	750	750	534	534	858	836
858	750	710	590	690	690	750	771	750	730	571	482	448	516	610	710
750	750	771	792	710	730	730	814	836	836	814	771	710	690	690	710
670	650	670	710	730	710	690	710	750	710	750	730	710	690	670	670
792	1160	1080	670	534	610	750	792	792	771	750	750	730	710		

(1973)

690	670	670	630	902	1650	2150	1560	1690	2300	2010	1450	1250	1160	1100	1080
968	902	1030	1010	990	946	880	858	836	771	730	730	750	814	836	636
516	690	771	771	771	771	750	750	750	750	670	630	670	771	771	690
670	670	792	836	836	814	836	902	946	968	968	0	968	946	924	880
858	836	836	814	814	814	858	858	814	836	880	946	990	1160	1450	1730
1920	1840	1450	1220	1080	858	836	858	750	710	730	771	814	814	710	750
710	710	730	771	880	990	1420	1880	2520	3150	2200	2410	3920	5010	4620	3520
3080	3150	3150	2520	2150	1730	1270	1330	1300	1250	1160	1190	1300	1300	1250	1160
1160	1080	1010	1010	968	946	1030	1160	1390	1390	1250	1190	1220	1300	1330	1300
1270	1190	1330	1250	1190	1160	1050	1010	990	968	968	990	1080	1100	1080	1080
1010	946	924	902	880	858	924	1080	1190	1270	1190	1130	1160	1220	1270	1190
1160	1130	1130	1130	1130	1130	1100	1080	1030	1010	990	990	990	990	968	946
924	902	902	880	858	858	814	814	814	814	814	814	814	814	814	792
771	750	771	771	771	750	771	792	771	880	990	858	814	792	792	792
792	836	771	792	792	771	750	730	730	730	730	730	730	750	771	792
750	750	750	750	771	750	730	730	730	792	730	730	710	710	710	690
690	690	690	690	690	710	710	710	690	690	771	814	836	880	792	771
750	730	836	836	858	771	792	792	858	990	792	792	771	771	771	690
630	690	610	610	650	730	690	792	880	814	670	710	670	670	1080	1360
1130	858	858	771	630	571	792	1130	968	814	730	690	534	670	670	670
630	750	836	836	858	858	946	968	880	814	750	690	690	670	670	670
902	924	858	771	730	771	792	814	792	771	750	650	771	814	814	902
814	710	650	610	590	571	552	552	516	482	465	465	465	465		

Vatnsdalsà (*cont.*)

(1974)

465	465	465	448	516	552	534	534	482	465	448	431	431	431	414	382
398	398	431	571	650	630	571	571	516	465	414	398	448	448	431	465
431	398	398	398	398	398	398	382	367	367	398	398	382	382	382	414
590	448	398	398	382	367	367	367	465	398	431	0	431	367	431	610
730	750	750	814	1080	1610	1480	1250	990	814	690	610	534	516	499	499
499	499	552	630	730	690	590	571	571	858	3150	3370	1840	1130	1610	3290
4530	5400	2570	1800	1590	1560	1450	1590	3590	3750	2940	2750	3010	2750	3080	2940
2200	2010	3590	3670	3290	2200	1800	1590	1520	1480	1300	1270	1250	1100	968	880
792	730	690	730	1030	1100	1130	1190	1250	1360	1220	1080	990	946	880	750
710	771	710	610	534	534	534	552	552	630	670	650	590	571	590	571
552	730	750	710	730	670	690	730	750	1080	1160	858	792	710	670	650
610	590	590	571	552	552	552	590	590	571	552	552	534	534	552	650
650	571	534	516	499	482	482	499	482	482	482	482	482	465	448	448
431	431	414	414	431	448	431	431	431	499	571	630	610	610	590	571
552	552	552	552	552	534	534	552	552	552	534	534	552	534	552	552
534	534	534	534	571	590	630	690	750	650	610	610	590	610	610	590
650	650	610	590	590	571	590	590	571	499	465	516	534	534	465	499
571	534	534	534	534	499	534	534	534	534	552	534	552	571	650	771
690	650	670	610	590	610	590	571	792	771	710	792	534	516	814	1010
792	730	690	690	690	858	730	690	730	630	516	610	552	499	534	534
534	516	571	552	552	516	482	552	610	590	571	552	516	499	448	482
516	516	516	516	516	482	465	382	414	465	465	431	431	516	516	516
516	516	499	465	516	516	516	516	516	516	516	516	534	534		

Format of data: typically, '(1972) 1610 1920 . . .' means observations in year 1972: River-flow on 1 January 1972 is $16.10 \, \text{m}^3/\text{s}^{-1}$ per day; River-flow on 2 January 1972 is $19.20 \, \text{m}^3 \, \text{s}^{-1}$ per day. See Note on Hveravellir data. The Vatnsdalsà data, the Jökulsà Eystri data and the Hveravellir data are by courtesy of the Hydrological Survey of the National Energy Authority of Iceland.

Jökulsà Eystri

(1972)

```
 3020  2900  2840  2780  2780  2780  2780  2780  2780  2730  2730  2730  2620  2520  2670  2670
 2670  2670  2670  2520  2570  2620  2620  2620  2620  2570  2620  2670  2840  2900  2780  2730
 2670  2620  2570  2620  2620  2570  2570  2570  2570  2570  2570  2570  2520  2520  2520  2460
 2520  2570  2670  2620  2570  2670  2670  2670  2620  2570  2570  2520  2520  2520  2460  2460
 2460  2460  2460  2460  2360  2410  2410  2460  2410  2460  2460  2570  2840  3140  3020  2900
 2840  2780  2670  2670  2780  2670  2620  2520  2520  2520  2460  2520  2520  2410  2410  2460
 2410  2410  2410  2410  2360  2360  2360  2360  2360  2360  2360  2410  2410  2410  2520  2520
 2670  3020  4170  5170  4400  4100  3570  3080  2780  2900  2900  2840  2780  3440  4700  5910
10100 10300  9000 11300 12100 10400  9480  7740  8300  8160  8020  8160  9000 10300 11100 10900
10300  9960  9160  6660  5910  5250  5170  5330  5250  5250  5830  6430  6780  7880  6660  5570
 5740  6340  6780  6900  7020  8440  9000  7880  6000  4850  4240  4170  4020  4540  5090  5410
 5010  5090  5250  5490  5910  6170  6340  6340  6550  5830  5830  6090  6660  7480  7370  7020
 6550  6170  6170  6780  6000  6260  6170  6170  6340  6090  6000  5830  5490  5330  6340  6430
 7740  8580  6780  5740  5410  5250  5170  4620  4320  4100  3960  3700  3640  3570  3570  3640
 3890  5330  5830  5740  5010  4540  4100  4100  4020  3760  4620  4540  4540  3960  4020  4620
 4770  5910  5830  4850  5660  5660  4470  5090  5830  4470  3890  3640  3440  3440  3440  3440
 3440  4170  4770  4400  3830  3960  3700  3760  3890  3640  3760  4400  4100  3890  3960  3890
 3700  3570  3440  3200  3320  3200  3440  4170  3640  3380  3260  3200  2900  3570  3890  3320
 3200  3570  3380  3440  3260  3080  3080  2840  2840  2780  2780  2780  2570  2200  2840  3020
 2960  2900  2840  2670  2730  2730  2730  2780  2670  2670  2670  2670  2620  2620  2620  2620
 2620  2620  2670  2780  2780  2780  2780  2780  2780  2780  2780  2780  2780  2780  2780  2780
 2780  2780  2780  2780  2780  2780  2780  2670  2670  2670  2670  2670  2670  2670  2670  2670
 2960  3440  3440  2840  2840  2780  2900  2960  3080  3020  2960  2960  2960  2780
```

(1973)

```
 2840  2730  2780  2730  3020  3440  3830  3830  4540  7020  5910  4170  3760  3510  3440  3380
 3140  3140  3140  3080  3020  2960  2960  2900  2840  2730  2730  2900  2840  2780  2730  2780
 2520  2780  2730  2730  2730  2730  2570  2570  2570  2620  2520  2570  2570  2570  2670  2670
 2570  2570  2620  2620  2570  2570  2460  2570  2570  2570  2520     0  2520  2520  2460  2520
 2460  2460  2520  2570  2460  2460  2670  2670  2620  2620  2670  2730  2730  2840  2960  2900
 2960  3080  2960  2730  2730  2620  2520  2570  2520  2360  2460  2460  2410  2410  2410  2410
 2410  2410  2410  2410  2520  2460  2620  2780  3200  3830  3640  3570  4470  5830  6780  6430
 6430  6000  6090  5570  4930  4170  3510  3320  3260  3080  3020  2960  2960  2960  2960  3200
 3020  2960  2730  2840  2780  2620  2730  2780  4020  6090  5660  4620  4540  4770  5170  5330
 5090  5170  5910  5570  5330  5170  5090  3890  3760  3760  3830  4240  4770  4700  4850  4930
 4770  4170  3890  3700  3510  3440  3640  4930  6550  8720 10900 11300  9800 10900 12700 12500
11500 11500  9160  8720  8580  7130  7020  6340  6170  6170  6090  6090  6340  6260  6660  7600
 9000 11600 11100 13200 12300 11300  9800  8720  7880  6900  6340  6170  6260  6260  6430  7600
 8440  8440  8440  6660  5490  5250  5250  5570  5570  5910  6430  4770  4400  4170  4170  4320
 4170  4770  5250  5490  5740  5490  4540  4170  4020  4020  3890  3960  4620  6430  6780  6340
 6170  6550  5740  5570  5330  4930  4700  4320  4240  4100  3960  3960  3640  3570  3760  4400
 5570  7020  6340  5330  5090  5250  5170  4770  4170  3830  3700  4020  4930  4470  3830  3510
 3510  3510  5090  6090  6000  4240  4400  4320  4240  3510  3380  3380  3380  3320  3260  3980
 3020  2900  2900  2900  3020  3140  3020  3260  3260  3320  3020  2900  2840  3080  3510  4170
 6090  4020  3570  3380  3020  2960  3140  3510  3510  3200  3140  3020  2780  2900  2900  2730
 2620  2730  2840  2840  2840  2840  2840  2840  2780  2780  2840  2900  2900  2900  2840  2960
 3570  2960  2840  2900  2780  2780  2780  2840  2780  2780  2780  2730  2730  2780  2840  2780
 2780  2780  2780  3200  2780  2780  2780  2840  2900  2840  2840  2780  2840  2840
```

Jökulsà Eystri (*cont.*)

(1974)

2840	2840	2840	2780	2730	2670	2570	2520	2520	2520	2570	2570	2570	2570	2570	2520
2520	2460	2520	2620	2570	2570	2520	2570	2460	2520	2520	2520	2520	2460	2460	2460
2460	2460	2460	2410	2410	2410	2360	2250	2250	2200	2200	2200	2200	2200	2200	2250
2460	2460	2570	2570	2410	2460	2620	2570	3200	2620	2670	0	2570	2520	2520	2570
2410	2410	2460	2730	3200	3200	3080	2960	2960	2900	2780	2670	2670	2620	2520	2520
2520	2460	2520	2360	2410	2410	2410	2410	2570	3080	5090	6260	5330	4320	5910	8580
11600	12100	7880	5740	5170	4770	4400	4020	4400	6090	6430	6900	7600	6900	6780	7880
7130	6430	8160	14100	14100	9000	7600	6900	6090	5910	5740	5740	5410	5250	4700	4320
3890	3510	3260	3380	4320	5250	7130	7370	9000	9640	9960	11600	9960	9480	11300	7600
7880	8160	6090	4770	4240	4020	3890	4240	5410	5740	7600	7250	7130	7130	6340	5740
4930	4620	4620	5010	14300	13400	8440	7600	6780	6260	5570	5170	5330	6260	8440	11300
9320	7880	7130	5910	4930	4400	4240	4700	4850	4470	4320	4020	4100	4930	5330	6550
6780	5910	5410	5250	5090	5090	6170	6660	7370	6660	5740	5250	4540	4470	4770	5090
5410	5660	4840	4320	3890	3760	3830	3830	3760	4020	4470	5570	6090	5910	5570	5490
5010	5330	4930	4620	4470	4320	4100	4100	4400	4100	3700	3380	3260	3200	3140	3020
3080	3200	3080	3380	3830	4400	4930	4930	5330	4930	4020	3570	3320	3260	3200	3140
3570	3380	3140	3080	3080	2780	2900	2900	2780	2900	2840	2840	2780	2780	2670	2730
2780	2780	2780	2780	2840	2840	2840	2780	2730	2780	2670	2670	2780	2840	3380	4100
3830	2900	2900	2960	2900	2840	2840	2730	3200	2900	2840	2780	2670	2460	2960	3760
3140	2960	2840	2900	3570	5410	2900	2900	3020	2840	2780	2840	2670	2730	2730	2670
2620	2620	2620	2620	2570	2460	2460	2620	2670	2670	2670	2620	2620	2570	2570	2460
2520	2570	2520	2570	2620	2520	2620	2520	2520	2520	2460	2460	2460	2460	2460	2460
2460	2460	2460	2460	2460	2460	2460	2460	2460	2460	2460	2460	2460	2570		

Same format as that of Vatnsdalsà data.

Hveravellir

(1972)

9	81	16	44	1	70	6	0	1	70	20	0	8	0	14	19	13	12	22	0	0	1	1	30	0	-2	2	-26	18	-38	2	9	2	19	2
-4	15	-60	92	-50	10	-46	2			-53	25	-73	1	-85	33	-99	2	-131	4	-102	0		-87	0	4	48	19	194	8	9	-16	1	-9	0
5	0	-41	0	-28	0	-26	2			-33	1	-28	0	-76	0	-58	38	-64	1	-59	1		-53	1	-86	1	-126	2	-153	0	-74	0	5	29
11	21	-24	67	-7	112	-45	61			-6	422	3	3	2	125	7	1	8	21	23	40		1	2	11	0	-14	12	-6	1	3	5	-11	0
-36	0	-19	0	1	17	-4	5			-39	21	-12	2	-40	161	-48	6	-78	18	-31	0		-46	40	22	13	10	224	-16	357	-32	87	1	12
-52	3	-65	1	-53	11	0	65			-68	6	-69	1	-50	2	-94	6	-94	70	-104	0		-84	0	9	0	-70	33	-117	3	-90	1	-79	1
-84	0	-98	16	-134	3	-28	19			-12	0	-16	1	-2	3	-26	13	-36	2	-21	0		-31	17	1	1	5	1	9	1	10	2	7	0
24	-1	30	1	27	2	0	1			-2	2	-3	0	-32	37	-68	1	-68	0	-64	18		18	0	-5	0	8	18	22	207	30	1	47	1
40	0	35	0	44	1	43	0			40	0	29	56	18	2	18	2	16	1	16	56		31	70	34	3	45	1	58	2	33	0	48	0
41	5	42	0	16	0	11	2			16	0	24	2	25	0	17	138	22	0	41	2		18	38	34	18	55	1	22	6	33	4	56	84
63	5	61	0	62	0	85	13			55	44	70	0	47	12	23	6	13	8	-2	0		31	3	29	3	45	6	59	3	44	24	22	51
44	63	44	22	34	44	52	16			62	22	65	136	70	17	61	28	19	0	35	54		69	11	62	1	64	26	65	114	67	7	67	14
76	1	61	4	51	32	36	102			48	84	75	0	61	0	68	0	67	70	79	19		70	25	58	48	60	0	61	0	75	0	78	49
91	29	71	55	64	0	68	0			74	0	67	54	37	2	47	148	34	42	14	1		26	13	25	2	32	1	58	2	72	50	62	19
89	4	72	80	55	108	44	36			49	1	47	18	44	1	35	4	42	1	50	26		52	53	55	0	36	3	34	0	65	0	64	10
88	21	61	60	43	39	45	2			69	6	48	2	58	0	60	70	26	0	-17	96		72	9	-8	250	1	0	-1	540	20	33	26	1
38	17	73	1	63	4	46	2			62	12	42	0	47	13	43	65	31	13	38	0		-24	9	46	6	64	6	61	3	45	34	42	12
29	54	11	52	9	2	21	7			10	0	6	3	53	62	17	2	1	62	-11	3		-47	0	-58	0	17	37	24	249	6	35	-14	3
21	15	-16	162	-2	0	26	1			-23	0	23	2	-13	43	-25	67	-49	10	-44	2		2	8	-54	24	-44	5	13	3	14	2	-13	12
-17	29	-29	0	-28	22	-29	7			-78	4	-31	0	-5	38	-43	0	-71	0	-75	99		-37	143	-50	8	-61	41	-85	46	-104	19	-152	3
-106	2	-93	0	-80	11	-79	4			-63	9	-89	0	-142	2	-36	0	-1	37	-24	117		-74	1	-13	0	-32	0	-57	5	-50	0	-42	0
-38	13	-63	0	-70	0	-62	0			-49	1	-54		-110	1	-85	26	-56	2	-95				8	-37	22	-41	91	-38	6	13		35	19
25	23	9	185	-15	108	-32	84			-49	14	-61		-34	0	14		-62		-52					-30				-65					

15	0	32	10	1	0	10	0	7	0	1	0	47	4	0	0	0	208	0	1	4		
−45	−25	−34	−77	6	−65	15	−2	26	19	57	93	83	53	72	85	−12	−50	43	−158	1	−224	
0	0	8	16	0	43	1	0	24	29	11	0	101	63	0	20	0	78	0	39			
13	−99	−48	−56	17	−80	19	−1	33	12	56	65	100	52	86	75	0	−14	23	−104	−38	−124	
1	12	7	0	1	1	1	0	1	26	2	0	8	34	0	120	2	0	0	25	0		
−14	−53	−112	−27	22	−50	23	−4	29	15	67	51	110	42	102	47	12	−35	−28	−91	−56	−62	−107
24	0	19	43	0	15	0	29	13	3	0	0	1	180	0	54	29	0	5			
−19	−22	−145	−48	−2	−158	26	−8	38	24	60	41	115	40	103	15	−9	−31	−41	−67	−147	−133	
17	94	16	0	26	0	11	0	0	0	2	124	1	20	0	2	57	0	177	1	3	8	19
6	−8	−145	0	16	−166	13	−33	20	26	42	55	105	24	103	13	33	−39	−6	−56	−46	−188	−123
1	0	8	67	103	0	8	0	2	8	115	0	0	220	1	0	0	10	41	17	46	3	
6	−64	−144	−36	4	−158	−15	−65	0	24	39	34	97	34	79	38	42	−42	−1	−91	−89	−84	−80
4	0	90	30	1	20	8	0	163	0	43	36	0	14	0	7	0	64	70	20	0	0	49
33	−109	−43	−28	10	−137	−4	−57	19	−5	60	54	79	45	53	31	22	1	8	−48	−163	−112	−88
41	0	0	2	29	10	1	161	0	21	36	0	14	0	1	8	1	51	98	9	2		
32	−56	−95	−108	10	−49	22	−51	24	−8	65	45	75	58	38	50	20	42	2	−8	−183	−112	−53
58	18	10	0	50	1	0	0	8	144	16	0	111	0	5	2	2	43	114	1	45	36	
17	−39	−124	−103	13	−67	9	−78	17	−7	69	33	101	68	28	42	21	61	15	13	−174	−42	−48
152	10	15	0	243	129	0	1	13	1	17	1	2	0	0	5	4	35	0	0	21	3	0
19	−28	−127	−183	−13	−56	28	−73	3	−14	30	17	98	64	18	38	50	46	−17	−27	−108	−54	−71
31	6	0	0	0	39	0	2	24	0	0	4	4	20	4	2	17	1	0	2	22	0	
24	−15	−149	−147	−27	−13	32	−82	−38	−5	26	15	84	84	20	43	75	17	−46	−115	−24	−163	−166
13	0	66	1	2	0	0	0	21	0	24	1	0	3	93	1	130	5	7	4	0	0	
19	−15	−51	−113	−60	−107	24	−16	−48	20	−9	52	102	67	67	48	87	39	−31	−77	−22	−155	−152
55	7	13	111	207	12	0	0	2	1	2	16	89	1	27	9	0	38	0	12	3	61	0
−7	16	−54	−62	−5	−134	22	0	−34	15	−17	48	117	35	85	60	73	69	−83	−39	−116	−57	−158
6	92	107	28	19	1	0	0	2	63	12	23	4	12	25	1	2	12	1	1	1	28	23
−17	−42	−33	−16	−1	−105	−15	17	−37	29	−28	41	93	54	61	71	73	63	−102	−13	−134	−28	−130
13	7	137	18	0	60	0	0	1	0	5	90	3	2	136	43	39	1	0	11	0	12	0
−68	1	−3	−62	−70	−31	−71	19	−39	27	−15	41	84	68	65	65	66	29	−73	−2	−153	−25	−140
28	9	82	109	1	75	1	2	30	0	3	2	0	19	0	93	1	0	0	376	0	56	0
−49	−61	−49	−105	−107	12	−70	14	−31	18	2	45	105	64	63	75	80	−3	−70	−2	−158	1	−214

(1974)

-94	30	-84	3	-33	0	-1	22	-4	7	1	29	-13	35	-32	7	-27	14	-41	46	-20	1	-35	16	-33	1	-39	0	-61	0	-79	16
-48	8	-82	25	-21	0	-19	308	-43	68	-6	19	-20	19	-34	4	-62	67	-47	16	-52	33	-81	30	-36	2	-56	0	-24	3	-43	1
-34	0	-17	0	-46	0	-94	0	-127	18	-147	1	-143	1	-142	0	-92	18	-94	6	-47	7	-85	2	-109	0	-152	0	-128	0	-15	5
-41	36	-35	23	-7	27	-34	19	-116	18	-13	15	-19	180	-143	0	-7	6	-30	173	-4	55	0	0	-54	46	-98	6	-15	9	10	54
5	29	1	1	-7	26	12	82	25	241	13	9	6	2	-4	603	-8	0	-30	0	-43	0	-47	0	-41	8	-29	0	-59	0	-67	0
-23	0	14	0	-1	43	4	58	-7	34	-34	1	-18	0	2	120	16	120	10	51	16	777	2	256	-19	30	-19	40	20	108	21	57
21	100	9	103	-4	105	-13	32	-14	0	-5	7	-8	4	-5	11	23	9	21	4	20	5	21	0	18	0	25	54	25	4	9	40
8	0	25	6	27	6	27	64	17	60	4	5	3	1	19	20	32	96	38	10	35	61	13	6	25	0	19	0	14	0	3	0
0	0	1	0	27	27	55	0	42	11	49	36	51	0	52	0	61	6	57	20	53	1	44	9	56	29	50	0	27	6	46	4
52	0	47	0	20	4	-9	36	6	0	16	0	24	0	55	1	62	49	75	39	49	39	38	62	59	9	44	14	39	1	12	0
20	0	31	134	40	29	69	57	68	793	34	194	42	72	33	82	30	54	20	12	30	38	59	9	88	1	131	0	139	0	124	0
120	0	101	0	63	0	30	12	31	0	42	0	39	1	51	25	63	4	63	4	30	0	74	27	77	2	98	20	103	57	95	55
82	134	40	0	69	0	83	0	85	0	69	0	85	0	81	36	77	2	65	10	56	2	37	29	79	30	97	0	109	21	97	0
115	14	90	1	35	0	40	0	33	21	61	2	57	5	59	2	72	15	89	16	89	6	101	15	94	102	92	30	107	21	93	0
100	0	74	1	66	1	55	2	60	0	68	0	63	5	63	28	54	54	31	16	16	1	29	1	15	35	6	4	-4	7	12	1
21	0	50	8	58	13	84	102	63	17	90	19	78	9	59	17	56	1	36	16	19	1	16	1	22	1	36	15	35	3	52	34
33	105	9	4	7	39	8	5	-28	15	-16	2	-12	1	14	1	-11	1	-39	0	-56	0	-46	0	-34	0	-32	2	-50	2	-47	0
-30	1	-8	0	-2	24	1	0	3	1	3	2	-27	3	-23	0	-20	0	-10	0	-6	1	9	0	21	2	25	1	53	63	42	71
20	161	1	64	14	49	-14	63	-31	1	-12	2	-12	0	-12	0	27	150	-43	259	-16	2	-11	108	-84	10	-106	0	6	35	7	13
-13	19	-11	20	-6	0	-1	1	20	0	-12	2	-13	70	3	18	-4	45	-48	3	-58	7	-26	3	-58	4	-42	2	-46	13	-40	5
-61	2	-86	2	-87	0	-46	0	-58	0	-46	185	-26	0	-20	0	-18	8	-28	7	-32	2	-59	35	-70	0	-18	0	-26	16	-35	28
-42	11	-47	2	-116	12	-59	1	-18	40	-53	3	-34	37	-105	8	-127	2	-132	1	-142	15	-38	4	-91	18	-111	1	-72	3	-91	3
-127	1	-132	1	-127	4	-170	12	-194	0	-116	0	-73	4	-98	81	-113	0	-41	0	-59	71	-68	1	-24	3	-54	81				

Format of data: typically, '(1972) 9 81 16 44 ...' means observations in year 1972: Temperature on 1 January 1972 is 0.9°C; precipitation on 1 January 1972 is 8.1 mm/day; temperature on 2 January 1972 is 1.6°C; precipitation on 2 January 1972 is 4.4 mm/day.

29 February is always allocated the same position and a zero is recorded when the year is not a leap year.

The data under the headings Hvervellir, Vatusdalsà, and Jökulsà Eystro were kindly supplied to the author by the Hydrological Survey of the National Energy Authority of Iceland.

Dissolved oxygen data, Butterfly Beach, Hong Kong (DW = day of the week, DO = dissolved oxygen)

Year	Month	Day	DW	DO
1980	1	4	5	6.5
1980	2	10	7	8.8
1980	2	29	5	9.5
1980	3	9	7	10.2
1980	3	19	3	9.2
1980	3	25	2	8.4
1980	4	20	7	9.4
1980	5	11	7	7.0
1980	5	20	2	7.0
1980	5	29	4	11.0
1980	6	13	5	15.2
1980	6	22	7	9.7
1980	6	25	3	16.4
1980	7	4	5	10.8
1980	7	13	7	8.4
1980	7	29	2	10.0
1980	8	1	5	10.8
1980	8	13	3	10.4
1980	8	24	7	9.2
1980	9	7	7	9.4
1980	9	15	1	8.4
1980	9	18	4	7.6
1980	10	8	3	13.0
1980	10	19	7	9.6
1980	10	23	4	9.0
1980	11	13	4	9.8
1980	11	16	7	9.8
1980	11	27	4	9.2
1980	12	7	7	9.7
1980	12	12	5	9.7
1981	1	11	7	9.4
1981	1	20	2	8.0
1981	1	30	5	9.0
1981	2	1	7	9.0
1981	2	13	5	10.5

The data under the headings Butterfly Beach, Anglers Beach, Shek O Beach, Repulse Bay Beach, Hong Kong were obtained by courtesy of the Engineering Development Department and the Environmental Protection Department, Hong Kong.

Year	Month	Day	DW	DO
1981	2	17	2	9.3
1981	3	2	1	9.0
1981	3	8	7	8.4
1981	3	13	5	9.8
1981	4	5	7	11.8
1981	4	8	3	11.5
1981	4	22	3	8.4
1981	5	3	7	8.9
1981	5	11	1	10.4
1981	5	21	4	7.2
1981	6	9	2	11.6
1981	6	14	7	10.6
1981	6	29	1	9.0
1981	7	12	7	9.4
1981	7	21	2	9.2
1981	8	18	2	8.2
1981	8	23	7	10.0
1981	9	9	3	12.5
1981	9	13	7	9.2
1981	9	23	3	8.4
1981	10	12	1	9.1
1981	10	28	3	9.7
1981	11	15	7	9.4
1981	11	17	2	9.4
1981	11	25	3	8.0
1981	12	4	5	12.0
1981	12	17	4	˙8.2
1982	1	18	1	9.0
1982	1	29	5	11.2
1982	2	3	3	9.2
1982	2	12	5	7.0
1982	3	8	1	8.4
1982	3	14	7	9.4
1982	3	22	1	9.0
1982	4	5	1	8.8
1982	4	14	3	10.8
1982	4	20	2	8.9
1982	5	11	2	9.2
1982	5	21	5	8.7
1982	5	30	7	8.8
1982	6	6	7	9.7

Year	Month	Day	DW	DO
1982	6	18	5	8.8
1982	6	28	1	8.2
1982	7	11	7	16.6
1982	7	21	3	8.4
1982	7	28	3	9.9
1982	8	5	4	9.9
1982	8	15	7	10.8
1982	8	23	1	7.9
1982	9	6	1	8.0
1982	9	19	7	7.3
1982	9	29	3	9.4
1982	10	10	7	9.8
1982	10	18	1	10.1
1982	10	27	3	10.1
1982	11	4	4	10.9
1982	11	14	7	12.4
1982	11	25	4	9.1
1982	12	5	7	11.2
1982	12	14	2	8.6
1982	12	29	3	11.0
1983	1	3	1	8.5
1983	1	13	4	8.8
1983	1	23	7	9.6
1983	2	1	2	9.9
1983	2	10	4	11.2
1983	2	20	7	10.4
1983	3	9	3	8.5
1983	4	13	3	10.9
1983	4	24	7	9.2
1983	5	4	3	11.5
1983	5	18	3	8.9
1983	5	29	7	11.0
1983	6	9	4	11.2
1983	6	19	7	10.8
1983	6	30	4	11.4
1983	7	7	4	8.8
1983	7	22	5	11.6
1983	7	31	7	12.0
1983	8	9	2	10.9
1983	8	16	2	9.8
1983	8	29	1	9.7

Year	Month	Day	DW	DO
1983	9	11	7	10.6
1983	9	20	2	10.8
1983	9	26	1	9.0
1983	10	6	4	10.3
1983	10	12	3	10.0
1983	10	30	7	9.6
1983	11	8	2	8.9
1983	11	18	5	9.9
1983	11	27	7	9.8
1983	12	4	7	9.7
1983	12	16	5	9.6
1983	12	28	3	8.9
1984	1	8	7	9.9
1984	1	18	3	9.5
1984	1	31	2	10.2
1984	2	12	7	9.8
1984	2	21	2	9.9
1984	3	3	6	9.8
1984	3	12	1	9.8
1984	3	26	1	8.5
1984	4	1	7	10.8
1984	4	10	2	9.9
1984	4	18	3	8.0
1984	5	1	2	9.3
1984	5	18	5	9.9
1984	5	25	5	8.2
1984	6	6	3	10.6
1984	6	10	7	11.5
1984	6	26	2	9.3
1984	7	2	1	10.4
1984	7	11	3	10.2
1984	7	22	7	12.3
1984	8	1	3	9.9
1984	8	12	7	8.2
1984	8	24	5	9.7
1984	9	5	3	8.0
1984	9	16	7	9.3
1984	9	28	5	8.9
1984	10	6	6	7.2
1984	10	12	5	9.8
1984	10	21	7	9.0

Year	Month	Day	DW	DO
1984	11	2	5	7.4
1984	11	11	7	8.0
1984	11	24	6	9.3
1984	12	4	2	7.3
1984	12	9	7	8.9
1985	1	10	4	9.5
1985	1	20	7	12.5
1985	2	3	7	8.9
1985	2	13	3	10.0
1985	2	26	2	9.0
1985	3	5	2	9.0
1985	3	17	7	8.0
1985	3	29	5	9.7
1985	4	12	5	9.4
1985	4	21	7	9.5
1985	4	30	2	10.4
1985	5	12	7	10.1
1985	5	23	4	10.2
1985	5	30	4	9.8
1985	6	9	7	9.6
1985	6	18	2	9.5
1985	6	28	5	7.2
1985	7	7	7	9.5
1985	7	18	4	8.8
1985	7	30	2	10.1
1985	8	4	7	11.0
1985	8	16	5	7.4
1985	8	28	3	9.5
1985	9	8	7	10.4
1985	9	13	5	10.3
1985	9	27	5	10.1
1985	10	10	4	10.0
1985	10	20	7	9.6
1985	10	29	2	10.3
1985	11	10	7	9.7
1985	11	22	5	9.7
1985	11	29	5	9.6
1985	12	9	1	10.0
1985	12	20	5	10.3

Dissolved oxygen, data, Anglers Beach, Hong Kong (DW = day of the week, DO = dissolved oxygen)

Year	Month	Day	DW	DO
1980	1	4	5	6.0
1980	2	10	7	11.0
1980	2	29	5	8.8
1980	3	9	7	9.6
1980	3	19	3	9.0
1980	3	25	2	8.3
1980	4	20	7	9.6
1980	5	11	7	7.6
1980	5	20	2	6.0
1980	5	29	4	7.9
1980	6	13	5	13.8
1980	6	22	7	9.5
1980	6	25	3	13.2
1980	7	4	5	8.8
1980	7	13	7	8.5
1980	7	29	2	8.6
1980	8	1	5	7.8
1980	8	13	3	8.3
1980	8	24	7	9.6
1980	9	7	7	8.6
1980	9	15	1	8.0
1980	9	18	4	6.9
1980	10	8	3	8.0
1980	10	19	7	8.9
1980	10	23	4	8.2
1980	11	13	4	10.0
1980	11	16	7	8.9
1980	11	27	4	9.0
1980	12	7	7	9.6
1980	12	12	5	9.7
1981	1	11	7	9.3
1981	1	20	2	8.5
1981	1	30	5	8.0
1981	2	1	7	9.3
1981	2	13	5	9.0
1981	2	17	2	9.0
1981	3	2	1	7.8

Year	Month	Day	DW	DO
1981	3	8	7	9.2
1981	3	13	5	9.8
1981	4	5	7	11.6
1981	4	8	3	10.8
1981	4	22	3	7.4
1981	5	3	7	8.8
1981	5	11	1	10.4
1981	5	21	4	6.8
1981	6	9	2	9.7
1981	6	14	7	9.8
1981	6	29	1	9.6
1981	7	3	5	9.0
1981	7	12	7	9.4
1981	7	21	2	7.9
1981	8	18	2	8.0
1981	8	23	7	9.5
1981	9	9	3	6.5
1981	9	12	6	8.0
1981	9	13	7	9.8
1981	9	23	3	8.2
1981	10	28	3	9.6
1981	11	15	7	9.2
1981	11	17	2	9.6
1981	11	25	3	6.7
1981	12	4	5	11.6
1981	12	17	4	8.5
1982	1	18	1	8.6
1982	1	29	5	8.8
1982	2	3	3	9.2
1982	2	12	5	7.8
1982	3	8	1	7.2
1982	3	14	7	9.7
1982	3	22	1	9.2
1982	4	5	1	9.2
1982	4	14	3	9.2
1982	4	20	2	7.8
1982	5	11	2	7.5
1982	5	21	5	9.2
1982	5	30	7	9.0
1982	6	6	7	8.8
1982	6	18	5	8.8

Year	Month	Day	DW	DO
1982	6	28	1	7.5
1982	7	11	7	8.2
1982	7	21	3	7.9
1982	7	28	3	9.6
1982	8	5	4	8.3
1982	8	15	7	9.6
1982	8	23	1	7.4
1982	9	6	1	7.1
1982	9	19	7	6.6
1982	9	29	3	7.2
1982	10	10	7	8.0
1982	10	18	1	9.8
1982	10	27	3	9.9
1982	11	4	4	9.7
1982	11	14	7	10.4
1982	11	25	4	8.8
1982	12	5	7	6.4
1982	12	14	2	7.2
1982	12	29	3	8.8
1983	1	3	1	8.6
1983	1	13	4	8.3
1983	1	23	7	8.7
1983	2	1	2	8.9
1983	2	10	4	10.0
1983	2	20	7	10.0
1983	3	9	3	7.6
1983	3	27	7	9.6
1983	4	13	3	9.2
1983	4	24	7	8.8
1983	5	4	3	9.3
1983	5	18	3	7.7
1983	5	29	7	8.4
1983	6	9	4	9.4
1983	6	19	7	9.9
1983	6	30	4	7.5
1983	7	7	4	9.8
1983	7	22	5	10.7
1983	7	31	7	9.4
1983	8	9	2	8.6
1983	8	16	2	8.8
1983	8	29	1	7.6

Year	Month	Day	DW	DO
1983	9	11	7	11.2
1983	9	20	2	9.2
1983	9	26	1	8.0
1983	10	6	4	10.3
1983	10	13	4	7.5
1983	10	30	7	8.4
1983	11	8	2	7.5
1983	11	18	5	9.5
1983	11	27	7	6.5
1983	12	4	7	9.0
1983	12	16	5	9.0
1983	12	28	3	8.4
1984	1	8	7	9.3
1984	1	18	3	9.5
1984	1	31	2	9.8
1984	2	12	7	9.3
1984	2	21	2	9.5
1984	3	3	6	9.6
1984	3	12	1	8.9
1984	3	25	7	8.0
1984	4	1	7	9.2
1984	4	10	2	8.9
1984	4	18	3	7.5
1984	5	1	2	9.0
1984	5	18	5	8.6
1984	5	25	5	7.6
1984	6	6	3	10.1
1984	6	10	7	8.9
1984	6	26	2	6.7
1984	7	2	1	8.8
1984	7	11	3	7.5
1984	7	22	7	9.7
1984	8	1	3	7.5
1984	8	12	7	8.4
1984	8	24	5	5.3
1984	9	5	3	6.8
1984	9	16	7	6.3
1984	9	28	5	7.4
1984	10	6	6	6.6
1984	10	21	7	7.5
1984	11	2	5	7.1

Year	Month	Day	DW	DO
1984	11	11	7	7.1
1984	11	24	6	8.1
1984	12	4	2	7.4
1984	12	9	7	8.1
1985	1	10	4	9.2
1985	1	20	7	8.7
1985	2	3	7	8.5
1985	2	13	3	8.4
1985	2	26	2	8.7
1985	3	5	2	8.0
1985	3	17	7	8.0
1985	3	29	5	8.8
1985	4	12	5	9.6
1985	4	21	7	9.2
1985	4	30	2	9.0
1985	5	12	7	4.3
1985	5	23	4	9.4
1985	5	30	4	7.0
1985	6	9	7	6.4
1985	6	18	2	9.0
1985	6	28	5	8.8
1985	7	7	7	9.1
1985	7	18	4	9.1
1985	7	30	2	9.7
1985	8	4	7	8.6
1985	8	16	5	6.6
1985	8	28	3	9.9
1985	9	8	7	9.0
1985	9	13	5	8.7
1985	9	27	5	9.5
1985	10	10	4	9.5
1985	10	20	7	8.4
1985	10	29	2	8.9
1985	11	10	7	7.9
1985	11	22	5	6.6
1985	11	29	5	9.2
1985	12	9	1	9.0
1985	12	20	5	8.6

Dissolved oxygen data, Shek O Beach, Hong
Kong (DW = day of the week, DO = dissolved
oxygen)

Year	Month	Day	DW	DO
1980	1	3	4	6.9
1980	2	5	2	8.7
1980	2	24	7	8.2
1980	3	2	7	8.5
1980	3	14	5	8.4
1980	3	26	3	9.2
1980	4	6	7	9.5
1980	5	4	7	8.3
1980	5	14	3	8.4
1980	5	27	2	10.2
1980	6	1	7	9.8
1980	6	18	3	16.4
1980	6	26	4	9.8
1980	7	11	5	10.0
1980	7	18	5	8.3
1980	8	10	7	8.8
1980	8	19	2	10.2
1980	8	29	5	9.0
1980	9	23	2	11.6
1980	9	28	7	8.6
1980	9	30	2	10.7
1980	10	5	7	9.9
1980	10	15	3	10.2
1980	10	31	5	10.6
1980	11	21	5	10.2
1980	11	23	7	9.9
1980	11	28	5	10.0
1980	12	4	4	11.6
1980	12	14	7	9.5
1980	12	30	2	10.4
1981	1	6	2	11.2
1981	1	18	7	9.8
1981	1	23	5	10.4
1981	2	3	2	10.2
1981	2	15	7	9.3
1981	2	18	3	9.4
1981	3	17	2	8.9

Year	Month	Day	DW	DO
1981	3	23	1	8.2
1981	3	29	7	8.6
1981	4	2	4	9.8
1981	4	13	1	6.1
1981	4	26	7	9.0
1981	5	8	5	8.8
1981	5	17	7	7.9
1981	5	22	5	9.7
1981	6	8	1	9.4
1981	6	24	3	9.2
1981	6	28	7	11.0
1981	7	5	7	9.4
1981	7	13	1	9.4
1981	7	22	3	9.8
1981	8	4	2	8.6
1981	8	9	7	10.2
1981	8	24	1	12.4
1981	9	2	3	8.8
1981	10	15	4	9.4
1981	10	30	5	9.2
1981	11	1	7	9.2
1981	11	4	3	8.0
1981	11	25	3	8.5
1981	12	13	7	8.8
1981	12	18	5	8.8
1981	12	28	1	9.0
1982	1	6	3	7.6
1982	1	19	2	9.6
1982	2	4	4	8.6
1982	2	19	5	8.6
1982	2	28	7	8.5
1982	3	7	7	9.8
1982	3	17	3	9.3
1982	3	24	3	9.4
1982	4	1	4	9.8
1982	4	25	7	8.0
1982	4	28	3	7.0
1982	5	2	7	9.4
1982	5	12	3	9.0
1982	5	31	1	7.7
1982	6	7	1	10.3

Year	Month	Day	DW	DO
1982	6	20	7	9.2
1982	6	29	2	8.2
1982	7	8	4	12.0
1982	7	19	1	8.8
1982	7	25	7	10.6
1982	8	8	7	9.0
1982	8	18	3	7.8
1982	9	12	7	7.8
1982	9	22	3	8.9
1982	9	28	2	9.6
1982	10	3	7	10.4
1982	10	13	3	10.7
1982	10	26	2	9.7
1982	11	1	1	10.2
1982	11	8	1	9.7
1982	11	21	7	9.7
1982	12	6	1	11.6
1982	12	19	7	9.0
1982	12	30	4	9.7
1983	1	10	1	10.2
1983	1	18	2	9.6
1983	1	30	7	10.8
1983	2	6	7	9.9
1983	2	18	5	10.6
1983	2	27	7	12.0
1983	3	11	5	8.3
1983	3	20	7	10.0
1983	3	30	3	10.8
1983	4	3	7	10.0
1983	4	22	5	9.8
1983	5	6	5	11.2
1983	5	24	2	10.4
1983	6	2	4	11.5
1983	6	26	7	9.2
1983	7	3	7	10.9
1983	7	16	6	11.8
1983	7	28	4	11.6
1983	8	7	7	10.2
1983	8	15	1	10.2
1983	8	26	5	10.4
1983	9	7	3	10.1

Year	Month	Day	DW	DO
1983	9	13	2	9.5
1983	9	25	7	10.4
1983	10	3	1	9.6
1983	10	15	6	9.9
1983	10	23	7	10.3
1983	11	1	2	10.0
1983	11	13	7	10.0
1983	11	25	5	10.1
1983	12	6	2	9.4
1983	12	15	4	10.0
1984	1	10	2	10.1
1984	1	15	7	10.2
1984	1	21	6	10.1
1984	2	6	1	9.7
1984	2	13	1	9.8
1984	2	26	7	10.0
1984	3	7	3	10.2
1984	3	18	7	10.1
1984	3	27	2	9.4
1984	4	8	7	9.9
1984	4	16	1	9.8
1984	4	24	2	9.6
1984	5	5	7	9.6
1984	5	17	4	7.9
1984	5	29	2	9.3
1984	6	3	7	9.2
1984	6	12	2	8.8
1984	6	21	4	8.9
1984	7	20	5	8.9
1984	7	29	7	9.4
1984	8	9	4	8.1
1984	8	27	1	8.9
1984	8	30	4	9.6
1984	9	4	2	9.3
1984	9	17	1	9.5
1984	9	23	7	9.7
1984	10	8	1	9.2
1984	10	14	7	9.5
1984	10	26	5	9.6
1984	11	8	4	7.8
1984	11	15	4	9.8

Year	Month	Day	DW	DO
1984	11	25	7	10.0
1984	12	7	5	7.7
1984	12	16	7	10.10
1985	1	11	5	0.86
1985	1	19	6	10.30
1985	1	27	7	10.50
1985	2	10	7	8.70
1985	2	14	4	9.90
1985	3	4	1	9.10
1985	3	9	6	10.90
1985	3	24	7	9.90
1985	4	4	4	9.90
1985	4	15	1	10.00
1985	4	28	7	10.30
1985	5	5	7	9.40
1985	5	14	2	10.40
1985	5	29	3	9.30
1985	6	10	1	9.40
1985	6	20	4	9.30
1985	6	30	7	9.50
1985	7	10	3	10.00
1985	7	21	7	2.50
1985	7	31	3	10.30
1985	8	11	7	9.60
1985	8	22	4	10.00
1985	8	29	4	11.70
1985	9	2	1	11.50
1985	9	15	7	10.30
1985	9	24	2	10.50
1985	10	1	2	9.70
1985	10	14	1	10.00
1985	10	27	7	9.50
1985	11	3	7	10.00
1985	11	12	2	9.30
1985	11	23	6	9.80
1985	12	1	7	8.00
1985	12	13	5	9.90

APPENDIX 3

Dissolved oxygen data, Repulse Bay Beach, Hong Kong (DW = day of the week, DO = dissolved oxygen)

Year	Month	Day	DW	DO
1980	1	3	4	6.5
1980	2	5	2	7.8
1980	2	24	7	7.7
1980	3	2	7	9.2
1980	3	14	5	8.8
1980	3	26	3	10.1
1980	4	6	7	10.2
1980	5	4	7	7.8
1980	5	14	3	7.9
1980	5	27	2	10.8
1980	6	1	7	10.2
1980	6	18	3	15.8
1980	6	26	4	8.6
1980	7	18	5	8.5
1980	8	10	7	11.9
1980	8	19	2	10.5
1980	8	29	5	9.6
1980	9	23	2	11.6
1980	9	28	7	8.2
1980	9	30	2	11.6
1980	10	5	7	10.0
1980	10	15	3	10.2
1980	10	31	5	10.7
1980	11	21	5	9.9
1980	11	23	7	9.8
1980	11	28	5	11.3
1980	12	4	4	10.2
1980	12	14	7	10.0
1980	12	30	2	9.7
1981	1	6	2	12.0
1981	1	18	7	9.7
1981	1	23	5	10.4
1981	2	3	2	10.6
1981	2	15	7	10.8
1981	2	18	3	9.6
1981	3	17	2	8.7
1981	3	23	1	9.4

Year	Month	Day	DW	DO
1981	3	29	7	10.0
1981	4	2	4	12.2
1981	4	13	1	6.0
1981	4	26	7	9.4
1981	5	8	5	9.4
1981	5	17	7	9.0
1981	5	22	5	9.8
1981	6	8	1	9.5
1981	6	24	3	9.2
1981	6	28	7	10.2
1981	7	5	7	9.2
1981	7	13	1	9.0
1981	7	22	3	8.9
1981	8	4	2	9.9
1981	8	9	7	11.4
1981	8	24	1	10.5
1981	9	2	3	9.6
1981	10	15	4	9.0
1981	10	30	5	10.0
1981	11	1	7	9.4
1981	11	4	3	8.5
1981	11	25	3	9.2
1981	12	13	7	10.0
1981	12	18	5	9.6
1981	12	28	1	8.6
1982	1	6	3	8.1
1982	1	19	2	11.2
1982	2	4	4	8.8
1982	2	19	5	9.0
1982	2	28	7	8.5
1982	3	7	7	9.5
1982	3	17	3	9.8
1982	3	24	3	10.4
1982	4	1	4	10.0
1982	4	25	7	8.6
1982	4	28	3	8.2
1982	5	2	7	9.0
1982	5	12	3	10.0
1982	5	31	1	8.0
1982	6	7	1	10.5
1982	6	20	7	8.8

Year	Month	Day	DW	DO
1982	6	29	2	7.8
1982	7	8	4	12.4
1982	7	19	1	8.0
1982	7	25	7	9.9
1982	8	8	7	9.2
1982	8	18	3	8.1
1982	9	12	7	8.6
1982	9	28	2	10.0
1982	10	3	7	11.9
1982	10	13	3	10.9
1982	10	26	2	9.4
1982	11	1	1	11.3
1982	11	8	1	9.8
1982	11	21	7	9.9
1982	12	6	1	12.0
1982	12	19	7	8.8
1982	12	30	4	10.0
1983	1	10	1	9.6
1983	1	18	2	9.0
1983	1	30	7	10.2
1983	2	6	7	10.0
1983	2	18	5	9.0
1983	2	27	7	9.7
1983	3	11	5	8.3
1983	3	20	7	10.0
1983	3	30	3	11.4
1983	4	3	7	9.9
1983	4	22	5	11.6
1983	5	6	5	11.0
1983	5	24	2	10.5
1983	6	2	4	9.0
1983	6	26	7	9.6
1983	7	3	7	8.6
1983	7	16	6	11.2
1983	7	28	4	12.0
1983	8	7	7	10.4
1983	8	15	1	10.8
1983	8	26	5	10.8
1983	9	7	3	10.8
1983	9	13	2	7.5
1983	9	25	7	11.5

Year	Month	Day	DW	DO
1983	10	3	1	9.3
1983	10	15	6	9.4
1983	10	23	7	9.7
1983	11	1	2	9.7
1983	11	13	7	10.1
1983	11	25	5	9.8
1983	12	6	2	7.8
1983	12	15	4	9.9
1984	1	10	2	10.3
1984	1	15	7	10.9
1984	1	21	6	9.8
1984	2	6	1	9.9
1984	2	13	1	10.0
1984	2	26	7	10.6
1984	3	7	3	10.1
1984	3	18	7	10.1
1984	3	27	2	10.3
1984	4	8	7	9.6
1984	4	16	1	9.9
1984	4	24	2	9.6
1984	5	6	7	9.7
1984	5	17	4	8.3
1984	5	29	2	9.6
1984	6	3	7	8.8
1984	6	12	2	9.0
1984	6	21	4	9.0
1984	7	20	5	8.7
1984	7	29	7	8.4
1984	8	9	4	8.7
1984	8	27	1	9.9
1984	8	30	4	9.7
1984	9	4	2	9.8
1984	9	17	1	9.3
1984	9	23	7	9.7
1984	10	8	1	9.8
1984	10	14	7	8.3
1984	10	26	5	9.5
1984	11	8	4	7.9
1984	11	15	4	11.5
1984	11	25	7	10.0
1984	12	7	5	6.6

APPENDIX 3

Year	Month	Day	DW	DO
1984	12	16	7	10.3
1985	1	11	5	9.3
1985	1	19	6	10.4
1985	1	27	7	10.2
1985	2	10	7	8.8
1985	2	14	4	9.5
1985	3	4	1	9.8
1985	3	9	6	10.9
1985	3	24	7	9.4
1985	4	4	4	9.8
1985	4	15	1	9.5
1985	4	28	7	9.2
1985	5	14	2	11.4
1985	5	29	3	9.3
1985	6	10	1	9.2
1985	6	20	4	9.0
1985	6	30	7	9.0
1985	7	10	3	10.4
1985	7	31	3	9.8
1985	8	11	7	9.8
1985	8	22	4	9.6
1985	8	29	4	10.2
1985	9	2	1	11.2
1985	9	15	7	10.1
1985	9	24	2	11.3
1985	10	1	2	9.8
1985	10	14	1	10.8
1985	10	27	7	10.0
1985	11	3	7	9.0
1985	11	12	2	9.6
1985	11	23	6	10.5
1985	12	1	7	9.6
1985	12	13	5	9.8

Lupus erythematosis data (by courtesy of Professor R. H. Jones)

Day	DB	SC
0.0	8.40	16.0
8.0	8.50	.
23.0	8.70	9.0
35.0	6.60	13.9
44.0	4.60	13.8
58.0	4.20	13.7
100.0	7.90	17.2
121.0	7.10	13.5
149.0	9.10	8.6
156.0	9.00	8.1
184.0	10.00	7.9
198.0	10.00	6.9
254.0	9.84	12.3
280.0	10.00	10.0
281.0	9.30	10.4
288.0	8.80	8.2
295.0	7.60	8.6
302.0	4.80	9.6
309.0	5.50	8.2
316.0	5.70	10.7
323.0	4.30	9.6
330.0	6.00	10.7
337.0	5.90	10.7
343.0	6.90	11.7
351.0	6.90	10.2
358.0	7.90	9.1
364.0	8.40	9.1
370.0	6.00	10.7
380.0	9.20	11.0
401.0	7.10	10.6
440.0	7.30	14.4
478.0	7.90	16.3
506.0	6.10	16.8
541.0	7.20	21.0
576.0	7.30	13.3
611.0	8.00	13.2
674.0	6.00	11.7
709.0	7.60	13.4
730.0	7.10	12.5
807.0	6.20	12.5
842.0	7.50	11.7
884.0	5.30	12.9
921.0	5.90	14.0
1011.0	5.50	12.0
1038.0	4.20	10.0
1046.0	4.90	9.0
1100.0	2.50	9.6
1121.0	3.20	12.5
1133.0	3.30	15.0
1137.0	3.60	11.8
1157.0	2.50	13.2
1213.0	2.70	20.0
1255.0	4.60	10.8
1297.0	3.60	12.0
1325.0	3.40	13.0
1353.0	5.80	14.5
1381.0	4.40	11.5
1437.0	3.82	13.0
1507.0	5.17	10.0
1535.0	5.57	12.9
1556.0	5.49	7.1
1584.0	6.96	16.0
1604.0	6.09	14.5
1618.0	5.69	10.0
1653.0	5.61	13.0
1689.0	6.64	15.0
1717.0	4.66	10.5
1738.0	5.41	10.5
1808.0	5.60	9.2
1850.0	5.26	13.4
1878.0	5.55	10.1
1906.0	5.61	12.0
1990.0	4.30	13.5
2025.0	3.79	11.8
2081.0	4.93	11.0
2102.0	5.23	10.8
2144.0	4.52	11.4
2186.0	3.55	11.0
2218.0	2.87	2.9
2263.0	3.20	12.8

Day	DB	SC
2284.0	3.09	12.8
2333.0	3.33	10.0
2361.0	2.80	12.7
2424.0	3.06	12.7
2452.0	2.03	11.2
2458.0	2.35	10.6
2501.0	1.88	12.2
2564.0	1.76	10.4
2599.0	1.17	12.8
2641.0	2.01	13.6
2676.0	1.16	13.8
2711.0	0.39	11.6
2739.0	1.25	10.7
2767.0	0.90	12.7
2823.0	1.49	11.7
2886.0	2.05	10.3
2928.0	1.97	5.4
2991.0	1.11	15.0
3061.0	0.84	10.0

Bone marrow transplant data (by courtesy of Professor R. H. Jones)

Post-transplant day	WBC	PLC	HCT
0	215	29 500	20.0
1	77	21 600	30.0
2	120	12 400	28.5
3	66	40 000	34.5
4	66	25 700	34.0
5	33	21 000	32.0
6	44	31 000	30.5
7	50	34 500	31.0
8	100	28 000	33.0
9	250	12 600	34.0
10	400	29 800	31.5
11	520	8 300	27.5
12	630	14 700	30.0
13	968	11 000	31.5
14	760	13 400	33.0
15	470	13 400	32.0
16	1350	39 500	33.0
17	1060	14 700	33.0
18	1290	37 000	33.0
19	1200	37 750	33.0
20	1306	57 500	·
21	1550	34 700	32.5
22	1500	54 500	31.5
23	1800	71 500	31.5
24	3100	80 000	29.5
25	2550	65 000	·
26	1980	76 500	28.0
27	3000	94 000	31.0
28	3700	88 000	30.5
29	3025	162 500	31.5
30	4500	195 200	31.0
31	3700	149 300	31.0
32	3650	152 500	31.5
33	6700	112 000	31.0
34	7100	170 000	31.5
35	8100	201 000	32.0
37	8000	165 000	30.0

Post-transplant day	WBC	PLC	HCT
38	8000	165 000	30.0
40	10 600	185 000	28.5
42	11 300	200 000	27.0
45	9150	237 500	28.5
47	6350	175 000	27.0
49	3600	136 000	31.0
52	3050	126 000	29.5
56	1780	145 000	27.0
59	1500	162 500	28.5
63	2300	121 700	35.0
66	3400	165 000	34.5
70	4700	217 500	35.0
73	7200	205 000	31.5
77	4500	190 000	30.0
80	3700	230 000	27.5
84	5500	181 000	35.0
87	3800	153 300	33.0
91	3250	267 500	31.5

Respiration data (by courtesy of Professor R. H. Jones)

Time	Work	VENT	Uptake	CO_2
1.38	1147.00	0.00	0.00	0.00
5.90	976.00	27.00	1178.66	923.45
11.24	876.00	26.00	1320.08	1057.66
16.94	1177.00	24.00	1041.68	827.90
22.72	1050.00	18.00	1228.24	931.51
28.38	959.00	17.00	1209.89	933.03
33.30	875.00	19.00	1136.38	867.66
39.50	1265.00	20.00	989.66	725.44
44.16	1197.00	19.00	1600.36	1185.99
48.00	1206.00	22.00	1212.01	862.14
52.32	1227.00	23.00	1483.40	1081.36
56.42	1373.00	23.00	1543.80	1137.85
59.82	1243.00	24.00	1312.64	945.79
64.66	1107.00	22.00	1579.21	1194.36
68.60	948.00	23.00	1407.67	1028.06
72.86	818.00	27.00	1610.95	1254.50
76.60	1083.00	26.00	1432.71	1111.51
81.02	1074.00	22.00	1479.89	1177.35
84.72	1221.00	20.00	1375.70	1073.93
88.68	1161.00	28.00	1667.25	1302.91
94.18	1299.00	22.00	1543.79	1232.92
98.02	1075.00	22.00	1371.72	1077.07
102.82	1486.00	25.00	1641.90	1315.03
106.58	1319.00	34.00	1709.40	1409.01
110.06	1169.00	34.00	1741.12	1451.37
115.28	1018.00	23.00	1497.58	1256.15
120.00	867.00	27.00	1529.83	1274.89
123.88	819.00	26.00	1452.19	1230.02
127.72	767.00	28.00	1522.05	1265.63
131.90	1083.00	31.00	1591.82	1376.84
136.10	1285.00	32.00	1711.77	1501.86
139.96	1228.00	35.00	1796.60	1597.68
143.46	1107.00	42.00	1799.06	1643.53
146.86	1059.00	44.00	1709.50	1622.61
151.26	1285.00	36.00	1534.12	1480.09
155.46	1027.00	34.00	1682.89	1610.71
159.64	788.00 •	29.00	1602.35	1517.59
164.12	375.00	24.00	1300.96	1209.25
169.08	838.00	21.00	1340.99	1203.58

Time	Work	VENT	Uptake	CO_2
172.54	735.00	27.00	1286.73	1141.20
176.50	777.00	26.00	1542.65	1370.54
180.28	1059.00	33.00	1628.77	1475.52
184.18	691.00	33.00	1672.77	1575.13
188.80	886.00	26.00	1405.50	1287.36
193.22	1153.00	28.00	1495.44	1382.37
197.34	1221.00	30.00	1465.51	1373.59
200.96	1333.00	25.00	1422.77	1268.86
204.18	1244.00	31.00	1402.37	1251.06
207.66	1220.00	33.00	1713.20	1536.09
211.62	1205.00	28.00	1488.95	1361.52
215.68	1340.00	31.00	1476.16	1329.82
218.42	1257.00	31.00	1250.29	1076.74
222.22	967.00	27.00	1673.19	1470.53
226.86	830.00	27.00	1552.46	1381.16
231.04	1050.00	25.00	1448.91	1284.31
235.58	1130.00	26.00	1490.65	1306.83
239.82	894.00	23.00	1359.42	1163.42
243.98	525.00	30.00	1618.23	1406.38
248.32	618.00	30.00	1682.94	1517.91
252.44	429.00	30.00	1547.55	1407.35
256.48	1170.00	31.00	1587.34	1461.52
260.54	1115.00	27.00	1558.48	1436.66
265.08	984.00	27.00	1477.63	1387.31
269.24	1067.00	28.00	1324.90	1191.91
273.98	1250.00	24.00	1591.03	1426.72
278.26	1497.00	30.00	1490.52	1335.68
281.80	1256.00	31.00	1595.82	1428.57
285.44	1311.00	32.00	1679.25	1494.85
289.56	1234.00	30.00	1620.38	1484.05
292.90	1414.00	20.00	824.91	744.72
298.46	1413.00	38.00	1160.20	1039.71
302.34	1315.00	36.00	1854.30	1630.64
306.12	966.00	34.00	1840.71	1655.60
310.06	867.00	32.00	1699.87	1525.20
314.00	940.00	27.00	1726.74	1569.80
318.04	777.00	29.00	1529.68	1382.75
322.56	1154.00	28.00	1730.47	1592.40
326.44	1394.00	28.00	1676.61	1530.17
330.04	1313.00	31.00	1680.86	1510.88
333.46	1074.00	38.00	1856.26	1671.53

Time	Work	VENT	Uptake	CO_2
336.88	914.00	36.00	1872.78	1705.88
340.66	975.00	31.00	1574.04	1410.14
344.76	630.00	31.00	1690.04	1545.04
347.84	644.00	29.00	1473.41	1335.53
351.96	22.00	30.00	1703.64	1591.65
356.34	374.00	28.00	1582.05	1482.45
360.28	867.00	28.00	1505.87	1434.46
364.24	866.00	27.00	1586.62	1488.13
368.30	757.00	31.00	1528.59	1468.53
372.26	1122.00	33.00	1507.19	1450.16
376.38	1027.00	32.00	1648.29	1616.46
381.16	1278.00	28.00	1501.71	1473.59
384.92	1353.00	30.00	1448.70	1397.15
388.62	1220.00	38.00	1543.22	1488.08
393.44	1099.00	27.00	1620.74	1596.13
398.08	1279.00	33.00	1360.27	1299.52
402.92	1271.00	27.00	1723.17	1634.98
407.24	1299.00	31.00	1591.02	1512.62
411.76	950.00	29.00	1501.48	1406.45
416.02	1138.00	29.00	1508.89	1380.82
420.80	1139.00	25.00	1534.08	1395.34
425.14	1043.00	34.00	1684.51	1526.22
429.16	1228.00	30.00	1699.16	1537.23
433.36	966.00	31.00	1673.78	1506.29
437.72	735.00	31.00	1648.44	1507.59
441.72	645.00	30.00	1700.89	1546.20
445.88	1176.00	29.00	1569.72	1444.39
449.68	1407.00	31.00	1616.62	1505.16
452.86	1292.00	39.00	1854.84	1720.92
456.80	1306.00	32.00	1599.86	1484.51
459.96	1313.00	34.00	1722.19	1575.86
462.58	1191.00	44.00	1859.81	1712.31
465.74	1066.00	36.00	1777.38	1658.67
469.42	1099.00	34.00	1647.98	1542.64
473.24	1249.00	33.00	1663.64	1542.23
477.28	838.00	32.00	1684.28	1586.36
481.02	199.00	36.00	1700.46	1587.49
484.80	525.00	31.00	1668.36	1576.43
488.76	1243.00	32.00	1541.87	1456.41
493.08	958.00	28.00	1637.92	1586.36
498.54	738.00	27.00	1422.72	1316.40

Time	Work	VENT	Uptake	CO_2
502.96	1026.00	26.00	1582.49	1480.23
507.32	1206.00	30.00	1446.06	1315.84
511.62	839.00	36.00	1649.67	1513.49
515.98	788.00	34.00	1721.26	1592.44
520.10	829.00	33.00	1608.39	1541.79
524.56	1066.00	34.00	1518.90	1472.89
528.84	914.00	32.00	1511.63	1478.26
533.58	885.00	29.00	1426.84	1396.20
538.54	1184.00	32.00	1451.10	1432.47
543.12	1380.00	32.00	1618.45	1589.25
546.44	1478.00	37.00	1467.46	1420.15
550.24	1227.00	34.00	1495.34	1440.86
553.90	1228.00	31.00	1548.53	1465.56
558.52	1242.00	29.00	1483.32	1409.98
562.72	1298.00	36.00	1551.44	1462.82
566.16	1381.00	34.00	1845.67	1719.03
569.82	1352.00	40.00	1664.39	1562.57
573.98	992.00	35.00	1754.97	1671.42
578.14	913.00	33.00	1641.31	1572.69
582.52	1146.00	33.00	1625.11	1558.72
587.40	1220.00	26.00	1638.03	1535.73
590.68	1473.00	40.00	1796.67	1693.64
594.14	1434.00	37.00	1877.78	1756.41

IBM (Part I) data (DW = day of the week; · = missing)

Year	Month	Day	DW	Stock price	Year	Month	Day	DW	Stock price
					1959	8	6	4	422
					1959	8	7	5	409
1959	6	29	1	445	1959	8	8	6	·
1959	6	30	2	448	1959	8	9	7	·
1959	7	1	3	450	1959	8	10	1	407
1959	7	2	4	447	1959	8	11	2	423
1959	7	3	5	·	1959	8	12	3	422
1959	7	4	6	·	1959	8	13	4	417
1959	7	5	7	·	1959	8	14	5	421
1959	7	6	1	451	1959	8	15	6	·
1959	7	7	2	453	1959	8	16	7	·
1959	7	8	3	454	1959	8	17	1	424
1959	7	9	4	454	1959	8	18	2	414
1959	7	10	5	459	1959	8	19	3	419
1959	7	11	6	·	1959	8	20	4	429
1959	7	12	7	·	1959	8	21	5	426
1959	7	12	1	440	1959	8	22	6	·
1959	7	14	2	446	1959	8	23	7	·
1959	7	15	3	443	1959	8	24	1	425
1959	7	16	4	443	1959	8	25	2	424
1959	7	17	5	440	1959	8	26	3	425
1959	7	18	6	·	1959	8	27	4	425
1959	7	19	7	·	1959	8	28	5	424
1959	7	20	1	439	1959	8	29	6	·
1959	7	21	2	435	1959	8	30	7	·
1959	7	22	3	435	1959	8	31	1	425
1959	7	23	4	436	1959	9	1	2	421
1959	7	24	5	435	1959	9	2	3	414
1959	7	25	6	·	1959	9	3	4	410
1959	7	26	7	·	1959	9	4	5	411
1959	7	27	1	435	1959	9	5	6	·
1959	7	28	2	435	1959	9	6	7	·
1959	7	29	3	433	1959	9	7	1	·
1959	7	30	4	429	1959	9	8	2	406
1959	7	31	5	428	1959	9	9	3	406
1959	8	1	6	·	1959	9	10	4	413
1959	8	2	7	·	1959	9	11	5	411
1959	8	3	1	425	1959	9	12	6	·
1959	8	4	2	427	1959	9	13	7	·
1959	8	5	3	425	1959	9	14	1	410
					1959	9	15	2	405

Year	Month	Day	DW	Stock price
1959	9	16	3	409
1959	9	17	4	410
1959	9	18	5	405
1959	9	19	6	·
1959	9	20	7	·
1959	9	21	1	401
1959	9	22	2	401
1959	9	23	3	401
1959	9	24	4	414
1959	9	25	5	419
1959	9	26	6	·
1959	9	27	7	·
1959	9	28	1	425
1959	9	29	2	423
1959	9	30	3	411
1959	10	1	4	414
1959	10	2	5	420
1959	10	3	6	·
1959	10	4	7	·
1959	10	5	1	412
1959	10	6	2	415
1959	10	7	3	412
1959	10	8	4	412
1959	10	9	5	411
1959	10	10	6	·
1959	10	11	7	·
1959	10	12	1	412
1959	10	13	2	409
1959	10	14	3	407
1959	10	15	4	408
1959	10	16	5	415
1959	10	17	6	·
1959	10	18	7	·
1959	10	19	1	413
1959	10	20	2	413
1959	10	21	3	410
1959	10	22	4	405
1959	10	23	5	410
1959	10	24	6	·
1959	10	25	7	·
1959	10	26	1	412
1959	10	27	2	413
1959	10	28	3	411
1959	10	29	4	411
1959	10	30	5	409
1959	10	31	6	·
1959	11	1	7	·
1959	11	2	1	406
1959	11	3	2	·
1959	11	4	3	407
1959	11	5	4	410
1959	11	6	5	408
1959	11	7	6	·
1959	11	8	7	·
1959	11	9	1	408
1959	11	10	2	409
1959	11	11	3	410
1959	11	12	4	409
1959	11	13	5	405
1959	11	14	6	·
1959	11	15	7	·
1959	11	16	1	406
1959	11	17	2	405
1959	11	18	3	407
1959	11	19	4	409
1959	11	20	5	407
1959	11	21	6	·
1959	11	22	7	·
1959	11	23	1	409
1959	11	24	2	425
1959	11	25	3	425
1959	11	26	4	·
1959	11	27	5	428
1959	11	28	6	·
1959	11	29	7	·
1959	11	30	1	436
1959	12	1	2	442
1959	12	2	3	442
1959	12	3	4	433
1959	12	4	5	435
1959	12	5	6	·
1959	12	6	7	·
1959	12	7	1	433

Year	Month	Day	DW	Stock price	1960	1	17	7	·
					1960	1	18	1	431
					1960	1	19	2	425
1959	12	8	2	435	1960	1	20	3	423
1959	12	9	3	429	1960	1	21	4	420
1959	12	10	4	439	1960	1	22	5	426
1959	12	11	5	437	1960	1	23	6	·
1959	12	12	6	·	1960	1	24	7	·
1959	12	13	7	·	1960	1	25	1	418
1959	12	14	1	439	1960	1	26	2	416
1959	12	15	2	438	1960	1	27	3	419
1959	12	16	3	435	1960	1	28	4	418
1959	12	17	4	433	1960	1	29	5	416
1959	12	18	5	437	1960	1	30	6	·
1959	12	19	6	·	1960	1	31	7	·
1959	12	20	7	·	1960	2	1	1	419
1959	12	21	1	437	1960	2	2	2	425
1959	12	22	2	444	1960	2	3	3	421
1959	12	23	3	441	1960	2	4	4	422
1959	12	24	4	440	1960	2	5	5	422
1959	12	25	5	·	1960	2	6	6	·
1959	12	26	6	·	1960	2	7	7	·
1959	12	27	7	·	1960	2	8	1	417
1959	12	28	1	441	1960	2	9	2	420
1959	12	29	2	439	1960	2	10	3	417
1959	12	30	3	439	1960	2	11	4	418
1959	12	31	4	438	1960	2	12	5	419
1960	1	1	5	·	1960	2	13	6	·
1960	1	2	6	·	1960	2	14	7	·
1960	1	3	7	·	1960	2	15	1	419
1960	1	4	1	437	1960	2	16	2	417
1960	1	5	2	441	1960	2	17	3	419
1960	1	6	3	442	1960	2	18	4	422
1960	1	7	4	441	1960	2	19	5	423
1960	1	8	5	437	1960	2	20	6	·
1960	1	9	6	·	1960	2	21	7	·
1960	1	10	7	·	1960	2	22	1	·
1960	1	11	1	427	1960	2	23	2	422
1960	1	12	2	423	1960	2	24	3	421
1960	1	13	3	424	1960	2	25	4	421
1960	1	14	4	428	1960	2	26	5	419
1960	1	15	5	428	1960	2	27	6	·
1960	1	16	6	·	1960	2	28	7	·

Year	Month	Day	DW	Stock price
1960	2	29	1	418
1960	3	1	2	421
1960	3	2	3	420
1960	3	3	4	413
1960	3	4	5	413
1960	3	5	6	.
1960	3	6	7	.
1960	3	7	1	408
1960	3	8	2	409
1960	3	9	3	415
1960	3	10	4	415
1960	3	11	5	420
1960	3	12	6	.
1960	3	13	7	.
1960	3	14	1	420
1960	3	15	2	424
1960	3	16	3	426
1960	3	17	4	423
1960	3	18	5	423
1960	3	19	6	.
1960	3	20	7	.
1960	3	21	1	425
1960	3	22	2	431
1960	3	23	3	436
1960	3	24	4	436
1960	3	25	5	440
1960	3	26	6	.
1960	3	27	7	.
1960	3	28	1	436
1960	3	29	2	443
1960	3	30	3	445
1960	3	31	4	439
1960	4	1	5	443
1960	4	2	6	.
1960	4	3	7	.
1960	4	4	1	445
1960	4	5	2	450
1960	4	6	3	461
1960	4	7	4	471
1960	4	8	5	467
1960	4	9	6	.
1960	4	10	7	.
1960	4	11	1	462
1960	4	12	2	456
1960	4	13	3	464
1960	4	14	4	463
1960	4	15	5	.
1960	4	16	6	.
1960	4	17	7	.
1960	4	18	1	465
1960	4	19	2	464
1960	4	20	3	456
1960	4	21	4	460
1960	4	22	5	458
1960	4	23	6	.
1960	4	24	7	.
1960	4	25	1	453
1960	4	26	2	453
1960	4	27	3	449
1960	4	28	4	447
1960	4	29	5	453
1960	4	30	6	.
1960	5	1	7	.
1960	5	2	1	450
1960	5	3	2	459
1960	5	4	3	457
1960	5	5	4	453
1960	5	6	5	455
1960	5	7	6	.
1960	5	8	7	.
1960	5	9	1	453
1960	5	10	2	450
1960	5	11	3	456
1960	5	12	4	461
1960	5	13	5	463
1960	5	14	6	.
1960	5	15	7	.
1960	5	16	1	463
1960	5	17	2	461
1960	5	18	3	465
1960	5	19	4	473
1960	5	20	5	473
1960	5	21	6	.

Year	Month	Day	DW	Stock price					
1960	5	22	7	·	1960	6	10	5	529
1960	5	23	1	475	1960	6	11	6	·
1960	5	24	2	499	1960	6	12	7	·
1960	5	25	3	485	1960	6	13	1	530
1960	5	26	4	491	1960	6	14	2	531
1960	5	27	5	496	1960	6	15	3	527
1960	5	28	6	·	1960	6	16	4	525
1960	5	29	7	·	1960	6	17	5	519
1960	5	30	1	·	1960	6	18	6	·
1960	5	31	2	504	1960	6	19	7	·
1960	6	1	3	504	1960	6	20	1	514
1960	6	2	4	509	1960	6	21	2	509
1960	6	3	5	511	1960	6	22	3	505
1960	6	4	6	·	1960	6	23	4	513
1960	6	5	7	·	1960	6	24	5	525
1960	6	6	1	524	1960	6	25	6	·
1960	6	7	2	525	1960	6	26	7	·
1960	6	8	3	541	1960	6	27	1	519
1960	6	9	4	531	1960	6	28	2	519
					1960	6	29	3	522
					1960	6	30	4	522

IBM (Part II) data (DW = day of the week; · = missing)

Year	Month	Day	DW	Stock price	Year	Month	Day	DW	Stock price
					1961	6	24	6	·
					1961	6	25	7	·
					1961	6	26	1	479
1961	5	17	3	460	1961	6	27	2	475
1961	5	18	4	457	1961	6	28	3	479
1961	5	19	5	452	1961	6	29	4	476
1961	5	20	6	·	1961	6	30	5	476
1961	5	21	7	·	1961	7	1	6	·
1961	5	22	1	459	1961	7	2	7	·
1961	5	23	2	462	1961	7	3	1	478
1961	5	24	3	459	1961	7	4	2	·
1961	5	25	4	463	1961	7	5	3	479
1961	5	26	5	479	1961	7	6	4	477
1961	5	27	6	·	1961	7	7	5	476
1961	5	28	7	·	1961	7	8	6	·
1961	5	29	1	·	1961	7	9	7	·
1961	5	30	2	·	1961	7	10	1	475
1961	5	31	3	493	1961	7	11	2	475
1961	6	1	4	490	1961	7	12	3	473
1961	6	2	5	492	1961	7	13	4	474
1961	6	3	6	·	1961	7	14	5	474
1961	6	4	7	·	1961	7	15	6	·
1961	6	5	1	498	1961	7	16	7	·
1961	6	6	2	499	1961	7	17	1	474
1961	6	7	3	497	1961	7	18	2	465
1961	6	8	4	496	1961	7	19	3	466
1961	6	9	5	490	1961	7	20	4	467
1961	6	10	6	·	1961	7	21	5	471
1961	6	11	7	·	1961	7	22	6	·
1961	6	12	1	489	1961	7	23	7	·
1961	6	13	2	478	1961	7	24	1	471
1961	6	14	3	487	1961	7	25	2	467
1961	6	15	4	491	1961	7	26	3	473
1961	6	16	5	487	1961	7	27	4	481
1961	6	17	6	·	1961	7	28	5	488
1961	6	18	7	·	1961	7	29	6	·
1961	6	19	1	482	1961	7	30	7	·
1961	6	20	2	479	1961	7	31	1	490
1961	6	21	3	478	1961	8	1	2	489
1961	6	22	4	479	1961	8	2	3	489
1961	6	23	5	477	1961	8	3	4	485

Year	Month	Day	DW	Stock price
1961	8	4	5	491
1961	8	5	6	·
1961	8	6	7	·
1961	8	7	1	492
1961	8	8	2	494
1961	8	9	3	499
1961	8	10	4	498
1961	8	11	5	500
1961	8	12	6	·
1961	8	13	7	·
1961	8	14	1	497
1961	8	15	2	494
1961	8	16	3	495
1961	8	17	4	500
1961	8	18	5	504
1961	8	19	6	·
1961	8	20	7	·
1961	8	21	1	513
1961	8	22	2	511
1961	8	23	3	514
1961	8	24	4	510
1961	8	25	5	509
1961	8	26	6	·
1961	8	27	7	·
1961	8	28	1	515
1961	8	29	2	519
1961	8	30	3	523
1961	8	31	4	519
1961	9	1	5	523
1961	9	2	6	·
1961	9	3	7	·
1961	9	4	1	·
1961	9	5	2	531
1961	9	6	3	547
1961	9	7	4	551
1961	9	8	5	547
1961	9	9	6	·
1961	9	10	7	·
1961	9	11	1	541
1961	9	12	2	545
1961	9	13	3	549
1961	9	14	4	545
1961	9	15	5	549
1961	9	16	6	·
1961	9	17	7	·
1961	9	18	1	547
1961	9	19	2	543
1961	9	20	3	540
1961	9	21	4	539
1961	9	22	5	532
1961	9	23	6	·
1961	9	24	7	·
1961	9	25	1	517
1961	9	26	2	527
1961	9	27	3	540
1961	9	28	4	542
1961	9	29	5	538
1961	9	30	6	·
1961	10	1	7	·
1961	10	2	1	541
1961	10	3	2	541
1961	10	4	3	547
1961	10	5	4	553
1961	10	6	5	559
1961	10	7	6	·
1961	10	8	7	·
1961	10	9	1	557
1961	10	10	2	557
1961	10	11	3	560
1961	10	12	4	571
1961	10	13	5	571
1961	10	14	6	·
1961	10	15	7	·
1961	10	16	1	569
1961	10	17	2	575
1961	10	18	3	580
1961	10	19	4	584
1961	10	20	5	585
1961	10	21	6	·
1961	10	22	7	·
1961	10	23	1	590
1961	10	24	2	599
1961	10	25	3	603

Year	Month	Day	DW	Stock price
1961	10	26	4	599
1961	10	27	5	596
1961	10	28	6	.
1961	10	29	7	.
1961	10	30	1	585
1961	10	31	2	587
1961	11	1	3	585
1961	11	2	4	581
1961	11	3	5	583
1961	11	4	6	.
1961	11	5	7	.
1961	11	6	1	592
1961	11	7	2	.
1961	11	8	3	592
1961	11	9	4	596
1961	11	10	5	596
1961	11	11	6	.
1961	11	12	7	.
1961	11	13	1	595
1961	11	14	2	598
1961	11	15	3	598
1961	11	16	4	595
1961	11	17	5	595
1961	11	18	6	.
1961	11	19	7	.
1961	11	20	1	592
1961	11	21	2	588
1961	11	22	3	582
1961	11	23	4	.
1961	11	24	5	576
1961	11	25	6	.
1961	11	26	7	.
1961	11	27	1	578
1961	11	28	2	589
1961	11	29	3	585
1961	11	30	4	580
1961	12	1	5	579
1961	12	2	6	.
1961	12	3	7	.
1961	12	4	1	584
1961	12	5	2	581
1961	12	6	3	581
1961	12	7	4	577
1961	12	8	5	577
1961	12	9	6	.
1961	12	10	7	.
1961	12	11	1	578
1961	12	12	2	580
1961	12	13	3	586
1961	12	14	4	583
1961	12	15	5	581
1961	12	16	6	.
1961	12	17	7	.
1961	12	18	1	576
1961	12	19	2	571
1961	12	20	3	575
1961	12	21	4	575
1961	12	22	5	573
1961	12	23	6	.
1961	12	24	7	.
1961	12	25	1	.
1961	12	26	2	577
1961	12	27	3	582
1961	12	28	4	584
1961	12	29	5	579
1961	12	30	6	.
1961	12	31	7	.
1962	1	1	1	.
1962	1	2	2	572
1962	1	3	3	577
1962	1	4	4	571
1962	1	5	5	560
1962	1	6	6	.
1962	1	7	7	.
1962	1	8	1	549
1962	1	9	2	556
1962	1	10	3	557
1962	1	11	4	563
1962	1	12	5	564
1962	1	13	6	.
1962	1	14	7	.
1962	1	15	1	567
1962	1	16	2	561

Year	Month	Day	DW	Stock price
1962	1	17	3	559
1962	1	18	4	553
1962	1	19	5	553
1962	1	20	6	·
1962	1	21	7	·
1962	1	22	1	553
1962	1	23	2	547
1962	1	24	3	550
1962	1	25	4	544
1962	1	26	5	541
1962	1	27	6	·
1962	1	28	7	·
1962	1	29	1	532
1962	1	30	2	525
1962	1	31	3	542
1962	2	1	4	555
1962	2	2	5	558
1962	2	3	6	·
1962	2	4	7	·
1962	2	5	1	551
1962	2	6	2	551
1962	2	7	3	552
1962	2	8	4	553
1962	2	9	5	557
1962	2	10	6	·
1962	2	11	7	·
1962	2	12	1	557
1962	2	13	2	548
1962	2	14	3	547
1962	2	15	4	545
1962	2	16	5	545
1962	2	17	6	·
1962	2	18	7	·
1962	2	19	1	539
1962	2	20	2	539
1962	2	21	3	535
1962	2	22	4	·
1962	2	23	5	537
1962	2	24	6	·
1962	2	25	7	·
1962	2	26	1	535
1962	2	27	2	536
1962	2	28	3	537
1962	3	1	4	543
1962	3	2	5	548
1962	3	3	6	·
1962	3	4	7	·
1962	3	5	1	546
1962	3	6	2	547
1962	3	7	3	548
1962	3	8	4	549
1962	3	9	5	553
1962	3	10	6	·
1962	3	11	7	·
1962	3	12	1	553
1962	3	13	2	552
1962	3	14	3	551
1962	3	15	4	550
1962	3	16	5	553
1962	3	17	6	·
1962	3	18	7	·
1962	3	19	1	554
1962	3	20	2	551
1962	3	21	3	551
1962	3	22	4	545
1962	3	23	5	547
1962	3	24	6	·
1962	3	25	7	·
1962	3	26	1	547
1962	3	27	2	537
1962	3	28	3	539
1962	3	29	4	538
1962	3	30	5	533
1962	3	31	6	·
1962	4	1	7	·
1962	4	2	1	525
1962	4	3	2	513
1962	4	4	3	510
1962	4	5	4	521
1962	4	6	5	521
1962	4	7	6	·
1962	4	8	7	·
1962	4	9	1	521

Year	Month	Day	DW	Stock price	Year	Month	Day	DW	Stock price
					1962	5	20	7	·
					1962	5	21	1	450
					1962	5	22	2	435
1962	4	10	2	523	1962	5	23	3	415
1962	4	11	3	516	1962	5	24	4	398
1962	4	12	4	511	1962	5	25	5	399
1962	4	13	5	518	1962	5	26	6	·
1962	4	14	6	·	1962	5	27	7	·
1962	4	15	7	·	1962	5	28	1	361
1962	4	16	1	517	1962	5	29	2	383
1962	4	17	2	520	1962	5	30	3	·
1962	4	18	3	519	1962	5	31	4	393
1962	4	19	4	519	1962	6	1	5	385
1962	4	20	5	·	1962	6	2	6	·
1962	4	21	6	·	1962	6	3	7	·
1962	4	22	7	·	1962	6	4	1	360
1962	4	23	1	519	1962	6	5	2	364
1962	4	24	2	518	1962	6	6	3	365
1962	4	25	3	513	1962	6	7	4	370
1962	4	26	4	499	1962	6	8	5	374
1962	4	27	5	485	1962	6	9	6	·
1962	4	28	6	·	1962	6	10	7	·
1962	4	29	7	·	1962	6	11	1	359
1962	4	30	1	454	1962	6	12	2	335
1962	5	1	2	462	1962	6	13	3	323
1962	5	2	3	473	1962	6	14	4	306
1962	5	3	4	482	1962	6	15	5	333
1962	5	4	5	486	1962	6	16	6	·
1962	5	5	6	·	1962	6	17	7	·
1962	5	6	7	·	1962	6	18	1	330
1962	5	7	1	475	1962	6	19	2	336
1962	5	8	2	459	1962	6	20	3	328
1962	5	9	3	451	1962	6	21	4	316
1962	5	10	4	453	1962	6	22	5	320
1962	5	11	5	446	1962	6	23	6	·
1962	5	12	6	·	1962	6	24	7	·
1962	5	13	7	·	1962	6	25	1	332
1962	5	14	1	455	1962	6	26	2	320
1962	5	15	2	452	1962	6	27	3	333
1962	5	16	3	457	1962	6	28	4	344
1962	5	17	4	449	1962	6	29	5	339
1962	5	18	5	·	1962	6	30	6	·
1962	5	19	6	·	1962	7	1	7	·

Year	Month	Day	DW	Stock price	Year	Month	Day	DW	Stock price
					1962	8	11	6	·
					1962	8	12	7	·
					1962	8	13	1	379
1962	7	2	1	350	1962	8	14	2	386
1962	7	3	2	351	1962	8	15	3	387
1962	7	4	3	·	1962	8	16	4	386
1962	7	5	4	350	1962	8	17	5	389
1962	7	6	5	345	1962	8	18	6	·
1962	7	7	6	·	1962	8	19	7	·
1962	7	8	7	·	1962	8	20	1	394
1962	7	9	1	350	1962	8	21	2	393
1962	7	10	2	359	1962	8	22	3	409
1962	7	11	3	375	1962	8	23	4	411
1962	7	12	4	379	1962	8	24	5	409
1962	7	13	5	376	1962	8	25	6	·
1962	7	14	6	·	1962	8	26	7	·
1962	7	15	7	·	1962	8	27	1	408
1962	7	16	1	382	1962	8	28	2	393
1962	7	17	2	370	1962	8	29	3	391
1962	7	18	3	365	1962	8	30	4	388
1962	7	19	4	367	1962	8	31	5	396
1962	7	20	5	372	1962	9	1	6	·
1962	7	21	6	·	1962	9	2	7	·
1962	7	22	7	·	1962	9	3	1	·
1962	7	23	1	373	1962	9	4	2	387
1962	7	24	2	363	1962	9	5	3	383
1962	7	25	3	371	1962	9	6	4	388
1962	7	26	4	369	1962	9	7	5	382
1962	7	27	5	376	1962	9	8	6	·
1962	7	28	6	·	1962	9	9	7	·
1962	7	29	7	·	1962	9	10	1	384
1962	7	30	1	387	1962	9	11	2	382
1962	7	31	2	387	1962	9	12	3	383
1962	8	1	3	376	1962	9	13	4	383
1962	8	2	4	385	1962	9	14	5	388
1962	8	3	5	385	1962	9	15	6	·
1962	8	4	6	·	1962	9	16	7	·
1962	8	5	7	·	1962	9	17	1	395
1962	8	6	1	380	1962	9	18	2	392
1962	8	7	2	373	1962	9	19	3	386
1962	8	8	3	382	1962	9	20	4	383
1962	8	9	4	377	1962	9	21	5	377
1962	8	10	5	376	1962	9	22	6	·

Year	Month	Day	DW	Stock price	Year	Month	Day	DW	Stock price
1962	9	23	7	·	1962	10	12	5	355
1962	9	24	1	364	1962	10	13	6	·
1962	9	25	2	369	1962	10	14	7	·
1962	9	26	3	355	1962	10	15	1	367
1962	9	27	4	350	1962	10	16	2	357
1962	9	28	5	353	1962	10	17	3	361
1962	9	29	6	·	1962	10	18	4	355
1962	9	30	7	·	1962	10	19	5	348
1962	10	1	1	340	1962	10	20	6	·
1962	10	2	2	350	1962	10	21	7	·
1962	10	3	3	349	1962	10	22	1	343
1962	10	4	4	358	1962	10	23	2	330
1962	10	5	5	360	1962	10	24	3	340
1962	10	6	6	·	1962	10	25	4	339
1962	10	7	7	·	1962	10	26	5	331
1962	10	8	1	360	1962	10	27	6	·
1962	10	9	2	366	1962	10	28	7	·
1962	10	10	3	359	1962	10	29	1	345
1962	10	11	4	356	1962	10	30	2	352
					1962	10	31	3	346
					1962	11	1	4	352
					1962	11	2	5	357

Hang Seng index (DW = day of the week (1 = Monday ... 7 = Sunday); · = missing)

Year	Month	Day	DW	Stock price*
1984	1	1	7	·
1984	1	2	1	·
1984	1	3	2	87 106
1984	1	4	3	87 726
1984	1	5	4	88 099
1984	1	6	5	90 956
1984	1	7	6	·
1984	1	8	7	·
1984	1	9	1	93 746
1984	1	10	2	94 334
1984	1	11	3	96 447
1984	1	12	4	97 858
1984	1	13	5	97 547
1984	1	14	6	·
1984	1	15	7	·
1984	1	16	1	97 517
1984	1	17	2	98 972
1984	1	18	3	101 807
1984	1	19	4	102 140
1984	1	20	5	103 400
1984	1	21	6	·
1984	1	22	7	·
1984	1	23	1	105 581
1984	1	24	2	103 528
1984	1	25	3	104 188
1984	1	26	4	104 757
1984	1	27	5	105 537
1984	1	28	6	·
1984	1	29	7	·
1984	1	30	1	109 763
1984	1	31	2	110 238
1984	2	1	3	110 854
1984	2	2	4	·
1984	2	3	5	·
1984	2	4	6	·
1984	2	5	7	·
1984	2	6	1	113 412
1984	2	7	2	108 540
1984	2	8	3	107 879
1984	2	9	4	109 008
1984	2	10	5	105 077
1984	2	11	6	·
1984	2	12	7	·
1984	2	13	1	106 236
1984	2	14	2	108 834
1984	2	15	3	109 065
1984	2	16	4	108 406
1984	2	17	5	109 487
1984	2	18	6	·
1984	2	19	7	·
1984	2	20	1	107 281
1984	2	21	2	106 691
1984	2	22	3	104 722
1984	2	23	4	106 729
1984	2	24	5	104 876
1984	2	25	6	·
1984	2	26	7	·
1984	2	27	1	102 285
1984	2	28	2	104 156
1984	2	29	3	105 929
1984	3	1	4	106 140
1984	3	2	5	107 963
1984	3	3	6	·
1984	3	4	7	·
1984	3	5	1	110 205
1984	3	6	2	109 168
1984	3	7	3	109 144
1984	3	8	4	107 755
1984	3	9	5	109 440
1984	3	10	6	·
1984	3	11	7	·
1984	3	12	1	108 774
1984	3	13	2	108 624
1984	3	14	3	109 926
1984	3	15	4	111 106
1984	3	16	5	113 069
1984	3	17	6	·

* (×100)

Year	Month	Day	DW	Stock price*	Year	Month	Day	DW	Stock price*
					1984	4	27	5	105 430
					1984	4	28	6	·
					1984	4	29	7	·
1984	3	18	7	·	1984	4	30	1	103 706
1984	3	19	1	117 035	1984	5	1	2	103 473
1984	3	20	2	116 912	1984	5	2	3	103 264
1984	3	21	3	115 729	1984	5	3	4	100 461
1984	3	22	4	115 607	1984	5	4	5	100 479
1984	3	23	5	116 165	1984	5	5	6	·
1984	3	24	6	·	1984	5	6	7	·
1984	3	25	7	·	1984	5	7	1	95 370
1984	3	26	1	115 695	1984	5	8	2	96 965
1984	3	27	2	113 125	1984	5	9	3	93 971
1984	3	28	3	111 885	1984	5	10	4	92 131
1984	3	29	4	105 709	1984	5	11	5	92 832
1984	3	30	5	101 438	1984	5	12	6	·
1984	3	31	6	·	1984	5	13	7	·
1984	4	1	7	·	1984	5	14	1	90 872
1984	4	2	1	102 396	1984	5	15	2	92 407
1984	4	3	2	103 319	1984	5	16	3	94 932
1984	4	4	3	·	1984	5	17	4	93 372
1984	4	5	4	108 367	1984	5	18	5	89 573
1984	4	6	5	106 432	1984	5	19	6	·
1984	4	7	6	·	1984	5	20	7	·
1984	4	8	7	·	1984	5	21	1	89 301
1984	4	9	1	107 027	1984	5	22	2	92 377
1984	4	10	2	109 612	1984	5	23	3	91 215
1984	4	11	3	108 890	1984	5	24	4	92 300
1984	4	12	4	109 141	1984	5	25	5	90 279
1984	4	13	5	107 570	1984	5	26	6	·
1984	4	14	6	·	1984	5	27	7	·
1984	4	15	7	·	1984	5	28	1	91 931
1984	4	16	1	107 548	1984	5	29	2	92 303
1984	4	17	2	108 812	1984	5	30	3	92 860
1984	4	18	3	109 020	1984	5	31	4	91 530
1984	4	19	4	111 585	1984	6	1	5	91 750
1984	4	20	5	·	1984	6	2	6	·
1984	4	21	6	·	1984	6	3	7	·
1984	4	22	7	·	1984	6	4	1	·
1984	4	23	1	·	1984	6	5	2	93 244
1984	4	24	2	107 002	1984	6	6	3	93 212
1984	4	25	3	108 272	1984	6	7	4	96 214
1984	4	26	4	107 070	1984	6	8	5	96 421

Year	Month	Day	DW	Stock price*	Year	Month	Day	DW	Stock price*
					1984	7	19	4	79 765
					1984	7	20	5	80 110
					1984	7	21	6	·
1984	6	9	6	·	1984	7	22	7	·
1984	6	10	7	·	1984	7	23	1	74 702
1984	6	11	1	96 612	1984	7	24	2	75 475
1984	6	12	2	95 890	1984	7	25	3	75 848
1984	6	13	3	96 122	1984	7	26	4	76 307
1984	6	14	4	95 315	1984	7	27	5	78 599
1984	6	15	5	93 237	1984	7	28	6	·
1984	6	16	6	·	1984	7	29	7	·
1984	6	17	7	·	1984	7	30	1	80 268
1984	6	18	1	·	1984	7	31	2	80 015
1984	6	19	2	92 739	1984	8	1	3	82 674
1984	6	20	3	93 105	1984	8	2	4	89 369
1984	6	21	4	92 912	1984	8	3	5	89 460
1984	6	22	5	93 738	1984	8	4	6	·
1984	6	23	6	·	1984	8	5	7	·
1984	6	24	7	·	1984	8	6	1	90 347
1984	6	25	1	93 637	1984	8	7	2	88 549
1984	6	26	2	92 792	1984	8	8	3	89 413
1984	6	27	3	92 497	1984	8	9	4	90 116
1984	6	28	4	90 383	1984	8	10	5	92 570
1984	6	29	5	90 107	1984	8	11	6	·
1984	6	30	6	·	1984	8	12	7	·
1984	7	1	7	·	1984	8	13	1	92 639
1984	7	2	1	86 863	1984	8	14	2	90 481
1984	7	3	2	86 183	1984	8	15	3	91 883
1984	7	4	3	85 033	1984	8	16	4	90 619
1984	7	5	4	82 897	1984	8	17	5	90 834
1984	7	6	5	82 286	1984	8	18	6	·
1984	7	7	6	·	1984	8	19	7	·
1984	7	8	7	·	1984	8	20	1	89 690
1984	7	9	1	77 360	1984	8	21	2	90 749
1984	7	10	2	80 531	1984	8	22	3	90 799
1984	7	11	3	76 361	1984	8	23	4	89 112
1984	7	12	4	76 378	1984	8	24	5	89 369
1984	7	13	5	74 602	1984	8	25	6	·
1984	7	14	6	·	1984	8	26	7	·
1984	7	15	7	·	1984	8	27	1	·
1984	7	16	1	79 116	1984	8	28	2	89 891
1984	7	17	2	79 369	1984	8	29	3	89 759
1984	7	18	3	79 199	1984	8	30	4	92 277

Year	Month	Day	DW	Stock price*
1984	8	31	5	92 678
1984	9	1	6	.
1984	9	2	7	.
1984	9	3	1	93 942
1984	9	4	2	94 702
1984	9	5	3	94 687
1984	9	6	4	93 593
1984	9	7	5	94 055
1984	9	8	6	.
1984	9	9	7	.
1984	9	10	1	94 606
1984	9	11	2	.
1984	9	12	3	93 240
1984	9	13	4	91 178
1984	9	14	5	94 544
1984	9	15	6	.
1984	9	16	7	.
1984	9	17	1	96 352
1984	9	18	2	97 492
1984	9	19	3	98 379
1984	9	20	4	100 213
1984	9	21	5	100 008
1984	9	22	6	.
1984	9	23	7	.
1984	9	24	1	99 082
1984	9	25	2	101 023
1984	9	26	3	99 979
1984	9	27	4	101 498
1984	9	28	5	100 250
1984	9	29	6	.
1984	9	30	7	.
1984	10	1	1	98 919
1984	10	2	2	98 510
1984	10	3	3	.
1984	10	4	4	98 947
1984	10	5	5	97 417
1984	10	6	6	.
1984	10	7	7	.
1984	10	8	1	96 350
1984	10	9	2	98 238
1984	10	10	3	98 313
1984	10	11	4	97 978
1984	10	12	5	98 314
1984	10	13	6	.
1984	10	14	7	.
1984	10	15	1	99 909
1984	10	16	2	102 001
1984	10	17	3	101 743
1984	10	18	4	102 811
1984	10	19	5	103 180
1984	10	20	6	.
1984	10	21	7	.
1984	10	22	1	105 305
1984	10	23	2	104 516
1984	10	24	3	105 431
1984	10	25	4	105 471
1984	10	26	5	105 684
1984	10	27	6	.
1984	10	28	7	.
1984	10	29	1	103 930
1984	10	30	2	101 921
1984	10	31	3	101 513
1984	11	1	4	102 926
1984	11	2	5	103 523
1984	11	3	6	.
1984	11	4	7	.
1984	11	5	1	102 748
1984	11	6	2	103 767
1984	11	7	3	104 603
1984	11	8	4	105 265
1984	11	9	5	104 372
1984	11	10	6	.
1984	11	11	7	.
1984	11	12	1	104 445
1984	11	13	2	106 613
1984	11	14	3	107 793
1984	11	15	4	107 484
1984	11	16	5	107 179
1984	11	17	6	.
1984	11	18	7	.
1984	11	19	1	106 761
1984	11	20	2	107 252
1984	11	21	3	108 435

Year	Month	Day	DW	Stock price*
1984	11	22	4	108 781
1984	11	23	5	109 604
1984	11	24	6	·
1984	11	25	7	·
1984	11	26	1	111 396
1984	11	27	2	111 273
1984	11	28	3	111 863
1984	11	29	4	113 611
1984	11	30	5	112 810
1984	12	1	6	·
1984	12	2	7	·
1984	12	3	1	112 226
1984	12	4	2	112 540
1984	12	5	3	113 608
1984	12	6	4	112 074
1984	12	7	5	112 212
1984	12	8	6	·
1984	12	9	7	·
1984	12	10	1	111 501
1984	12	11	2	111 838
1984	12	12	3	111 723
1984	12	13	4	112 649
1984	12	14	5	114 209
1984	12	15	6	·
1984	12	16	7	·
1984	12	17	1	116 642
1984	12	18	2	116 613
1984	12	19	3	117 331
1984	12	20	4	118 442
1984	12	21	5	119 859
1984	12	22	6	·
1984	12	23	7	·
1984	12	24	1	120 683
1984	12	25	2	·
1984	12	26	3	·
1984	12	27	4	117 693
1984	12	28	5	118 567
1984	12	29	6	·
1984	12	30	7	·
1984	12	31	1	120 038
1985	1	1	2	·
1985	1	2	3	122 074
1985	1	3	4	123 598
1985	1	4	5	126 230
1985	1	5	6	·
1985	1	6	7	·
1985	1	7	1	128 187
1985	1	8	2	128 301
1985	1	9	3	126 995
1985	1	10	4	131 855
1985	1	11	5	135 269
1985	1	12	6	·
1985	1	13	7	·
1985	1	14	1	135 806
1985	1	15	2	133 100
1985	1	16	3	135 881
1985	1	17	4	138 842
1985	1	18	5	136 033
1985	1	19	6	·
1985	1	20	7	·
1985	1	21	1	135 000
1985	1	22	2	137 362
1985	1	23	3	135 784
1985	1	24	4	138 487
1985	1	25	5	137 391
1985	1	26	6	·
1985	1	27	7	·
1985	1	28	1	137 489
1985	1	29	2	133 887
1985	1	30	3	133 504
1985	1	31	4	136 502
1985	2	1	5	135 626
1985	2	2	6	·
1985	2	3	7	·
1985	2	4	1	136 322
1985	2	5	2	135 247
1985	2	6	3	133 331
1985	2	7	4	131 243
1985	2	8	5	134 788
1985	2	9	6	·
1985	2	10	7	·
1985	2	11	1	135 794
1985	2	12	2	135 722

Year	Month	Day	DW	Stock price*	Year	Month	Day	DW	Stock price*
1985	2	13	3	133 632	1985	3	25	1	136 223
1985	2	14	4	135 439	1985	3	26	2	134 413
1985	2	15	5	140 593	1985	3	27	3	135 065
1985	2	16	6	·	1985	3	28	4	135 290
1985	2	17	7	·	1985	3	29	5	138 204
1985	2	18	1	142 718	1985	3	30	6	·
1985	2	19	2	143 517	1985	3	31	7	·
1985	2	20	3	·	1985	4	1	1	138 913
1985	2	21	4	·	1985	4	2	2	143 036
1985	2	22	5	·	1985	4	3	3	145 035
1985	2	23	6	·	1985	4	4	4	147 125
1985	2	24	7	·	1985	4	5	5	·
1985	2	25	1	138 916	1985	4	6	6	·
1985	2	26	2	140 286	1985	4	7	7	·
1985	2	27	3	138 762·	1985	4	8	1	·
1985	2	28	4	137 525	1985	4	9	2	148 022
1985	3	1	5	140 115	1985	4	10	3	147 061
1985	3	2	6	·	1985	4	11	4	148 339
1985	3	3	7	·	1985	4	12	5	149 218
1985	3	4	1	139 946	1985	4	13	6	·
1985	3	5	2	136 794	1985	4	14	7	·
1985	3	6	3	138 328	1985	4	15	1	150 544
1985	3	7	4	138 914	1985	4	16	2	152 130
1985	3	8	5	139 527	1985	4	17	3	150 597
1985	3	9	6	·	1985	4	18	4	150 009
1985	3	10	7	·	1985	4	19	5	147 421
1985	3	11	1	138 011	1985	4	20	6	·
1985	3	12	2	137 151	1985	4	21	7	·
1985	3	13	3	133 582	1985	4	22	1	148 740
1985	3	14	4	135 635	1985	4	23	2	151 163
1985	3	15	5	133 376	1985	4	24	3	151 730
1985	3	16	6	·	1985	4	25	4	151 077
1985	3	17	7	·	1985	4	26	5	150 649
1985	3	18	1	131 047	1985	4	27	6	·
1985	3	19	2	130 097	1985	4	28	7	·
1985	3	20	3	131 256	1985	4	29	1	149 737
1985	3	21	4	134 773	1985	4	30	2	152 056
1985	3	22	5	136 069	1985	5	1	3	151 673
1985	3	23	6	·	1985	5	2	4	151 621
1985	3	24	7	·	1985	5	3	5	155 080
					1985	5	4	6	·
					1985	5	5	7	·
					1985	5	6	1	159 643

Year	Month	Day	DW	Stock price*
1985	5	7	2	159 326
1985	5	8	3	162 145
1985	5	9	4	161 009
1985	5	10	5	161 336
1985	5	11	6	·
1985	5	12	7	·
1985	5	13	1	162 829
1985	5	14	2	161 500
1985	5	15	3	161 261
1985	5	16	4	163 588
1985	5	17	5	164 788
1985	5	18	6	·
1985	5	19	7	·
1985	5	20	1	163 847
1985	5	21	2	161 222
1985	5	22	3	159 964
1985	5	23	4	161 730
1985	5	24	5	159 684
1985	5	25	6	·
1985	5	26	7	·
1985	5	27	1	155 778
1985	5	28	2	157 084
1985	5	29	3	159 771
1985	5	30	4	162 166
1985	5	31	5	161 387
1985	6	1	6	·
1985	6	2	7	·
1985	6	3	1	164 125
1985	6	4	2	164 335
1985	6	5	3	162 782
1985	6	6	4	162 950
1985	6	7	5	154 255
1985	6	8	6	·
1985	6	9	7	·
1985	6	10	1	157 187
1985	6	11	2	149 213
1985	6	12	3	150 294
1985	6	13	4	148 291
1985	6	14	5	144 197
1985	6	15	6	·
1985	6	16	7	·
1985	6	17	1	·
1985	6	18	2	142 708
1985	6	19	3	151 028
1985	6	20	4	154 215
1985	6	21	5	156 113
1985	6	22	6	·
1985	6	23	7	·
1985	6	24	1	·
1985	6	25	2	157 515
1985	6	26	3	156 519
1985	6	27	4	158 170
1985	6	28	5	157 061
1985	6	29	6	·
1985	6	30	7	·
1985	7	1	1	157 060
1985	7	2	2	159 133
1985	7	3	3	159 816
1985	7	4	4	157 437
1985	7	5	5	157 030
1985	7	6	6	·
1985	7	7	7	·
1985	7	8	1	156 668
1985	7	9	2	156 504
1985	7	10	3	157 341
1985	7	11	4	159 781
1985	7	12	5	161 578
1985	7	13	6	·
1985	7	14	7	·
1985	7	15	1	164 049
1985	7	16	2	163 299
1985	7	17	3	164 790
1985	7	18	4	167 204
1985	7	19	5	167 887
1985	7	20	6	·
1985	7	21	7	·
1985	7	22	1	168 985
1985	7	23	2	167 385
1985	7	24	3	166 563
1985	7	25	4	169 206
1985	7	26	5	168 358
1985	7	27	6	·
1985	7	28	7	·

Year	Month	Day	DW	Stock price*
1985	7	29	1	·
1985	7	30	2	168 624
1985	7	31	3	168 062
1985	8	1	4	167 895
1985	8	2	5	166 559
1985	8	3	6	·
1985	8	4	7	·
1985	8	5	1	167 190
1985	8	6	2	170 093
1985	8	7	3	169 866
1985	8	8	4	167 355
1985	8	9	5	167 651
1985	8	10	6	·
1985	8	11	7	·
1985	8	12	1	169 943
1985	8	13	2	168 709
1985	8	14	3	169 173
1985	8	15	4	168 455
1985	8	16	5	170 037
1985	8	17	6	·
1985	8	18	7	·
1985	8	19	1	171 151
1985	8	20	2	169 274
1985	8	21	3	165 078
1985	8	22	4	167 187
1985	8	23	5	166 998
1985	8	24	6	·
1985	8	25	7	·
1985	8	26	1	·
1985	8	27	2	166 730
1985	8	28	3	166 885
1985	8	29	4	165 219
1985	8	30	5	165 610
1985	8	31	6	·
1985	9	1	7	·
1985	9	2	1	161 617
1985	9	3	2	158 622
1985	9	4	3	157 854
1985	9	5	4	159 668
1985	9	6	5	157 906
1985	9	7	6	·
1985	9	8	7	·
1985	9	9	1	155 083
1985	9	10	2	154 631
1985	9	11	3	157 195
1985	9	12	4	159 642
1985	9	13	5	160 584
1985	9	14	6	·
1985	9	15	7	·
1985	9	16	1	160 023
1985	9	17	2	156 940
1985	9	18	3	156 362
1985	9	19	4	156 327
1985	9	20	5	154 946
1985	9	21	6	·
1985	9	22	7	·
1985	9	23	1	153 545
1985	9	24	2	153 324
1985	9	25	3	154 768
1985	9	26	4	151 187
1985	9	27	5	151 180
1985	9	28	6	·
1985	9	29	7	·
1985	9	30	1	·
1985	10	1	2	152 099
1985	10	2	3	155 313
1985	10	3	4	158 107
1985	10	4	5	158 744
1985	10	5	6	·
1985	10	6	7	·
1985	10	7	1	161 776
1985	10	8	2	160 653
1985	10	9	3	158 799
1985	10	10	4	158 913
1985	10	11	5	158 355
1985	10	12	6	·
1985	10	13	7	·
1985	10	14	1	159 435
1985	10	15	2	160 289
1985	10	16	3	161 837
1985	10	17	4	162 479
1985	10	18	5	163 989
1985	10	19	6	·

Year	Month	Day	DW	Stock price*
1985	10	20	7	·
1985	10	21	1	166 606
1985	10	22	2	·
1985	10	23	3	166 671
1985	10	24	4	167 051
1985	10	25	5	167 173
1985	10	26	6	·
1985	10	27	7	·
1985	10	28	1	165 125
1985	10	29	2	165 403
1985	10	30	3	165 468
1985	10	31	4	166 539
1985	11	1	5	168 065
1985	11	2	6	·
1985	11	3	7	·
1985	11	4	1	170 219
1985	11	5	2	169 271
1985	11	6	3	170 076
1985	11	7	4	172 193
1985	11	8	5	172 238
1985	11	9	6	·
1985	11	10	7	·
1985	11	11	1	172 240
1985	11	12	2	173 015
1985	11	13	3	174 718
1985	11	14	4	174 514
1985	11	15	5	173 607
1985	11	16	6	·
1985	11	17	7	·
1985	11	18	1	174 420
1985	11	19	2	175 468
1985	11	20	3	175 729
1985	11	21	4	176 251
1985	11	22	5	171 282
1985	11	23	6	·
1985	11	24	7	·
1985	11	25	1	173 649
1985	11	26	2	173 835
1985	11	27	3	170 638
1985	11	28	4	168 550
1985	11	29	5	171 695
1985	11	30	6	·
1985	12	1	7	·
1985	12	2	1	169 457
1985	12	3	2	166 406
1985	12	4	3	170 096
1985	12	5	4	169 391
1985	12	6	5	172 189
1985	12	7	6	·
1985	12	8	7	·
1985	12	9	1	172 427
1985	12	10	2	172 829
1985	12	11	3	172 305
1985	12	12	4	174 040
1985	12	13	5	173 558
1985	12	14	6	·
1985	12	15	7	·
1985	12	16	1	172 821
1985	12	17	2	172 045
1985	12	18	3	172 694
1985	12	19	4	172 605
1985	12	20	5	172 016
1985	12	21	6	·
1985	12	22	7	·
1985	12	23	1	170 429
1985	12	24	2	171 754
1985	12	25	3	·
1985	12	26	4	·
1985	12	27	5	173 037
1985	12	28	6	·
1985	12	29	7	·
1985	12	30	1	175 262
1985	12	31	2	175 245
1986	1	1	3	·
1986	1	2	4	177 438
1986	1	3	5	179 123
1986	1	4	6	·
1986	1	5	7	·
1986	1	6	1	179 659
1986	1	7	2	181 553
1986	1	8	3	182 684
1986	1	9	4	179 851
1986	1	10	5	180 794

Year	Month	Day	DW	Stock price*
1986	1	11	6	·
1986	1	12	7	·
1986	1	13	1	179 961
1986	1	14	2	178 223
1986	1	15	3	178 366
1986	1	16	4	179 722
1986	1	17	5	180 686
1986	1	18	6	·
1986	1	19	7	·
1986	1	20	1	177 582
1986	1	21	2	177 619
1986	1	22	3	173 794
1986	1	23	4	176 229
1986	1	24	5	174 580
1986	1	25	6	·
1986	1	26	7	·
1986	1	27	1	174 411
1986	1	28	2	175 438
1986	1	29	3	173 635
1986	1	30	4	172 021
1986	1	31	5	169 578
1986	2	1	6	·
1986	2	2	7	·
1986	2	3	1	170 238
1986	2	4	2	172 881
1986	2	5	3	172 308
1986	2	6	4	171 967
1986	2	7	5	173 404
1986	2	8	6	·
1986	2	9	7	·
1986	2	10	1	·
1986	2	11	2	·
1986	2	12	3	174 303
1986	2	13	4	174 640
1986	2	14	5	177 754
1986	2	15	6	·
1986	2	16	7	·
1986	2	17	1	178 308
1986	2	18	2	177 141
1986	2	19	3	175 167
1986	2	20	4	173 317
1986	2	21	5	174 706
1986	2	22	6	·
1986	2	23	7	·
1986	2	24	1	174 237
1986	2	25	2	174 605
1986	2	26	3	174 630
1986	2	27	4	172 051
1986	2	28	5	169 530
1986	3	1	6	·
1986	3	2	7	·
1986	3	3	1	168 506
1986	3	4	2	169 577
1986	3	5	3	166 433
1986	3	6	4	166 851
1986	3	7	5	168 265
1986	3	8	6	·
1986	3	9	7	·
1986	3	10	1	166 707
1986	3	11	2	163 915
1986	3	12	3	159 039
1986	3	13	4	161 267
1986	3	14	5	160 763
1986	3	15	6	·
1986	3	16	7	·
1986	3	17	1	156 649
1986	3	18	2	156 172
1986	3	19	3	155 994
1986	3	20	4	160 570
1986	3	21	5	161 173
1986	3	22	6	·
1986	3	23	7	·
1986	3	24	1	163 529
1986	3	25	2	162 671
1986	3	26	3	161 880
1986	3	27	4	162 594
1986	3	28	5	·
1986	3	29	6	·
1986	3	30	7	·
1986	3	31	1	·
1986	4	1	2	·
1986	4	2	3	160 327
1986	4	3	4	162 520

Year	Month	Day	DW	Stock price*	Year	Month	Day	DW	Stock price*
1986	4	4	5	164 380	1986	5	14	3	182 068
1986	4	5	6	·	1986	5	15	4	179 417
1986	4	6	7	·	1986	5	16	5	178 708
1986	4	7	1	169 160	1986	5	17	6	·
1986	4	8	2	172 793	1986	5	18	7	·
1986	4	9	3	175 234	1986	5	19	1	176 502
1986	4	10	4	175 857	1986	5	20	2	177 727
1986	4	11	5	178 421	1986	5	21	3	179 494
1986	4	12	6	·	1986	5	22	4	182 098
1986	4	13	7	·	1986	5	23	5	181 592
1986	4	14	1	178 545	1986	5	24	6	·
1986	4	15	2	176 373	1986	5	25	7	·
1986	4	16	3	179 119	1986	5	26	1	181 187
1986	4	17	4	181 200	1986	5	27	2	181 630
1986	4	18	5	179 040	1986	5	28	3	177 747
1986	4	19	6	·	1986	5	29	4	177 276
1986	4	20	7	·	1986	5	30	5	178 796
1986	4	21	1	178 838	1986	5	31	6	·
1986	4	22	2	179 290	1986	6	1	7	·
1986	4	23	3	178 319	1986	6	2	1	178 194
1986	4	24	4	182 451	1986	6	3	2	175 791
1986	4	25	5	183 462	1986	6	4	3	175 667
1986	4	26	6	·	1986	6	5	4	174 856
1986	4	27	7	·	1986	6	6	5	174 709
1986	4	28	1	184 865	1986	6	7	6	·
1986	4	29	2	182 629	1986	6	8	7	·
1986	4	30	3	183 699	1986	6	9	1	174 824
1986	5	1	4	184 865	1986	6	10	2	175 136
1986	5	2	5	184 314	1986	6	11	3	·
1986	5	3	6	·	1986	6	12	4	175 279
1986	5	4	7	·	1986	6	13	5	176 565
1986	5	5	1	184 244	1986	6	14	6	·
1986	5	6	2	185 816	1986	6	15	7	·
1986	5	7	3	186 565	1986	6	16	1	·
1986	5	8	4	186 421	1986	6	17	2	178 934
1986	5	9	5	185 221	1986	6	18	3	178 978
1986	5	10	6	·	1986	6	19	4	177 829
1986	5	11	7	·	1986	6	20	5	178 104
1986	5	12	1	183 250	1986	6	21	6	·
1986	5	13	2	180 373	1986	6	22	7	·
					1986	6	23	1	177 715
					1986	6	24	2	176 390
					1986	6	25	3	175 972

Year	Month	Day	DW	Stock price*
1986	6	26	4	175 038
1986	6	27	5	175 098
1986	6	28	6	·
1986	6	29	7	·
1986	6	30	1	173 911
1986	7	1	2	173 351
1986	7	2	3	176 021
1986	7	3	4	175 758
1986	7	4	5	175 676
1986	7	5	6	·
1986	7	6	7	·
1986	7	7	1	176 152
1986	7	8	2	175 224
1986	7	9	3	174 761
1986	7	10	4	171 830
1986	7	11	5	172 169
1986	7	12	6	·
1986	7	13	7	·
1986	7	14	1	173 993
1986	7	15	2	176 413
1986	7	16	3	176 338
1986	7	17	4	175 971
1986	7	18	5	175 960
1986	7	19	6	·
1986	7	20	7	·
1986	7	21	1	177 773
1986	7	22	2	179 153
1986	7	23	3	181 696
1986	7	24	4	183 600
1986	7	25	5	184 357
1986	7	26	6	·
1986	7	27	7	·
1986	7	28	1	184 729
1986	7	29	2	186 001
1986	7	30	3	184 794
1986	7	31	4	185 546
1986	8	1	5	187 411
1986	8	2	6	·
1986	8	3	7	·
1986	8	4	1	190 628
1986	8	5	2	188 904
1986	8	6	3	188 783
1986	8	7	4	192 018
1986	8	8	5	193 129
1986	8	9	6	·
1986	8	10	7	·
1986	8	11	1	192 704
1986	8	12	2	190 500
1986	8	13	3	190 802
1986	8	14	4	192 516
1986	8	15	5	193 576
1986	8	16	6	·
1986	8	17	7	·
1986	8	18	1	195 012
1986	8	19	2	193 569
1986	8	20	3	194 128
1986	8	21	4	194 136
1986	8	22	5	194 603
1986	8	23	6	·
1986	8	24	7	·
1986	8	25	1	·
1986	8	26	2	191 700
1986	8	27	3	193 299
1986	8	28	4	193 420
1986	8	29	5	191 300
1986	8	30	6	·
1986	8	31	7	·
1986	9	1	1	190 302
1986	9	2	2	193 061
1986	9	3	3	194 499
1986	9	4	4	194 670
1986	9	5	5	196 853
1986	9	6	6	·
1986	9	7	7	·
1986	9	8	1	196 998
1986	9	9	2	196 602
1986	9	10	3	197 616
1986	9	11	4	199 792
1986	9	12	5	196 633
1986	9	13	6	·
1986	9	14	7	·
1986	9	15	1	194 234
1986	9	16	2	102 797

Year	Month	Day	DW	Stock price*	Year	Month	Day	DW	Stock price*
1986	9	17	3	192 199	1986	10	27	1	234 366
1986	9	18	4	192 582	1986	10	28	2	235 593
1986	9	19	5	·	1986	10	29	3	234 524
1986	9	20	6	·	1986	10	30	4	231 281
1986	9	21	7	·	1986	10	31	5	231 563
1986	9	22	1	195 360	1986	11	1	6	·
1986	9	23	2	199 260	1986	11	2	7	·
1986	9	24	3	200 830	1986	11	3	1	225 878
1986	9	25	4	201 170	1986	11	4	2	226 582
1986	9	26	5	203 436	1986	11	5	3	220 371
1986	9	27	6	·	1986	11	6	4	223 065
1986	9	28	7	·	1986	11	7	5	221 838
1986	9	29	1	206 430	1986	11	8	6	·
1986	9	30	2	206 844	1986	11	9	7	·
1986	10	1	3	209 024	1986	11	10	1	220 676
1986	10	2	4	212 014	1986	11	11	2	220 725
1986	10	3	5	213 480	1986	11	12	3	223 971
1986	10	4	6	·	1986	11	13	4	226 145
1986	10	5	7	·	1986	11	14	5	224 403
1986	10	6	1	208 493	1986	11	15	6	·
1986	10	7	2	216 276	1986	11	16	7	·
1986	10	8	3	220 441	1986	11	17	1	224 289
1986	10	9	4	227 115	1986	11	18	2	224 997
1986	10	10	5	227 952	1986	11	19	3	224 334
1986	10	11	6	·	1986	11	20	4	224 595
1986	10	12	7	·	1986	11	21	5	227 398
1986	10	13	1	·	1986	11	22	6	·
1986	10	14	2	224 922	1986	11	23	7	·
1986	10	15	3	228 965	1986	11	24	1	234 359
1986	10	16	4	227 777	1986	11	25	2	236 112
1986	10	17	5	223 489	1986	11	26	3	237 771
1986	10	18	6	·	1986	11	27	4	235 433
1986	10	19	7	·	1986	11	28	5	241 875
1986	10	20	1	222 776	1986	11	29	6	·
1986	10	21	2	223 829	1986	11	30	7	·
1986	10	22	3	·	1986	12	1	1	245 215
1986	10	23	4	225 479	1986	12	2	2	245 820
1986	10	24	5	228 607	1986	12	3	3	246 000
1986	10	25	6	·	1986	12	4	4	243 052
1986	10	26	7	·	1986	12	5	5	240 072
					1986	12	6	6	·
					1986	12	7	7	·
					1986	12	8	1	243 129

Year	Month	Day	DW	Stock price*	1987	1	19	1	246 046
					1987	1	20	2	244 988
					1987	1	21	3	253 390
1986	12	9	2	140 035	1987	1	22	4	253 694
1986	12	10	3	244 259	1987	1	23	5	249 943
1986	12	11	4	246 713	1987	1	24	6	·
1986	12	12	5	246 323	1987	1	25	7	·
1986	12	13	6	·	1987	1	26	1	248 435
1986	12	14	7	·	1987	1	27	2	252 401
1986	12	15	1	244 943	1987	1	28	3	255 325
1986	12	16	2	244 068	1987	1	29	4	·
1986	12	17	3	241 108	1987	1	30	5	·
1986	12	18	4	242 222	1987	1	31	6	·
1986	12	19	5	246 381	1987	2	1	7	·
1986	12	20	6	·	1987	2	2	1	258 522
1986	12	21	7	·	1987	2	3	2	260 638
1986	12	22	1	250 377	1987	2	4	3	263 663
1986	12	23	2	250 194	1987	2	5	4	265 214
1986	12	24	3	252 392	1987	2	6	5	267 357
1986	12	25	4	·	1987	2	7	6	·
1986	12	26	5	·	1987	2	8	7	·
1986	12	27	6	·	1987	2	9	1	271 367
1986	12	28	7	·	1987	2	10	2	269 485
1986	12	29	1	255 245	1987	2	11	3	273 947
1986	12	30	2	255 936	1987	2	12	4	275 472
1986	12	31	3	256 830	1987	2	13	5	274 049
1987	1	1	4	·	1987	2	14	6	·
1987	1	2	5	254 006	1987	2	15	7	·
1987	1	3	6	·	1987	2	16	1	276 606
1987	1	4	7	·	1987	2	17	2	279 208
1987	1	5	1	255 240	1987	2	18	3	280 148
1987	1	6	2	258 387	1987	2	19	4	277 582
1987	1	7	3	260 711	1987	2	20	5	282 740
1987	1	8	4	260 333	1987	2	21	6	·
1987	1	9	5	256 173	1987	2	22	7	·
1987	1	10	6	·	1987	2	23	1	287 901
1987	1	11	7	·	1987	2	24	2	284 819
1987	1	12	1	261 487	1987	2	25	3	287 358
1987	1	13	2	259 083	1987	2	26	4	284 360
1987	1	14	3	257 823	1987	2	27	5	287 787
1987	1	15	4	255 912	1987	2	28	6	·
1987	1	16	5	254 257	1987	3	1	7	·
1987	1	17	6	·	1987	3	2	1	289 426
1987	1	18	7	·	1987	3	3	2	293 905

Year	Month	Day	DW	Stock price*	Year	Month	Day	DW	Stock price*
					1987	4	14	2	266 835
					1987	4	15	3	269 362
					1987	4	16	4	272 112
1987	3	4	3	289 093	1987	4	17	5	·
1987	3	5	4	279 844	1987	4	18	6	·
1987	3	6	5	279 864	1987	4	19	7	·
1987	3	7	6	·	1987	4	20	1	·
1987	3	8	7	·	1987	4	21	2	271 336
1987	3	9	1	282 038	1987	4	22	3	271 689
1987	3	10	2	273 105	1987	4	23	4	271 989
1987	3	11	3	276 090	1987	4	24	5	270 761
1987	3	12	4	275 014	1987	4	25	6	·
1987	3	13	5	272 117	1987	4	26	7	·
1987	3	14	6	·	1987	4	27	1	263 647
1987	3	15	7	·	1987	4	28	2	261 708
1987	3	16	1	266 957	1987	4	29	3	258 954
1987	3	17	2	262 928	1987	4	30	4	265 985
1987	3	18	3	272 401	1987	5	1	5	268 537
1987	3	19	4	272 128	1987	5	2	6	·
1987	3	20	5	278 055	1987	5	3	7	·
1987	3	21	6	·	1987	5	4	1	268 575
1987	3	22	7	·	1987	5	5	2	271 383
1987	3	23	1	281 340	1987	5	6	3	279 289
1987	3	24	2	282 807	1987	5	7	4	278 556
1987	3	25	3	283 150	1987	5	8	5	280 506
1987	3	26	4	278 312	1987	5	9	6	·
1987	3	27	5	279 874	1987	5	10	7	·
1987	3	28	6	·	1987	5	11	1	284 693
1987	3	29	7	·	1987	5	12	2	285 342
1987	3	30	1	277 488	1987	5	13	3	283 353
1987	3	31	2	271 381	1987	5	14	4	385 392
1987	4	1	3	269 591	1987	5	15	5	287 219
1987	4	2	4	270 941	1987	5	16	6	·
1987	4	3	5	267 999	1987	5	17	7	·
1987	4	4	6	·	1987	5	18	1	287 545
1987	4	5	7	·	1987	5	19	2	288 147
1987	4	6	1	·	1987	5	20	3	287 810
1987	4	7	2	266 470	1987	5	21	4	287 091
1987	4	8	3	272 955	1987	5	22	5	289 762
1987	4	9	4	278 547	1987	5	23	6	·
1987	4	10	5	276 641	1987	5	24	7	·
1987	4	11	6	·	1987	5	25	1	292 610
1987	4	12	7	·	1987	5	26	2	293 588
1987	4	13	1	270 894	1987	5	27	3	294 117

Year	Month	Day	DW	Stock price*
1987	5	28	4	294 906
1987	5	29	5	291 970
1987	5	30	6	·
1987	5	31	7	·
1987	6	1	1	·
1987	6	2	2	293 419
1987	6	3	3	298 510
1987	6	4	4	302 360
1987	6	5	5	306 433
1987	6	6	6	·
1987	6	7	7	·
1987	6	8	1	306 806
1987	6	9	2	310 857
1987	6	10	3	309 733
1987	6	11	4	308 752
1987	6	12	5	312 988
1987	6	13	6	·
1987	6	14	7	·
1987	6	15	1	·
1987	6	16	2	317 088
1987	6	17	3	317 862
1987	6	18	4	313 374
1987	6	19	5	316 564
1987	6	20	6	·
1987	6	21	7	·
1987	6	22	1	313 119
1987	6	23	2	311 041
1987	6	24	3	317 898
1987	6	25	4	313 631
1987	6	26	5	313 868
1987	6	27	6	·
1987	6	28	7	·
1987	6	29	1	315 198
1987	6	30	2	317 819
1987	7	1	3	316 399
1987	7	2	4	322 915
1987	7	3	5	320 884
1987	7	4	6	·
1987	7	5	7	·
1987	7	6	1	322 068
1987	7	7	2	323 641
1987	7	8	3	325 138
1987	7	9	4	322 597
1987	7	10	5	320 721
1987	7	11	6	·
1987	7	12	7	·
1987	7	13	1	321 611
1987	7	14	2	325 342
1987	7	15	3	326 230
1987	7	16	4	330 582
1987	7	17	5	334 213
1987	7	18	6	·
1987	7	19	7	·
1987	7	20	1	338 609
1987	7	21	2	335 378
1987	7	22	3	338 041
1987	7	23	4	336 682
1987	7	24	5	334 360
1987	7	25	6	·
1987	7	26	7	·
1987	7	27	1	334 687
1987	7	28	2	333 746
1987	7	29	3	338 973
1987	7	30	4	341 928
1987	7	31	5	347 924
1987	8	1	6	·
1987	8	2	7	·
1987	8	3	1	351 425
1987	8	4	2	353 188
1987	8	5	3	351 713
1987	8	6	4	349 795
1987	8	7	5	353 619
1987	8	8	6	·
1987	8	9	7	·
1987	8	10	1	354 376
1987	8	11	2	354 652
1987	8	12	3	355 743
1987	8	13	4	351 427
1987	8	14	5	351 215
1987	8	15	6	·
1987	8	16	7	·
1987	8	17	1	351 066
1987	8	18	2	350 487

Year	Month	Day	DW	Stock price*	Year	Month	Day	DW	Stock price*
1987	8	19	3	345 064	1987	9	9	3	357 764
1987	8	20	4	340 801	1987	9	10	4	360 096
1987	8	21	5	344 659	1987	9	11	5	366 050
1987	8	22	6	·	1987	9	12	6	·
1987	8	23	7	·	1987	9	13	7	·
1987	8	24	1	339 126	1987	9	14	1	364 984
1987	8	25	2	344 730	1987	9	15	2	364 692
1987	8	26	3	352 626	1987	9	16	3	360 464
1987	8	27	4	358 333	1987	9	17	4	357 136
1987	8	28	5	361 174	1987	9	18	5	374 996
1987	8	29	6	·	1987	9	19	6	·
1987	8	30	7	·	1987	9	20	7	·
1987	8	31	1	·	1987	9	21	1	366 795
1987	9	1	2	364 428	1987	9	22	2	369 553
1987	9	2	3	363 586	1987	9	23	3	376 311
1987	9	3	4	365 395	1987	9	24	4	376 842
1987	9	4	5	365 448	1987	9	25	5	384 011
1987	9	5	6	·	1987	9	26	6	·
1987	9	6	7	·	1987	9	27	7	·
1987	9	7	1	364 633	1987	9	28	1	388 465
1987	9	8	2	360 154	1987	9	29	2	385 948
					1987	9	30	3	394 364

References

Aase, K. K. (1983). Recursive estimation in non-linear time series models of autoregressive type. *J. R. Stat. Soc.*, **B45**, 228–37.

Abramowitz, M. and Stegun, I. A. (1972). *Handbook of mathematical functions.* Dover, New York.

Akaike, H. (1973*a*). Information theory and an extension of the maximum likelihood principle. *2nd Int. Symp. on Inf. Th.*, (eds. B. N. Petrov and F. Caski), pp. 267–810 Akademia Kiado, Budapest.

Akaike, H. (1973*b*). Block Toeplitz matrix inversion. *SIAM J. Appl. Math.* **24**, 234–41.

Akaike, H. (1974*a*). Markovian representation of stochastic processes and its application to the analysis of autoregressive moving average processes. *Ann. Inst. Stat. Math.*, **26**, 363–87.

Akaike, H. (1974*b*). A new look at the statistical model identification. *IEEE Trans. Autom. Control*, **AC-19**, 716–23.

Akaike, H. (1977). On entropy maximization principle. *Applications of Statistics*, (ed. P. R. Krishnaiah), pp. 27–41 North Holland, Amsterdam.

Akaike, H. (1978*a*). On the likelihood of a time series model. *The Statistician*, **27**, 217–35.

Akaike, H. (1978*b*). A Bayesian analysis of the minimum AIC procedure. *Ann. Inst. Stat. Math.*, **30**, A, 9–14.

Akaike, H. (1978*c*). On newer statistical approaches to parameter estimation of structure denomination. *A link between science and applications of automatic control*, (ed. A. Niemi), p. 3. Pergamon, Oxford.

Akaike, H. (1978*d*). Comments on 'On model structured testing in system identification'. *Int. J. Control*, **27**, 323–4.

Akaike, H. (1979). A Bayesian extension of the minimum AIC procedure of autoregressive model fitting. *Biometrika*, **66**, 237–42.

Akaike, H. (1981). Abstract and commentary on 'A new look at the statistical model identification'. *Curr. Contents, Eng. Tech. Appl. Sci.*, **12**, No. 51, 22.

Akaike, H. (1985). Prediction and entropy. *A celebration of statistics: the ISI centenary volume*, (ed. A. C. Atkinson and S. E. Fienberg). Springer, New York.

Al-Quassem, M. S. and Lane, J. A. (1987). Forecasting exponential autoregressive models of order 1. *J. Time Ser. Anal.*, **10**, 95–113.

Andel, J. (1976). Autoregressive series with random parameters *Math. Op. Stat.*, **7**, 735–41.

Andel, J. and Barton, T. (1986). A note on threshold AR(1) model with Cauchy innovations. *J. Time Ser. Anal.*, **7**, 1–5.

Andel, J., Netuka, I., and Svara, K. (1984). On threshold autoregressive processes. *Kybernetika*, **20**, 89–106.

Anderson, B. D. O. and Moore, J. B. (1979). *Optimal filtering*. Prentice-Hall, Englewood Cliffs, NJ.

Anderson, T. W. and Darling, D. A. (1952). Asymptotic theory of certain goodness of fit criterion based on stochastic processes. *Ann. Math. Stat.*, **23**, 193–211.

Andronov, A. A. and Khaikin, S. E. (1937). *Theory of oscillations* (in Russian), Moscow. English trans. by S. Lefschetz, (1949) Princeton University Press, Princeton, NJ; 2nd Russian edn by A. Andronov, A. A. Vitt, and S. E. Khaikin (1989) with English trans. published by Pergamon, Oxford (1966).

Armitage, P., McPherson, C. K., and Rowe, B. C. (1969). Repeated significance tests on accumulated data. *J. R. Stat. Soc.*, **A132**, 235–44.

Ashley, R. A., Patterson, D. M., and Hinich, M. J. (1986). A diagnostic test for nonlinear serial dependence in time series fitting errors. *J. Time Ser. Anal.*, **7**, 165–78.

Atkinson, A. C. (1978). Posterior probabilities for choosing a regression model. *Biometrika*, **65**, 39–48.

Azzalini, A., Bowman, A. W., and Hàrdle, W. (1989). On the use of nonparametric regression for model checking. *Biometrika*, **76**, 1–11.

Baconnier, P., Benchetrit, G., Demongeot, J., and Pham Dinh Tuan (1983). Simulation of the entrainment of the respiratory rhythm by two conceptually different models. In *Rhythms in biology and other fields of application*, (ed. M. Cosnard, J. Demongeot, and A. Le Breton), Lecture Notes in Biomathematics. Springer, Heidelberg.

Barnett, W., Geweke, J., and Shell, K. (eds) (1988). *Economic complexity: chaos, sunspots, bubbles and non-linearity*. Cambridge University Press.

Barrett, J. F. (1963). The use of functionals in the analysis of non-linear physical systems. *J. Electr. Control*, **15**, 567–615.

Bartlett, M. S. (1954). Problémes de l'analyse spectrale des series temporelles stationnaires. *Publ. Inst. Stat. (Univ. de Paris)*, Fasc. **3**, 119–34.

Basawa, I. V. and Prakasa Rao, B. L. S. (1980). *Statistical inference for stochastic processes*. Academic Press, London.

Bellman, R. and Cooke, K. L. (1963). *Differential–difference equations*. Academic Press, New York.

Bhansali, R. J. (1978). Estimation of the order of an autoregessive model: a review of some recent developments. *Rep.*, No. CSS 78/10/1, Dept of Computational & Statistical Science, University of Liverpool.

Bhansali, R. J. (1986). A derivation of the information criterion for selecting autoregressive models. *Adv. Appl. Probab.*, **18**, 360–87.

Bhansali, R. J. and Downham, D. Y. (1977). Some properties of the order of an autoregressive model selected by a generalization of Akaike's FPE criterion. *Biometrika*, **64**, 547–51.

Bhaskara Rao, M., Subba Rao, T., and Walker, A. M. (1983). On the existence of some bilinear time series models. *J. Time Ser. Anal.*, **4**, 95–110.

Billingsley, P. (1961). *Statistical inference for Markov processes*. Holt, New York.

Birkhoff, G. and MacLane, S. (1953). *A survey of modern algebra.* Macmillan, New York.

Bollerslev, T. (1986). Generalised autoregressive conditional heteroscedasticity. *J. Econ..*, **31**, 307–27.

Boltzmann, L. (1877). Uber die Beziehung zwischen dem zweiten Hauptsatze der mechanischen Warmtheorie und der Wahrscheinlichkeitzrechnung respectiv den Satzen uber das Warmegleichgemicht. *Wiener Ber.*, **76**, 373–435.

Bonilla, L. L. and Velarde, M. G. (1982). The spruce budworm–forest and other ecosystems. *Rhythms in biology and fields of applications. Lecture notes in synergetics,* Springer, Heidelberg, pp. 94–100.

Boole, G. (1880). *Finite differences.* Macmillan, London.

Box, G. E. P. (1980). Sampling and Bayes' inference in scientific modelling and robustness. *J. R. Stat. Soc.* **A143**, 383–430.

Box, G. E. P. and Jenkins, G. M. (1976). *Time series analysis, forecasting and control,* (revised edn). Holden-Day, San Francisco.

Bray, R. J. and Loughhead, R. E. (1964). *Sunspots.* Chapman and Hall, London.

Breiman, L. (1968). *Probability.* Addison-Wesley, Reading, MA.

Brillinger, D. R. (1965). An introduction to polyspectra, *Ann. Math. Stat.*, **36**, 1351–74.

Brillinger, D. R. (1966). An extremal property of the conditional expectation. *Biometrika*, **53**, 594–5.

Brillinger, D. R. (1975). *Time series data analysis and theory.* Holt, Rinehart and Winston, New York.

Brillinger, D. R. and Rosenblatt, M. (1967a). Asymptotic theory of estimates of kth order spectra. *Spectral analysis of time series,* (ed. B. Harris), pp. 153–88. Wiley, New York.

Brillinger, D. R. and Rosenblatt, M. (1967b). Computation and interpretation of kth order spectra. *Spectral analysis of time series,* (ed. B. Harris), pp. 189–232. Wiley, New York.

Brillinger, D. R. and Segundo, P. (1979). Empirical examination of the threshold model of neuron firing. *Biol. Cybern.*, **35**, 213–220.

Brock, W. M. and Sayers, C. L. (1988). Is the business cycle characterized by deterministic chaos? *J. Monetary Econ.*, **22**, 71–90.

Brockett, P. L., Hinich, M. J., and Patterson, D. (1988). Bispectral-based tests for the detection of Gaussianity and linearity in time series. *J. Am. Stat. Assoc.*, **83**, 657–64.

Brockett, R. W. (1976). Volterra series and geometric control theory. *Automatica*, **12**, 167–76.

Brockett, R. W. (1977). Convergence of Volterra series on infinite intervals and bilinear approximations. In *Nonlinear systems and applications,* (ed. V. Lakshmikathan), pp. 39–46. Academic Press, New York.

Brockwell, P. J. and Davis, R. A. (1987). *Time series: theory and methods.* Springer, New York.

Brown, R. G. (1962). *Smoothing, forecasting and prediction of discrete time series.* Prentice-Hall, Englewood Cliffs, NJ.

Bruce, A. and Martin, R. D. (1989). Leave-k-out diagnostics for time series. *J. R. Stat. Soc.*, **B51**.

Buse, A. (1982). The likelihood ratio, Wald and Lagrange multiplier tests: an expository note. *Am. Stat.*, **36**, 153–7.

Campbell, M. J. and Walker, A. M. (1977). A survey of statistical work on the McKenzie River series of annual Canadian lynx trappings for the years 1821–1934, and a new analysis. *J. R. Stat. Soc.*, **A140**, 411–31, discussion 448–68.

The Canadian Encyclopaedia (1985). Hurtig, Edmonton.

Cartwright, P. A. (1985). Forecasting time series: a comparative analysis of alternative classes of time series models. *J. Time Ser. Anal.*, **6**, 203–11.

Casdagli, M. (1987). Nonlinear prediction of chaotic time series. *Techn. Report.*, Mathematics Department, Queen Mary College, London.

Chan, K. S. (1986). Topics in nonlinear time series analysis. *Doctoral Thesis*, Mathematics Department, Princeton University.

Chan, K. S. (1988*a*). On the existence of the stationary and ergodic NEAR (p) model. *J. Time Ser. Anal.*, **9**, 319–28.

Chan, K. S. (1988*b*). Testing for threshold autoregression. *Tech. Rep.* No. 243, Deparment of Statistics, University of Chicago.

Chan, K. S. (1988*c*). Consistency and limiting distribution of least squares estimator of a threshold autoregressive model. *Tech. Rep.*, No. 245, Department of Statistics, University of Chicago.

Chan, K. S. and Tong, H. (1984). A note on sub-system stability and system stability. *J. Eng. Math.*, **1**, 43–51.

Chan, K. S. and Tong, H. (1985). On the use of the deterministic Lyapunov function for the ergodicity of stochastic difference equations. *Adv. Appl. Probab.*, **17**, 666–78.

Chan, K. S. and Tong, H. (1986*a*). On estimating thresholds in autoregressive models. *J. Time Ser. Anal.*, **7**, 178–90.

Chan, K. S. and Tong, H. (1986*b*). A note on certain integral equations associated with non-linear time series analysis. *Prob. Th. Rel. Fields*, **73**, 153–9.

Chan, K. S. and Tong, H. (1987). A note on embedding a discrete parameter ARMA model in a continuous parameter ARMA model. *J. Time Ser. Anal.*, **8**, 277–81.

Chan, K. S. and Tong, H. (1988). On likelihood ratio tests for threshold autoregression. *Tech. Rep.*, Institute of Mathematics, University of Kent.

Chan, K. S., Petruccelli, J. D., Tong, H., and Woolford, S. W. (1985). A multiple threshold AR(1) model. *J. Appl. Probab.*, **22**, 267–79.

Chan, K. S., Moeanaddin, R., and Tong, H. (1988). Some difficulties of non-linear time series modelling. *Tech. Rep.*, Institute of Mathematics, University of Kent.

Chan, W. S. and Tong, H. (1986) On tests for non-linearity in time series analysis. *J. Forecasting*, **5**, 217–28.

Chen, C. F. (1971). Hurwitz's stability criterion and Fuller's aperiodicity criterion in non-linear systems analysis. *Int. J. Electron.*, **31**, 609–19.

Childers, D. G. (1978). *Modern spectral analysis*. IEEE Press, New York.

Cleveland, W. S. and McGill, R. (1987). Graphical perception: the visual decoding of quantitative information on graphical displays of data. *J. R. Stat. Soc.*, **A150**, 300.

Cobb, L. and Zacks, S. (1988). Nonlinear time series analysis for dynamical systems of catastrophe type. In *Nonlinear time series and signal processing,* (ed. R. R. Mohler), Lecture Notes in Control and Information Sciences. Springer, Heidelberg.

Cox, D. R. (1977). Discussion of papers by Campbell and Walker, Tong and Morris. *J. R. Stat. Soc.,* **A140,** 453–4.

Cox, D. R. (1981). Statistical analysis of time series: some recent developments. *Scand. J. Stat.,* **8,** 93–115.

Cox, D. R. and Hinkley, D. V. (1974). *Theoretical statistics.* Chapman and Hall, London.

Cox, D. R. and Miller, H. D. (1965). *The theory of stochastic processes.* Methuen, London.

Cox, D. R. and Reid, N. (1987). Parameter orthogonality and approximate conditional inference (with discussion). *J. R. Stat. Soc.,* **B49,** 1–39.

Cox, D. R. and Small, N. J. H. (1978). Testing multivariate normality. *Biometrika,* **65,** 263–82.

Davies, N. and Petruccelli, J. D. (1985). Experience with detecting non-linearity in time series: identification and diagnostic checking. *Res. Rep.,* MSOR/8/85, Trent Polytechnic, Nottingham.

Davies, R. B. (1977). Hypothesis testing when a nuisance parameter is present only under the alternative. *Biometrika,* **64,** 247–54.

Davies, R. B. (1987). Hypothesis testing when a nuisance parameter is present only under the alternative. *Biometrika,* **74,** 33–43.

Dawid, A. P. (1984). Statistical theory: the prequential approach. *J. R. Stat. Soc.,* **A147,** 278–92.

Dempster, A. P., Laird, N. M., and Rubin, D. B. (1977). Maximum likelihood from incomplete data via EM algorithm (with discussion) *J. R. Stat. Soc.,* **B39,** 1–38.

Dirkse, J. P. (1975). An absorption probability for the Ornstein–Uhlenbeck process. *J. Appl. Prob.,* **12,** 595–9.

Doob, J. L. (1953). *Stochastic processes.* Wiley, New York.

Doukhan, P. (1983). Simulation in the general first order autoregressive process. In *Specifying statistical models,* (ed. J. P. Florens *et al.*), Lecture Notes in Statistics No. 16. Springer, New York.

Draper, N. R. and Smith, H. (1981). *Applied regression analysis,* 2nd ed. Wiley, New York.

Durbin, J. (1971). Boundary-crossing probabilities for Brownian motion and Poisson processes and techniques for computing the power of the Kolmogorov–Smirnov test. *J. Appl. Probab.,* **8,** 431–3.

Eckmann, J. P. and Ruelle, D. (1985). Ergodic theory of chaos and strange attractors. *Rev. Mod. Phys.,* **57,** 617.

Elton, C. and Nicholson, M. (1942). The ten-year cycle in numbers of the lynx in Canada. *J. Anim. Ecol.,* **11,** 215–44.

Engle, R. F. (1982). Autoregressive conditional heteroscedasticity with estimates of the variance of U.K. inflation. *Econometrica,* **50,** 987–1008.

Engle, R. F. and Bollerslev, T. (1986). Modelling the persistence of conditional variances. *Res. Rep.,* Department of Economics, University of California at San Diego.

Farmer, J. D. and Sidorowich, J. J. (1988). Exploiting chaos to predict the future and reduce noise. *Tech. Rep.*, LA-UR-88-901, Los Alamos National Lab.

Farmer, J. D., Ott, E., and York, J. A. (1983). The dimension of chaotic attractors. *Physica*, **7D**, 153–80.

Feder, P. T. (1975). On asymptotic distribution theory in segmented regression problems—identified case. *Ann. Stat.*, **3**, 49–83.

Feigin, P. D. and Tweedie, R. L. (1985). Random coefficient autoregressive processes—a Markov chain analysis of stationarity and finiteness of moments. *J. Time Ser. Anal.*, **6**, 1–14.

Feller, W. (1966). *An introduction to probability theory and its applications*, Vol. II. Wiley, New York.

Findley, D. F. (1983). On the unbiasedness property of AIC for exact or approximating multivariate ARMA models. *Res. Rep.*, Statistical Research Division, US Bureau of Census.

Fisz, M. (1963). *Probability theory and mathematical statistics*. Wiley, New York.

Foster, F. G. (1953). On the stochastic matrices associated with certain queueing processes. *Ann. Math. Stat.*, **24**, 355–60.

Fox, A. J. (1972). Outliers in time series. *J. R. Stat. Soc.*, **B34**, 350–63.

Freidlin, M. I. and Wentzill, A. D. (1984). *Random perturbations of dynamical systems*. Springer, Heidelberg.

Gabr, M. M. (1988). On the third-order moment structure and bispectral analysis of some bilinear time series. *J. Time Ser. Anal.*, **9**, 11–20.

Gabr, M. M. and Subba Rao, T. (1981). The estimation and prediction of subset bilinear time series models with applications. *J. Time Ser. Anal.*, **2**, 153–71.

Ghaddar, D. K. and Tong, H. (1981). Data transformation and self-exciting threshold autoregression. *J. R. Stat. Soc.*, **C30**, 238–48.

Gladyshev, E. G. (1961). Periodically correlated random sequences. *Sov. Math.*, **2**, 385–8.

Godambe, V. P. (1960). An optimum property of regular maximum likelihood equation. *Ann. Math. Stat.*, **31**, 1208–11.

Godambe, V. P. (1985). The foundations of finite sample estimation in stochastic processes. *Biometrika*, **72**, 419–28.

Gooijer, J. G., Abraham, B., Gould, A., and Robinson, L. (1984). Methods for determining the order of an autoregressive-moving average process: a survey. *Int. Stat. Rev.*, **53**, 301–29.

Granger, C. W. J. and Andersen, A. P. (1978). *An introduction to bilinear time series models*. Vandenhoek and Ruprecht, Gottingen.

Granger, C. W. J. and Newbold, P. (1977). *Forecasting economic time series*. Academic Press, New York.

Guckenheimer, J. and Holmes, P. (1983). *Nonlinear oscillations, dynamical systems and bifurcations of vector fields*. Springer, Heidelberg.

Gudmundsson, G. (1970). Short term variations of a glacier-fed river. *Tellus*, **22**, 341–53.

Gudmundsson, G. (1975). Seasonal variations and stationarity. *Nord. Hydrol.*, **6**, 137–44.

Guegan, D. (1981). Etude d'un modèle nonlinéaire, le modèle superdiagonal d'ordre. *C. R. Acad. Sci. Paris*, **293**, Ser. 1, 95–8.

Guegan, D. (1987). Different representations for bilinear models. *J. Time Ser. Anal.*, **8**, 389–408.

Guegan, D. and Pham Dinh Tuan (1987). Minimalité et inversibilité des modèles bilinèares á temps discret. *C. R. Acad. Sci. Paris*, **304**, 159–62.

Guegan, D. and Pham Dinh Tuan (1988). A note on the estimation of the parameters of the diagonal bilinear model by the least squares method. *Scand. J. Stat.*, **16**, 129–136.

Gumowski, I. (1981). Qualitative properties of some dynamic systems with pure delay. *Modeles mathematiques en biologie,* (ed. C. Chevalet and A. Micali), Lecture Notes in Biomathematics. Springer, Heidelberg.

Gumowski, I. and Mira, C. (1980). *Recurrences and discrete dynamic systems.* Springer, Heidelberg.

Gurney, W. S. C., Blythe, S. P., and Nisbet, R. M. (1981). Letter to the editor. *Nature*, **292**, 178.

Haggan, V. and Ozaki, T. (1981). Modelling non-linear random vibrations using an amplitude-dependent autoregressive time series model. *Biometrika*, **68**, 189–96.

Haggan, V., Heravi, S. M., and Priestley, M. B. (1984). A study of the application of state-dependent models in non-linear time series analysis. *J. Time Ser. Anal.*, **5**, 69–102.

Hall, P. and Heyde, C. C. (1980). *Martingale limit theory and its applications.* Academic Press, New York.

Hallin, M., Le Fevre, C., and Puri, M. L. (1988). On time-reversibility and the uniqueness of moving average representations for non-Gaussian stationary time series. *Biometrika*, **75**, 170–71.

Hannan, E. J. (1960). *Time series analysis.* Methuen, London.

Hannan, E. J. (1980). The estimation of the order of an ARMA process. *Ann. Stat.*, **8**, 1071–81.

Hannan, E. J. (1982). A note on bilinear time series models. *Stochastic Processes Appl.*, **12**, 221–4.

Hannan, E. J. and Quinn, B. G. (1979). The determination of the order of an autoregression. *J. R. Stat. Soc.*, **B41**, 190–5.

Harrison, P. J. and Stevens, C. F. (1976). Bayesian forecasting. *J. R. Stat. Soc.*, **B38**, 205–47.

Hau, M. C. and Tong, H. (1984). Outlier detection in autoregressive time series modelling. *Tech. Rep.* No. 15, Department of Statistics, Chinese University of Hong Kong. *Stochastic Hydrol. Hydraul.* **3**, 241–260.

Hinich, M. (1982). Testing for Gaussianity and linearity of a stationary time series. *J. Time Ser. Anal.*, **3**, 169–76.

Hinkley, D. V. (1969). Inference about the intersection in two-phase regression. *Biometrika*, **56**, 495–504.

Högnäs, G. (1986). Comparison of some non-linear autoregressive processes. *J. Time Ser. Anal.*, **7**, 205–12.

Holden, A. V. (1986). *Chaos.* Manchester University Press.

Hsu, C.S. (1970). Application of the tau-decomposition method to dynamical systems subjected to retarded follower forces. *J. Appl. Mech.*, **37**, 259–66.

Huang, L. and Li, Z. (1987). Some problems of second method of Lyapunov in discrete systems. *Tech. Rep.*, Department of Mechanics, Peking University.

Hung, G., Brillinger, D. R., and Stark, L. (1979). Interpretation of kernels, II, same-signed 1st-and-2nd degree kernels of the human pupillary system. *Math. Biosci.*, **46**, 159–87.

Hutchinson, G. E. (1948). Circular causal systems in ecology. *Ann. NY Acad. Sci.*, **50**, 221–46.

Hyndman, B. W., Kitney, R. I., and Sayers, B. McA. (1971). Spontaneous rhythms in physiological control systems. *Nature*, **233**, 339–41.

Ivakhnenko, A. G. (1971). Polynomial theory of complex systems. *IEEE Trans. Syst. Man Cybern.*, **SMC-1**, 364–78.

Izenman, A. J. (1983). J. R. Wolf and H. A. Wolfer: an historical note on Zurich sunspot relative numbers. *J. R. Stat. Soc.*, **A146**, 311–18.

Jeffreys, H. (1936). Further significance tests. *Proc. Camb. Philos. Soc.*, **32**, 416–45.

Jenkins, G. M. and Watts, D. G. (1968). *Spectral analysis and its applications*. Holden-Day, San Francisco.

Jones, D. A. (1976). Non-linear autoregressive processes. Unpublished PhD Thesis, University of London.

Jones, D. A. (1978). Nonlinear autoregressive processes. *Proc. R. Soc.*, **A360**, 71–95.

Jones, R. H. (1965). An experiment in non-linear prediction. *J. Appl. Meteorol.*, **4**, 701–5.

Jones, R. H. (1984). Fitting multivariate models to unequally spaced data. In *Tiome series analysis of irregularly observed data*, Lecture Notes in Statistics, **25**, pp. 158–88. Springer, New York.

Jones, R. H. and Brelsford, W. M. (1967). Time series with periodic structure. *Biometrika*, **54**, 403–8.

Kalman, R. E. (1955). Analysis and design principles of second and higher order saturating servomechanisms. *Trans IEEE*, **74**, 294–310.

Kalman, R. E. (1956). Nonlinear aspects of sampled-data control systems. *Proc. Symp. Nonlinear Circuit Analysis*, pp. 273–313. Polytechnic Institute of Brooklyn, U.S.A.

Kalman, R. E. (1957). Physical and mathematical mechanisms of instability in nonlinear automatic control systems. *Trans. ASME*, **79**, 553–66.

Kalman, R. E. (1980). Pattern recognition properties of multilinear response functions, Part I. *Control Cybern.*, **9**, 5–31. (Original Russian version presented in 1968).

Kalman, R. E., Falb, P. L., and Arbib, M. A. (1969). *Topics in mathematical system theory*. McGraw-Hill, New York.

Kaplan, W. (1950). Dynamical systems with indeterminacy. *Am. J. Math.*, **72**, 573–94.

Karlsen, H. and Tjøstheim, D. (1988). Consistent estimates for the NEAR(2) and NLAR(2) time series models. *J. R. Stat. Soc.*, **B50**, 313–20.

Kavvas, M. L. and Delleur, J. W. (1984). A statistical analysis of the daily streamflow hydrograph. *J. Hydrol.*, **71**, 253–76.

✱Keenan, D. M. (1985). A Tukey non-additivity-type test for time series nonlinearity. *Biometrika*, **72**, 39–44.

Kent, J. T. (1982). Robust properties of likelihood ratio tests. *Biometrika*, **69**, 19–27.

Kifer, Yu. (1986). *Ergodic theory of random transformations.* Birkhäuser, Boston.

Kitagaura, G. (1987). Non-Gaussian state space modeling of non-stationary time series. *J. Am. Stat. Assoc.*, **82**, 1032–63.

Kingman, J. F. C. and Taylor, S. J. (1966). *Introduction to measure and probability.* Cambridge University Press.

Kleiner, B., Martin, R. D., and Thomson, D. J. (1979). Robust estimation of power spectra (with Discussion). *J. R. Stat. Soc.*, **B41**, 313–51.

Klimko, L. A. and Nelson, P. I. (1978). On conditional least squares estimation for stochastic processes. *Ann. Stat.*, **6**, 629–42.

Kumar, K. (1986). On the identification of some bilinear time series models. *J. Time Ser. Anal.*, **7**, 117–22.

Künsch, H. (1984). Infinitesimal robustness for autoregressive processes. *Ann. Stat.*, **12**, 843–63.

Kushner, H. H. (1971). *Introduction to stochastic control.* Holt, Rinehart & Winston, New York.

Larimore, W. E. (1983). Predictive inference, sufficiency, entropy and an asymptotic likelihood principle. *Biometrika*, **70**, 175–81.

La Salle, J. P. (1976). *The stability of dynamical systems,* CMBS 25. SIAM, Philadelphia.

La Salle, J. P. (1977). Stability theory for difference equations. *Studies in ordinary differential equations,* MAA Studies in Mathematics, pp. 1–31. Am. Math. Assoc.

Lawrance, A. J. (1987). Directionality and reversibility in time series. *Tech. Rep.*, Department of Statistics, Birmingham University.

Lawrance, A. J. and Kottegoda, N. T. (1977). Stochastic modelling of riverflow time series (with discussion). *J. R. Stat. Soc.*, **A140**, 1–47.

Lawrance, A. J. and Lewis, P. A. W. (1980). The exponential autoregressive moving average EARMA(p, q) process. *J. R. Stat. Soc.*, **B42**, 150–61.

Lawrance, A. J. and Lewis, P. A. W. (1985). Modelling and residual analysis of non-linear autoregressive time series in exponential variables (with Discussion). *J. R. Stat. Soc.*, **B47**, 165–202.

Levin, S. A. and May, R. M. (1976). A note on difference–delay equations. *Theor. Popul. Biol.*, **9**, 178–187.

Li, L.-Y. and Liu, D.-F. (1985). Threshold modelling on the earthquake magnitude series. *Acta Geophys. Sin.*, **28**, 303–10.

Li, T.-Y. and Yorke, J. A. (1975). Period three implies chaos. *Am. Math. Mon.*, **82**, 988–92.

Li, W. K. (1988). The Akaike information criterion in threshold modelling. In *Nonlinear time series and signal processing,* (ed. R. R. Mohler), Lecture Notes in Control and Information Sciences, pp. 88–96. Springer, New York.

Li, W. K. and McLeod, A. I. (1988). ARMA modelling with non-Gaussian innovations. *J. Time Ser. Anal.*, **9**, 155–68.

Lim, K. S. (1981). On threshold time series modelling. Unpublished Doctoral Thesis, University of Manchester.

Lim, K. S. (1987). A comparative study of various univariate time series models for Canadian lynx data. *J. Time Ser. Anal.*, **8**, 161–76.

Lin, C.-C. and Mudholkar, G. S. (1980). A simple test for normality against asymmetric alternatives. *Biometrika*, **67**, 455–61.

Liu, J. (1989). Simple condition for the existence of some stationary bilinear time series. *J. Time Ser. Anal.*, **10**, 33–40.

Liu, J. and Brockwell, P. J. (1988). On the general bilinear time series models. *J. Appl. Probab.*, **25**, 553–64.

Ljung, G. M. and Box, G. E. P. (1978). On a measure of lack of fit in time series models. *Biometrika*, **65**, 297–303.

Lukacs, E. (1960). *Characteristic functions.* Methuen, London.

Luukkonen, R. and Teräsvirta, T. (1988). Testing linearity of economic time series against cyclical asymmetry. *Res. Rep.* No. 262, Research Institute of the Finnish Economy, Helsinki,.

Luukkonen, R., Saikkonen, P., and Teräsvirta, T. (1988a). Testing linearity against smooth transition autoregressive models. *Biometrika*, **75**, 491, 499.

Luukkonen, R., Saikkonen, P., and Teräsvirta, T. (1988b). Testing linearity in univariate time series models. *Scand. J. Stat.*, **15**, 161–75.

Lyapunov, A. M. (1892). *General problems of stability of motion.* (Original in Russian.)

McKenzie, E. (1982). Product autoregression: a time-series characterization of the gamma distribution. *J. Appl. Probab.*, **19**, 463–8.

McKenzie, E. (1985). Some simple models for discrete variate time series. In *Time series analysis in water resources*, (ed. K. W. Hipel), pp. 645–50. Am. Water Res. Assoc.

McLeod, A. I. and Li, W. K. (1983). Diagnostic checking ARMA time series models using squared-residual autocorrelations. *J. Time Ser. Anal.*, **4**, 269–73.

Maravall, A. (1983). An application of nonlinear time series forecasting. *J. Bus. Econ. Stat.*, **1**, 66–74.

May, R. M. (1976). Simple mathematical models with very complicated dynamics. *Nature*, **261**, 459–67.

May, R. M. and Oster, G. F. (1976). Bifurcations and dynamic complexity in simple ecological models. *Am. Nat.*, **110**, 573–99.

Mélard, G. and Roy, R. (1988). Modèles de series chronologiques avec seuils. (*Rev. Stat. Appl.*).

Milhøj, A. (1985). The moment structure of ARCH processes. *Scand. J. Stat.*, **12**, 281–92.

Minorsky, N. (1962). *Non-linear oscillations.* Van Nostrand, Princeton, NJ.

Moeanaddin, R. (1989). Aspects of non-linear time series analysis. Unpublished PhD Thesis, University of Kent.

Moeanaddin, R. and Tong, H. (1988). A comparison of likelihood ratio test and CUSUM test for threshold autoregression. *The Statistician*, **37**, 213–25. (Corrigenda and Addenda in *The Statistician*, **37**, 473–4.)

Moeanaddin, R. and Tong, H. (1989a). Numerical evaluation of distributions in non-linear autoregression. *J. Time Ser. Anal.*, **10**.

Moeanaddin, R. and Tong, H. (1989*b*). Is a bilinear model an illusion? *Tech. Rep.*, Dept of Statistics, University of Kent.

Moran, P. A. P. (1953). The statistical analysis of the Canadian lynx cycle, I: structure and prediction. *Aust. J. Zool.*, **1**, 163–73.

Nachbin, L. (1965). *The Haar integral*. Van Nostrand, Princeton, N.J.

Needham, J. (1959). *Science and civilisation in China*, Vol. III. Cambridge University Press.

Neveu, J. (1965). *Mathematical foundations of the calculus of probability*. Holden-Day, San Francisco.

Newbold, P. (1981). Some recent developments in time series analysis. *Int. Stat. Rev.*, **49**, 53–66.

Nicholls, D. F. and Quinn, B. G. (1982). *Random coefficient autoregressive models: an introduction*, Lecture Notes in Statistics, Vol. No. 11. Springer, New York.

Nield, D. (1982). Threshold time series modelling of Nicholson's blow-fly data. Unpublished MSc dissertation, University of Manchester.

Nisio, M. (1960). On polynomial approximation for strictly stationary processes. *J. Math. Soc. Jpn*, **12**, 207–26.

Nummelin, E. (1984). *General irreducible Markov chains and non-negative operators*. Cambridge University Press.

Orey, S. (1971). *Lecture notes on limit theorems for Markov chain transition probabilities*. Van Nostrand, London.

Oseledec, V. I. (1968). A multiplicative ergodic theorem: Liapunov characteristic numbers for dynamical systems. *Trans. Moscow Math. Soc.*, **19**, 197–231.

Oster, G. and Ipaktchi, A. (1978). Population cycles. In *Theoretical Chemistry: periodicities in chemistry and biology*, (ed. H. Eyring and D. Henderson), pp. 111–32. Academic Press, New York.

Otomo, T., Nakagawa, T., and Akaike, H. (1972). Statistical approach to computer control of cement rotary kilns. *Automatica*, **8**, 35–48.

Ozaki, T. (1981). Non-linear threshold autoregressive models for non-linear random vibrations. *J. Appl. Probab.*, **18**, 443–51.

Ozaki, T. (1982). The statistical analysis of perturbed limit cycle processes using nonlinear time series models. *J. Time Ser. Anal.*, **3**, 29–41.

Ozaki, T. (1985*a*). Non-linear time series models and dynamical systems. *Handbook of statistics*, **5**, (ed. E. J. Hannan, P. R. Krishnaiah, and M. M. Rao). North-Holland, Amsterdam.

Ozaki, T. (1985*b*). Statistical identification of storage models with applications to stochastic hydrology. In *Time series analysis in water resources*, (ed. K. W. Hipel), pp. 663–76. Am. Water. Res. Assoc.

Ozaki, T. and Oda, H. (1978). Non-linear time series model identification by Akaike's information criterion. *Proc. IFAC Workshop on Information and Systems, Compiegn, France, October 1977.*

Packard, N. H., Crutchfield, J. P., Farmer, J. D. R., and Shaw, R. S. (1980). Geometry from a time series. *Phys. Rev. Lett.*, **45**, 712–16.

Parthasarathy, K. R. (1967). *Probability measures on metric spaces*. Academic Press, New York.

Parzen, E. (1962). *Stochastic processes*. Holden-Day, San Francisco.

Parzen, E. (1974). Some recent advances in time series modelling. *IEEE Trans. Autom. Control*, **AC-19**, 723–9.

Pemberton, J. (1985). Contributions to the theory of non-linear time series models. PhD Thesis, University of Manchester.

Pemberton, J. (1987). Exact least squares multi-step prediction from non-linear autoregressive models. *J. Time Ser. Anal.*, **8**, 443–8.

Pemberton, J. (1989). Forecasting accuracy of non-linear time series models. Tech. Rep. Dept. of Maths, University of Salford, UK, August 1989.

Pemberton, J. and Tong, H. (1981). A note on the distribution of non-linear autoregressive stochastic models. *J. Time Ser. Anal.*, **2**, 49–52.

Petruccelli, J. D. (1987). On tests for SETAR-type non-linearity in time series. *Tech. Rep.*, Worcester Polytechnic Institute, MA.

Petruccelli, J. D. and Davies, N. (1986a). A portmanteau test for self-exciting threshold autoregressive-type non-linearity in time series. *Biometrika*, **73**, 687–94.

Petruccelli, J. D. and Davies, N. (1986b). Experience with testing for SETAR-type nonlinearity in time series. *Res. Rep.*, Department of Mathematics, Trent Polytechnic, Nottingham.

Petruccelli, J. D. and Woolford, S. W. (1984). A threshold AR(1) model. *J. Appl. Probab.*, **21**, 207–86.

Pham Dinh Tuan (1985). Bilinear Markovian representation and bilinear models. *Stochastic Processes Appl.*, **20**, 295–306.

Pham Dinh Tuan (1986). The mixing property of bilinear and generalised random coefficient autoregressive models. *Stochastic Processes Appl.*, **23**, 291–300.

Pham Dinh Tuan and Lanh Tat Tran (1981). On first-order bilinear time series models. *J. Appl. Probab.*, **18**, 617–27.

Pham Dinh Tuan, Chan, K. S., and Tong, H. (1989). Strong consistency of the least squares estimator for a non-stationary threshold autoregressive model. Contributed paper to *47th Session of Int. Stat. Inst., Paris, 1989.*

Pielou, E. C. (1974). *Population and community ecology*. Gordon and Breach, New York.

Pole, A. M. and Smith, A. F. M. (1985). A Bayesian analysis of some threshold switching models. *J. Econ.*, **29**, 97–119.

Pollard, D. (1984). *Convergence of stochastic processes*. Springer-Verlag, New York.

Popper, K. (1972). *Conjectures and refutations: the growth of scientific knowledge*. Routledge & Kegan Paul, London.

Poston, T. and Stewart, I. (1978). *Catastrophe theory and its applications*. Pitman, London.

Pourahmadi, M. (1986). On stationarity of the solution of a doubly stochastic model. *J. Time Ser. Anal.*, **7**, 123–32.

Powell, M. J. D. (1976). *Bull. Math. Appl.*, **12**, 79.

Priestley, M. B. (1980). State dependent models: a general approach to non-linear time series analysis. *J. Time Ser. Anal.*, **1**, 57–71.

Priestley, M. B. (1981). *Spectral analysis and time series*, Vols I and II. Academic Press, London.

Priestley, M. B. (1988). *Nonlinear and non-stationary time series analysis*. Academic Press, London.

Quinn, B. G. (1982). A note on the existence of strictly stationary solutions to bilinear equations. *J. Time Ser. Anal.*, **3**, 249–52.

Readshaw, J. L. and Cuff, W. R. (1980). A model of Nicholson's blowfly cycles and its relevance to predation theory. *J. Anim. Ecol.*, **49**, 1005–10.

Richter, K. and Schunke, E. (1981). Runoff and water budget of the Blanda and and Vatnsdalsà Periglacial River Basins, Central Iceland. *Bull.*, **34**, Research Institute, Nedri As., Hveragdodi, Iceland.

Rissanen, J. (1987). Stochastic complexity. *J. R. Stat. Soc.* **B49**, 223–39, 253–65.

Rist, S. (1983). Floods and flood danger in Iceland. *Jökull*, **33**, 119–32.

Robinson, P. M. (1972). The estimation of continuous-time systems using discrete data. Unpublished PhD Thesis, Australian National University.

Robinson, P. M. (1974). Stochastic difference equations with non-integral differences. *Adv. Appl. Probab.*, **6**, 524–45.

Robinson, P. M. (1975). Continuous time regressions with discrete data. *Ann. Stat.*, **3**, 688–97.

Robinson, P. M. (1977a). The construction and estimation of continuous time models and discrete approximations in econometrics. *J. Econ.*, **6**, 173–97.

Robinson, P. M. (1977b). The estimation of a nonlinear moving average model. *Stochastic Processes Appl.*, **5**, 81–90.

Robinson, P. M. (1978). Statistical inference for a random coefficient autoregressive model. *Scand. J. Stat.*, **5**, 163–8.

Robinson, P. M. (1983). Non-parametric estimation for time series models. *J. Time Ser. Anal.*, **4**, 185–208.

Rosenblatt, M. (1969). Conditional probability density and regression estimators. *Multivariate Anal.*, **2**, 25–31.

Rosenblatt, M. (1971). *Markov processes, structure and asymptotic behaviour.* Springer, New York.

Rosenblatt, M. (1979). Linearity and non-linearity on time series prediction. *Proc. 42nd ISI Meeting, Manila, Phillipines.*

Rugh, W. J. (1981). *Nonlinear system theory—the Volterra/Wiener approach.* Johns Hopkins University Press, Baltimore, MD).

Saikkonen, P. and Luukkonen, R. (1988). Lagrange multiplier tests for testing non-linearities in time series models. *Scand. J. Stat.*, **15**, 55–68.

Sanov, I. N. (1961). On the probability of large deviations of random variables. *IMS and ASM Selected Translations in Mathematical Statistics and Probability*, **1**, 213–44.

Schaffer, W. M. (1984). Stretching and folding in lynx fur returns: evidence for a strange attractor? *Am. Nat.*, **124**, 798–820.

Schuster, A. (1898). On the investigation of hidden periodicities with application to a supposed 26-day period of meteorological phenomena. *Terr. Magn. Atmos. Electr.*, **3**, 13–41.

Schuster, A. (1906). On the periodicities of sunspots. *Philos. Trans. R. Soc.*, **A206**, 69–100.

Schwarz, G. (1978). Estimating the dimension of a model. *Ann. Stat.*, **6**, 461–4.

Sesay, S. A. O. (1982). Sampling properties of estimates of the parameters of the bilinear model BL(1, 0, 1, 1). Unpublished MSc Dissertation, UMIST.

Shepp, L. A., Slepian, D., and Wyner, A. D. (1980). On prediction of moving average processes. *Bell Syst. Tech. J.*, **59**, 367–415.

Shibata, R. (1976). Selection of the order of an autoregressive model by Akaike fms information criterion. *Biometrika*, **63**, 117–26.

Shibata, R. (1980). Asymptotically efficient selection of the order of the model for estimating parameters of a linear process. *Ann. Stat.*, **8**, 147–64.

Shibata, A. (1981). An optimal selection of regression variables. *Biometrika*, **68**, 45–54.

Shimizu, R. (1978). Entropy maximization principle and selection of the order of an autoregressive Gaussian process. *Ann. Inst. Stat. Math.*, **30**, 263–70.

Shorack, G. and Wellner, J. (1986). *Empirical processes with applications to statistics*. Wiley, New York.

Shumway, R. H. (1988). *Applied statistical time series analysis*. Prentice-Hall, Englewood Cliffs, NJ.

Siegmund, D. (1977). Repeated significance tests for a normal mean. *Biometrika*, **64**, 177–89.

Silverman, B. W. (1981). Using kernel density estimates to investigate multi-modality. *J. R. Stat. Soc.*, **B53**, 97–9.

Smith, A. F. M. and Spiegelhalter, D. J. (1980). Bayes factors and choice criteria for linear models. *J. R. Stat. Soc.*, **B42**, 213–20.

Smith, J. Q., Harrison, P. J., and Zeeman, E. C. (1981). The analysis of some discontinuous decision processes. *Eur. J. Oper. Res.*, **7**, 30–43.

Smith, R. L. (1989). A survey of nonregular problems. *Proc. 47th Session, ISI, Paris.*

Snorrason, A., Newbold, P., and Maxwell, W. H. C. (1984). Multiple input transfer function–noise modelling of riverflow. In *Frontiers in hydrology*, (ed. W. H. C. Maxwell and L. R. Beard), pp. 111–26. Water Resources Publications, Littleton, CO.

Söderström, T. (1977). On model structure testing in system identification. *Int. J. Control*, **26**, 1–18.

Stoker, J. J. (1950). *Nonlinear vibrations*. Interscience, New York.

Stone, C. J. (1982). Local asymptotic admissibility of a generalisation of Akaike's model selection rule. *Ann. Inst. Stat. Math.*, **34**, 123–234.

Stone, M. (1974). Cross-validatory choice and assessment of statistical predictions (with Discussion). *J. R. Stat. Soc.*, **B36**, 111–47.

Stone, M. (1977). An asymptotic equivalence of choice of model by cross-validation and Akaike's criterion. *J. R. Stat. Soc.*, **B39**, 44–7.

Stone, M. (1979). Comments on model selection criteria of Akaike and Schwarz. *J. R. Stat. Soc.*, **B41**, 276–8.

Subba Rao, T. (1980). Discussion of paper by Tong and Lim. *J. R. Stat. Soc.*, **B42**, 278–80.

Subba Rao, T. (1981). On the theory of bilinear time series models. *J. R. Stat. Soc.*, **B43**, 244–55.

Subba Rao, T. (1988). Spectral and bispectral methods for the analysis of nonlinear (non-Gaussian) time series signals. In *Nonlinear time series and signal processing*, (ed. R. R. Mohler), Lecture Notes in Control and Information Sciences. Springer, New York.

Subba Rao, T. and Gabr, M. M. (1980). A test for linearity of stationary time series. *J. Time Ser. Anal.*, **1**, 145–58.

Subba Rao, T. and Gabr, M. M. (1984). *An introduction to bispectral analysis and bilinear time series models,* Lecture Notes in Statistics, **24**. Springer, New York.

Sugawara, M. (1961). On the analysis of run-off structure about several Japanese rivers. *Jpn. J. Geophys.*, **2**, 1–76.

Takens, F. (1981). *Dynamical systems and turbulence.* Warwick 1980. Proc. ed. by D. A. Rand and L. S. Young. Lecture Notes on Maths No. 898. Springer Verlag, Heidelberg.

Thanoon, B. Y. (1984). A study of threshold autoregressive models with some applications. Unpublished PhD Thesis, University of Manchester.

Thavaneswaran, A. and Abraham, B. (1988). Estimation for nonlinear time series models using estimating equations. *J. Time Ser. Anal.*, **9**, 99–108.

Titterington, D. M. (1988). Some recent research in the analysis of mixture distributions. *Paper presented at the 18th European Meeting of Statisticians, Berlin, DDR, 1988.*

Tjøstheim, D. (1986a). Some doubly stochastic time series models. *J. Time Ser. Analysis*, **7**, 51–72.

Tjøstheim, D. (1986b). Estimation in nonlinear time series models I: stationary series. *Stochastic Processes Appl.*, **21**, 225–73.

Tjøstheim, D. (1989). Nonlinear time series and Markov chain. *Tech. Rep. Dept of Mathematics*, University of Bergen. (To appear in *Adv. Appl. Probab.*)

Tjur, T. (1980). *Probability based on radon measures.* Wiley, New York.

Tong, H. (1975). Determination of the order of a Markov chain by Akaike's information criteria. *J. Appl. Probab.*, **12**, 488–97.

Tong, H. (1976). Fitting a smooth moving average to noisy data. *IEEE Trans. Inf. Theory.*, **IT-26**, 493–6.

Tong, H. (1977a). Discussion of a paper by A. J. Lawrance and N. T. Kottegoda. *J. R. Stat. Soc.*, **A140**, 34–5.

Tong, H. (1977b). Some comments on the Canadian lynx data—with Discussion. *J. R. Stat. Soc.*, **A140**, 432–5, 448–68.

Tong, H. (1978). On a threshold model. In *Pattern recognition and signal processing,* (ed. C. H. Chen). Sijthoff and Noordhoff, Amsterdam.

Tong, H. (1979). A note on a local equivalence of two recent approaches to autoregressive order determination. *Int. J. Control*, **29**, 441–6.

Tong, H. (1980a). Catastrophe theory and threshold autoregressive modelling. *Tech. Rep.*, No. 125. Dept of Mathematics (Statistics), UMIST. (Abstract in *J. Stat., Resume Commun., Toulouse,* 19–22 May 1980, p. 106.)

Tong, H. (1980b). A view on non-linear time series model building. In *Time series,* (ed. O. D. Anderson). North Holland, Amsterdam.

Tong, H. (1981). A note on a Markov bilinear stochastic process in discrete time. *J. Time Ser. Anal.*, **2**, 279–84.

Tong, H. (1982). Discontinuous decision processes and threshold autoregressive time series modelling. *Biometrika*, **69**, 274–6.

Tong, H. (1983a). *Threshold models in non-linear time series analysis,* Lecture Notes in Statistics, No. 21. Springer, Heidelberg.

Tong, H. (1983b). A note on a delayed autoregressive process in continuous time. *Biometrika*, **70**, 710–12.

Tong, H. (1987). Non-linear time series models of regularly sampled data: A survey. *Proc. 1st World Congress of the Bernoulli Society, 1986,* (ed. Y. V. Prohrov and V. V. Sansonov), **2**, pp. 355–67. VNU Science Press, Holland (Amsterdam).

Tong, H. (1988). Contribution to the discussion of papers by D. V. Hinkley and T. J. Dibiccio and J. P. Romano. *J. R. Stat. Soc.,* **B50**, 359–60.

Tong, H. (1989). Thresholds, stability, non-linear forecasting and irregularly sampled data. In *Statistical analysis and forecasting economic structural change,* (ed. P. Hackl). Heidelberg: Springer Verlag, pp. 279–296.

Tong, H. and Dabas, P. (1989). Clusters of time series models: an example. *Tech. Rep.,* University of Kent, June 1989.

Tong, H. and Lim, K. S. (1980). Threshold autoregression, limit cycles and cyclical data (with Discussion). *J. R. Stat. Soc.,* **B42**, 245–92.

Tong, H. and Moeanaddin, R. (1988). On multi-step non-linear least squares prediction. *The Statistician,* **37**, 101–10.

Tong, H. and Wu, Z. M. (1982). Multi-step-ahead forecasting of cyclical data by threshold autoregression. *Time Series Analysis: Theory and Practice 1.* North-Holland, Amsterdam, pp. 733–53.

Tong, H. and Yeung, I. (1988a). On tests for SETAR-type non-linearity in partially observed time series. *Tech. Rep,* Institute of Mathematics, University of Kent.

Tong, H. and Yeung, I. (1988b). On tests for SETAR-type non-linearity in irregularly spaced time series. *Tech. Rep.,* Institute of Mathematics, University of Kent.

Tong, H., Thanoon, B., and Gudmundsson, G. (1985). Threshold time series modelling of two Icelandic riverflow systems. In *Time series analysis in water resources,* (ed. K. W. Hipel). Am. Water Res. Assoc.

Tsay, R. S. (1986). Nonlinearity tests for time series. *Biometrika,* **73**, 461–6.

Tsay, R. S. (1988). Non-linear time series analysis of blowfly population. *J. Time Ser. Anal.,* **9**, 247–64.

Tsay, R. S. (1989). Testing and modelling threshold autoregressive processes. *J. Am. Stat. Assoc.,* **84**, 231–40.

Tweedie, R. L. (1975). Sufficient conditions for ergodicity and recurrence of Markov chain on a general state space. *Stochastic Processes Appl.,* **3**, 385–403.

Tweedie, R. L. (1983). The existence of moments for stationary Markov chains. *J. Appl. Probab.,* **20**, 191–6.

Tyssedal, J. S. and Tjøstheim, D. (1988). An autoregressive model with suddenly changing parameters and an application to stockmarket prices. *Appl. Stat.,* **37**, 300.

Veres, S. (1988). Asymptotic distributions of likelihood ratios for overparametrized ARMA processes. *J. Time Ser. Anal.,* **8**, 345–57.

Volterra, V. (1930). *Theory of functionals.* Blackie, London.

Wallace, C. S. and Freeman, P. R. (1987). Estimation and inference by compact coding. *J. R. Stat. Soc.,* **B49**, 240–65.

Wang, S. R., An, H. Z., and Tong, H. (1983). On the distribution of a simple stationary bilinear process. *J. Time Ser. Anal.,* **4**, 209–16.

Wang, W.-Y., Du, J.-G., and Xiang, J.-T. (1984). Threshold autoregressive moving average model. *Comput. Math.*, **4**, 414–19 (in Chinese).

Watson, G. S. (1964). Smooth regression analysis. *Sankya*, **A26**, 359–72.

Wecker, W. E. (1981). Asymmetric time series. *J. Am. Stat. Assoc.*, **76**, 16–21.

Weiss, A. A. (1986). ARCH and bilinear time series models: comparison and combination. *J. Bus. Econ. Stat.*, **4**, 59–70.

Weiss, G. (1975). Time-reversibility of linear stochastic processes. *J. Appl. Probab.*, **12**, 831–6.

West, M., Harrison, P. J., and Migon, H. S. (1985). Dynamic generalized linear models and Bayesian forecasting (with Discussion). *J. Am. Stat. Assoc.*, **80**, 73–97.

Whittle, P. (1963*a*). *Prediction and regulation by linear least-square methods.* English University Press, London. (2nd ed. (1983), Blackwell, Oxford.)

Whittle, P. (1963*b*). On the fitting of multivariate autoregressions and the approximate factorization of a spectral density matrix. *Biometrika*, **50**, 129–34.

Wiener, N. (1948). *Cybernetics.* Wiley, New York.

Wiener, N. (1958). *Nonlinear problems in random theory.* MIT Press, Cambridge, MA.

Wilkinson, J. H. (1965). *The algebraic eigenvalue problem.* Clarendon Press, Oxford.

Williamson, M. (1972). *The analysis of biological populations.* Edward Arnold, London.

Yamaguti, M. and Ushiki, S. (1981). Chaos in numerical analysis of ordinary differential equations. *Physica D*, **3**, 618–28.

Yeung, I. (1989). Continuous time threshold autoregressive models. Unpublished Ph.D. thesis, University of Kent.

Yoshimura, H. (1979). The solar-cycle period–amplitude relation as evidence of hysteresis of the solar-cycle non-linear magnetic oscillation and the long-term (55 year) cycle modulation. *Astrophys. J.*, **227**, 1047–58.

Yu, J. (1986). On invariant measures associated with piecewise linear maps. Master Thesis, Department of Physics, Peking University.

Yule, G. U. (1927). On a method of investigating periodicities in disturbed series with special reference to Wolfer's sunspot numbers. *Philos. Trans. R. Soc.*, **A226**, 267–98.

Zheng, D. W. and Chen, Z. G. (1982). Predictions of the earth rotation parameters. *Ann. Shanghai Obs., Acad. Sin.*, **4**, 116–20.

Zhu, Z.-X. (1984). On the conservative Hénon map. *Tech. Rep.*, Department of Mechanics, Peking University.

Zhu, Z.-X. (1985). What is chaos? *Mechanics and Practice*, **7**, 1–7 (in Chinese).

Subject index

Name index

STAR

A microcomputer software package for the testing for nonlinearity, the fitting of threshold autoregressive models and multi-step-ahead nonlinear forecasting is available as a companion to this book.

   STAR is a user-friendly, menu-driven interactive microcomputer statistical package containing the computing package and some of the data sets from *Non-Linear Time Series*: *A Dynamical System Approach*. **STAR** may be run on IBM-PC or its compatible. Substantial graphics facilities are available, using a built-in automatic configuration.

MICROSTAR SOFTWARE
Old House Meadow, Long Hill
Old Wives Lees, Canterbury,
Kent CT4 8BN, England

☐ Please send me _____ sets of **STAR** @ £300 (plus 15% VAT).

☐ Cheque drawable in a bank in the United Kingdom enclosed.

☐ Send me a pro-forma invoice.

☐ I am a bona fida academic and will be using **STAR** exclusively for my scientific pursuit. Please send me details of discounts for academic users.

☐ Please send me a demo diskette for £20 (I understand that this sum minus packaging and postage will be refunded to me if and only if I subsequently decided to purchase STAR).

Orders must be accompanied by a cheque drawable in a U.K. bank.

send to:

_____

Name

_____

Address

_____

_____